Recent Progress in

HORMONE RESEARCH

The Proceedings of the Laurentian Hormone Conference

VOLUME 35

RECENT PROGRESS IN

HORMONE RESEARCH

Proceedings of the
1978 Laurentian Hormone Conference

Edited by

ROY O. GREEP

VOLUME 35

PROGRAM COMMITTEE

E. Alpert   D. T. Krieger
G. D. Aurbach   E. E. McGarry
J. C. Beck   H. Papkoff
I. S. Edelman   J. E. Rall
L. L. Engel   K. J. Ryan
R. O. Greep   K. Savard
M. M. Grumbach   N. B. Schwartz
E. Knobil   J. L. Vaitukaitis

A. White

ACADEMIC PRESS   New York   San Francisco   London

A Subsidiary of Harcourt Brace Jovanovich, Publishers

ACADEMIC PRESS, INC.
111 Fifth Avenue, New York, New York 10003

United Kingdom Edition published by
ACADEMIC PRESS, INC. (LONDON) LTD.
24/28 Oval Road, London NW1 7DX

LIBRARY OF CONGRESS CATALOG CARD NUMBER: Med. 47–38

ISBN 0–12–571135–2

PRINTED IN THE UNITED STATES OF AMERICA

79 80 81 82   9 8 7 6 5 4 3 2 1

CONTENTS

v

*Manuscript not submitted.

LIST OF CONTRIBUTORS AND DISCUSSANTS

K. Ahren
J. Alvarado
J. W. Apriletti
D. T. Armstrong
G. Aurbach
U. K. Banik
G. Baumann
John D. Baxter
J. C. Beck
T. A. Bewley
H. S. Bhakoo
L. Birnbaumer
D. K. Biswas
H. L. Bradlow
Michael S. Brown
L. Bullock
J. Carter
J. F. Catterall
A. Charles
S. Ciccarese
J. H. Clark
S. L. Cohen
D. A. Colbert
A. Crastes de Paulet
W. F. Crowley
T. F. Davies
H. W. Dickerman
O. Dominguez
P. K. Donahoe
J. H. Dorrington
W. L. Duax
A. Dugaiczyk
N. L. Eberhardt
N. Eigler
L. E. Faber
P. Felig
E. R. Ferguson
G. L. Flickinger
E. H. Frieden
H. Friesen
O. P. Ganda
J. Geller
D. Goldberg
J. L. Goldstein
A. L. Goodman
H. M. Goodman
D. Gospodarowicz

G. Greenburg
R. O. Greep
M. M. Grumbach
W. Hansel
K. M. Henderson
R. Hendler
A. Hirsch
R. D. Ivarie
H. Iwata
L. S. Jacobs
R. Jewelewicz
L. K. Johnson
B. S. Katzenellenbogen
J. A. Katzenellenbogen
J. Kellett
A. D. Kenny
H. Keutmann
L. Kornel
I. A. Kourides
P. T. Kovanen
J. Kowal
E. C. Lai
N. C. Lan
T. Landefeld
K. R. Latham
C. Lazier
R. Levine
J. W. McArthur
J. M. McKenzie
J. A. Martial
S. Marx
C. Monder
J. Moran
J. A. Morris
T. G. Muldoon
B. E. P. Murphy
F. Naftolin
Y. Nagai
D. Nelson
M. New
J. L. Nordstrom
A. Nureddin
W. Odell
S. Ohno
B. W. O'Malley
D. N. Orth
H. Papkoff

PREFACE

This volume is based on the proceedings of the 1978 Laurentian Hormone Conference held August 27 through September 1 at the Mont Tremblant Lodge, Mont Tremblant, Quebec, Canada. The opening Gregory Pincus Memorial Lecture by Bert O'Malley led off a series of related reports dealing with hormonal regulation of gene expression, work that is opening new vistas on the basic mechanisms whereby hormones exert their actions. On the same level of technological expertise others addressed problems at the cutting edge in endocrine research. These included advanced work on gonadotropins, antiestrogens, steroid metabolism, H-Y antigen, protein kinases, cell growth factors, opiate receptors, and blood glucose regulation. These dazzling portrayals of recent progress in hormone research mark this as a field to watch for breakthroughs of major significance in biology and medicine.

It is a pleasure to thank Drs. John C. Beck, Lutz Birnbaumer, James H. Clark, Frederick Naftolin, Joseph E. Rall, Kenneth J. Ryan, Marvin D. Siperstein, and Darrell N. Ward for chairing the various sessions and guiding the discussions that form such a valuable contribution to the Conference and to this volume. For on-the-spot transcriptions of these lengthy discussions we are much indebted to Lucy Felicissimo for her arduous and skillful efforts. The ever pleasant and courteous service by the management and staff of the Mont Tremblant Lodge is deeply appreciated and contributive to the main purpose of the Conference, which is formal and informal scientific communication at its best. To this end I am most grateful for the invaluable assistance of Miss Martha Wright and the staff of Academic Press for dedicated attention to the production of another fine addition to this series of volumes aptly titled *Recent Progress in Hormone Research*.

Roy O. Greep

The Ovalbumin Gene: Organization, Structure, Transcription, and Regulation[1]

B. W. O'MALLEY, D. R. ROOP, E. C. LAI, J. L. NORDSTROM,
J. F. CATTERALL, G. E. SWANECK, D. A. COLBERT, M.-J. TSAI,
A. DUGAICZYK, AND S. L. C. WOO

Department of Cell Biology, Baylor College of Medicine, Houston, Texas

I. Introduction

A. INDUCTION OF SPECIFIC PROTEIN SYNTHESIS BY STEROID HORMONES

The regulation of specific gene expression is undoubtedly a major mechanism of action of the steroid hormones. Much of our present knowledge has been derived from studies on a limited number of systems. The topic has been recently reviewed by a number of authors (Gorski and Gannon, 1976; Yamamoto and Albert, 1976; Liao, 1977; Jensen and De Sombre, 1974) and by ourselves (O'Malley and Means, 1974; Vedeckis *et al.*, 1978; Chan and O'Malley, 1976a–c). In this field, the major advances during the past 6 years have been in the area of steroid hormone regulation of specific mRNA synthesis and translation.

A large number of proteins have been reported to increase in concentration or activity after steroid hormone treatment (Pitot and Yatvin, 1973; Gelehrter, 1973). However, the exact level of regulation of most of these proteins is unclear. These are indirect studies involving drugs like actinomycin D, from which conclusions have been drawn. However, such studies are fraught with dangers of over- and misinterpretation because of the multiplicity of action of most drugs. We might expect that major conceptual advances will occur primarily either through use of purified, reconstituted cell-free systems for transcription and translation or via cell culture systems amenable to genetic manipulations. To assess the level of regulation and to separate translation from pretranslational events, the mRNAs of several such proteins have been partially purified and their activities assayed using *in vitro* translation systems (Table I). In a few instances, the mRNAs have been purified to homogeneity and their complementary DNAs (cDNAs) have been synthesized *in vitro*. More precise studies using the

---

[1] The Gregory Pincus Memorial Lecture.

TABLE I

Specific Proteins Induced by Steroid Hormones[a]

Hormone	Tissue	Protein	References
I. Estrogen	Chick oviduct	Ovalbumin	Chan *et al.*, 1973; Cox *et al.*, 1974; Harris *et al.*, 1975; McKnight *et al.*, 1975; Roop *et al.*, 1978
	Chick oviduct	Conalbumin	Palmiter *et al.*, 1976
	Chick oviduct	Ovomucoid	S. Y. Tsai *et al.*, 1978; Hynes *et al.*, 1977
	Chick oviduct	Lysozyme	Hynes *et al.*, 1977
	Chick liver	ApoVLDL-II	Chan *et al.*, 1976
	Chick liver	Vitellogenin	Mullinix *et al.*, 1976; Deeley *et al.*, 1977
	Xenopus liver	Vitellogenin	Shapiro *et al.*, 1976; Baker and Shapiro, 1977; Ryffel *et al.*, 1977
	Rat pituitary	Prolactin	Stone *et al.*, 1977
II. Progesterone	Chick oviduct	Avidin	Chan *et al.*, 1973
	Rabbit uterus	Uteroglobin	Beato and Rungger, 1975; Levey and Daniel, 1976; Bullock *et al.*, 1976
III. Androgen	Rat liver	α-2u Globulin	Sippel *et al.*, 1975; Kurtz and Feigelson, 1977
	Mouse liver	Major urinary protein complex	Osawa and Tomino, 1977
	Rat prostate	Aldolase	Mainwaring *et al.*, 1977
IV. Glucocorticoids	Rat liver	Tyrosine aminotransferase	Roewekamp *et al.*, 1976; Nickol *et al.*, 1976; Diesterhaft *et al.*, 1977
	Rat liver	Tryptophan oxygenase	Schultz *et al.*, 1975
	Rat kidney	Phosphoenolpyruvate carboxykinase	Hynedjian and Hanson, 1977
	Mouse mammary cells	Mammary tumor virus RNA	Parks *et al.*, 1974; Ringold *et al.*, 1975; Young *et al.*, 1977

TABLE I (*continued*)

Hormone	Tissue	Protein	References
	Embryonic chicken retina	Glutamine synthetase	Sarkar and Griffith, 1976
	Rat pituitary cell culture	Growth hormone	Tushinski *et al.*, 1977; Martial *et al.*, 1977
	Rat pituitary	Corticotropin[b]	Nakanishi *et al.*, 1977

[a] Includes those proteins the mRNAs of which have been demonstrated by translation or nucleic acid hybridization. The level of regulation can be evaluated only in these instances.

[b] Corticotropin mRNA is "turned off" rather than induced by glucocorticoids.

radiolabeled cDNAs as hybridization probes have generally confirmed the results obtained via the translation experiments. Taken together, the experimental evidence currently available strongly supports the idea that steroid hormones act primarily at the level of nuclear transcription. Perhaps future studies will provide evidence for effects on mRNA processing as well.

For our studies on the molecular mechanism of steroid hormone action, we have utilized the chick oviduct model, an experimental system developed in our laboratory over a decade ago (O'Malley, 1967, O'Malley *et al.*, 1967, 1969; O'Malley and McGuire, 1968). In oviduct tubular gland cells, estrogen (or progesterone) induces the synthesis of egg-white proteins, of which ovalbumin is the major component (O'Malley *et al.*, 1969; Kohler *et al.*, 1969).

The purpose of this manuscript is to review our laboratory's efforts over the past 5 years to understand the regulation of expression of the chicken ovalbumin gene by steroid hormones. However, a number of excellent laboratories have utilized this model system for investigations of eukaryotic molecular biology. A selected group of these publications is listed for reference (Oka and Schimke, 1969; Palmiter and Schimke, 1973; Palmiter *et al.*, 1976; Cox, 1977; Hynes *et al.*, 1977; Garapin *et al.*, 1978; Mandel *et al.*, 1978). For the remainder of this review, we will confine our comments primarily to our own work on the chick oviduct. In this animal model, we have studied steroid hormone-mediated accumulation and synthesis of ovalbumin mRNA ($mRNA_{ov}$); purified, characterized, and sequenced this mRNA; determined the rate of accumulation and synthesis of $mRNA_{ov}$; determined the organization and structure of the ovalbumin gene; described the primary transcription product; and studied the processing of the hormone-inducible mRNA. This work is summarized in the following sections.

B. RECEPTORS AND STEROID HORMONE ACTION

Upon entering the cell, steroid hormones are initially bound to specific cytoplasmic protein receptors. The hormone–receptor complex undergoes "activation'' and translocates from the cytoplasm into the nucleus. In the nuclear compartment, the hormone–receptor complex binds to ''acceptor sites'' on the target cell chromatin. This is followed by the activation (and perhaps in some cases inactivation) of specific genes resulting in the appearance of new species of RNA. This general model seems to hold for all the major steroid hormones examined, including estrogens (Gorski, 1964; Raynaud-Jammet et al., 1971), progesterone (McGuire and O'Malley, 1968; Schrader and O'Malley, 1971), glucocorticoids (Dukes et al., 1966; Sajdel and Jacob, 1971), aldosterone (Feldman et al., 1972; Swaneck et al., 1970), and vitamin D (Zerwekh et al., 1974).

In an effort to determine the molecular biology of receptors and their functional relationships to hormone action, we have invested a great deal of effort over the past 4 years in purifying the progesterone receptor of chick oviduct and determining its subunit structure and binding affinities for nuclear constituents (Vedeckis et al., 1978). This receptor is a dimer composed of A and B subunits. This subunit structure has been confirmed recently by use of a reversible cross-linking reagent that will cross-link the native dimer. After extraction and partial purification, the dimer can be dissociated, releasing equimolar amounts of the A and B proteins. Both of the two subunits have been purified.

The A protein has a molecular weight of 79,000, and that of the B protein is 117,000. The hormone-binding specificity and kinetics for the two receptor proteins are virtually identical, suggesting that their hormone-binding sites may be very similar. The intact 6 S dimer containing 1 mol each of A and B is located in the cytoplasm of the target cell in the absence of hormone stimulation and translocates to the nuclear compartment on administration of progesterone. The B subunit binds to the nonhistone protein–DNA complexes of oviduct chromatin but only weakly to pure DNA, whereas the A subunit binds to pure DNA but poorly to chromatin. These observations on the properties of the A and B subunits have led to a hypothesis of their mechanism of interaction with the target-cell genome. It is believed that the A subunit could be the actual gene regulatory protein. In the absence of the B protein, the A subunit would encounter difficulty in locating the specific chromosomal regions it is to regulate, while the B subunit, the ''specifier'' protein, should be totally inactive as the sole transcriptional regulator. Consistent with this concept was the observation that purified A subunit protein was capable of stimulating transcription on hormone-withdrawn chromatin, but only at much higher concentrations (approximately 10- to 50-fold) than that required for the intact dimer. The isolated B subunit was totally ineffective in stimulating transcription from oviduct chromatin at any concentration tested. These observations are consistent with a model in which the B subunit acts as a binding-site specifier protein to localize the dimer in certain regions of chromatin, whereas the A subunit may alter the local structure or conformation of a portion of the chromatin DNA so that initiation of new RNA synthesis can occur.

II. Ovalbumin Messenger RNA

A. PURIFICATION

For our early studies, large quantities of highly purified mRNA were needed in order to study its physical and chemical properties. More important, pure $mRNA_{ov}$ was required for the synthesis of complementary DNA strands (cDNA) to be used as hybridization probes for the study of the regulation of gene expression and for the identification and isolation of the natural ovalbumin gene from total chicken DNA. Preparation of milligram amounts of purified ovalbumin mRNA was accomplished by a combination of techniques based on absorption chromatography, precise size separation, and selective purification of the polyadenylic acid containing RNA (Rosenfeld *et al.*, 1972; Rosen *et al.*, 1975).

Total nucleic acid was extracted with phenol from hen oviducts, and the poly(A)-containing RNA was selectively enriched by either nitrocellulose filtration or oligo(dT)-cellulose column chromatography (Rosen *et al.*, 1975; Woo *et al.*, 1975). The mRNA was further purified by a gel filtration step using Sepharose 4B chromatography and by preparative agarose gel electrophoresis in the presence of 6 *M* urea at pH 3.5 (Woo *et al.*, 1975). These methods were applicable to the purification of most eukaryotic mRNAs present in a concentration greater than 1% of the cellular mRNA. For ovalbumin mRNA, 0.5–1.0 mg of purified RNA was routinely obtained from 1–1.5 gm of total nucleic acid extract (Table II).

The purity of the ovalbumin mRNA was assessed by several independent criteria. (1) Purified ovalbumin mRNA migrated as a single band during both agarose–urea and formamide–polyacrylamide gel electrophoresis at pH 3.5 and 7.4, respectively. A single absorbance peak at about 17 S and containing all the ovalbumin mRNA activity was also found using linear sucrose gradients containing 70% formamide (Woo *et al.*, 1975). (2) Determination of both total mRNA activity and ovalbumin mRNA activity in the wheat germ cell-free translation

TABLE II

Purification of Ovalbumin mRNA from Hen Oviducts[a]

Procedure	RNA (mg)	Specific activity pmoles valine incorp. into ovalbumin/μg RNA	Purification (fold)	Yield (%)
Total nucleic acid extract	1300.0	0.63	1.0	100
Nitrocellulose absorbed RNA	22.2	11.6	18.4	31
Sepharose peak RNA	7.2	22.9	36.3	20
Nitrocellulose readsorbed RNA	3.6	25.7	40.8	11
Preparative gel RNA	0.6	92.5	146.8	6

[a] From Woo *et al.* (1975).

assay revealed that 92% of the total peptides synthesized were specifically immunoprecipitable with an ovalbumin antiserum (Rosen *et al.*, 1975). Furthermore, analysis of the total peptides synthesized in the wheat germ assay by sodium dodecyl sulfate (SDS)–polyacrylamide gel electrophoresis demonstrated the presence of a single radioactive peak that corresponded exactly to a specifically immunoprecipitable ovalbumin standard. (3) The purified ovalbumin mRNA was free of ribosomal RNA contamination since its oligonucleotide fingerprint map, after complete T1 ribonuclease digestion, contained no detectable specific large oligonucleotide markers of ribosomal RNAs (Woo *et al.*, 1975). (4) Ovalbumin mRNA molecules were examined by electron microscopy in the presence of 4 *M* urea dissolved in formamide. Length measurements on two independent preparations provided length distributions that were representative of a homogeneous species of RNA (Fig. 1). Thus, these observations indicate that the ovalbumin mRNA was more than 95% pure.

B. CHARACTERIZATION

Our initial estimates of the molecular weight of ovalbumin mRNA were 530,000, 510,000, and 540,000 by sucrose gradient centrifugation, poly(A) analysis, and sedimentation velocity determination, respectively (Woo *et al.*, 1975). However, the molecular weight was estimated by two independent gel electrophoresis methods carried out under denaturing conditions to be 900,000 (Rosen *et al.*, 1975). It was clear that the secondary structure of mRNA was preventing an accurate assessment of size. Our most reliable estimation of molecular size of RNA was accomplished by measuring its length directly by electron microscopy under denaturing conditions because this method is inde-

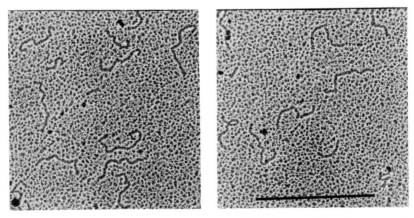

FIG. 1. Formamide–urea spreading of ovalbumin mRNA from two independent preparations. The magnification was the same in the two representative fields, as indicated by the bar length of 1 μm. From Woo *et al.* (1975).

pendent of RNA secondary structure and G + C contents (Robberson et al., 1971). A molecular weight of 650,000 ± 63,000 was obtained from electron microscopy for ovalbumin mRNA, and this value corresponded to a polynucleotide chain length of 1890 ± 180 residues (Woo et al., 1975). Ovalbumin mRNA is thus more than 600 nucleotides longer than the minimum nucleotide number required to code for ovalbumin, a protein composed of 387 amino acids. Analysis of the poly(A) content by a hybridization assay with [³H]poly(U) revealed the presence of a heterogeneous poly(A) region containing 20–140 adenosine residues with a number average chain length of 62. Ovalbumin mRNA has a nucleotide composition of 32.3% A, 21.0% G, 25.7% U, and 20.7% C, with an (A + U)/(G + C) ratio of 1.41. When ¹²⁵I-labeled ovalbumin mRNA was allowed to hybridize with a large excess of chick DNA, the observed kinetics of hybridization revealed no appreciable reaction between the mRNA and the repeated sequences of the chick DNA (Woo et al., 1975). This result indicated that the vast majority of ovalbumin mRNA sequence was transcribed from a unique DNA sequence in the chick genome. This observation was later confirmed with the use of a ³H-labeled ovalbumin cDNA and cloned ovalbumin structural DNA probes that contained complete copies of ovalbumin mRNA (Monahan et al., 1976b; Roop et al., 1978).

The secondary structure of highly purified ovalbumin mRNA was studied by automated thermal denaturation techniques, and the data were subjected to computer processing (Van et al., 1976). Comparative studies with 20 natural and synthetic model nucleic acids suggested that the secondary structure of ovalbumin mRNA possessed the following features: (1) the extent of base pairing of ovalbumin mRNA was similar to that found in tRNAs or ribosomal RNAs; (2) the secondary structure of ovalbumin mRNA was more thermolabile than any of the model compounds tested, including the copolymer poly (A-U); (3) ovalbumin mRNA did not have extensive G-C rich stems as found in tRNAs or ribosomal RNAs; (4) the renaturation kinetics of ovalbumin mRNA supported models in which base-paired regions are formed between neighboring sequences (model A, Fig. 2) rather than by extensive refolding and base pairing between distant sequences (model B, Fig. 2); (5) the base composition of the double-stranded regions revealed 54% G-C residues, which was significantly higher than that noted in the whole molecule (41.5% G-C). The presence of 46% A-U pairs in short stems of about five base pairs would have a very large destabilizing effect on the secondary structure of ovalbumin mRNA. However, at 0.175 M monovalent cations and at 36°C most of the secondary structure of ovalbumin mRNA appeared to be preserved. These data suggested that the double-stranded regions in ovalbumin mRNA were of sufficient length to provide the necessary stability for maintaining certain open-loop regions in an appropriate conformation which may be required for the biological function of ovalbumin mRNA. Furthermore, the lability of the double-stranded regions in ovalbumin mRNA may also be important for the biological function of the mRNA.

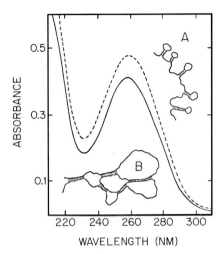

FIG. 2. Room temperature and 90°C spectra of ovalbumin mRNA. Buffer: 0.2 *M* KCl, 0.001 *M* Tris, 0.0001 *M* EDTA. ———, Room temperature; –––, 90°C. Repeated (up to six times) heating and cooling in the range 20–90°C yielded coincidental spectra. Model A showed base pairing between neighboring sequences, and model B involved refolding and pairing between distant sequences. From Van *et al.* (1976).

C. SEQUENCE DETERMINATION

The complete sequence of chicken ovalbumin mRNA was determined by the established chemical degradation method of Maxam and Gilbert (1977) on a full length duplex DNA copy of the mRNA cloned in the *Escherichia coli* plasmid pMB9 (McReynolds *et al.*, 1978) and is presented in Fig. 3. It was 1859 residues long, excluding its terminal "cap" and poly(A), and represented the third eukaryotic mRNA to be sequenced in its entirety, the other two being rabbit and human globin mRNAs (Efstratiadis *et al.*, 1977; Marotta *et al.*, 1977). The region coding for ovalbumin was situated toward the 5' end of the molecule. Interestingly, there was a leader sequence of 64 noncoding nucleotides preceding the coding sequence at the 5' end of the mRNA. The coding sequence (1158 nucleotides) was separated from the poly(A) by an extensive 3' noncoding region of 637 nucleotides, which may have no function that is precisely dependent on its sequence. The significance of the mRNA sequence in terms of secondary structure, translation, and allelic forms has been described in detail in the original publication (McReynolds *et al.*, 1978).

III. Messenger RNA and the Steroid Response

A. ACCUMULATION OF mRNA

The purification of ovalbumin RNA enabled us to synthesize DNA complementary to mRNA$_{ov}$ (cDNA$_{ov}$), which provided us with a method to study quantitatively the estrogen-mediated accumulation of $mRNA_{ov}$ in the chick oviduct (Harris *et al.*, 1975). The concentration of $mRNA_{ov}$ in total oviduct RNA was measured in immature chicks during primary stimulation, after hormone withdrawal, and again following secondary stimulation with estrogen. Daily estrogen administration to the immature chick resulted in the growth of the oviduct, differentiation of epithelial cells to tubular glands, and a corresponding increase in the concentration of $mRNA_{ov}$ in the tubular gland cell from essentially zero before estrogen administration to ~48,000 molecules per cell after 18 days of estrogen treatment (Table III). Upon withdrawal of estrogen from the chick for 12 days, the $mRNA_{ov}$ concentration decreased to a level of 0–4 molecules per tubular gland cell. Readministration of a single dose of estrogen to these chicks resulted in a dramatic and rapid increase in the concentration of $mRNA_{ov}$. Within 30 minutes the $mRNA_{ov}$ concentration more than doubled, and by 29 hours the tubular gland cell concentration had reached 17,000 molecules. Using these data, a half-life for ovalbumin mRNA of approximately 24–40 hours was calculated. These data lent support to the hypothesis that estrogen exerts its primary action at the level of transcription.

B. INDUCTION OF SYNTHESIS OF mRNA

Although the results described above are consistent with the primary effect of estrogen being at the level of transcription, it could be argued that the rate of transcription is unchanged during induction and that the accumulation of $mRNA_{ov}$ is due simply to the prevention of RNA degradation by estrogen. Since reports existed that the withdrawal of hormone resulted in a decrease in the half-life for $mRNA_{ov}$ from 40–50 hours to 2–3 hours (Palmiter and Carey, 1974; Cox, 1977), it was important to study the *de novo* rate of $mRNA_{ov}$ synthesis.

We have accomplished this by synthesizing labeled RNA in nuclei *in vitro* and determining the concentration of $mRNA_{ov}$ sequences by hybridization to filters containing pOV230 DNA (Roop *et al.*, 1978; Swaneck *et al.*, 1978). The ovalbumin gene was preferentially transcribed in nuclei isolated from estrogen-stimulated oviducts since ~ 0.2% of the total RNA synthesized with $mRNA_{ov}$ sequence (Table IV). This value was approximately 50- to 100-fold greater than would be expected if random transcription of the available genes in oviduct chromatin (haploid number) occurred. The presence of $5\mu g$ of α-amanitin per milliliter inhibited the synthesis of $mRNA_{ov}$ sequences by 98%, indicating that these sequences were transcribed by RNA polymerase II (Table IV). Also, total [³H]RNA and [³H]mRNA$_{ov}$ synthesis were inhibited about 96% and 97%, respectively, when actinomycin D (150 $\mu g/ml$) was present in the reaction mixture. The specificity of RNA synthesized *in vitro* was further demonstrated by the absence of detectable [³H]mRNA$_{ov}$ sequences in RNA synthesized in chick nuclei isolated from hormonally unresponsive tissues, such as liver and spleen (Table III). Finally, specific repression was maintained in oviduct nuclei since

F
C

M Q S I G A A S M I C F D V F A E L

10   20   30   40   50   60   70   80   90   100 110 120

M V H A N E N I F Y C P I A I M S A L A H V Y L G A K D G T K T Q I N A V V R

130 140 150 160 170 180 190 200 210 220 230 240

F D K L P G F G D S I E A Q C G T S V N V H S S L R D I L N Q I T K P N D V Y S

250 260 270 280 290 300 310 320 330 340 350 360

F S L A S R L Y A E E R Y P I L P E Y L Q C V K E L Y R G G L E P I N F Q T A A

370 380 390 400 410 420 430 440 450 460 470 480

D Q A R E L I N S W V E S Q T N G I I R N V L Q P S S V D S Q T A M V L V N A I

490 500 510 520 530 540 550 560 570 580 590 600

V F K G L W E K A F K D E D T Q A M P F R V T E Q E S K P V Q M M Y Q I G L F K

610 620 630 640 650 660 670 680 690 700 710 720

V A S M A S E K M K I L E L P F A S Q T M S M L V L L P D E V S G L E Q L E S I

730 740 750 760 770 780 790 800 810 820 830 840

CHO

I N F E K L T E W T S S N V M E E R K I K V Y L P R M K M E E K Y N L T S V L M

850 860 870 880 890 900 910 920 930 940 950 960

10

A M G I T D V F S S S A N L S G I S S A E S L K I S Q A V H A A H A E I N E A G
GCCUAUGGCAUUACUGACUGUGUUAGCUCUUCAGCCAACUGUCUGGCAUCUCCUCAGCAGAGAGCCUGAGAUAUUCUCAAGCUGUCCAUGCAGCACAUGGCAGAAAUCAAUUAAAGCAGG
970   980   990   1000   1010   1020   1030   1040   1050   1060   1070   1080

R E V U U G S A E A G V D A A S V S E E F R A D H P F L F C I K H I A T N A V L F
CAGAGAGGUAGGGUCAGCAGAGGGAUGGCUGGAAGCGUCUCUGAAGAAUUAGGGCUGCUCUCUGUAUCAAGCACACUGCCAACCAAGCGCGGUCCUCUU
1090   1100   1110   1120   1130   1140   1150   1160   1170   1180   1190   1200

F S R C V S P *
CUUUGGCAAUGUGUUUCCCUUAAAAAGAAGGGCUGAAAAACUCUGUCCCCUUCCAACCAGAGACCCACUGAACAGUAGUCACUGCUGCGAUCCUGCGCAUCCCACCCA
1210   1220   1230   1240   1250   1260   1270   1280   1290   1300   1310   1320

GACUUCAUAAAAGCUGGAGCUUAAAUCUAGAAAAAAAAUCAGAAAGAAAUUACACUGUGCAAUUCAUCUUUUCCUUUACACAGAGUAAAUACUGGUAAACUCAUGGCAUAGAAGGC
1330   1340   1350   1360   1370   1380   1390   1400   1410   1420   1430   1440

UUAAGGCAANGAAAUUGGAUUCAUCACCACUGAUAAAAAUGCAAUCUUAUAUCAUCAGCAGAAGGGUUAUGGGGGAAAAANGCAGCCUUCCAAUNAANCCAGAUAAUCUUGUAUACCAAACUUUCU
1450   1460   1470   1480   1490   1500   1510   1520   1530   1540   1550   1560

CCAGAAUUAGUCACUCAAAAUCUCACAGAUAUAUAAUUAAUCAACCAUUCUUAUGUCUUAUGUCUGGACAAGACAAUGGCUUGUUCUGGAUACUCUCUAUCCUGGAUCUGGACCAUGCAAGGUCUUUAUCUGACUU
1570   1580   1590   1600   1610   1620   1630   1640   1650   1660   1670   1680

CCUAAAGAGAGCAUAUAUAAAAUCUUAUAUAUUGCACAUUCUCUAAAGAUACAUUUUUGAUUUGAUUCAAAUAUUGUAAAUAUAUUUGCAAAAUUUGAAAUUUGUAAUAUAUUUACCAUAUNUU
1690   1700   1710   1720   1730   1740   1750   1760   1770   1780   1790   1800

AAUGGCGUCUUUAUAAUUGCUCUCUUUUUUUUCUUUUUUCUUUUUCUUUUUUUUUUUUUUUUAAUAUAAUUAACAAUGUUUUUUAAUUC—Poly(A)
1810   1820   1830   1840   1850   1860

FIG. 3.   Sequence of ovalbumin mRNA. Residues 13–1859 were present in the plasmid pOV230; residues 1–12 and 1731–1859 were sequenced directly from mRNA. * Marks the terminator; P, the serine phosphate residues; and CHO, the carbohydrate. Mature ovalbumin lacks the N-terminal methionine; the resultant N-terminal glycine is N-acetylated. The amino acid composition, excluding the initiator Met, is Ala (A), 35; Arg (R), 15; Asn (N), 17; Asp (D), 14; Cys (C), 6; Gln (Q), 15; Glu (E), 33; Gly (G), 19; His (H), 7; Ile (I), 25; Leu (L), 32; Lys (K), 20; Met (M), 16; Phe (F), 20; Pro (P), 14; Ser (S), 38; Thr (T), 15; Trp (W), 3; Tyr (Y), 10; and Val (V), 31. Total, 385 residues. This information is taken from the original publication (McReynolds et al., 1978) and for the most part was obtained by a collaborative effort in the laboratory of Dr. George Brownlee, Cambridge, England.

TABLE III

Induction of mRNA$_{ov}$ during Primary and Secondary Stimulation with Estrogen

Hormonal state[a]	Molecules mRNA$_{ov}$ per tubular gland cell[b]
Unstimulated	—
4 Days × DES	20,000
9 Days × DES	44,000
18 Days × DES	48,000
Withdrawn	0–4
0.5 Hour × DES	9
1.0 Hours × DES	50
4.0 Hours × DES	2,300
8.0 Hours × DES	5,100
29.0 Hours × DES	17,000

[a] Ten-day-old White Leghorn chicks received daily subcutaneous injections of diethylstilbestrol (DES, 2.5 mg in oil) and were killed at the indicated times. For experiments involving secondary stimulation with estrogen, the chicks were first treated with DES for 10 days followed by 11 days of withdrawal from hormone. On day 12 of withdrawal, chicks were given one subcutaneous injection of 2.5 mg of DES and oviducts were collected at the indicated time intervals.

[b] ^{3}H-labeled cDNA$_{ov}$ was hybridized to total oviduct RNA extracted from chicks treated as indicated. The number of molecules of mRNA$_{ov}$ was calculated as previously described (Harris *et al.*, 1975).

the [^{3}H]RNA did not hybridize to filters containing the chick β-globin gene (Roop *et al.*, 1978).

We examined the time course of the decrease in expression of the ovalbumin gene in oviduct nuclei after withdrawal from diethylstilbestrol (DES) and found that after 60 hours there was no detectable mRNA$_{ov}$ in the nascent radioactive transcripts (Swaneck *et al.*, 1979); (Table V). This loss of expression of the ovalbumin gene was reversible by readministration of a single injection of estrogen (Table V). There was an induction within 1 hour in the synthesis of mRNA$_{ov}$ sequences that increased in rate by 4 hours. These results support the hypothesis that estrogen induces the accumulation of mRNA$_{ov}$ primarily by increasing the rate of transcription. If the concentration of mRNA$_{ov}$ was primarily regulated by its rate of degradation, then the rate of transcription of the ovalbumin gene should be relatively independent of the hormonal state of the chick. However, since we detect no synthesis and very little mRNA$_{ov}$ mass (Roop *et al.*, 1978; Harris *et al.*, 1975) in oviducts from withdrawn chicks, the rate of degradation of ovalbumin sequence would have to be equal to the rate of synthesis. Although the presence of estrogen does seem to have an effect on the stability of mRNA$_{ov}$ (Cox, 1977), the primary effect of estrogen on the accumulation of mRNA$_{ov}$ in the oviduct appears to be at the level of gene transcription.

TABLE IV

Specificity of in Vitro Transcription in Nuclei

Nuclei from	Competitor	$[^3\mathrm{H}]$RNA hybridized (cpm)	$[^{32}\mathrm{P}]$cDNA$_{ov}$ recovery (%)	Hybridizable gene sequences (cpm)	Input $\times 10^{-6}$	Percent of total RNA
Oviduct DES[a]	—	1215	14.7	6950	2.92	0.238
	mRNA$_{ov}$	244				
	—	549	18.6	2350	1.02	0.231
	mRNA$_{ov}$	112				
Oviduct DES[a] + α-amanitin (0.5 µg/ml)	—	52	18.3	33	1.63	0.002
	mRNA$_{ov}$	46				
Oviduct DES + actinomycin D	—	469	18.2	2576	1.1	0.234
Oviduct W[b] 3 days	—	121	17.1	0	1.05	<0.001[c]
	mRNA$_{ov}$	131				
Oviduct W[b] 14 days	—	99	26.6	0	0.35	<0.001[c]
	mRNA$_{ov}$	103				
Spleen	—	62	18.9	0	3.10	<0.001[c]
	mRNA$_{ov}$	87				
Liver	—	33	16.9	23	0.59	<0.001[c]
	mRNA$_{ov}$	29				

[a] Chickens were implanted with diethylstilbestrol (DES) pellets weekly.

[b] Chickens were injected daily with 2.5 mg of DES in 0.25 ml of sesame oil. Withdrawn (W) indicates the number of elapsed days after the last injection.

[c] mRNA$_{ov}$ sequences cannot be measured at a concentration less than 0.001% in our assay. Hybridization conditions were as previously described (Swaneck et al., 1979).

TABLE V

In Vitro Transcription of Ovalbumin Gene Structural Sequences in Nuclei[a]

Hormonal state	Percent of total RNA hybridized
DES[b] daily	0.23
Withdrawn 60 hours	<0.001
+1 Hour DES	0.010
+2 Hours DES	0.031
+4 Hours DES	0.060

[a] [^{3}H]RNA (1–5 × 10^6 cpm) synthesized in nuclei from oviducts of stimulated, withdrawn, and secondarily stimulated chicks was incubated with filters containing pOV230 DNA and [^{32}P]cRNA$_{ov}$ internal standard (2000 cpm). Competitor RNA (7.5 μg of mRNA$_{ov}$) was also present in duplicate vials. Hybridization conditions were as previously described (Swaneck *et al.*, 1979).

[b] DES, diethylstilbestrol.

IV. The Ovalbumin Gene

In order to fully understand the detailed molecular mechanism involved in the hormonal regulation of the expression of the ovalbumin gene in the chicken oviduct, we felt compelled to elucidate the organizational structure of this interesting eukaryotic gene. In addition, our future experiments would require large quantities of purified natural ovalbumin gene sequences in order to study their interactions with hormone–receptor complexes, RNA polymerase, and chromosomal proteins *in vitro*. This task was initiated by first synthesizing a DNA-copy of the pure mRNA$_{ov}$ (cDNA$_{ov}$). The structure and organization of the cDNA$_{ov}$ was determined, and this DNA was amplified by molecular cloning. This synthetic ovalbumin structural (mRNA coding) gene could then be used as hybridization probe to identify the natural gene coding for ovalbumin in native chicken DNA, so that this natural gene could be subsequently purified and amplified.

A. SYNTHESIS OF A COMPLETE DOUBLE-STRANDED cDNA$_{ov}$

Large quantities of a highly radioactively labeled complementary DNA copy to purified ovalbumin mRNA (cDNA$_{ov}$) was synthesized using avian myeloblastosis virus reverse transcriptase (Monahan *et al.*, 1976a). In the absence of monovalent cation, at 46°C and at high concentration of deoxyribonucleoside triphosphates, a complete transcript of ovalbumin mRNA could be generated by the enzyme, a result that has been previously unobtainable using other conditions. The size of the product was analyzed on an alkaline sucrose gradient (Fig. 4) to be ≥ 10.5 S. Upon analysis by polyacrylamide gel electrophoresis in the presence of 98% formamide, the cDNA$_{ov}$ migrated as a polynucleotide with a weight-average size of 1800 nucleotides. Furthermore, the cDNA product was

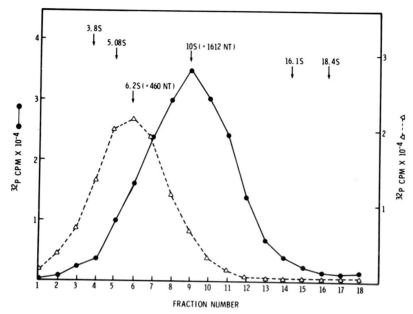

FIG. 4. Alkaline sucrose gradient of ³²P-labeled cDNA$_{ov}$ synthesized in △----△: 50 mM Tris·HCl (pH 8.3), 20 mM dithiothreitol, 6 mM MgCl$_2$, 96 mM KCl, 200 μM dTTP, 35 μM each of dGTP, dCTP, dATP, 5 μg/ml of oligo(dT$_{18-20}$), 36 μg/ml of actinomycin D, 1% ethanol, 25 μg/ml of mRNA, 50 μCi/ml of [³²P]dGTP, and 60 units/ml of reverse transcriptase. Synthesis was for 1 hour at 37°C. ○——○: Alkaline sucrose gradient of "long" ³²P-labeled cDNA$_{ov}$ synthesized in the buffer described above with no KCl present. Synthesis was for 5 minutes at 46°C. The samples were centrifuged in an SW40 rotor at 5°C for 24 hours at 38,000 rmp. From Monahan *et al.* (1976a).

capable of protecting quantitatively ¹²⁵I-labeled mRNA from nuclease digestion, indicating that an essentially complete complement of the ovalbumin mRNA has been synthesized. The cDNA/mRNA hybrid had a T_m on hydroxyapatite of 92°C, indicating the synthesis of a RNA transcript with high fidelity. When such a complete ovalbumin ³H-labeled cDNA was hybridized to an excess of chick DNA, the kinetics of hybridization indicated again that the cDNA was comprised of a nonrepetitive sequence.

Using purified single-stranded ovalbumin cDNA as a template for avian myeloblastosis virus (AMV) reverse transcriptase, a complete double-stranded ovalbumin cDNA sequence was synthesized (Monahan *et al.*, 1976a). The majority of the single-stranded cDNA molecules contained at their 3′ termini short double-stranded sequences (hairpins) that are capable of acting as primers for the synthesis of the second strand. Optimal conditions for synthesis of the double-stranded ovalbumin cDNA were found to be a high temperature (46°C) and a low salt concentration. After synthesis, the second DNA strand was found to be covalently linked to the first cDNA strand. The closed 5′ loop of the double-stranded cDNA could be opened with S1 nuclease. On a neutral sucrose gradient, the DNA sedimented at an average of 10 S, corresponding to a mean length of 1600 base pairs (Fig. 5). Greater than 30% of the final product was 1800 base pairs in length and thus contained the complete coding portion of the ovalbumin structural gene. The two strands of the cDNA had a high T_m on hydroxyapatite (89°C). These double-stranded ovalbumin cDNA molecules had a buoyant density in cesium chloride gradients of 1.700 gm/cm^3 and renatured after heat denaturation with a $C_{0}t_{1/2}$ value of 1.89×10^{-3} mol-sec liter^{-1}.

This full length, double-stranded ovalbumin cDNA, synthesized *in vitro* was used as a substrate to assay the capacity of 36 separate restriction endonucleases to cut the structural DNA sequence coding for mRNA (Monahan *et al.*, 1977). Some 22 enzymes, including *Bam*HI, *Hin*dIII, and *Eco*RI, failed to cut such a DNA sequence. However, fourteen enzymes did cut the DNA; they were *Hae*III, *Pst*I and its isoschizomer *Xma*II, *Sst*I, *Hga*I, *Xho*II, *Hph*I, *Eco*RII, *Hin*fI, *Mnl*I, *Mbo*I, *Mbo*II, *Taq*I, and *Alu*I. A map of the restriction enzyme recognition sites for some of these restriction endonucleases was determined as summarized in Fig. 6.

The ovalbumin structural gene was purified and amplified by cloning in the bacterial strain X1776 (Curtiss *et al.*, 1976) using the tetracycline-resistant plasmid pMB9 (Rodriquez *et al.*, 1976). All bacterial transformations were carried out according to NIH guidelines, and P3 physical and EK2 biological containments were employed. To construct this recombinant plasmid, a full-length double-stranded DNA copy of the ovalbumin mRNA was first synthe-

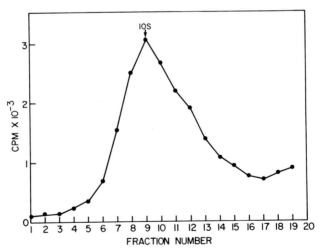

FIG. 5. Sedimentation of the ^{32}P-labeled synthetic double-stranded ovalbumin gene on a neutral 5 to 25% sucrose gradient containing 0.01 M Tris-HCl, pH 7.0, and 2 mM EDTA. Centrifugation was carried out at 4°C for 16 hours at 35,000 rpm in an SW40 rotor. The gradient was fractionated, and radioactivity content in each fraction was determined. DNA standards of various sizes were run on parallel tubes. From Monahan *et al.* (1976b).

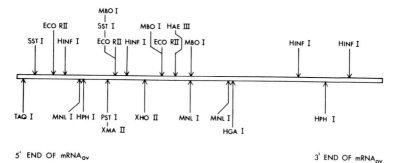

FIG. 6. Summary map of the sequence-specific sites for 12 restriction enzymes upon the ovalbumin structural DNA sequence. From Monahan *et al.* (1977).

sized; after S1 nuclease treatment, poly(dA) was added to both 3′ termini, using terminal deoxynucleotidyl transferase. The DNA was then hybridized to an *Eco*RI linearized plasmid DNA, pMB9, containing 3′-poly(dT) termini (Fig. 7). This hybrid molecule was used to transform *E. coli* strain X1776. Transformed colonies containing ovalbumin DNA were selected by *in situ* hybridization with [^{32}P]RNA transcribed from ovalbumin cDNA (McReynolds *et al.*, 1977a).

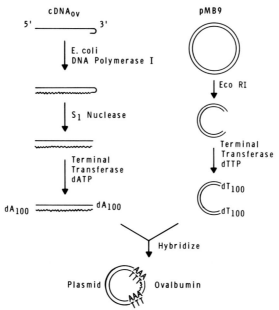

FIG. 7. Schematic diagram of the construction of the chimeric plasmids between double-stranded ovalbumin cDNA and pMB9. The wavy line represents the synthesis of second-strand DNA complementary to cDNA$_{ov}$. From McReynolds *et al.* (1977a).

One chimeric plasmid, pOV230, contained a 1950 base-pair insert that was slightly longer than the 1850 bases on the ovalbumin mRNA. By far the greater part of this insert DNA was complementary to ovalbumin gene sequences, since more than 95% of a complete DNA copy of the ovalbumin mRNA (1850 nucleotides in length) was protected from S1 nuclease digestion by pOV230. The remaining "extra" bases were thought to be comprised of the poly(dA-dT) linkers. Multiple restriction endonuclease digests of the inserted ovalbumin DNA demonstrated that the sites present in the double-stranded ovalbumin DNA were preserved also in the chimeric plasmid (McReynolds, 1977b).

This new recombinant plasmid (pOV230) was cultured in its bacterial host and amplified by the addition of chloramphenicol (Dugaiczyk *et al.*, 1975). Plasmid DNA was isolated from the bacterial cells by the clear lysate procedure (Katz *et al.*, 1973) and further purified by equilibrium centrifugation in CsCl gradients containing ethidium bromide. With *E. coli* χ1776 as host, about 200 μg of purified plasmid DNA could be produced per liter of bacterial culture.

B. A SURPRISING ORGANIZATION OF THE OVALBUMIN GENE (INTERVENING SEQUENCES)

With the cloned and now unquestionably pure ovalbumin structural gene in hand, it was possible to study the structure and organization of the ovalbumin gene in native chicken DNA in much greater detail. Chimeric plasmid pOV230 was digested with restriction endonucleases *Hae*III and *Hind*III to yield two DNA fragments containing the left and right halves of the ovalbumin DNA insert, designated OV_L and OV_R, respectively (Fig. 8). These two fragments were separated by preparative agarose gel electrophoresis and labeled to high

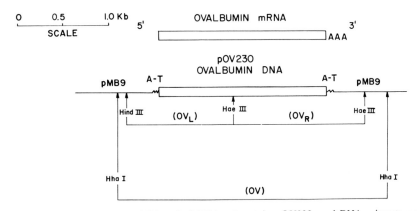

FIG. 8. Orientation of the full-length $dsDNA_{ov}$ insert in pOV230. , $dsDNA_{ov}$ insert; ∿, dA-dT linkers; ——, pMB9 DNA. The sites of cleavage of this recombinant DNA by *Hha*I, *Hind*-III, and *Hae*III are indicated by arrows. OV_L and OV_R, left half and right half of insert, respectively. From Lai *et al.* (1978).

specific radioactivity with ^{32}P-labeled dCTP and dTTP by "nick translation" (Maniatis *et al.*, 1975) and employed as specific hybridization probes (Lai *et al.*, 1978). Total chicken DNA was digested with restriction endonuclease *Eco*RI and transferred to a nitrocellulose filter using the method of Southern (1977) after agarose gel electrophoresis. The filter was then hybridized with the radioactive probes, OV_L and OV_R, followed by radioautography. We had previously reported that *Eco*RI does not cleave the ovalbumin structural gene (McReynolds *et al.*, 1978) and should thus place all of the ovalbumin gene sequence in a single band. To our great surprise, however, it produced at least three detectable DNA fragments that contained ovalbumin sequence (Fig. 9). While the 9.5 Kb fragment formed a hybrid only with OV_R, the 2.4 and 1.8 Kb fragments hybridized only with OV_L. A faint 1.3 Kb fragment was often detected by OV_L alone. The fidelity of these fragments was established by the fact that they could be enriched by "R-loop" formation (White and Hogness, 1977) using highly purified ovalbumin mRNA followed by oligo(dT)-cellulose column chromatography (Lai *et al.*, 1978). This result was consistent with the interpretation that within the native ovalbumin gene were two or more nonstructural sequences that were cleaved by *Eco*RI. Similar experiments were carried out with total chicken DNA digested with a variety of restriction endonucleases, namely *Hin*dIII, *Bam*HI, *Pst*I, and *Hae*III. The sizes of DNA fragments that resulted from these digests and contained ovalbumin structural gene sequence were measured. From the fragments, we obtained the probable locations of the nonstructural or intervening sequences within the native ovalbumin structural gene. A preliminary organization map of the native ovalbumin gene was drawn and is reproduced in Fig. 10. At this point, it was clear that each of these *Eco*RI fragments of the ovalbumin gene would have to be obtained in large amounts so that a definitive structure could be ascertained.

C. CLONING OF FRAGMENTS OF THE NATURAL GENE

Total chicken DNA was digested with *Eco*RI. Next, the 2.4, 1.8 and 9.5 Kb DNA fragments of the natural ovalbumin gene were enriched about 200-fold and separated from one another by a combination of RPC-5 column chromatography (Hardies and Wells, 1976) and gel electrophoresis. The enriched 2.4 Kb DNA fragment was cloned in bacteria using the certified EK2 vector λgtWES.λB (Leder *et al.*, 1977) and according to NIH guidelines in a P3 facility (Woo *et al.*, 1978). The cloning procedure is illustrated diagrammatically in Fig. 11. Five out of approximately 20,000 recombinant phage plaques were capable of hybridizing with a ^{32}P-labeled *Hha*I fragment of pOV230 containing the entire ovalbumin structural gene (Fig. 12). The 1.8 Kb fragment was cloned using an identical procedure. The 9.5 Kb fragment was cloned similarly but with a Charon 4A vector (Blattner *et al.*, 1977), which accepts a larger-size insert fragment. Although the lambda phage is an extremely efficient cloning system, it is not

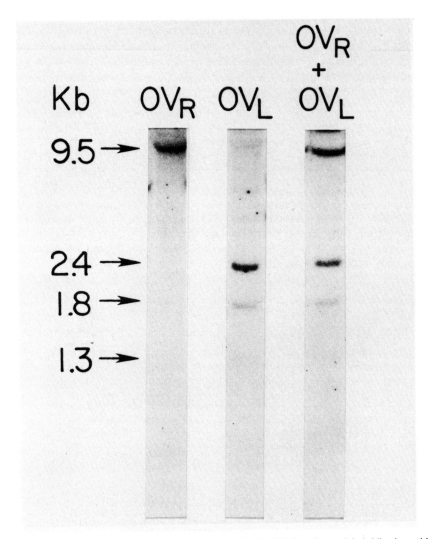

FIG. 9. Radioautogram of total chicken DNA after *Eco*RI digestion and hybridization with
[32]P-labeled ovalbumin DNA probes. Chick liver DNA (12 μg) as digested with *Eco*RI and
electrophoresed in a 1% agarose slab gel. DNA transfer and Southern hybridization were performed
as described in Lai *et al.* (1978). OV_L and OV_R are DNA fragments containing the left and right half
of the structural ovalbumin gene, respectively.

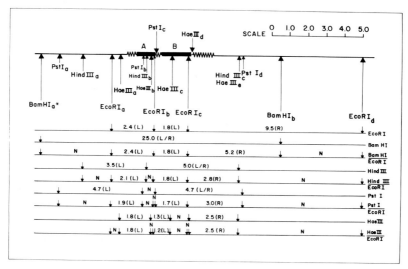

FIG. 10. Model for the organization of the natural ovalbumin gene in chicken DNA. DNA sequences present in cDNA$_{ov}$ are represented by ∿, insertion sequences are represented by ■, and flanking DNA sequences are represented by ——. Various restriction sites on the DNA are shown by the arrows. Those above the line are restriction sites present in dsDNA$_{ov}$. An exception to the scale is the *Bam*HI$_a$* site, which should be 25 Kb to the left of the *Bam*HI$_b$ site. The generation of DNA fragments of different sizes by various restriction digestions of this DNA is shown below the model: numbers represent the sizes of DNA fragments in kilobases; (L), (R), and (L/R) indicate that the DNA fragment was detected by hybridization with OV$_L$, OV$_R$, or both OV$_L$ and OV$_R$ respectively. N represents DNA fragments that should have resulted from various restriction digestions but were not detected in the radioautograms because there was no DNA sequence complementary to the probes used or the lengths of the complementary sequences were insufficient to form stable hybrids under the conditions used. From Lai *et al.* (1978).

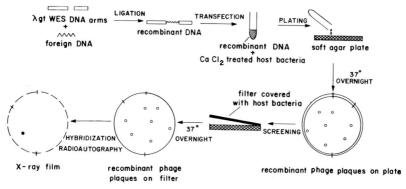

FIG. 11. Schematic diagram of the cloning of the natural ovalbumin gene. A detailed description of the procedure is presented in Woo *et al.* (1978).

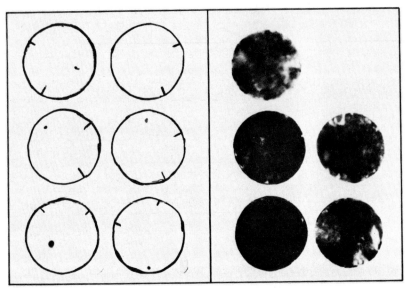

FIG. 12. Screening of the phage plaques by hybridization with the ^{32}P-labeled *Hha*I fragment of pOV230(OV). Phage particles were transferred from plaque on individual agar plates to nitrocellulose filters and subsequently amplified on fresh agar plates. Radioautography was carried out for 10 hours at −20°C. *Left:* Radioautogram of all the filters that yielded hybridization signals. The radioautogram of one of the filters not showing a hybridization signal is also shown in the upper right-hand corner. *Right:* Rescreening of the positive plaques. Individual phage plaques corresponding to the spots shown on the Left were picked for plate lysis and screening. The plates with hybridization signals are again shown; the upper right-hand corner is a radioautogram of the filter containing control plaques. From Woo *et al.* (1978).

suited for the production of bulk quantities of recombinant DNA. Thus these DNA inserts were cleaved from their respective recombinant phages and recloned in *E. coli* X1776 after ligation with *Eco*RI-digested plasmid (pBR322) DNA.

D. STRUCTURE OF THE NATURAL OVALBUMIN GENE

The cloned *Eco*RI fragments of the natural ovalbumin gene, designated OV2.4, OV1.8, and OV9.5, respectively, were amplified and purified from their recombinant plasmids. They were then studied by hybridization with mature ovalbumin mRNA, electron microscopy, restriction enzyme mapping, and DNA sequence analysis (Dugaiczyk *et al.*, 1978). Instead of two intervening sequence regions within the gene, we were surprised to find that the structural gene sequence coding for ovalbumin was separated into eight sequentially oriented pieces by seven intervening sequences of varying lengths. A more precise restriction map of the natural ovalbumin gene could then be constructed (Fig. 13). The distribution of the intervening sequences was nonrandom since all seven

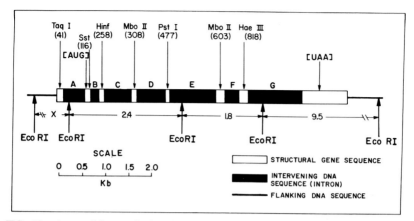

FIG. 13. A map of the organization of structural and intervening DNA sequences comprising the chick ovalbumin gene. Each of the noncontinuous structural segments is identified by one restriction endonuclease site. This amazing organization was revealed only after the natural ovalbumin gene was cloned and studied by restriction endonuclease mapping, electron microscopy, and limited sequence analysis. From Dugaiczyk *et al.* (1978).

were found in the left-hand half (leader sequence and peptide coding region) of the gene (Dugaiczyk *et al.*, 1978; Mandel *et al.*, 1978). Direct sequence analysis indicated that the OV2.4 does not encompass the 5′ terminus of the ovalbumin gene, but contains the ovalbumin sequence starting from nucleotide 46 of the structural gene. The cloning of the 5′ terminus of the ovalbumin gene as well as the 22 Kb *Bam*HI fragment that should contain the entire ovalbumin gene is presently being carried out.

Also of major interest was the observation that more than 8000 bases of DNA are required to code for an 1859-base mRNA (Roop *et al.*, 1978). These studies generated a great deal of speculation concerning the possible mechanisms for transcription of this fascinating structure.

E. GENETIC ALLELES OF THE OVALBUMIN GENE

The cloned 2.4, 1.8, and 9.5 Kb DNA fragments have been shown to be unique chicken DNA sequences (Roop *et al.*, 1978) and to contain various portions of the ovalbumin structural gene. When these three DNA fragments were labeled with ^{32}P by "nick translation" and used as probes to hybridize with *Eco*RI digested total chicken DNA (extracted from a group of hens) by the method of Southern (1977), OV2.4 and OV9.5 each detected only one distinct DNA fragment corresponding to its own size. However, with OV1.8 as probe, a total of three discrete fragments was observed (Lai *et al.*, 1979). In addition to a 1.8 Kb DNA fragment as expected, this probe also hybridized with a 1.3 Kb and 0.5 Kb fragment. This result indicated that there was significant homology among these three DNA fragments. The 1.3 Kb fragment was enriched and cloned using the λ phage cloning system. Detailed restriction endonuclease mapping analyses and direct DNA sequence data of the cloned 1.8 Kb and 1.3 Kb DNA fragments showed identical sequence organization of the interspersed structural and intervening sequences except for the presence of an extra *Eco*RI cleavage site. Sequence data of the cloned DNAs suggest that this *Eco*RI site may be created or eliminated by a single base mutation in the intervening sequence of the ovalbumin gene. Therefore, OV1.8 and OV1.3 are two allelic forms of the natural chicken ovalbumin gene.

The occurrence of apparent homozygous and heterozygous allelic forms of the ovalbumin gene in individual hens and roosters within the same breed has been observed. Of the chickens examined, 10% and 40% are homozygous for the ovalbumin gene with and without the extra *Eco*RI site, respectively, and 50% of them are heterozygous for this restriction site. Further analysis of individual chicken DNA cleaved by restriction endonuclease *Hae*III has revealed that there may be a series of such mutational variations within the ovalbumin gene. We have identified two *Hae*III cleavage sites that do not occur in all the chickens, thus giving rise to several additional allelic variations of the ovalbumin gene. At least one of these *Hae*III sites is situated in the intervening sequence of the ovalbumin gene, and its location has been mapped. A restriction endonuclease map of the ovalbumin gene showing common and variable *Eco*RI and *Hae*III cleavage sites is presented in Fig. 14. Contrary to prior speculations, this observation suggests that there may be a large amount of gene heterogeneity within species of eukaryotes. This type of mutation within the intervening sequences of an eukaryotic gene has no known phenotypic manifestation and may represent a new class of extrastructural silent mutations.

F. ORIGIN AND FUNCTIONS OF INTERVENING SEQUENCES IN THE EUKARYOTIC GENOME

The existence of intervening sequences was entirely unpredicted by our prior understanding of eukaryotic genes. From the gene studies to date (Lai *et al.*, 1978; Breathnach *et al.*, 1977; Doel *et al.*, 1977; Weinstock *et al.*, 1978; Jeffreys and Flavell, 1977; Tilghman *et al.*, 1978a; Goodman *et al.*, 1977; Valenzuela *et al.*, 1978; Tonegawa *et al.*, 1978; Mears *et al.*, 1978), it appears that structural genes are frequently interrupted by intervening sequences that are quite ubiquitous. Evidence indicates that the entire gene is transcribed as a unit into a primary transcript of RNA that appears to be subsequently processed into mature mRNA by reactions of precise cleavage and ligation. Thus, an abundant amount of intracistronic DNA will never be expressed in the phenotype as proteins.

The meaning or role of the intervening sequences is of current topical interest. At least three putative explanations can be set forth for the existence of these intervening sequences. (1) They may be recombinant accidents of nature that

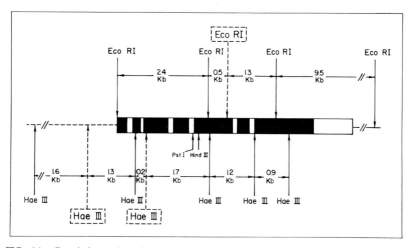

FIG. 14. Restriction endonuclease map of the natural ovalbumin gene showing common and variable *Eco*RI and *Hae*III cleavage sites. The map was generated from data obtained from *Eco*RI and *Hae*III digest of DNA from individual hens. Black sections on the map denote intervening sequences, and white sections represent ovalbumin structural DNA. A solid line represents flanking sequence, and a dotted line represents DNA sequence presently under investigation. Restriction endonuclease cleavage sites common in individual chickens are indicated by solid arrows, and variable sites are indicated by dash-line arrows. From Lai *et al.* (1979).

have never served a specific purpose and are simply eliminated by an eukaryotic RNA processing mechanism. This possibility seems unlikely because few accidental events in biology are perpetuated in the absence of any selective advantage. (2) These sequences may be of major regulatory importance for acute or developmental gene expression. At present we have uncovered no regulatory role for any of the seven intervening sequences inherent to the ovalbumin gene in chicken. However, further studies have to be carried out before a definite conclusion can be reached. (3) They may be the result of advantageous recombination events, which at one time during evolution provided a selective benefit to the organism in terms of the ultimate gene product. Since the cell is under environmental pressure to construct proteins (enzymes) with a particular set of characteristics, the cell could have been encouraged to splice together new polypeptides via assembly of various segments of DNA into a "gene region." As the desired sequences required to code for a given successful enzyme were assembled by recombination events, extraneous (intervening sequence) DNA was likely "brought along" due to a lack of precision in the recombination process. Cells carrying out such evolutionary recombinations were obviously under no pressure to prevent such accumulation of intracistronic DNA since eukaryotic RNA processing systems have evolved as efficient and accurate mechanisms to functionally remove them by splicing and reassembly of the primary transcripts into a mature RNA capable of coding for the appropriate protein. After evolutionary assembly of the gene, the intervening sequences of that gene were most likely unnecessary and may be in the process of being removed over a period of time in order to maximize the transcriptional efficiency of the gene. Since our current experiments view the gene at a particular evolutionary point in time, these intervening sequences may be present in varying numbers and sizes, or may, in fact, be already eliminated in certain genes. Alternatively, the intervening sequences may continue to play an important role in the transcription of certain differentiation-specific genes that are responsible for mRNAs present in high concentrations in cells. When more genes from the less abundant mRNA class are cloned (e.g., enzymes of intermediate metabolism, membrane proteins) this question can be resolved. In a sense, eukaryotic genomes could be viewed as inefficient in that the amount of DNA they continue to possess is far in excess of the minimum genetic information required to code for cellular proteins. However, because of this, they may be more flexible and adaptive to evolutionary pressures and environmental insults.

V. Transcription of the Natural Ovalbumin Gene

After the presence of the intervening sequences within the ovalbumin gene was revealed, the functional importance of these sequences became of interest. Therefore, we addressed the following questions: Do intervening sequences affect the transcription of different structural regions of the ovalbumin gene? Are the intervening sequences themselves transcribed? Do steroid hormones regulate the transcription of structural and intervening sequences in a coordinate fashion? Is the entire ovalbumin gene transcribed as a large precursor that is processed to form mature ovalbumin mRNA? What is the mechanism for processing precursor molecules?

A. TRANSCRIPTION OF STRUCTURAL VS. INTERVENING SEQUENCES

To determine whether the intervening sequences within the ovalbumin gene affect the expression of different structural regions of the gene in target and nontarget tissue, total nuclear RNA from estrogen-stimulated oviduct, estrogen-withdrawn oviduct, unstimulated liver, and unstimulated spleen were hybridized in excess to probes for the OV_L and OV_R regions of the ovalbumin structural gene to measure the concentration of $mRNA_{ov}$ sequences corresponding to these regions. The OV_L probe contains structural sequences located in the 2.4 and 1.8 Kb fragment of the ovalbumin gene, and the OV_R probe contains structural sequences located in the 9.5 Kb fragment. [The *Hae*III site shown in the 1.8 Kb fragment (Fig. 12) is the *Hae*III site at position 818 used to prepare the OV_L and OV_R probes (Fig. 8).] Equimolar amounts of RNA corresponding to the OV_L and OV_R regions were detected in each tissue (Fig. 15). Using the data

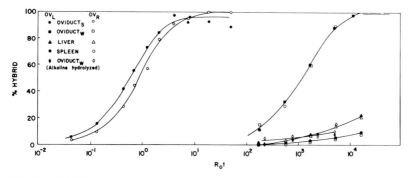

FIG. 15.   Hybridization of nuclear RNA to ^{3}H probes corresponding to structural sequences in the ovalbumin gene. The probes used were OV_L (filled symbols) and OV_R (open symbols). The RNAs used were extracted from stimulated oviduct ($\bullet$, $\bigcirc$) withdrawn oviduct ($\blacksquare$, $\square$) liver ($\blacktriangle$, $\triangle$), spleen, ($\blacksquare$, $\square$), and withdrawn oviduct, subjected to alkaline hydrolysis prior to hybridization ($\blacklozenge$, $\lozenge$). Hybridization was performed as previously described (Roop *et al.*, 1978).

in Fig. 15, we have calculated that there are approximately 3075 molecules of $mRNA_{ov}$ per tubular gland cell nucleus in estrogen-stimulated oviduct and approximately 2 molecules of $mRNA_{ov}$ tubular gland cell nucleus in estrogen-withdrawn oviduct nucleus (Table VI). Very low levels of structural gene transcripts were detected in nuclear RNA from unstimulated liver and spleen. Since equimolar amounts of RNA corresponding to OV_L and OV_R were detected in all four tissues, it appears that the structural sequence regions of the ovalbumin gene are under coordinate control in these tissues and that the intervening

TABLE VI

Concentration of Sequences Corresponding to Structural and Intervening Sequences within the Ovalbumin Gene in Total Nuclear RNA

	Molecules/tubular gland cell nucleus[b]		
Tissue[a]	Structural sequences	Intervening sequences 2.4	Intervening sequences 1.8
Oviduct$_S$	3075	233	286
Oviduct$_W$	2	<1	<1
Oviduct$_W$ + 2 hours DES	6	2	3
Oviduct$_W$ + 4 hours DES	71	—	15
Oviduct$_W$ + 8 hours DES	460	25	33
Oviduct$_W$ + 16 hours DES	995	9	26
Oviduct$_W$ + 24 hours DES	—	5	22
Oviduct$_W$ + 48 hours DES	3049	59	93

[a] DES, diethylstilbestrol; subscript S, estrogen-stimulated; subscript W, estrogen-withdrawn.

[b] Structural and intervening sequence probes were hybridized to nuclear RNA from the indicated tissues, and the number of molecules per tubular gland cell nucleus was calculated as previously described (Roop *et al.*, 1978).

sequences do not function as attenuators or terminators in estrogen-withdrawn oviduct or nontarget tissues, such as liver and spleen.

Nuclear RNA from the tissues described above were also assayed for the presence of transcripts corresponding to the intervening sequences within the ovalbumin gene. This was accomplished by hybridization with purified labeled 2.4 and 1.8 Kb fragments obtained from pOV2.4 and pOV1.8 cloned DNA (Roop *et al.*, 1978). Transcripts complementary to these fragments were detected in all the RNAs assayed; however, their concentration was greatly reduced compared to those for structural gene sequence (Fig. 16). We have calculated that there are approximately 233 molecules of RNA corresponding to the 2.4 Kb fragment intervening sequences, and approximately 286 molecules or RNA corresponding to the 1.8 Kb fragment intervening sequences, per tubular gland cell nucleus in estrogen-stimulated oviduct. Less than one molecule of RNA corresponding to each fragment per tubular gland cell nucleus was present in estrogen-withdrawn oviduct (Table VI). It should be noted that the extent of hybridization of both 2.4 and 1.8 Kb fragments to RNA from stimulated oviduct was approximately 50% (Fig. 16). This is equivalent to 100% hybridization assuming that both DNA strands of the fragments were labeled to the same degree by nick translation and that only the coding DNA strand was transcribed into RNA *in vivo*. These results suggest that all intervening sequences within the 2.4 and 1.8 Kb fragments of the ovalbumin gene are transcribed *in vivo*.

Since the withdrawal of estrogen from chronically stimulated chicks resulted in a marked decrease in the concentration of RNA corresponding to structural sequences (from 3075 molecules to 2 molecules, Table VI) and intervening

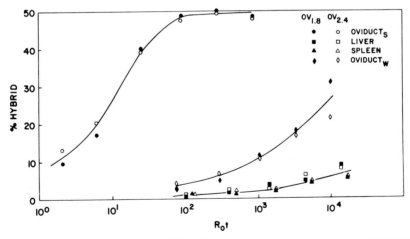

FIG. 16. Hybridization of nuclear RNA to ^3H probes corresponding to intervening sequences in the ovalbumin gene. The probes used were OV1.8 (filled symbols) and OV2.4 (open symbols). The RNAs used were extracted from stimulated oviduct (●, ○), withdrawn oviduct (◆, ◇), liver (■, □), and spleen (▲, △). Hybridization was performed as previously described (Roop *et al.*, 1978).

sequences (from approximately 250 molecules to less than 1 molecule, Table VI) in the ovalbumin gene, it was of interest to study the expression of these sequences during acute estrogen stimulation (Roop *et al.*, 1978). The accumulation of RNA corresponding to structural regions of the gene begins slowly during the first 2 hours after secondary stimulation (Table VI). By 4 hours, there is a dramatic increase in the accumulation of $mRNA_{ov}$ sequence, which continues at a constant rate. This type of secondary response observed for nuclear RNA is in agreement with that obtained when total cellular RNA was assayed (Harris *et al.*, 1975). The initial rate of accumulation of intervening sequence transcripts (2 hour point) is similar to that observed for structural sequence transcripts (Fig. 17). This indicates that transcription of structural and intervening sequences is coordinately induced by readministration of estrogen. The rate of accumulation of intervening sequence transcripts after the initial period is significantly less than that observed for structural sequence transcripts. Also an accumulation of intervening sequence RNA is observed for only 8 hours, and then a decrease occurs.

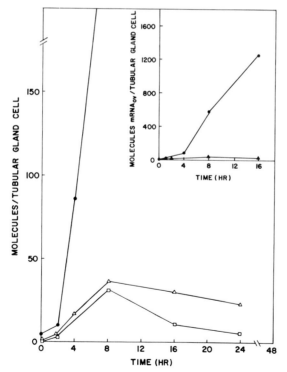

FIG. 17. Accumulation of RNA corresponding to structural and intervening sequences in the ovalbumin gene during secondary stimulation with estrogen. The data used to plot these curves were taken from Table VI. Plotted are the number of molecules corresponding to structural sequences (●), intervening sequences in OV2.4 (□), and intervening sequences in OV1.8 (△ and ▲).

These results raise the question whether RNA corresponding to intervening sequences is preferentially processed and degraded.

In an attempt to further investigate whether the transcription of structural and intervening sequences within the ovalbumin gene occurs at similar rates, we have examined their synthesis *in vitro* in nuclei. The synthesis in nuclei of RNA corresponding to structural sequences was assayed as described above in Section III,B. The synthesis of RNA corresponding to intervening sequences was determined by hybridizing labeled RNA synthesized in nuclei to filters containing pOV1.8 and pOV2.4 DNA (Roop *et al.*, 1978) (Table VII). Competition with $mRNA_{ov}$ was included in these experiments, since pOV2.4 and pOV1.8 contain approximately 20% structural sequences. An average of 0.055% and 0.051% of the total RNA synthesized corresponded to the intervening sequences in the 2.4 and 1.8 Kb fragments, respectively. These values are surprisingly similar to the value of 0.1% obtained under identical conditions for the structural sequences (Table III) and suggest that structural and intervening sequences within the ovalbumin gene are transcribed with similar kinetics. The fact that the amount of *in vitro* synthesized RNA corresponding to structural gene sequences was slightly greater than that observed for intervening sequences may indicate that some processing of RNA transcribed from the intervening sequences is occurring in nuclei.

Evidence that the intervening sequence transcripts were preferentially processed and not transported to cytoplasmic polysomes was obtained by measuring the concentration of RNA transcripts corresponding to structural and intervening sequences in total cellular RNA, nuclear RNA and polysomal RNA from chick oviduct (M.-J. Tsai *et al.*, 1978) (Table VIII). Oviduct tissue prepared from chicks chronically stimulated with DES contained approximately 58,000 molecules of $mRNA_{ov}$ sequence per tubular gland cell. The majority of these sequences were found in the cytoplasm bound to polysomes. There were only 200–300 molecules of RNA per cell transcribed from the intervening sequences of the 2.4 and 1.8 Kb fragments. In contrast, almost all these transcripts were found in the nucleus. The fact that a substantial difference in the ratio of $mRNA_{ov}$ to intervening sequence RNA exists in the nucleus (10-fold) and cytoplasm (2000-fold) suggests either that the intervening sequence transcripts are rapidly processed (degraded) as soon as they reach the cytoplasm, or, more likely, that they are degraded in the nucleus.

The small amount of intervening sequence RNA detected in polysomes (~20 copies) may arise from contamination of the polysome preparation by nuclear leakage. However, even if we assume that no contamination from nuclear leakage occurred, this value is substantially lower than the abundant number of cytoplasmic mRNA sequences synthesized from other hormone-dependent structural gene sequences, such as ovalbumin, ovomucoid, conalbumin, and lysozyme (S. Y. Tsai *et al.*, 1978; Hynes *et al.*, 1977; Lee *et al.*, 1978) and suggest that RNA transcripts from intervening sequences within the ovalbumin

TABLE VII

In Vitro Transcription of Ovalbumin Gene Intervening Sequences in Nuclei

Filter	Competitor	[³H]RNA hybridized[a] (cpm)	[³²P]cRNA recovery (%)	Hybridizable gene sequences (cpm)	Percent of total RNA	Average[b]
pOV230	—	1009	16.4	4499	0.110	0.10 ± 0.009
	mRNA$_{ov}$	271	—	—	—	—
pOV2.4	—	715	21.7	2295	0.056	0.058 ± 0.004
	mRNA$_{ov}$	712	20.7	2391	0.058	0.055 ± 0.003
	mRNA$_{ov}$ + RNA$_{2.4}$	217	—	—	—	—
pOV1.8	—	624	15.1	2616	0.064	0.057 ± 0.003
	mRNA$_{ov}$	668	18.4	2385	0.058	0.051 ± 0.006
	mRNA$_{ov}$ + RNA$_{1.8}$	229	—	—	—	—

[a] Input [³H]RNA = 4.09×10^6 cpm.

[b] Average and standard error of the mean determined on results from three separate experiments. Hybridization conditions were as previously described (Roop et al., 1978).

TABLE VIII
Ovalbumin RNA in Various RNA Preparations

RNA	Sequence of OV gene transcripts	$R_o t_{1/2}$	Fraction of OV RNA sequence in total RNA[a]	RNA:DNA[b]	Number of molecules per tubular gland cell[c]
Total RNA	$mRNA_{ov}$	5.4×10^{-1}	5.6×10^{-3}	3.5	58,000
	RNA 2.4	1.4×10^{2}	2.1×10^{-5}		228
	RNA 1.8	1.4×10^{2}	1.8×10^{-5}		233
Nuclear RNA	$mRNA_{ov}$	9.2×10^{-1}	3.3×10^{-3}	0.25	2,500
	RNA 2.4	1.0×10^{1}	3.0×10^{-4}		233
	RNA 1.8	1.0×10^{1}	2.7×10^{-4}		250
Polysomal RNA	$mRNA_{ov}$	5.5×10^{-1}	5.5×10^{-3}	2.9	47,000
	RNA 2.4	1.3×10^{3}	2.3×10^{-6}		20
	RNA 1.8	1.3×10^{3}	2.0×10^{-6}		21

[a] Fraction of OV RNA sequence in total RNA was estimated by comparing the $R_o t_{1/2}$ of individual RNA with $R_o t_{1/2}$ of back hybridization between mRNA and its DNA probe. The $R_o t_{1/2}$ of back hybridization for $mRNA_{ov}$ is 3×10^{-3}. The $R_o t_{1/2}$ for back hybridization of intervening sequences in RNA 1.8 and RNA 2.4 to their probes are calculated to be 2.65×10^{-3} and 2.98×10^{-3}, respectively, after taking into account their size (Roop et al., 1978).

[b] RNA:DNA ratio in oviduct cell was obtained as previously described (Harris et al., 1975).

[c] Number of molecules per tubular gland cell was calculated as described previously (Roop et al., 1978) after taking into account that only 80% of oviduct cells are tubular gland cells and the size of $mRNA_{ov}$ sequences is 1930 nucleotides. Intervening sequences in OV1.8 are 1500 nucleotides, and intervening sequences in OV2.4 are 1900 nucleotides.

gene do not function as components of mRNA for these other hormone-dependent genes. Furthermore, the ovalbumin gene intervening sequence transcripts were not detected in other tissues, such as liver and spleen (less than 0.1 molecule/cell: Fig. 16). Thus, it appears unlikely that the ovalbumin intervening sequences ever serve as templates for synthesis of any other mRNA sequences in these tissues. This is further supported by DNA-sequence analysis of the intervening sequences, which revealed the presence of numerous nonsense codons for translation in these regions of the ovalbumin gene (George Brownlee et al., unpublished observations).

B. THE PRIMARY TRANSCRIPT OF THE OVALBUMIN GENE

In the experiments described above we demonstrated that structural sequences separated by intervening sequence regions were coordinately regulated, that the intervening sequences themselves were transcribed in their entirety with kinetics similar to that observed for structural sequences, and that intervening sequence transcripts appear to be preferentially processed and degraded. Since these results are consistent with the hypothesis that the entire ovalbumin gene is transcribed as a large precursor molecule followed by processing (excision and degradation) of the intervening sequence transcripts, it was of interest to examine nuclear RNA for the presence of precursor molecules. This was accomplished by fractionating oviduct nuclear RNA by electrophoresis on agarose gels in the presence of methylmercury hydroxide, transferring the RNA to diazobenzyloxymethyl paper, and hybridizing the covalently bound RNA to ^{32}P-labeled pOV230 probe (Roop et al., 1978). Multiple discrete bands containing ovalbumin structural sequences were observed (Fig. 18, slot B). The most intense band of nuclear ovalbumin RNA ran similar to that observed using cytoplasmic RNA (Fig. 18, slot A) and represented mature ovalbumin mRNA. The sizes of the other species of ovalbumin RNA range from approximately 1.3 to more than 4 times the size of ovalbumin mRNA (~2000 nucleotides). These high molecular weight species of RNA that contain ovalbumin sequences are detected only in oviduct tissue, and estrogen administration is necessary for their induction (Roop et al., 1978).

Hybridization of the transferred RNA to ^{32}P-labeled 2.4 and 1.8 Kb fragments demonstrated that these high molecular weight species of RNA also contain RNA transcripts complementary to the intervening sequences of the ovalbumin gene (Roop et al., 1978) (Fig. 19). Most of the major bands of oviduct nuclear RNA that hybridized to the pOV230 DNA probe were again detected when hybridized to either the 2.4 Kb or 1.8 Kb probes (Fig. 19, lane B). This is to be expected, since both probes contain structural (about 20%) as well as intervening sequences. To determine whether RNA corresponding exclusively to the intervening sequences could be detected, excess unlabeled $mRNA_{ov}$ was added to the hybridization reaction to act as a competitor for the structural sequences present in the 2.4 and 1.8 Kb probes. Under these hybridization conditions, detection of

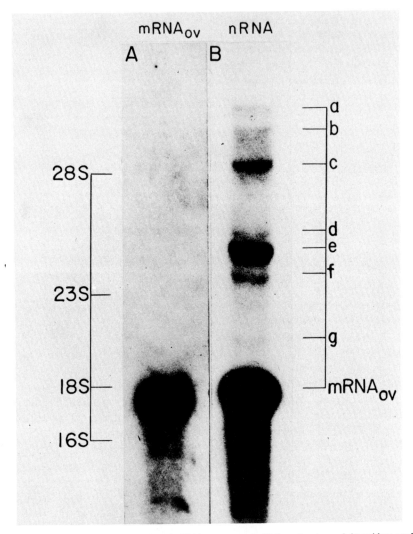

FIG. 18. Identification of ovalbumin RNA sequences in high molecular weight oviduct nuclear RNA. Oviduct RNA from chicks stimulated with diethylstilbestrol was subjected to electrophoresis (40 V, 16 hours), transferred to DBM paper, and hybridized with the ^{32}P-labeled ovalbumin structural sequence probe, pOV230. The mobility of the ribosomal RNA markers was determined by ethidium bromide staining. (A) Purified cytoplasmic mRNA$_{ov}$, 0.1 μg. (B) Oviduct nuclear RNA, 20 μg. The ovalbumin sequence-containing RNA bands were arbitrarily labeled from a to g. From Roop *et al.* (1978).

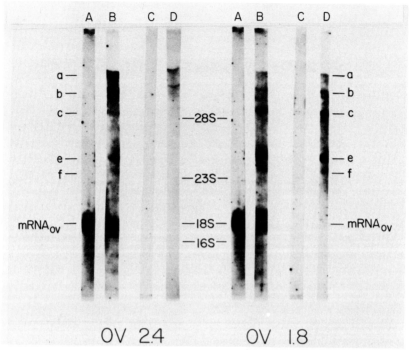

FIG. 19. Identification of sequences complementary to the intervening DNA sequences of the ovalbumin gene in oviduct nuclear RNA. Oviduct nuclear RNA was subjected to electrophoresis (50 V, 20 hours), transferred to DBM paper, and allowed to hybridize to the ^{32}P-labeled 2.4 and 1.8 Kb EcoRI fragments either in the presence or in the absence of excess unlabeled mRNA$_{ov}$ as a competitor. A: Purified, cytoplasmic ovalbumin mRNA, 0.1 μg. B: Oviduct nuclear RNA, 20 μg. C: Purified, cytoplasmic ovalbumin mRNA, 0.1 μg. Unlabeled mRNA$_{ov}$ (20 μg) present during hybridization. D: Oviduct nuclear RNA, 20 μg. Unlabeled mRNA$_{ov}$ (20 μg) present during hybridization. Left panel: Hybridization with ^{32}P-labeled 2.4 Kb EcoRI fragment of the ovalbumin gene. Right panel: Hybridization with the ^{32}P-labeled 1.8 Kb EcoRI fragment of the ovalbumin gene. From Roop et al. (1978).

the band corresponding to mature mRNA$_{ov}$ was eliminated (Fig. 19, lane C). The OV2.4 probe hybridized only to bands a and b, and OV1.8 probe hybridized to all the major bands (a, b, c, e, and f) (Fig. 19, slot D). Thus, RNA corresponding to the intervening sequences of OV1.8 are present in all the prominent high molecular weight ovalbumin species, while those of OV2.4 are present in greater amounts in the two larger species. These results are consistent with the hypothesis that the intervening sequences of the ovalbumin gene are transcribed into high molecular weight precursors and that the intervening sequences of OV2.4 appear to be removed prior to those of OV1.8. A schematic representation of transcription of the ovalbumin gene and processing of this transcript is shown in Fig. 20. We postulate that the entire natural gene is transcribed into a

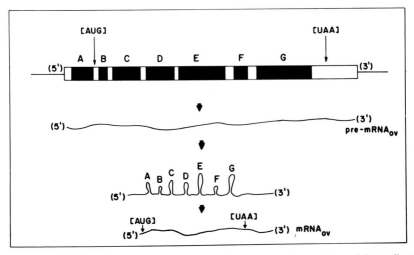

FIG. 20. Schematic representation of a proposed mechanism of transcription of the ovalbumin gene and processing of its primary transcript.

giant precursor RNA and that this molecule is processed so that the intervening sequence transcripts are removed to produce the intact, colinear mature $mRNA_{ov}$. Our laboratory results indicate that poly(A) is attached at the initial precursor stage and remains on the molecule while processing takes place.

It was also of interest to analyze the size of ovalbumin sequence-containing RNA in oviduct nuclei after hormone withdrawal during readministration of estrogen. Withdrawal of DES resulted in a depletion in the level of high molecular weight ovalbumin RNA as well as that of mature $mRNA_{ov}$ (Fig. 21). Since we were able to detect $mRNA_{ov}$ only when 100 μg of withdrawn nuclear RNA was assayed, we have estimated that approximately one part per 10^6 of this nuclear RNA contains ovalbumin sequences (Swaneck *et al.*, 1979). This value agrees well with the value of 1.9×10^{-6} obtained from RNA excess hybridization experiments (Table VI). The kinetics of induction of high molecular weight ovalbumin RNA in Fig. 21 is also similar to that observed by RNA excess hybridization to the intervening sequence probes (Fig. 17). These high molecular weight species increase coordinately with mature $mRNA_{ov}$ for the first few hours after estrogen readministration and then level off. The concentration of mature $mRNA_{ov}$, however, continues to increase for at least 16 hours. The observations that withdrawal of hormone depletes the nucleus of high molecular weight ovalbumin RNA as well as that of mature $mRNA_{ov}$ and that readministration of estrogen induces the accumulation of both species are consistent with the hypothesis that the ovalbumin gene is regulated by estrogen at the transcriptional level. These results rule out the unlikely possibility that the rapid accumulation of mature $mRNA_{ov}$ after secondary stimulation occurs by processing of ovalbumin

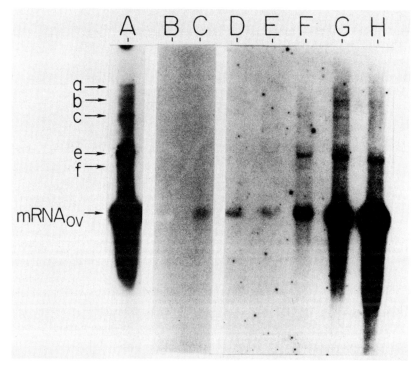

FIG. 21. Induction of high molecular weight ovalbumin RNA by secondary estrogen stimulation. Oviduct nuclear RNA, isolated from chicks subjected to the indicated hormonal treatments, was electrophoresed (40 V, 16 hours) on 1.5% agarose gels containing 10 mM methylmercury hydroxide. The RNA was transferred to DBM paper (12 × 14 cm) and hybridized with the ^{32}P-labeled pOV230 probe (2 × 10^7 cpm, specific activity 2.5 × 10^8 cpm/μg). Species of ovalbumin RNA larger than mRNA$_{ov}$ were arbitrarily labeled a–g (1). Bands d and g, which are minor species, were not detected in this figure. A: Oviduct nuclear RNA (20 μg) from chicks chronically stimulated with DES. B: Oviduct nuclear RNA (20 μg) from chicks stimulated with diethylstilbestrol (DES) and then withdrawn from hormone for 14 days. C: Same as lane B, except 100 μg. D: Oviduct nuclear RNA (20 μg) from chicks withdrawn for 14 days and restimulated with DES for 1 hour. E: Same as D except restimulation period was 2 hours. F: Same as D except restimulation period was 4 hours. G: Same as D except for 8 hours. H: Same as D except for 16 hours. From Roop et al. (1978).

RNA precursors that might have been stored in the withdrawn oviduct and are in agreement with the *in vitro* transcription experiments discussed in Section III, B.

C. PROCESSING OF THE PRIMARY TRANSCRIPT TO MATURE mRNA

In an attempt to gain some insight into the process by which intervening sequence RNA is converted from precursor molecules to mature messenger RNA$_{ov}$, a collaborative effort between George Brownlee's laboratory (MRC,

Cambridge) and our laboratory has resulted in determination of the DNA sequence in the junctions between structural and intervening sequences in the ovalbumin gene (Catterall *et al.*, 1978). An analysis of these data revealed the following points of interest. (1) The intervening sequences are rich in pyrimidine residues, especially at the 3' ends. (2) There is a redundancy of the structural sequence at each structural-intervening sequence junction, which probably represents an evolutionary conservation of homology. (3) The basic redundancy at all junctions was contained within the hexonucleotide (5') T-C-A-G-G-T (3'). (4) A "consensus" sequence C-A-G-G could be derived by counting the frequency of each nucleotide present in each junction. (5) The consensus sequence is well conserved in each of the ovalbumin junctions in addition to those found in immunoglobin λ chain (Tonegawa *et al.*, 1978) and a mouse β-globin gene (Tilghman *et al.*, 1978b), and again suggest that this sequence is conserved in evolution. (6) The exact splice point appears to occur at the G-G position in the consensus sequence. (7) The first cut by the processing enzyme in the consensus intersequence occurs immediately 5' to a G-T doublet (G-U in RNA) at one end and immediately 3' to an A-G doublet at the other end. (8) No evidence was found for strong Watson–Crick base pairing between sequences adjacent to any of the junctions. Taking the information derived above into account, an example of a typical processing reaction is demonstrated in Fig. 22.

Since there appears to be an insufficient amount of conserved sequence to allow for a specific protein–RNA interaction at these structural-intervening sequence junctions, it seems that the tertiary structure of the RNA in these regions must play some role in processing enzyme recognition of the appropriate RNA splicing sequence. Elucidation of the mechanism of splicing must await

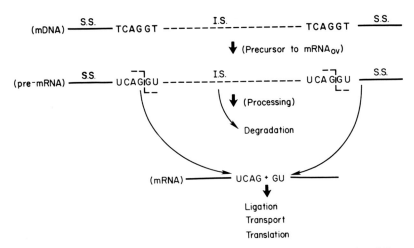

FIG. 22.   Hypothetical excision and splicing reaction during $mRNA_{ov}$ processing. S.S., structured sequence; I.S., intervening sequence.

isolation of the enzyme, or enzymes, involved. At the present time we have limited information concerning the effect of estrogen on RNA processing. However, since high molecular weight ovalbumin RNA did not accumulate prior to that of mature messenger RNA_{ov} during estrogen readministration (Fig. 21), sufficient processing enzyme activity must be present in the withdrawn oviduct to convert the initial estrogen-induced primary transcripts to mature messenger RNA_{ov}.

VI. The Future

At present there seems to be little doubt that steroid hormones can initiate a transcriptional response at the level of the gene and that receptors are requisite intermediates in this response. In the past year our knowledge of the organization and structure of eukaryotic genes has expanded greatly. Nevertheless, our understanding of genetic regulatory regions (i.e., promoters) in DNA is practically nonexistent. Perhaps an even greater mystery is the regulatory mechanisms of the nonhistone and histone protein coat of the DNA. To date, the complexity of the nonhistone protein population has defied any attempt at mechanistic analyses, but its importance is intuitive. Finally, much more remains to be learned about posttranscriptional RNA processing, including purification of the enzyme(s) involved and definition of their actions. Obviously then, a great deal of experimentation must be completed before the chemistry of the regulatory processes for gene expression is defined in precise detail. Nevertheless, the last 5 years have demonstrated that the complexities of eukaryotic gene expression are certainly not beyond a definitive solution in the not-too-distant future.

REFERENCES

Baker, H. J., and Shapiro, D. J. (1977). *J. Biol. Chem.* **252**, 8428.
Beato, M., and Rungger, D. (1975). *FEBS Lett.* **59**, 305.
Blattner, F. R., Williams, B. J., Blechl, A. E., Denniston-Thompson, K., Faber, H. E., Furlong, L.-A., Grunwald, D. J., Kiefer, D. O., Moore, D. D., Schummn, J. W., Sheldon, R. L., and Smithies, O. (1977). *Science* **196**, 161.
Breathnach, R., Mandel, J. L., and Chambon, P. (1977). *Nature (London)* **270**, 314.
Bullock, D. W., Woo, S. L. C., and O'Malley, B. W. (1976). *Biol. Reprod.* **15**, 435.
Catterall, J. F., O'Malley, B. W., Robertson, M. A., Staden, R., Tanaka, Y., and Brownlee, G. G. (1978). *Nature (London)* (in press).
Chan, L., and O'Malley, B. W. (1976a). *N. Engl. J. Med.* **294**, 1322.
Chan, L., and O'Malley, B. W. (1976b). *N. Engl. J. Med.* **294**, 1372.
Chan, L., and O'Malley, B. W. (1976c). *N. Engl. J. Med.* **294**, 1430.
Chan, L., Jackson, R. L., O'Malley, B. W., and Means, A. R. (1976). *J. Clin. Invest.* **58**, 368.
Chan, L., Means, A. R., and O'Malley, B. W. (1973). *Proc. Natl. Acad. Sci. U.S.A.* **70**, 1870.
Cox, R. R. (1977). *Biochemistry* **16**, 3433.
Cox, R. R., Hines, M. E., and Emtage, S. (1974). *Eur. J. Biochem.* **49**, 225.
Curtiss, R., III (1977). *In* "Molecular Cloning of Recombinant DNA" (W. A. Scott and R. Werner, eds.), p. 99. Academic Press, New York.

Deeley, R. G., Gurdon, J. L., Burns, A. T. H., Mullinix, K. P., Bina-Stein, M., and Goldberger, R. G. (1977). *J. Biol. Chem.* **252,** 8310.

Diesterhaft, M., Noguchi, T., Hargrove, J., Thornton, C., and Granner, D. (1977). *Biochem. Biophys. Res. Commun.* **79,** 1015.

Doel, M. T., Houghton, M., Cook, E. A., and Carey, N. H. (1977). *Nucl. Acid Res.* **4,** 3701.

Dugaiczyk, A., Boyer, H. W., and Goodman, H. M. (1975). *J. Mol. Biol.* **96,** 171.

Dugaiczyk, A., Woo, S. L. C., Lai, E. C., Mace, M. L., McReynolds, L. A., and O'Malley, B. W. (1978). *Nature (London)* **274,** 328.

Dukes, P. P., Sekeris, C. E., and Schmid, W. (1966). *Biochim. Biophys. Acta* **123,** 126.

Efstratiadis, A., Kafatos, F. C., and Maniatis, T. (1977). *Cell* **10,** 571.

Feldman, D., Funder, J. W., and Edelman, I. S. (1972). *Am. J. Med.* **53,** 545.

Garapin, A. C., Lepennec, J. P., Roskam, W., Perrin, F., Cami, B., Krust, A., Breathnach, R., Chambon, P., and Kourilsky, P. (1978). *Nature (London)* **273,** 349.

Gelehrter, T. D. (1973). *Metabolism* **22,** 85.

Goodman, H. M., Olson, M. V., and Hall, B. D. (1977). *Proc. Natl. Acad. Sci. U.S.A.* **74,** 5453.

Gorski, J. (1964). *J. Biol. Chem.* **230,** 889.

Gorski, J. and Gannon, F. (1976). *Annu. Rev. Physiol.* **38,** 425.

Hardies, S. C., and Wells, R. D. (1976). *Proc. Natl. Acad. Sci. U.S.A.* **73,** 3117.

Harris, S. E., Rosen, J. M., Means, A. R., and O'Malley, B. W. (1975). *Biochemistry* **14,** 2072.

Hynes, N. E., Groner, B., Sippel, A. E., Njuyen-Huu, M. C., and Schütz, G. (1977). *Cell* **11,** 923.

Iynedjian, P. B., and Hanson, R. W. (1977). *J. Biol. Chem.* **252,** 8398.

Jeffreys, A. J., and Flavell, R. A. (1977). *Cell* **12,** 1097.

Jensen, E. V., and De Sombre, E. R. (1974). *Vitam. Horm. (New York)* **32,** 89.

Katz, L., Kingsbury, D. T., and Helinski, D. R. (1973). *J. Bacteriol.* **114,** 577.

Kohler, P. O., Grimley, P. M., and O'Malley, B. W. (1969). *J. Cell Biol.* **40,** 8.

Kurtz, D. T., and Feigelson, P. (1977). *Proc. Natl. Acad. Sci. U.S.A.* **74,** 4791.

Lai, E. C., Woo, S. L. C., Dugaiczky, A., Catterall, J. F., and O'Malley, B. W. (1978). *Proc. Natl. Acad. Sci. U.S.A.* **75,** 2205.

Lai, E. C., Woo, S. L. C., Dugaiczyk, A., and O'Malley, B. W. (1979). *Cell* (in press).

Liao, S. (1977). *Biochem. Action Horm.* **4,** 351.

Leder, P., Tiemeier, D., and Enquist, L. (1977). *Science* **196,** 175.

Lee, D. C., McKnight, G. S., and Palmiter, R. D. (1978). *J. Biol. Chem.* **253,** 3494.

Levey, I. L., and Daniel, J. C., Jr. (1976). *Biol. Reprod.* **14,** 194.

McGuire, W. L., and O'Malley, B. W. (1968). *Biochim. Biophys. Acta* **157,** 187.

McKnight, G. S., Pennequin, P., and Schimke, R. T. (1975). *J. Biol. Chem.* **250,** 8105.

McReynolds, L. A., Catterall, J. F., and O'Malley, B. W. (1977b). *Gene* **2,** 217.

McReynolds, L. A., Monahan, J. J., Bendure, D. W., Woo, S. L. C., Paddock, G. V., Salser, W., Dorsen, J., Moses, R. E., and O'Malley, B. W. (1977a). *J. Biol. Chem.* **252,** 1840.

McReynolds, L. A., O'Malley, B. W., Misbet, A. D., Fothergill, J. E., Givole, D., Fields, S., Robertson, M., and Brownlee, G. G. (1978). *Nature (London)* **273,** 723.

Mainwaring, W. I. P., Mangan, F. R., Irving, R. A., and Jones, D. A. (1974). *Biochem. J.* **144,** 413.

Mandel, J. L., Breathnach, R., Gerlinger, P., Le Meur, M., Gannon, F., and Chambon, P. (1978). *Cell* **14,** 641.

Maniatis, T., Jeffrey, A., and Kleid, D. G. (1975). *Proc. Natl. Acad. Sci. U.S.A.* **72,** 1184.

Marotta, C. A., Wilson, J. T., Forget, B. G., and Weissman, S. M. (1977). *J. Biol. Chem.* **252,** 5040.

Martial, J. A., Baxter, J. D., Goodman, H. M., and Seeburg, P. H. (1977). *Proc. Natl. Acad. Sci. U.S.A.* **74,** 1816.

Maxam, A. M., and Gilbert, W. (1977). *Proc. Natl. Acad. Sci. U.S.A.* **74,** 560.

Mears, J. G., Ramirez, F., Leibowitz, D., and Bank, A. (1978). *Cell* **15,** 15.

Monahan, J. J., Harris, S. E., Woo, S. L. C., Robberson, D. L., and O'Malley, B. W. (1976a). *Biochemistry* **15,** 223.

Monahan, J. J., Harris, S. E., and O'Malley, B. W. (1976b). *J. Biol. Chem.* **251,** 3738.

Monahan, J. J., Woo, S. L. C., Liarakos, C. D., and O'Malley, B. W. (1977). *J. Biol. Chem.* **252,** 4722.

Mullinix, K. P., Wetekam, W., Deeley, R. G., Gordon, J. I., Meyers, M., Kent, K. A., and Goldberger, R. F. (1976). *Proc. Natl. Acad. Sci. U.S.A.* **73,** 1442.

Nakanishi, S., Kita, T., Taii, S., Imura, H., and Numa, S. (1977). *Proc. Natl. Acad. Sci. U.S.A.* **74,** 3283.

Nickol, J. M., Lee, K.-L., Hollinger, T. G., and Kenney, F. T. (1976). *Biochem. Biophys. Res. Commun.* **72,** 687.

Oka, T., and Schimke, R. T. (1969). *J. Cell Biol.* **43,** 123.

O'Malley, B. W. (1967). *Biochemistry* **6,** 2546.

O'Malley, B. W., and McGuire, W. L. (1968). *Proc. Natl. Acad. Sci. U.S.A.* **60,** 1527.

O'Malley, B. W., and Means, A. R. (1974). *Science* **183,** 610.

O'Malley, B. W., McGuire, W. L., and Korenman, S. G. (1967). *Biochim. Biophys. Acta* **145,** 204.

O'Malley, B. W., McGuire, W. L., Kohler, P. O., and Korenman, S. G. (1969). *Recent Prog. Horm. Res.* **25,** 105.

Osawa, S., and Tomino, S. (1977). *Biochem. Biophys. Res. Commun.* **77,** 628.

Palmiter, R. D., and Carey, N. H. (1974). *Proc. Natl. Acad. Sci. U.S.A.* **71,** 2357.

Palmiter, R. D., and Schimke, R. T. (1973). *J. Biol. Chem.* **248,** 1502.

Palmiter, R. D., Moore, P. B., and Mulvihill, E. R. (1976). *Cell* **8,** 557.

Parks, W. P., Scolnick, E. M., and Kozikowski, E. H. (1974). *Science* **184,** 158.

Pitot, H. C., and Yatvin, M. B. (1973). *Physiol. Rev.* **53,** 228.

Raynaud-Jammet, C., Bieri, F., and Baulieu, E. (1971). *Biochim. Biophys. Acta* **247,** 355.

Ringold, G., Yamamoto, K. R., Tomkins, G. M., Bishop, J. M., and Varmus, H. E., (1975) *Cell* **6,** 299.

Robberson, D., Alonis, Y., Attardi, G., and Davidson, N. (1971). *J. Mol. Biol.* **60,** 473.

Rodriquez, R. L., Bolivar, F., Goodman, H. M., Boyer, H. W., and Betlach, M. C. (1976). *In* "Molecular Mechanisms in the Control of Gene Expression" (D. P. Nierlich, W. J. Rutter, and C. F. Fox, eds.), p. 471. Academic Press, New York.

Roewekamp, W. G., Hofer, E., and Sekeris, C. E. (1976). *Eur. J. Biochem.* **70,** 259.

Roop, D. R., Nordstrom, J. L., Tsai, S. Y., Tsai, M.-J., and O'Malley, B. W. (1978). *Cell* **15,** 671.

Rosen, J. M., Woo, S. L. C., Holder, J. W., Means, A. R., and O'Malley, B. W. (1975). *Biochemistry* **14,** 69.

Rosenfeld, G. C., Comstock, J. P., Means, A. R., and O'Malley, B. W. (1972). *Biochem. Biophys. Res. Commun.* **47,** 387.

Ryffel, G. V., Wakli, W., and Weber, R. (1977). *Cell* **11,** 213.

Sajdel, E. M., and Jacob, S. T. (1971). *Biochem. Biophys. Res. Commun.* **45,** 707.

Sarkar, P. K., and Griffith, B. (1976). *Biochem Biophys. Res. Commun.* **68,** 675.

Schrader, W. T., and O'Malley, B. W. (1971). *J. Biol. Chem.* **247,** 51.

Schultz, G., Killewich, L., Chen, G., and Feigelson, P. (1975). *Proc. Natl. Acad. Sci. U.S.A.* **72,** 1017.

Shapiro, D. J., Baker, H. J., and Stitt, D. T. (1976). *J. Biol. Chem.* **251,** 3105.

Sippel, A. E., Feigelson, P., and Roy, A. K. (1975). *Biochemistry* **14,** 825.

Southern, E. M. (1975). *J. Mol. Biol.* **98,** 503.

Swaneck, G. E., Chu, L. L. H., and Edelman, I. S. (1970). *J. Biol. Chem.* **245,** 5382.

Swaneck, G. E., Nordstrom, J. L., Kreuzaler, F., Tsai, M.-J., and O'Malley, B. W. (1979). *Proc. Natl. Acad. Sci. U.S.A.* (in press).

Tilghman, S. M., Tiemeier, D. C., Seidman, J. G., Peterkin, B. M., Sullivan, M., Maizel, G. V., and Leder, P. (1978a). *Proc. Natl. Acad. Sci. U.S.A.* **75,** 725.

Tilghman, S. M., Curtis, P. J., Tiemeier, D. C., Leder, P., and Weissman, C. (1978b). *Proc. Natl. Acad. Sci. U.S.A.* **75**, 1309.

Tonegawa, S., Maxam, A. M., Tizard, R., Bernard, O., and Gilbert, W. (1978). *Proc. Natl. Acad. Sci. U.S.A.* **75**, 1485.

Tsai, M.-J., Tsai, S. Y., and O'Malley, B. W. (1979). *Science* **204**, 314.

Tsai, S. Y., Roop, D. R., Tsai, M.-J., Stein, J. P., Means, A. R., and O'Malley, B. W. (1978). *Biochemistry* **17**, 5773.

Tushinski, R. J., Sussman, P. M., Yu, L.-Y., and Bancroft, F. C. (1977). *Proc. Natl. Acad. Sci. U.S.A.* **74**, 2357.

Valenzuela, P., Venegas, A., Weinberg, F., Bishop, R., and Rutter, W. J. (1978). *Proc. Natl. Acad. Sci. U.S.A.* **75**, 190.

Van, N. T., Holder, J. W., Woo, S. L. C., Means, A. R., and O'Malley, B. W. (1976). *Biochemistry* **15**, 2054.

Vedeckis, W. V., Schrader, W. T., and O'Malley, B. W. (1978). *In* "Biochemical Actions of Hormones" (G. Litwack, ed.), Vol. 5, 321. Academic Press, New York.

Weinstock, R., Sweet, R., Weiss, M., Cedar, H., and Axel, R. (1978). *Proc. Natl. Acad. Sci. U.S.A.* **75**, 1299.

White, R. L., and Hogness, D. S. (1977). *Cell* **10**, 177.

Woo, S. L. C., Dugaiczyk, A., Tsai, M.-J., Lai, E. C., Catterall, J. F., and O'Malley, B. W. (1978). *Proc. Natl. Acad. Sci. U.S.A.* **75**, 3688.

Woo, S. L. C., Rosen, J. M., Liarakos, C. D., Choi, Y. C., Busch, H., Means, A. R., and O'Malley, B. W. (1975). *J. Biol. Chem.* **250**, 7027.

Yamamoto, K. R., and Albert, B. W. (1976). *Annu. Rev. Biochem.* **45**, 721.

Young, H. A., Shih, T. Y., Scolnick, E. M., and Parks, W. P. (1977). *J. Virol.* **21**, 139.

Zerwekh, J. E., Haussler, M. R., and Lindell, T. J. (1974). *Proc. Natl. Acad. Sci. U.S.A.* **71**, 2377.

DISCUSSION

F. Naftolin: Does the proposed sequence of events hold during the period of chromatin dispersion—as *in vivo* life situations require? Do the chromosomes interact, or are they as compartmentalized as your description, if taken literally, would suggest?

B. O'Malley: These genes are split into pieces, but are localized to one chromosome. Although they cover about 8000 bases, this is a rather small area compared to the overall length of eukaryotic DNA ($\sim$ 1 to 3 $\times$ 10^9 bases). They will probably always be localized to a single chromosome and would not translocate in the DNA. If though, for any reason, one lost a piece of this large gene, the gene might become inactive. It is possible, however, that an interior piece of intervening sequence DNA could be lost without disturbing structural mRNA since the intervening sequence transcripts appear to be edited out and degraded. I should comment that the large size of these eukaryotic genes provides a larger area for recombination events, so that one has a greater possibility of recombination: If the gene is 10-fold greater in size, the recombination rate could then be 10-fold greater than expected.

B. F. Rice: You have given us a very nice presentation as to how the steroid hormone might turn the gene on, and I have a specific question as to how the steroid hormone might turn the gene off. It relates to an observation that I heard at a meeting about the cortisol in very low molar concentrations inhibiting the synthesis and the rates of which is activated, and presumably this is an explanation for the anti-inflammatory type of cortisol. Do you have some explanation as to how you might explain this with your scheme?

B. O'Malley: We have had so much to do to figure out how this gene was turned on that we have not had time to work on any other aspects of the process. In the type of response that we are monitoring, it seems that the action of the hormone is to turn on transcription of the gene, and that transcription decreases very quickly as the concentration of inducer steroid in the blood drops. Under these conditions, a nonequilibrium condition exists for the hormone–receptor complex, and at body temperature the receptor tends to loose its bound hormone within a few minutes; when the hormone dissociates from receptor, the receptor no longer binds to the chromosomes. This dissociation of hormone–receptor complex from the DNA during hormone withdrawal might be the impetus for transcription of that gene to shut down. Another quite different shutdown of gene transcription could also occur. In this model, the hormone–receptor complex could act primarily to shut down transcription of certain genes. The details of this type of response, however, are less well understood. Finally, when we consider negative responses in which things seem to be shut off by steroid hormones, we should consider a well known model in which glucocorticoids act to suppress (or even kill) thymocytes.

A question could be raised as to how such a kill response relates to the positive inductive response seen in the chick oviduct. There was a time when such a model system was used as an illustration of how steroids act differently in each cell type. Recently we have come to understand how such negative responses may come to pass through virtually the same series of events as positive growth response. In fact, such responses work through a similar mechanism in that there is receptor for the hormone in that cell. The receptor binds the hormone and translocates to the nucleus, where it binds to chromatin. Next there is an RNA-dependent response that can be inhibited by actinomycin D, thereby blocking the response. Subsequent to these events something is made in the cell that shuts off membrane transport or glucose metabolism (probably a protein). Thus, via the same pathway a protein can be induced that has a positive effect on the cell or, in another case, actually kills the cell. Finally, in certain systems, a hormone may directly shut down transcription. The glucocorticoid effect on pituitary ACTH production is a prime candidate for such a response, but the definite studies on ACTH mRNA synthesis have not yet been done to the best of my knowledge.

A. L. Goodman: How can you determine what is being regulated? Is it the gene itself, or is it the enzyme that seems to cleave out the intervening sequence? If I understood you correctly, an intermediate (i.e., mRNA) is transcribed that includes all the sequences of the structural gene as well as some intervening sequences. If there were no active enzyme present, then there would be no net ovalbumin synthesis, because the intermediate mRNA would not be the proper message. Is that correct? So, the enzyme is required to align, in appropriate linear order, the structural gene mRNA. How can you distinguish between the action of the hormone in stimulating the reading of the gene as opposed to an action of the hormone in activating the enzyme that gives the net (i.e., mRNA) message?

B. O'Malley: I have previously mentioned a few reasons for this, but I will focus on the two major ones. I might say first, however, that we do not have evidence that the enzyme system is not regulated. There could be some induction of this enzyme as part of a coordinated growth response in the cell. What I wanted to focus on was the primary action of the hormone. In the unstimulated cell, is the precursor made from that gene and cannot be processed to the mature $mRNA_{ov}$—and therefore we have no biologic message in the cell—or are we turning on the synthesis as the precursor to $mRNA_{ov}$. We have radioactive probes now for the precusor and we have filters containing large amounts of intervening-sequence DNA, so that we can monitor the rate of synthesis of all the structural components in that long gene and all the intervening sequences. (1) We observe that with hormone we stimulate in a coordinate fashion a net synthesis of precursor to $mRNA_{ov}$ which are complementary to both structural and intervening sequences. (2) We now see an appearance of these precursors in mass assays in the cells which we assay by those insert-specific probes using the Northern gels (3) At early inductive times, what would you expect if the enzyme system was rate limiting? You would expect to turn on synthesis of the precursor, and it would build up and would be unable to be converted to the biologically active message. We do not see this. We see that the initial precursor to $mRNA_{ov}$ is converted immediately to 18 S $mRNA_{ov}$. Thus the processing enzyme system does not seem to be "rate-limiting" for initial production of mRNA (within 1 hour of hormone stimulation).

A. L. Goodman: Have you any evidence of the specificity of the enzyme that cleaves out the intervening sequences?

B. O'Malley: No, we have not yet isolated the enzyme. We are working on it at present. We may have to assay for it. We hope to have some information on this aspect of the problem later this year.

R. Levine: Do the intervening pieces—the insertions into the large genes—occur randomly in all kinds of genes, or is this phenomenon restricted to inducible genes? Do common "proletarian" genes that serve every cell, e.g., the one for hexokinase or the one for phosphofructokinase, contain these large insertions? Is there a method in this madness that has to do with inducibility or the differentiation properties, and does not this apply to the ordinary "household" genes? I hope that you may have some information on this problem.

B. O'Malley: This is a question that we too have considered but have no answer for at present. I can say that not just inducible genes have intervening sequences. Globin, immunoglobin E tRNA primary transcripts also have them.

J. Baxter: I wanted first to make a comment relating to the question about glucocorticoids. It is clear of course that glucocorticoids negatively regulate cellular functions in a lot of tissues, and one of the leading models has been that the steroid induces some gene product that in turn is inhibitory to the cell. In several systems, in particular the mouse thymocyte system, there is some indirect evidence based on inhibitor studies that they may be the case. More recently, we have collected data looking at a specific messenger RNA, that for the common precursor to ACTH and β-endorphin (J. Roberts, E. Herbert, and J. D. Baxter, in preparation). The glucocorticoids specifically decrease this mRNA. In this system, the steroid can also decrease this RNA when protein synthesis is totally blocked. Thus, this is a case where a steroid hormone can lower a specific messenger RNA without having to induce any intermediary protein. Findings such as this one will ultimately have to be considered in developing any detailed models for steroid hormone action.

In regard to measurements of the incorporation of precursors into ovalbumin mRNA, if the receptor–estrogen complex is stimulating transcription of the ovalbumin gene, why does it do it a lot better at 24 hours than at 1 or 2 hours, by which time there is maximal nuclear binding? That came out in both your studies of cell-free transcription and of the incorporation of precursors *in vivo*.

B. O'Malley: There is no doubt that the induction of $mRNA_{ov}$ is a two-phase response. After the initial induction of synthesis at 1 hour, the response becomes more efficient at about 4 hours. We do not completely understand this observation at the present time. The possible explanations range from differential temporal recruitment of oviduct cells to synthesis of an amplification factor.

J. Baxter: I am aware of your earlier cell free studies of stimulation by receptors of oviduct chromatin, but do you think that the lag in kinetics could mean that estrogens are inducing some other protein(s), that is, are in turn secondarily stimulating the transcription of the ovalbumin gene?

B. O'Malley: Not in terms of the primary induction, because it happens too quickly for RNA to be synthesized, processed, transported to cytoplasmic ribosomes, translated into protein, and have the protein reenter in the nucleus. But it does not rule out the possibility that, in the initial coordinated induction of gene products for the response, one of these mRNAs codes for the synthesis of a protein that makes the response more efficient.

J. E. Rall: You did not say very much about the sequences to the left of the start signal. You must have quite a few, and I suspect using different restriction fragments you could get even larger fragments. This is, of course, the promoter region, and I wonder if you could say something about that? Incidentally, I think it is confusing to call these spacers IS, because the insertion segments in bacteria and phage are well known and seem to be quite different with inverted repeats. They have been called IS elements for some years, and I think it is a confusing terminology.

B. O'Malley: This whole terminology for intervening sequences is a little confusing. You will see in the literature that the intervening sequences are also being referred to as inserts and introns, and intervening sequence seems to be the appropriate term at present.

The question you asked concerning the sequences to the left of the structural gene is, of course, a key one. Unfortunately, we have no detailed information on these sequences yet. As fate would have it, they have been the hardest to obtain, and we are only now cloning this region. We will be most interested in doing polymerase and receptor-binding experiments with these fragments.

S. L. Cohen: I would like to point out that this business of making more than is required for a structure is not uncommon to the gene, the big hormones, the bigger hormones, and the biggest hormones at the C peptides, and even the conversion of cholesterol to a hormone, that is, by chopping off the 6-carbon side chain. I have never heard anyone ask what happens to the 6-carbon atom chain that comes off the cholesterol. I also have a question. This relates to the translocation of your estrogen-receptor molecule into the nucleus. McGuire, as you know, has recently proposed that the estrogen is not necessary as a component of that receptor–estrogen complex. I wonder if you might comment on that.

B. O'Malley: I have done no experiments that would either confirm or contradict McGuire's "unoccupied nuclear receptor" theory. I do not object to it in principle.

S. L. Cohen: The estrogen receptor will bind steroids on the basis of affinity and concentration. If one could saturate the estrogen receptor with large amounts of androgen ($100+$-fold excess) it may then translocate the nucleus and carry out certain estrogen-associated events.

G. Baumann: I wonder whether you would be willing to speculate a little more about the possible function of the intervening sequences. You answered this question partially. You mentioned increased chance for crossing over and exchange of genetic material. If so, do you think the exchange of partial genes such as one-tenth or one-half of a gene would be advantageous in evolution? Do you have any other speculations regarding possible functions of intervening sequences?

B. O'Malley: Although this represents sheer speculation, scientists working in this area fall into three camps. Some take the point of view that intervening sequences have absolutely no function— that they are just results of recombination events that the cell has been able to deal with (and there is no doubt that the cell is able to deal with it, because the gene functions well with them present). A second group takes the point of view that the intervening sequences are regulatory in nature. I think one cannot rule this out at present except that there is no known regulatory role on intervening sequences of which I am aware. A third possibility exists that these intervening sequences are a result of previous evolutionary recombination events—events that have allowed, over a period of time, the construction of a gene that codes for a particular peptide with a particular set of characteristics or functions. I will summarize my feelings on this question more fully in the written text of my talk [see above], but I prefer the latter of these three possible explanations.

O. Dominguez: This comment is related to Dr. Rice's earlier question regarding the on and off mechanisms. It could be possible to consider that the positive or negative responses to steroid action might be due to relative concentrations of the steroids themselves, similarly as seems to occur, in a very gross manner, in the feedback mechanisms. As an example, pharmacological concentrations of testosterone block LH secretion; however, when one has a castrated animal and very small amounts of testosterone are given, over the already high levels of circulating LH, a stimulation of LH release still occurs. I was wondering if, after you had shown, through a sequence of steroid concentrations, a clear increment in response, you had arrived to a point at which you find inhibition or a way of turning off the system, owing perhaps to differences in relative affinities for specific receptor sites.

B. O'Malley: I think that is a good point. Although it might vary among species and cell types, there is a concentration of dependence for a positive steroid effect in which at too low concentration the response does not occur—then at concentrations above the physiologic range the response is often blocked or inhibited. This inhibitory response is used to advantage in the treatment of breast cancer, in which very high concentrations of estrogen often cause tumor regression.

A. Nureddin: I gather that the ligation step is also enzymic; if so, has there been a ligase isolated from eukaryotes?

B. O'Malley: Yes, in yeast the tRNA processing enzyme has been identified and solubilized. Apparently it carries out simultaneous excision and ligation. No other enzymes have been identified as yet.

D. N. Orth: It occurs to me that you have uncovered a question of which came first, the chicken or the egg, within the question of which came first, the chicken or the egg. That is to say, what enzyme processes the pre-mRNA of the enzyme that then possesses the pre-mRNAs for all the other proteins produced by the cell? It seems to me that there are two possible answers to this, one of which is that there are no intervening sequences in the gene for the processing enzyme and, therefore, that it does not need to be processed, and the other of which is that, like the reverse transcriptase carried by RNA tumor viruses, either the sperm or the ovum, or both, carries the critical amounts of the processing enzyme required to initiate pre-mRNA processing after fertilization. I wonder, in that regard, whether it is possible to study the unfertilized chicken egg to see whether, in fact, there are enzymes present that can carry out the pre-mRNA processing function?

B. O'Malley: That is an interesting point. Our best guess is that one enzyme system (or a limited number) processes all mRNAs. Whether the gene(s) coding for the processing enzyme(s) have intervening sequences is unknown. I would speculate, however, that this enzyme system is primitive and was present during the early stages of gene evolution.

J. H. Clark: My comments relate to some of the questions that were asked earlier. One concerned androgen binding and estrogen-induced responses. Androgen at high concentration are known to bind to estrogen receptor and will elicit estrogenlike responses. No steroid hormone receptor manifests absolute steroid specificity, and therefore when the concentration of ligand is sufficiently high, the binding site can no longer distinguish between estrogens and androgens. In addition, as I will discuss later in this meeting, the binding of the ligand to the receptor does not necessarily correlate with response. Triphenylethylene derivatives, such as Nafoxidine or Clomiphene, bind to estrogen receptor in all tissue layers of the uterus. Yet they stimulate only typical estrogenic responses in the epithelial cells. In the stroma and myometrium very little or no growth response occurs. This differential cell stimulation probably occurs in other organs, such as the brain, and may explain why triphenylethylene derivatives have such diverse effects in the central nervous system with respect to unfilled or unoccupied sites in the nucleus; it is not possible to tell whether they are truly unfilled, because they may be filled by a ligand of very weak binding affinity. If so, one will observe displacement and exchange at 4°C as McGuire has done. I have no bias against the concept of unfilled sites, but it is difficult to prove. With respect to John Baxter's question concerning estrogen-induced responses increasing at a time when receptor binding in the nucleus is low, this is not the case. Receptor retention in the oviduct is over very long periods of time and continues to increase with subsequent injections, and the number of receptors per nucleus is quite high during the time of elevated response.

I. A. Kourides: Dr. O'Malley, you have stated that steroids affect the rate of transcription of ovalbumin RNA rather than affecting only the processing of RNA from large nuclear to mature cytoplasmic mRNA; yet is has been suggested that hormones may act specificially by affecting only the processing of RNA. Do you know of any specific examples where it has been clearly demonstrated that a hormone acts strictly at the level of processing of RNA, rather than on both the rate of transcription and then subsequent processing of the RNA?

B. O'Malley: No, I know of no example of a "primary action" of steroid hormones at the posttranscriptional and RNA processing level. I would think it safe to assume, however, that steroids could coordinately enhance all steps in RNA synthesis and processing, protein synthesis and transport. This is only reasonable if the cell must grow and function at maximal efficiency. This pleiotypic or amplification response should be differentiated from the primary inductive response. So far, available evidence indicates that this primary response occurs at the level of the chromatin template and results in enhanced gene expression.

Vitellogenesis: A Versatile Model for Hormonal Regulation of Gene Expression

J. R. TATA AND D. F. SMITH[1]

National Institute for Medical Research,
Mill Hill, London, England

I. Introduction

Selective gene expression is now considered to be central to our understanding of cellular differentiation and the regulation of developmental processes (David-son, 1976). Although the term gene expression is not always clearly defined, it is often meant to indicate a change in the nature of, or rate at which, different genes are transcribed. Recent work on the organization of eukaryotic genes has also focused attention on the importance of structural features of expressed and unexpressed genes and on the posttranscriptional mechanisms that would deter-mine the processing of primary transcripts into the correct messenger sequences (Nierlich *et al.*, 1976; O'Malley *et al.*, 1977; Lewin, 1975; Davidson *et al.*, 1977). Despite these reservations, considerable progress has been made in recent years in piecing together information on how such processes may be regulated.

Biologists have used many different approaches and systems to study the question of gene expression during development. Among the most fruitful has been the exploitation of developmental hormones, particularly steroid hormones, to selectively induce well-defined gene products. It is generally agreed that the study of the expression of the ovalbumin gene as regulated by estrogen has made a major contribution to our knowledge of gene organization and transcription (O'Malley and Means, 1974; Schimke *et al.*, 1975; Palmiter, 1975; O'Malley, *et al.* 1977, and this volume, Chapter 1). If a successful system of hormonal regulation of selective gene expression has already been established, one may well ask why it is necessary to initiate work on another apparently similar model. It is intended to demonstrate in this review that indeed another system, based on the same hormone in vertebrates but involving a different gene, is justified not merely to extend or complement the existing information obtained from genes coding for ovalbumin and other egg white proteins, but to offer novel approaches and insights into the question of regulation of gene expression.

---

[1]Present address: Department of Biochemistry, Imperial College of Science and Technology, London SW7 2AZ, England.

In studying the expression of the vitellogenin gene, we have, in our laboratory, tried to avoid duplicating what has already been established by work on estrogenic induction of ovalbumin but have instead tried to develop those features of egg yolk protein synthesis that permit new insights into transcriptional as well as posttranscriptional events following hormonal induction. Although much of the work reported here is from our laboratory, many other laboratories are now engaged in studying vitellogenesis, and their work too will be considered. Some of the earlier studies from various laboratories have also been reviewed extensively (Follett and Redshaw, 1974; Clemens, 1974; Bergink et al., 1974; Tata, 1976, 1978; Gruber et al. 1976; Ryffel, 1978).

II. Yolk Proteins and Vitellogenin

A. EGG-YOLK PROTEINS

Egg-yolk proteins have been intensively studied over the last four or five decades, and considerable information is now available on their chemical nature in a wide range of birds, amphibians, reptiles, fish, insects, and other egg-laying animals (see Wallace, 1963, 1965; Redshaw and Follet, 1971; Clemens, 1974; Follett and Redshaw, 1974; Christmann et al., 1977; Ohlendorf et al., 1977). Two major classes of egg-yolk proteins are found in all these animals: the phosphoserine-rich glycosylated components termed phosvitins and the lipoprotein lipovitellins. In some species, particularly amphibians, the two proteins form crystalline complexes known as yolk platelets and lend themselves admirably well for ultrastructural and physical analysis of naturally occurring protein crystals (Karasaki, 1963; Wallace, 1963; Ohlendorf et al., 1978). The high density of such complexes and other special features, such as strong affinity for Ca^{2+}, have made their purification and characterization relatively simple and unambiguous.

Table I lists some of the main characteristics of phosvitins and lipovitellins in a variety of species of animals. Each of these yolk components can be subdivided into various fractions termed α, β, γ, etc.—phosvitins, lipovitellins, or livetins—the heterogeneity being particularly well studied in the chicken. It is not always clear whether the detection of multiple phosvitins and lipovitellins reflects a real polypeptide heterogeneity or different degrees of phosphorylation, glycosylation, and lipidation of the same polypeptide. Recent data on both the yolk proteins and their precursor in the chicken suggests that, whereas there are two distinct phosvitin polypeptide residues, lipovitellin may exist as a single component (Christmann et al., 1977; Gordon et al., 1977). In amphibians, too, there seems to be a unique lipovitellin residue (Wallace, 1965).

The major characteristic of phosvitin is the very high serine content of 56% of all amino acid residues, most of which are phosphorylated, a relatively high

TABLE I

Properties of Principal Egg-Yolk Proteins in Xenopus, Chicken, and Insects

Egg-yolk-protein	Species	Molecular weight	Amino acid residues (mol %)		Phosphorus (%)	Lipid (%)	Carbohydrate (%)
			Serine	Methionine			
Phosvitin	Xenopus	32×10^3	56	<0.4	10.0	0.5	10.0
	Chicken	32×10^3	56	<0.4	10.1	0.3	11.3
Lipovitellin	Xenopus	115×10^3	6	2.2	0.5	20.0	0.3
	Chicken	130×10^3	5	2.1	0.4	21.1	0.3
Vitellin	Insect[a]	100×10^3	7	2.0	0.4	16.0	0.5

[a] Values averaged from those reported for the major silk moth, cockroach, and locust egg-yolk protein.

sugar content, and a single methionine. Lipovitellins have a high lipid content, which includes cholesterol, are relatively rich in methionine, with a serine content of 4% of the residues. Virtually nothing is known of the amino acid sequence of these egg-yolk proteins. That such information would be most interesting is suggested by the few observations available indicating a high degree of conservation in egg-yolk amino acid protein composition in all vertebrates studied. Recent work on insect vitellogenins, except perhaps in lower flies such as *Drosophila* and *Calliphora* (Bownes and Hames, 1977) reveals a remarkable similarity in molecular weight, amino acid composition, etc. with that of the yolk protein precursor in vertebrates (Kunkel and Pan, 1976; Koeppe and Offengand, 1976; Chen *et al.*, 1978).

B. VITELLOGENIN

Although egg-yolk proteins have been intensively studied over the past 40 years and chemically well characterized, it is only recently that we know that these are not individually synthesized but derived from a common precursor called vitellogenin. The generic term vitellogenins was first used for insect yolk proteins, to refer to all the plasma precursors of egg-yolk proteins (Pan *et al.*, 1969). It is synthesized in the liver of all egg-laying animals and transported in the blood to the ovary, where it is cleaved to the final egg-yolk proteins, and is best characterized in the chicken and *Xenopus*. Table II lists some of the characteristics of vitellogenin found in blood or hemolymph of amphibians, birds, and insects, and it is interesting to compare them with those of its products, phosvitin and lipovitellin or vitellin as derived from eggs, described in Table I. Further accounts of the nature of chicken and *Xenopus* vitellogenin can be found in some recent reviews and original papers (Wallace, 1963, 1970; Redshaw and Follett, 1971; Ansari *et al.*, 1971; Follett and Redshaw, 1974; Clemens 1974; Tata, 1976, 1978; Jackson *et al.*, 1977; Smith *et al.*, 1978). There is still some doubt about the exact size of the native protein as found in *Xenopus* blood (MW 4.9–6.0×10^5), but its single subunit seems to have a molecular weight of 2.1–2.2×10^5 as judged by polyacrylamide gel electrophoresis under denaturing conditions (Clemens, 1974; Bergink and Wallace, 1974; Clemens *et al.*, 1975; Tata, 1976; Berridge *et al.*, 1976; Penning *et al.*, 1977). A similar large protein (subunit of 2.4–2.5×10^5 MW), which would be the precursor of yolk proteins, has been reported in chicken blood (Jost and Pehling, 1976; Gruber *et al.*, 1976; Deeley *et al.*, 1975; Wetekam *et al.*, 1975; Christmann *et al.*, 1977; Gordon *et al.*, 1977).

More recently Gordon *et al.* (1977) introduced a novel approach to determine the organization of the two phosvitin and the single lipovitellin moieties in the chicken vitellogenin molecule. These workers have analyzed the product of translation of chicken vitellogenin mRNA in a heterologous cell-free wheat-germ system and derived a model depicted in Fig. 1. Cyanogen bromide cleavage of

TABLE II

Properties of Amphibian, Avian, and Insect Vitellogenins

Species	Subunit molecular weight	Amino acid residues (mol %)		Phosporus (%)	Lipid (%)	Carbohydrate (%)
		Serine	Methionine			
Xenopus	215×10^3	12	2	1.6	12	2
Chicken	240×10^3	14	2	2.4	12	2
Insect[a]	260×10^3	10	2	1.5	15	3

[a] Values for locust and silk moth vitellogenins averaged.

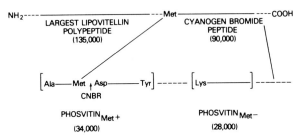

FIG. 1. Organization of lipovitellin and two residues of phosvitin in chicken vitellogenin, as deduced from analysis of cell free translation product of chicken vitellogenin messenger RNA From Gordon *et al.* (1977).

[³H]serine-labeled vitellogenin formed *in vitro* showed that both phosvitin residues were grouped together at the carboxyl end of the precursor molecule. Of the two phosvitins, only one contains a single methionine, the methionine-lacking component being located at the C terminus. It will be interesting to see whether a similar organization of the two very different egg-yolk proteins has been retained in vitellogenin in other species.

III. Vitellogenesis

A. HORMONAL REGULATION

The formation of egg-yolk proteins is under the control of estrogenic hormones (Follett and Redshaw, 1974; Clemens, 1974; Bergink *et al.*, 1974). Figure 2

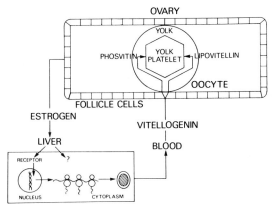

FIG. 2. Scheme depicting the regulation by estrogen of vitellogenesis in *Xenopus* (and other egg-laying vertebrates).

summarizes the major physiological aspects of the formation of egg-yolk proteins in the liver and their deposition in the egg of most egg-laying vertebrates (Tata, 1976). In invertebrates, particularly insects, vitellogenesis is under juvenile hormone control, although ecdysone has also been implicated (Koeppe and Offengand, 1976; Kunkel and Pan, 1976; Bownes and Hames, 1977; Kelly and Telfer, 1977).

In vertebrates, after the initial stimulus from the environment (temperature, length of daylight, etc.) and its transmission via the neuroendocrine hypothalamopituitary complex to the ovary, circulating estrogen levels build up rapidly immediately prior to vitellogenesis. Similarly in invertebrates, the environmental changes acting via the central nervous system cause the buildup of juvenile hormone. Vitellogenin is then synthesized in the liver (vertebrates) or fat body (insects) and then secreted into the blood (or other body fluids) to be taken up in the ovary or oocytes.

The administration of a single injection of estrogen to male vertebrates of egg-laying species results in the formation and secretion into the blood stream of substantial amounts of vitellogenin. This competence of male liver to respond to estrogen offers an experimental control of "zero" background. In *Xenopus,* the chronic exposure of both males and females to estradiol will result in vitellogenin almost totally replacing all the normal serum proteins, including albumin (Follett and Redshaw, 1968; Wallace and Jared, 1968a; Redshaw and Follett, 1971). This is, to some extent, due to the very long life of vitellogenin in male amphibian blood ($T_{1/2} > 40$ days) relative to that in females ($T_{1/2} < 2$ days), the latter arising from the rapid uptake, cleavage, and platelet formation in the ovary (Wallace and Jared, 1968b). At the same time, administration of estrogen causes the synthesis of plasma proteins normally made only in the liver, particularly serum albumin, to be slowed down or cease altogether. It was felt for a number of years that other hormones or factors, particularly of pituitary origin, or insulin, might play a "permissive" role (see Follett and Redshaw, 1974; Clemens, 1974). However, as also mentioned below, vitellogenin synthesis can be induced by the hormone directly in *Xenopus* liver tissue cultures, thus establishing that estrogen alone is responsible for vitellogenin synthesis in both male and female animals (Wangh and Knowland, 1975; Green and Tata, 1976).

Although vitellogenin as such was not identified, Wallace and Jared (1969) were able to demonstrate that a lipophosphoprotein, secreted into the blood of the female *Xenopus,* was selectively taken up by the ovary, where it was converted into crystalline yolk platelet proteins. Later work from the same laboratory (Bergink and Wallace, 1974) conclusively established this precursor–product relationship and showed that the ovary contains a specific enzyme to cleave vitellogenin to yield phosvitin and lipovitellin. These workers had also established that the oocyte itself does not synthesize yolk proteins, which are exclusively derived from circulating vitellogenin (Wallace and Jared, 1969; Wallace *et al.*, 1972; Bergink and Wallace, 1974). The process of vitellogenin uptake by oocytes itself seems to be based on pinocytosis following adsorption to plasma membranes (Wallace and Jared, 1976; Brummett and Dumont, 1977). Interestingly, Schuetz *et al.* (1977) have suggested the presence in the cytoplasm of mature *Xenopus* oocytes of a factor that alters the capacity of plasma membranes of immature oocytes to take up vitellogenin.

B. PRIMARY VS. SECONDARY INDUCTION

A general feature of the action of most growth and developmental hormones is a lag period preceding the onset of a given response that is typical for a particular hormone and its target tissue (see Tata, 1970). This latent period, which is important in explaining the early events underlying hormone action, can vary according to whether or not the target has been previously primed by the hormone. In the liver of male *Xenopus* exposed for the first time to estrogen, there is a lag period before the appearance of vitellogenin in the blood, as measured by radioimmunoassay (see Fig. 3). A shorter lag period has been reported for birds (Gruber *et al.*, 1976). The length of the latent period for such a primary induction in absolute terms is a function of the sensitivity of the assay used for detecting vitellogenin and would vary according to whether vitellogenin

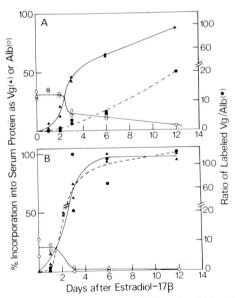

FIG. 3.   Immunological quantitation of labeled vitellogenin, (Vg) and albumin (Alb) in the serum of male *Xenopus* as a function of time during the onset of primary and secondary responses to estradiol. At 24 hours before drawing blood, each frog was injected with 200 μCi of [³⁵S]methionine. ○, Albumin; ▲, vitellogenin; ●, ratio of incorporation into vitellogenin to that into albumin. (A) Primary response; (B) Secondary response (a second injection of 1 mg of estradiol given to frogs treated with the same dose 41 days earlier). From Farmer *et al.* (1978).

is induced *in vivo* or in tissue culture, according to whether one is trying to measure the level of the protein in the tissue or after it is secreted into blood or the culture medium, the quality of antibody preparations, etc. (Dolphin *et al.*, 1971; Clemens *et al.*, 1975; Green and Tata, 1976; Berridge *et al.*, 1976; Farmer *et al.*, 1978).

Upon withdrawal of the primary hormonal stimulus, the production of this protein gradually returns to zero levels. If a second dose of estrogen is given, the lag period is virtually abolished or much reduced and the synthesis of the respective proteins is rapidly established at a maximal rate, which is termed the secondary response. A similar more rapid enhancement of secondary vitellogenic response coupled with a shorter lag period has been observed in the induction by estradiol in chicken blood of phosvitin and other phosphoproteins (Beuving and Gruber, 1971; Jailkhani and Talwar, 1972a,b; Mäenpää, 1976), which is in some ways similar to that observed for ovalbumin in the chick oviduct (Schimke *et al.*, 1975; Palmiter, 1975). A comparison in tissue culture of the lag period in primary and secondary stimulations makes it possible to establish with more precision the primary events associated with the induction process as well as study some aspects of the utilization of mRNA for vitellogenin, as will be discussed later (see Section III, C). The magnitude of the induction of vitellogenin during both primary and secondary responses in male *Xenopus* can also be judged from a direct electrophoretic analysis of plasma obtained at different times after hormone administration (see Fig. 4). The extent of vitellogenin secretion is well visualized by comparing panels 3–12 in Fig. 4, in which the output of newly synthesized protein far exceeds that of albumin (panel 0), which is the most abundant plasma protein synthesized over the same period of time of labeling in control animals. The gel electrophoretic patterns also show the disappearance of the albumin band by day 12 after secondary hormone administration. The different lag periods preceding the primary and secondary responses have also been important in designing experiments for testing the possibility of specific translational control (see Section VI).

C. INDUCTION OF VITELLOGENIN SYNTHESIS IN TISSUE CULTURE

Several questions concerning the mechanism of hormonal induction of proteins, especially the early events, can be better examined in cultured cells or organs than in the whole animal. Furthermore, tissue culture studies also allow us to better analyze questions relating to the dynamics of hormone distribution and receptor interaction, the role of obligatory DNA synthesis in induction, the requirement for possible "permissive" hormones or factors, etc. In recent years, it has been possible to obtain a full vitellogenic response to estradiol added *in vitro*, at first in organ cultures of male *Xenopus* liver (Wangh and Knowland, 1975; Green and Tata, 1976) and, more recently, in plated, disaggregated hepato-

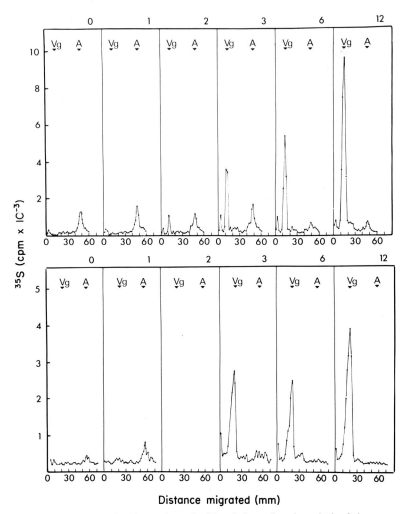

FIG. 4.   Sodium dodecyl sulfate–polyacrylamide gel electrophoretic analysis of plasma proteins synthesized following a 24-hour pulse of [^{35}S]methionine during primary (top panels) and secondary (bottom panels) responses of male *Xenopus* to estradiol. Vg, vitellogenin; A, albumin. All conditions are the same as those for the experiment shown in Fig. 3. Data were provided by S. R. Farmer.

cytes from *Xenopus* liver (Stanchfield and Yager, 1977; Wangh and Osborne, 1979; Felber *et al.*, 1979). In view of the heterogeneity of cell populations in *Xenopus* liver and the necessity to study only the parenchymal or estrogen-responsive cells, a major difficulty in such primary cell cultures is to fractionate the cells without too much perturbing their ability to synthesize vitellogenin. So far, it has been possible to establish a competent cell or organ culture system only from *Xenopus,* although some success has been reported for *Drosophila* cell lines induced to synthesize vitellogenin in culture.

Direct induction of vitellogenin *in vitro* has already established that estrogen is the sole inducer and that the process does not require other steroids, insulin, or pituitary hormones to play a "permissive" role, as had previously been suggested (see Follett and Redshaw, 1974). Not only does estrogen alone trigger the initial induction of vitellogenin, but its continuous presence is required during the lag period for the maintenance of vitellogenin synthesis, as depicted in Fig. 5 (Green and Tata, 1976). The cessation of vitellogenin synthesis upon withdrawal of the hormone in tissue culture is compatible with the response *in vivo,* and the reversibility of the phenomenon is useful in designing experiments on control of translation of mRNA, in a manner analogous to that established for estrogen-induced ovalbumin synthesis in chick oviduct (Palmiter, 1975). Induction of vitellogenin in organ cultures has also confirmed that an obligatory round of DNA synthesis is not essential for the initial stages of induction. However, it is quite likely that an uninterrupted DNA synthesis may be essential for the long-term maintenance or amplification of response to the hormone in the intact animal.

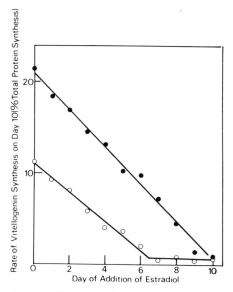

FIG. 5. Experiment demonstrating the requirement for the continuous presence of estradiol throughout the culture period of *Xenopus* liver explants during both primary (O———O) and secondary (●———●) induction of vitellogenin *in vitro.* Organ cultures were exposed to $10^{-6}\,M$ estradiol for decreasing length of time by delaying addition of the hormone until the indicated day after the start of culture. The vitellogenic response *in vitro* was quantitated by measuring the incorporation of [^{35}S]methionine into vitellogenin and total protein, as described by Green and Tata (1976).

Tissue culture studies also facilitate a more accurate analysis of the difference between primary and secondary responses to the hormone than is possible *in vivo*. Figure 6 is a typical result showing the induction of vitellogenin, as well as the deinduction of albumin, in cultured tissue as determined by radioimmunoassay of the two proteins. The lag period for the appearance of vitellogenin in the culture medium for the secondary response is half that observed for the primary response, but, as already mentioned, the absolute value for the lag period depends on the sensitivity of the assay method used for detecting vitellogenin. The mechanism of the deinduction of albumin in cultured tissue is not understood but it is worth comparing the phenomenon with observations of the virtual disappearance of this protein from blood, as well as of other serum proteins synthesized by the liver, following exposure to estradiol *in vivo* (Follett and Redshaw, 1968; Wallace and Jared, 1968a; Redshaw and Follett, 1971; Clemens *et al.*, 1975). Recently, Wangh and Osborne (1979) have found that, in dispersed hepatocytes in culture, vitellogenin and albumin are the most prominent of two groups of secreted proteins whose synthesis is induced or deinduced. Furthermore, glucocorticoids diminish the response of hepatocytes to estrogen while enhancing the production of the group of proteins including albumin, whose synthesis is lowered in the presence of estrogen.

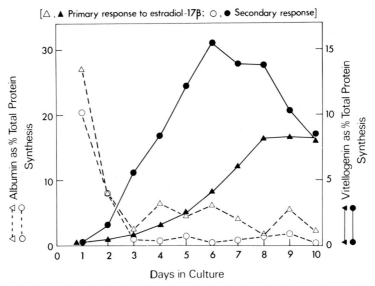

FIG. 6.   Rates of synthesis of vitellogenin and albumin by male *Xenopus* liver maintained in organ culture during primary and secondary response to estradiol added directly to the culture medium. Liver explants from untreated males (primary) and from males treated with 1 mg of estradiol-17β 35 days earlier (secondary) were cultured for the times indicated. The rates of incorporation of [^{35}S]methionine into vitellogenin and albumin were determined immunologically each day between 18 and 24 hours after addition of 5 μCi of [^{35}S]methionine to culture dishes containing 10^{-6} M estradiol. ▲, Vitellogenin in primary induction; ●, vitellogenin in secondary induction; △, albumin (primary); ○, albumin (secondary). Data from Green and Tata (1976).

From the dose-response curves of induction *in vitro* (see Fig. 7), vitellogenesis in culture was detectable at almost $10^{-10} M$ estradiol, being maximal at around $10^{-8} M$ for both primary and secondary inductions (Wangh and Knowland, 1975; Green and Tata, 1976), which is surprisingly low in comparison with the high levels of 1 mg per 100 gm of body weight needed for full induction *in vivo* (Clemens, 1974). The estradiol dose-response curve *in vitro* as well as the relative potency of other steroids tested are compatible with the properties of estradiol receptor found in the chick oviduct and other mammalian target tissues (O'Malley and Means, 1974; Jensen and De Sombre, 1973; King and Mainwaring, 1974). Thus, the establishment of a culture system for directly inducing vitellogenin synthesis *in vitro* opens the way for further studies on several aspects of the induction process which cannot be easily studied *in vivo*. The validity of

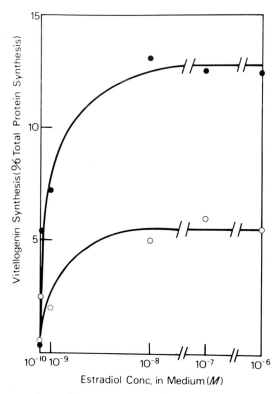

FIG. 7.   Primary and secondary response to estradiol in organ cultures of *Xenopus* liver as a function of concentration of hormone added to culture medium. Liver explants from untreated males (O——O; primary response) and from males injected with 1 mg of estradiol 30 days prior to culture (●——●; secondary response) were cultured for 8 days in medium containing different concentrations of estradiol, as indicated. The vitellogenic response was determined from the incorporation of [^{35}S]methionine into vitellogenin and total protein over a 6-hour period on day 8 of culture. From Green and Tata (1976).

the tissue culture system also rests on the fact that the only difference between induction *in vitro* and *in vivo* seems to be a quantitative one.

D. VITELLOGENESIS AS A MODEL SYSTEM FOR STUDYING HORMONAL REGULATION OF GENE EXPRESSION

It is obvious from the above characteristics of the hormonal regulation of vitellogenin that they constitute a unique combination of advantages for studying the cell biology of regulation of gene expression. The most important advantages are briefly listed below.

1. Vitellogenin is a unique, stable protein whose synthesis is regulated by a single hormone (estrogen in vertebrates, juvenile hormone in most insects).

2. The hormonal induction is completely reversible; i.e., the synthesis of vitellogenin ceases immediately upon withdrawal of the hormone, while the cells retain competence for subsequent reinduction.

3. Primary and secondary induction occurs in fully differentiated cells (hepatocytes in vertebrates, fat body cells in insects) in the virtual absence of cell proliferation of DNA synthesis. The latter often vitiates an analysis of the early events occurring in other hormonal induction systems.

4. Both the primary and secondary induction of the protein can be faithfully reproduced in tissue culture, which is particularly advantageous in analyzing the role of receptor–hormone interaction and the early transcriptional events.

5. The multicomponent nature of vitellogenin and its cleavage in cells (oocytes) different from those in which it is synthesized (hepatocytes) makes it particularly attractive in studying precursor-product processing. The unequal distribution of amino acids, such as serine and methionine, phosphate, sugars, and lipids on the phosvitin and lipovitellin moieties is an added advantage in designing experiments for studying posttranslational or even cotranslational modifications and processing.

6. The simultaneous deinduction of albumin synthesis in the same cells in which vitellogenin is induced by estrogen (Wachsmuth and Jost, 1976; Wangh and Osborne, 1979) offers a "built-in" control for studying differential gene transcription and translation.

7. The hormonal induction of egg-yolk proteins in cells from male animals, in which these would normally never be synthesized, constitutes a further unique advantage in designing experiments to study gene expression.

IV. RNA Synthesis and Transcription of the Vitellogenin Gene

A. OVERALL RNA SYNTHESIS

An uninterrupted RNA synthesis is essential for obtaining the full hormonal induction of vitellogenesis. The first studies in chicken showed that inhibition of

RNA synthesis with actinomycin D at, or soon after, the time of administration of estradiol blocked the subsequent appearance of phosvitin (Greengard *et al.*, 1964), although there has been some controversy over the effect of inhibiting RNA synthesis on the secondary response to the hormone (Beuving and Gruber, 1971; Jost *et al.*, 1973). In *Xenopus* also, actinomycin D will block the synthesis of vitellogenin (Clemens *et al.*, 1975). The induction of vitellogenesis by estradiol is characterized by a massive accumulation in the liver of total RNA (Schjeide and Lai, 1970; Wittliff and Kenney, 1972b; Jost *et al.*, 1973; Tata and Baker, 1975; Lewis *et al.*, 1976). Much of the extra RNA synthesized is found to be ribosomal RNA if cytoplasmic or total liver RNA is determined at the height of the vitellogenic response (Wittliff and Kenney, 1972b; Lewis *et al.*, 1976). In addition to the doubling or tripling of ribosomal population in hepatocytes at the height of the vitellogenic response (Lewis *et al.*, 1976; Mäenpää, 1976; Bast *et al.*, 1977), there occurs a massive proliferation of endoplasmic reticulum, Golgi bodies, mitochondria, etc., so that a large amount of extra RNA synthesized following estrogen administration must code for proteins other than vitellogenin, which are not induced *de novo* (Lewis *et al.*, 1976).

B. VITELLOGENIN mRNA

The early studies on the cessation of vitellogenin synthesis following treatment with actinomycin D also indicated a relatively long half-life of avian and amphibian vitellogenin mRNA (Greengard *et al.*, 1964; Beuving and Gruber, 1971; Clemens *et al.*, 1975; Gruber *et al.*, 1976). More precise quantitation of mRNA levels measured by hybridization to complementary DNA or by cell-free translation assays have placed the $T_{1/2}$ at 30–45 hours for chicken and *Xenopus* messenger (Ryffel *et al.*, 1977; Deeley *et al.*, 1977a; Burns *et al.*, 1978).

The relative stability of vitellogenin mRNA, and the massive hepatic accumulation of the messenger occurring soon after estrogen administration to male animals, has facilitated purification of the mRNA. Additionally, the large size of vitellogenin mRNA (minimum MW $2.2–2.5 \times 10^6$) has allowed it to be readily isolated from other cellular messengers, although initial difficulties were encountered due to degradation by the high levels of ribonuclease present in amphibian and avian livers. Thus, it has been necessary to develop specific conditions for the isolation procedure, and this is exemplified by the work of Berridge *et al.* (1976), who used high ionic strength and high pH, together with the ribonuclease inhibitors heparin or diethylpyrocarbonate, for the isolation of large, vitellogenin-synthesizing polysomes. Several workers have reported that vitellogenin mRNA and vitellogenin-synthesizing polysomes are the most abundant species in the liver of estrogenized male frogs and chickens. The actual estimates of the values vary from 10 to 50% of the total RNA and depend on the precision of the method used for quantitating mRNA or the nascent proteins, according to whether the induction is *in vivo* or in culture or is primary or secondary induction (Clemens, 1974; Gruber *et al.*, 1976; Berridge *et al.*, 1976; Green and Tata, 1976; Wahli *et al.*, 1976; Mullinix *et al.*, 1976; D. F. Smith, unpublished observation).

Vitellogenin mRNA has now been purified to homogeneity using several combinations of a number of techniques. In *Xenopus,* Shapiro and Baker (1977) used oligo(dT)-cellulose chromatography of total cellular RNA to produce a poly(A)-containing fraction that was subsequently fractionated on isokinetic sucrose gradients to yield vitellogenin mRNA. The purification factor was approximately 170-fold by this procedure, as judged by cDNA hybridization and assay in a rabbit reticulocyte lysate protein-synthesizing system. Other workers have used similar procedures to purify the messenger (Wahli *et al.*, 1976; D. F. Smith, unpublished data) and have shown that it comprises 12–20% of all cytoplasmic poly(A)-containing RNA from estrogen-treated males, whereas in untreated animals, it is absent or at least 2000-fold less abundant.

The gel electrophoretic pattern in Fig. 8 illustrates the exploitation of the large size of vitellogenin mRNA for its isolation from total cytoplasmic RNA. Fractio-

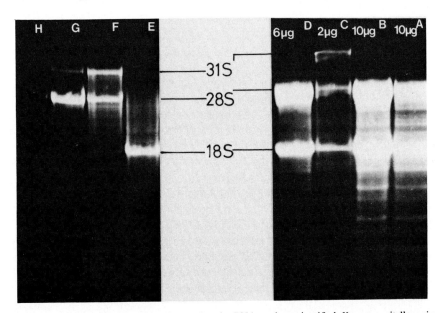

FIG. 8. Electrophoresis of total cytoplasmic RNA and semipurified *Xenopus* vitellogenin mRNA fractions in 1.5% agarose gels containing 5 m*M* methylmercuric hydroxide. Total cytoplasmic RNA was fractionated by chromatography on oligo(dT)-cellulose and centrifugation on log-linear sucrose gradients, prior to electrophoresis. The figure shown is a photograph of the ethidium bromide-stained gel, exposed under ultraviolet light. The amounts of RNA loaded onto the gel are indicated, together with the positions of vitellogenin mRNA and 28 S and 18 S ribosomal RNA. Track A: total RNA from normal male *Xenopus* liver; B: total RNA from estrogen-treated male liver; C: high molecular weight, poly(A)$^+$-RNA derived from B; D: high molecular weight, poly(A)$^-$-RNA derived from B; E–H: fractionation of C on a log-linear sucrose gradient.

nation of this RNA to yield a high molecular weight fraction, followed by affinity chromatography to produce a poly(A)$^+$-RNA population, gives a considerable enrichment for vitellogenin messenger, as is shown in track C of the electrophoretic gel. Subsequent centrifugation of this fraction on log-linear sucrose gradients allows a more specific selection to be made for the mRNA (tracks E–H), and recycling through these two last purification steps allows a 99% pure messenger fraction to be isolated. In chicken, Deeley et al. (1977b) have also purified vitellogenin mRNA from total cellular RNA, which was extracted by tissue disruption at low temperature ($-25°$C) in 8 M guanidine HCl and dithiothreitol, to minimize ribonuclease activity. Subsequent purification involved the sequential use of poly(U)-Sephadex G-10 chromatography and centrifugation in isokinetic sucrose gradients of low ionic strength; using these techniques, a purification factor of 550-fold was recorded. Other workers have extracted the messenger from large polysomes that would be expected to code for vitellogenin (AB et al., 1976; Jost and Pehling, 1976; Jost et al., 1978), although a completely homogeneous RNA species has not been obtained.

Vitellogenin mRNA has a molecular weight of $2.0–2.3 \times 10^6$ in Xenopus (Shapiro and Baker, 1977; Wahli et al., 1976, 1978) and $2.3–2.8 \times 10^6$ in avian species (AB et al., 1976; Jost and Pehling, 1976; Deeley et al., 1977b), as determined either by gel electrophoresis under denaturing conditions or by electron microscopy. It has a 3′ poly(A)tail, estimated to be 117 residues in Xenopus (Shapiro and Baker, 1977) and approximately 220 residues in chicken (M. Willems, personal communication). Vitellogenin mRNA therefore shows a structure common with that of other eukaryotic messengers and may thus also be assumed to have 5′ and 3′ noncoding regions, as suggested by the size and sequence complexity measurements of Shapiro and Baker (1977) and Deeley et al. (1977b).

The levels of vitellogenin mRNA present during response to estrogen have been determined either directly, by hybridization using a complementary DNA (cDNA) probe, or indirectly by translational analysis. Figure 9 illustrates the use of a cDNA probe to vitellogenin mRNA in determining the presence of specific sequences in total cytoplasmic RNA from the livers of both estrogen-treated (E) and untreated (U) male Xenopus. Whereas the kinetics of hybridization of the cDNA with its messenger template are characteristic of those of a pure message species, the hybridization with total RNA E indicates that approximately 0.9% of the RNA is vitellogenin mRNA. Conversely, little detectable hybridization is recorded with RNA U. In chicken, cDNA hybridization analysis suggests that vitellogenin mRNA comprises 8.3% and 0.007% of the total poly(A)$^+$ RNA from livers of estrogen-treated and normal roosters, respectively (Deeley et al., 1977b).

Hybridization analyses have also given very accurate determinations of the number of vitellogenin mRNA sequences present per cell, and these are summarized in Table III. It is evident from these data that in Xenopus, accumulation

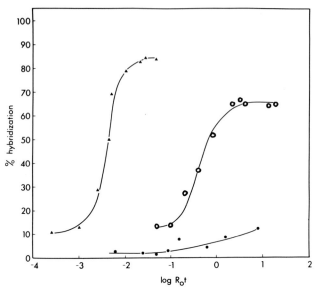

FIG. 9. Hybridization of vitellogenin complementary DNA (cDNA) to purified vitellogenin mRNA and to total cytoplasmic RNA from the livers of estrogen-treated and untreated male *Xenopus*. Vitellogenin cDNA was incubated with either purified vitellogenin mRNA (▲———▲) or total cytoplasmic RNA from the livers of estrogen-treated (○———○, E) or untreated (●———●, U) male *Xenopus*. Incubations were carried out at 70°C in 0.24 M phosphate buffer, pH 6.8, containing 1 mM EDTA and 0.02% sodium dodecyl sulfate to the R_ot values indicated. The extent of hybridization was determined with S1 nuclease and expressed as the fraction of radioactivity in the hybrid resistant to digestion by the enzyme.

of mRNA sequences occurs more rapidly during secondary response to estrogen; in both *Xenopus* and chicken higher maximum levels are attained than those measured during primary response (Baker and Shapiro, 1977, 1978; Deeley *et al.*, 1977a,b). This difference in mRNA accumulation almost certainly accounts for the more rapid appearance of newly synthesized vitellogenin observed during the secondary response. However, during primary response the events occurring are more complex. Ryffel *et al.* (1977) have observed that in *Xenopus* mRNA accumulation levels off between 3 and 7 days during primary response whereas vitellogenin synthesis continues to increase up to 12–15 days, suggesting some mechanism of translational control of the mRNA. Conversely, Deeley *et al.* (1977b) have demonstrated that in primary response in chicken, vitellogenin mRNA initially accumulates at a slow rate and then shifts to a higher rate of accumulation, which could explain the relatively slow appearance of newly synthesized vitellogenin in terms of mRNA availability alone. However, ancillary changes in the hepatocyte and also of considerable importance in the primary hormonal response, and these are discussed in Sections V, B, C. The data recorded in Table III also highlight the extremely low levels of vitellogenin

TABLE III

Accumulation in Xenopus Liver of Vitellogenin mRNA Sequences during Primary and Secondary
Responses to Estradiol Assayed by mRNA–cDNA Hybridization Analysis[a]

Induction	Time after estradiol	Vitellogenin mRNA sequences	
		% Total RNA	Molecules/cell
Primary	0 Hours	3.9×10^{-6}	<0.15
	3 Hours	3.9×10^{-6}	0.17
	6 Hours	4.7×10^{-4}	25
	12 Hours	6.8×10^{-3}	260
	24 Hours	9.0×10^{-2}	3200
	12 Days	3.0×10^{-1}	36000
Secondary	0 Hours	9.6×10^{-6}	<0.40
	3 Hours	3.0×10^{-4}	10
	6 Hours	7.6×10^{-3}	260
	12 Hours	2.5×10^{-2}	1110
	24 Hours	7.6×10^{-2}	2900
	12 Days	6.9×10^{-1}	82000

[a] Adapted from data of Baker and Shapiro (1977, 1978).

mRNA sequences present in uninduced tissue and the drop in sequence number to its original level, observed several weeks after primary estrogen response. The former observation prompts the question whether there is any transcription at all of the vitellogenin gene in untreated animals, whereas the latter point eliminates the possibility that stored mRNA in an untranslatable form might provide for a more rapid secondary response to estrogen.

Although cDNA hybridization analysis has allowed for very accurate determinations of the number of mRNA sequences present during the estrogen response, it can give no indication as to the functional state of these sequences. For this purpose, heterologous cell-free translation systems are invaluable. Figure 10 is an example of the result obtained when mRNA preparations from estrogen-treated and control male *Xenopus* liver were translated in a rabbit reticulocyte cell-free system and the translation products were identified by immunoprecipitation followed by gel electrophoresis. The large polypeptide of molecular weight 210,000 is vitellogenin (mostly unmodified), and smaller immunoreactive peptides are most likely to be degradation products of the primary translation product. Neither vitellogenin nor the smaller polypeptides reacting with antivitellogenin antibodies could be detected among translation products of RNA from non-estrogen-treated *Xenopus* liver. Although not as accurate as hybridization assay, the heterologous cell-free assay gives a similar trend in the rate of accumulation of vitellogenin mRNA at the longer time intervals after hormone administration (see Section VI).

Assay of vitellogenin mRNA by its translational activity was initially used to identify the messenger's presence in either total RNA or polysomal RNA frac-

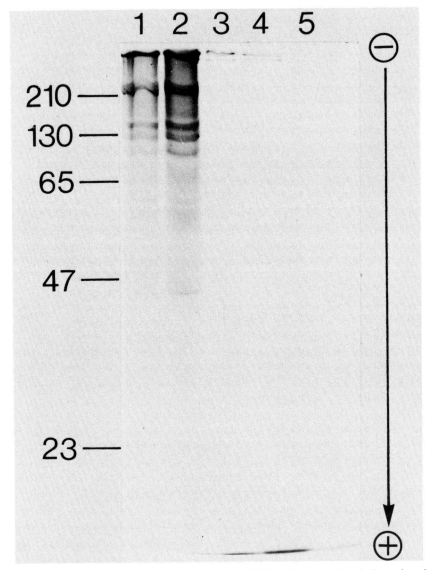

FIG. 10. Autoradiogram of sodium dodecyl sulfate (SDS)–polyacrylamide gel electrophoresis of the vitellogenin-specific immunoprecipitation of the translation product of rabbit reticulocyte lysate programmed with liver RNA from untreated (slots 3–5) and estradiol-treated (slots 1 and 2) male *Xenopus*. Total postnuclear RNA, 50 μg, was added to a reticulocyte cell-free system incorporating [^{35}S]methionine into protein. The latter was treated with rabbit antivitellogenin antibody, and the immunoprecipitate was analyzed on 10% SDS–polyacrylamide gels. Figures on left represent molecular weight markers; that of 210,000 is for the vitellogenin subunit. Data were provided by S. R. Farmer.

tion. Berridge *et al.* (1976) were able to characterize vitellogenin-synthesizing polysomes by the ability of the polysomal RNA to direct the synthesis of immunoprecipitable vitellogenin in a rabbit reticulocyte cell-free protein-synthesizing system. Subsequently, Shapiro *et al.* (1976) used translation to quantitate the levels of mRNA up to 12 days after estrogen treatment and recorded a lag between mRNA level and the intracellular rate of vitellogenin synthesis up to 4 days, after which, the two parameters could be closely correlated. In this connection, the sensitivity of the immunological assay for vitellogenin synthesis is most critical, and this point, along with the evidence for the translational control of vitellogenin synthesis, will be further discussed in Section VI. In any case, more recently the use of translational analysis as a quantitative tool in the estimation of vitellogenin mRNA sequences has been superseded by cDNA hybridization analysis, and, indeed, it has been shown to be somewhat unreliable unless the immunoprecipitable translation products are critically evaluated (Mullinix *et al.*, 1976; Burns *et al.*, 1978). However, translation analysis can answer a number of important questions regarding the structure of the synthesized polypeptide (Gordon *et al.*, 1977) as has previously been discussed (Section II, B).

C. NUCLEAR RNA SYNTHESIS AND PROCESSING

Relatively little work has been done so far on the synthesis of vitellogenin mRNA and its processing in the nucleus. From the few studies that have been reported, a rather more complex picture emerges than that seen for cytoplasmic mRNA, if one measures RNA synthesis in the nucleus during the lag period preceding the onset of vitellogenin synthesis. A massive increase in the rate of nuclear RNA synthesis *in vivo* can be observed within 3 hours after the injection of estradiol to the male *Xenopus,* reaching a maximum elevation of 8-fold the control values by 11 hours (Tata and Baker, 1975). Much of the newly made hormone-induced RNA made at 3–6 hours after the administration of the hormone is nonribosomal, an increasing proportion of ribosomal RNA being synthesized after 11 hours (Wittliff and Kenney, 1972b; Tata and Baker, 1975; Mäenpää, 1976). It is therefore not surprising that a stimulation of both RNA polymerase I and II activities was observed in liver nuclei at 24 hours after the injection of estradiol into male chickens (Weckler and Gschwendt, 1976; Bieri-Boniot *et al.*, 1977; Panyim *et al.*, 1978). It is also quite possible that vitellogenin mRNA synthesis begins very soon after hormone administration; analysis of nuclear RNA by hybridization to DNA complementary to vitellogenin mRNA could confirm this possibility. Hybridization studies on nuclear RNA will also establish the presence or the absence of vitellogenin mRNA sequences in the nuclei of uninduced male livers although several hybridization studies report that there are virtually no sequences (<1–5 copies per cell) detectable in total liver

RNA from male chickens or frogs not treated with estrogen (Baker and Shapiro, 1977; Ryffel *et al.*, 1977; Deeley *et al.*, 1977a,b; Burns *et al.*, 1978; Jost *et al.*, 1978).

Synthesis and processing of RNA is known to be compartmentalized within the nucleus, and this can be easily observed upon nuclear fractionation (Tata and Baker, 1974, 1978). When nuclei were fractionated into their structurally different components, additional newly labeled RNA in hormone-treated animals was recovered in all the major subnuclear fractions (Tata and Baker, 1975). However, quite marked differences were noted in the nature and metabolism of RNA associated with the different nuclear fractions from treated and untreated animals.

Polyadenylation, "capping," cleavage and degradation of the HnRNA precursor for messenger RNA are the major posttranscriptional processing steps in the nucleus (Lewin, 1975). Although the importance of these processes in determining the nature and speed of an induction phenomenon is in no doubt, again very little work has been done on posttranscriptional modification and processing during vitellogenesis. In one study, Tata and Baker (1975) observed a 2- to 10-fold increase in the poly(A) content of male *Xenopus* liver nuclear RNA accompanying the estrogen-induced increase in the total amount of newly synthesized RNA, much of the increase being associated with the euchromatin fraction. The differential subnuclear distribution of newly synthesized poly(A)-containing RNA was further emphasized in the size distribution of RNA in the different subnuclear fractions. A large proportion of the poly(A)-rich RNA found in the nuclear sap was of small molecular weight, presumably reflecting intranuclear degradation and turnover, whereas most of the total or polyadenylated RNA associated with the euchromatin fraction was of high molecular weight when analyzed by SDS- or formamide-polyacrylamide gel electrophoresis (Tata and Baker, 1975) (see Fig. 11). Besides a marked increase in the high molecular weight RNA fraction, presumably corresponding to HnRNA (>50 S), induction of vitellogenin synthesis in male frogs was characterized by the appearance of polyadenylated high molecular weight (32–36 S) RNA of approximately 2.2×10^6, i.e., close to the calculated minimum size of the cytoplasmic mRNA for vitellogenin. In such studies, in order to eliminate the problem of background "noise" due to preexisting mRNA sequences, it would be preferable to probe newly transcribed labeled nuclear RNA with cDNA to vitellogenin, amplified by bacterial cloning techniques. If DNA excess hybridization studies do indeed show that vitellogenin mRNA sequences are present in nuclear RNA of a well-defined size class (~35 S), then it can be concluded that the most stable form of putative precursor nuclear RNA containing vitellogenin sequences is only slightly larger than the cytoplasmic mRNA and that this form is closely associated with the transcriptionally active fraction of the nucleus. This conclusion could not, however, rule out the existence of a larger primary transcript of a much shorter life, as has been recently suggested for chicken vitellogenin pre-mRNA (Jost *et al.*, 1978).

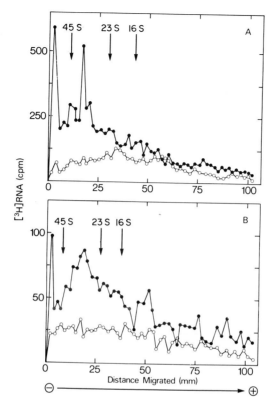

FIG. 11. Sodium dodecyl sulfate (SDS)-polyacrylamide gel electrophoresis of total and poly(A)-rich nuclear RNA from liver of control and estradiol-treated male *Xenopus*. RNA was labeled with 400 μCi of [³H]orotic acid injected 1.6 hours before death into 2 groups of 3 frogs each; one group served as control (○), and the other had been treated with 1 mg of estradiol 11 hours before death (●). RNA was extracted from nuclei and then resolved into poly(A)-poor and poly(A)-rich RNA by chromatography on oligo(dT)-cellulose. Electrophoresis was carried out on 2.3% polyacrylamide–SDS gels, and the radioactivity was measured in 2-mm slices. (A) Total nuclear RNA; (B) poly(A)-rich nuclear RNA. From Tata and Baker (1975).

The importance of characterizing primary gene transcripts has recently been highlighted very dramatically by studies on the organization of several eukaryotic genes. Genes for hemoglobin, ovalbumin, and immunoglobulin have now all been found to have long stretches of inserts interrupting their coding sequences (Tilghman *et al.*, 1978a; Breathnach *et al.*, 1977). From a recent study (Tilghman *et al.*, 1978b), it has emerged that the DNA of the inserts is transcribed contiguously with that of the coding regions and that the primary transcript is then cleaved, the insert transcripts eliminated, and the coding transcripts somehow resealed or "spliced" to give the correct messenger RNA. If this process proves to be generally applicable to other genes, then there is much to be gained by applying such an approach to the vitellogenin gene. Not only would it yield information on the organization of the vitellogenin gene and the formation of its primary transcription product, but the multicomponent nature of vitellogenin particularly makes it interesting to determine whether or not the arrangement of lipovitellin and phosvitin residues in the gene corresponds to that in the precursor polypeptide.

D. APPLICATION OF RECOMBINANT DNA TECHNOLOGY

It is clear from the above discussion that recombinant DNA technology offers a most powerful and direct approach to understanding the regulation of expression of the vitellogenin gene. Our laboratory is adopting two approaches in this exploitation of bacterial cloning: (a) the amplification of plasmid DNA containing complementary DNA to vitellogenin mRNA by transformation into a bacterial host; (b) the cloning of larger genomic DNA fragments bearing not only the vitellogenin gene but its flanking sequences.

These operations are schematically summarized in Fig. 12, where these two approaches (a and b) are depicted on the left and right halves of the scheme. As shown in Fig. 12(a), messenger RNA for vitellogenin (or albumin) is reverse transcribed to yield a cDNA copy that is subsequently made double-stranded using DNA polymerase I. After S1 nuclease cleavage of the single-stranded portion of the molecule and "tailing" with poly(A) (or C), the modified species is ready for insertion into the bacterial plasmid of choice. This is prepared by cutting the plasmid DNA with an appropriate restriction enzyme and "tailing" the cut ends with poly(T) (or G) to produce so-called "sticky ends." Annealing of the modified cDNA and plasmid species produces a plasmid containing an inserted sequence complementary to vitellogenin mRNA, which can now be amplified in a bacterial host cell. Alternatively, as shown in Fig. 12(b), genomic DNA and the plasmid DNA may be cleaved by the same restriction enzyme to yield complementary sites for annealing on both molecules. The production of such "genomic" plasmids must then be followed by a rigorous screening procedure to select those plasmids containing the inserted sequences of choice, particularly when the inserted DNA is of eukaryotic origin and therefore represents a very small fraction of the total genome. Procedures similar to those outlined in Fig. 12 have been used to clone cDNAs to globin mRNA in rabbit (Maniatis *et al.*, 1976; Rougeon and Mach, 1976; Rabbitts, 1976) and *Xenopus* (C. C. Hentschel, R. M. Kay, and J. G. Williams, personal communication) and to ovalbumin mRNA in chicken (McReynolds *et al.*, 1977), among others.

We have now prepared cDNA clones to vitellogenin mRNA (D. F. Smith *et al.*, 1979) using the plasmid pBR 322 as vector (Bolivar *et al.*, 1977) and inserting foreign DNA into the *Pst* site in the ampicillin gene of this plasmid, using poly(dC) - poly(dG) "tailing." Transformed colonies of the *Escherichia coli* host containing vitellogenin cDNA were then selected by *in situ*

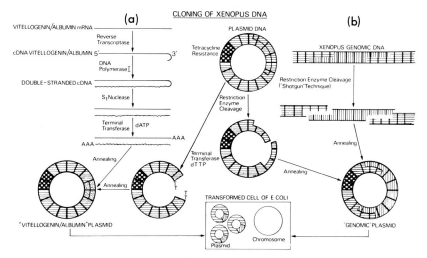

FIG. 12. Scheme illustrating the two principal approaches taken in our laboratory to the cloning of DNA coding for vitellogenin or albumin mRNAs in bacterial plasmids. In approach (a) complementary DNA to purified messenger RNA is amplified by cloning in bacterial plasmids, whereas in (b) genomic clones carrying DNA sequences coding for these two proteins are prepared. See text for further details.

hybridization with ^{32}P-labeled vitellogenin mRNA. These clones will be used to probe the primary events that follow the "switching-on" of the vitellogenin gene by estradiol. Wahli *et al.* (1979) have also reported the cloning of *Xenopus* vitellogenin cDNA and have also shown that vitellogenin is encoded in a small family of genes, at least four of which are expressed.

Cloning of genomic DNA has also been carried out for the globin gene (Tilghman *et al.*, 1977), and, similarly, cloning of genomic DNA for vitellogenin will facilitate the elucidation of the structure and function of the vitellogenin gene and its regulatory sequences.

Additionally, cDNA and genomic cloning for the *Xenopus* albumin gene is being pursued in parallel, in order to correlate the activity of a gene that is not estrogen-induced with that of the vitellogenin gene. In view of our recent evidence suggesting that the albumin gene may in fact be "switched-off" after estrogen treatment (see Section VI), the parallel study of the two genes is made all the more interesting.

V. Synthesis of Vitellogenin and Translation of Messenger RNA

A. OVERALL PROTEIN SYNTHESIS

The first studies on male frog and chicken liver showed that the overall protein synthetic capacity of the tissue was markedly enhanced after the administration of estrogen and that the stimulation preceded the appearance of egg-yolk protein in the blood (Wittliff and Kenney, 1972a; see Follett and Redshaw, 1974; Clemens, 1974). The same was true for total protein synthesis as opposed to vitellogenin secreted into culture medium when studying *Xenopus* liver explants at different times after hormonal treatment of male *Xenopus in vivo* or following direct hormonal induction in culture (Clemens *et al.*, 1975; Green and Tata, 1976). When protein synthesis was studied in cell-free systems, the capacity of *Xenopus* liver ribosomes to incorporate amino acid into protein was found to be enhanced by estrogen administration *in vivo* in addition to that due to the accumulation of vitellogenin mRNA (Clemens and Tata, 1973). At the same time, the stimulation was selective according to the amino acid studied. The incorporation of serine relative to that of phenylalanine in preparations from estrogen-stimulated animals was twice as high as that noted for control preparations. As already mentioned, Gordon *et al.* (1977) have exploited this preferential incorporation of serine into vitellogenin for deducing the organization of phosvitin and lipovitellin residues by temporally following the translation of vitellogenin mRNA in a heterologous cell-free system. An interesting observation also emerging from the earlier study of Clemens and Tata (1973) was that the n..aximum effect of hormonal treatment on the incorporation of serine could be observed only if ribosomes from treated animals were incubated with cell sap also derived from treated animals. It would be important if one is to understand translational control to learn more about the cell sap factor(s) responsible for this cooperative effect between ribosomes and cell sap. Because of the extraordinarily high serine content (56%) of phosvitin, possible differences in seryl-tRNA species in vitellogenic and nonvitellogenic animals would be expected. It is therefore of interest that the pattern of seryl-tRNAs was found to be altered during estrogen-induced vitellogenesis, including the appearance of two new tRNA isoacceptor species (Mäenpää and Bernfield, 1969, 1975; Mäenpää, 1972). Unfortunately, these observations have not been followed up in either birds or amphibians. Perhaps the cell-sap effect noted for *Xenopus* liver may reflect a change in seryl tRNA pattern and may also underlie a specific mechanism of translational control of vitellogenin mRNA.

B. POLYRIBOSOMES SYNTHESIZING VITELLOGENIN AND ALBUMIN AND THEIR CYTOPLASMIC DISTRIBUTION

The identity of serine-rich protein synthesized by cell-free systems as vitellogenin was established by electrophoretic and immunological analysis of the product of polyribosomal protein synthesis (Clemens, *et al.*, 1975; Lewis *et al.*, 1976; Berridge *et al.*, 1976; Wetekam *et al.*, 1975; Jost and Pehling, 1976; Roskam *et al.*, 1976b). The first attempts to identify and isolate intact vitellogenin-synthesizing polysomes ended in failure owing to the higher sensitivity of the large mRNA to degradative enzymes and the high level of ribonuclease in avian and amphibian livers. This difficulty was overcome by lowering the ribonuclease activity with high pH (8.5), heparin, diethylpyrocarbonate, etc. Figure 13 shows profiles of polysomes from estrogenized male and female *Xenopus* liver in which the large 30–40 ribosome aggregates are retained. Control male *Xenopus* liver does not have polysomes of more than 20 monomeric units (Berridge *et al.*, 1976). Berridge *et al.* (1976) also characterized *Xenopus* vitellogenin- and albumin-synthesizing polyribosomes simultaneously in the same sample by radioimmunoassay and by immunoprecipitation, using double antibody techniques analogous to those so successfully used for identifying ovalbumin synthesizing polysomes in chick oviductal cells (Palmiter, 1975). Jost and Pehling (1976) and Roskam *et al.* (1976a,b) have also described large polysomes induced in rooster liver by estradiol treatment. As would be expected, polysomes of about 35 monomeric units were found to be engaged in the synthesis of vitellogenin, whereas much smaller polyribosomes were found to be engaged in synthesizing albumin. In our laboratory we have characterized mRNA for both proteins from livers of estradiol-treated male *Xenopus* from polyribosomes immunoprecipitated with antivitellogenin or antialbumin antibodies, and later assayed in a rabbit reticulocyte or wheat germ cell-free translational system.

In common with all secretory proteins (Palade, 1975; Shore and Tata, 1977), vitellogenin is synthesized on membrane-bound ribosomes (Lewis *et al.*, 1976). As shown in Fig. 14, a characteristic feature of induction of vitellogenesis is the parallel increase in the amount of ribosomal or polyribosomal populations of *Xenopus* hepatocytes (Clemens, 1974; Berridge *et al.*, 1976; Lewis *et al.*, 1976; Skipper and Hamilton, 1977). As mentioned earlier, the massive accumulation of ribosomes following hormone administration is not only a characteristic of vitellogenesis (Wittliff and Kenney, 1972b; Tata and Baker, 1975; Mäenpää, 1976) but also a general feature of all developmental hormone-induced induction phenomena (see Tata, 1970). We have found that the buildup of additional ribosomes is coordinated with that of the proliferation of the membranes of the endoplasmic reticulum to which these ribosomes are bound, as established both by electron microscopy and biochemical analysis (Lewis *et al.*, 1976). A question that is seldom considered is whether or not any other significance could be attached to the synthesis of induced proteins on membrane-bound ribosomes, besides that of secretion. Two such possible functions are briefly discussed below: (a) segregation of polyribosomes; (b) posttranslational modification of nascent protein. These two features have been considered in detail elsewhere (Shore and Tata, 1977).

The concept of segregation of different populations of polyribosomes bound to membranes and engaged in the synthesis of different classes of protein is less easy to establish than the role of attachment to membranes of ribosomes engaged in synthesizing secretory proteins. For the latter, it suffices to separate membrane-bound from free polysomes and to demonstrate that secretory proteins

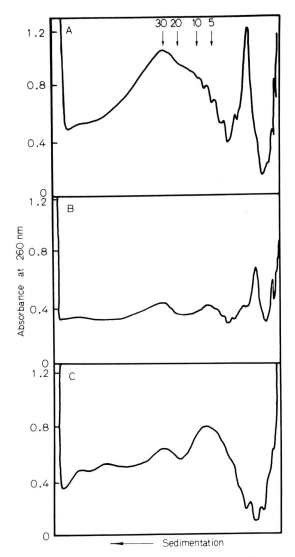

FIG. 13. Liver polysomes from (A) female and (B) male *Xenopus* after treatment with estrogen. Polysomes were prepared from estrogen-treated *Xenopus* and analyzed on linear 20 to 50% sucrose gradients. Polysome size, determined by extrapolation of the log-linear relationship between ribosome monomeric units and distance of migration in sucrose gradients, is shown at the top. Panel (C) shows profile of *Xenopus* tadpole tail polysomes that synthesize the large myosin polypeptide as the major protein. From Berridge *et al.* (1976).

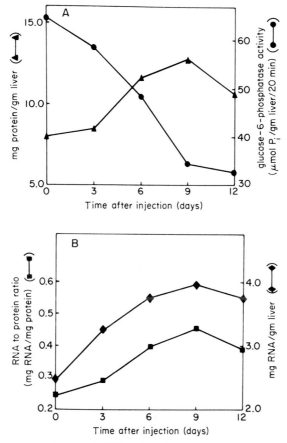

FIG. 14.   Time course of changes in RNA and protein content and glucose-6-phosphatase activity (as an index of microsomal membrane proliferation) after estradiol-17β treatment. Groups of 3 male *Xenopus* each were injected with 1 mg of estradiol-17β at various times before death. Subcellular fractionation of the livers was carried out as described by Lewis *et al.* (1976). The fractions (homogenate, smooth and rough microsomes, and total microsomes) were assayed for protein and RNA content and glucose-6-phosphatase activity. (A) Changes in total liver glucose-6-phosphatase activity (●———●) and in total microsomal protein (▲———▲); (B) Changes in total RNA content of liver (◆———◆) and in rough microsomal RNA:protein ratio (■———■). A lowering in specific activity of glucose-6-phosphatase indicates proliferation of endoplasmic reticulum. From Lewis *et al.* (1976).

are preferentially synthesized on membrane-bound ribosomes but not on free ones (Tata, 1973; Shore and Tata, 1977). A minimum requirement for the demonstration of topological segregation is to obtain two or more distinguishable subclasses of membrane-bound ribosomes. Lewis and Tata (1973) have described a procedure based on rate-sedimentation through discontinuous sucrose gradients which resolves the total membrane-bound population of polysomes into two operational subclasses of endoplasmic reticulum (rapidly sedimenting and buoyant). Using this procedure, we have recently found that in rat liver there is an 8-fold difference between the rapidly sedimenting and the buoyant fractions of membrane-bound ribosomes in the relative distribution of translatable mRNA coding for albumin and for those mitochondrial proteins that are synthesized on cytoplasmic ribosomes (Shore and Tata, 1977). Although by itself this does not constitute definitive evidence for a topological segregation, it strongly suggests an unequal distribution of polysomes on membranes that would not be incompatible with a possible topological segregation *in vivo*.

Zehavi-Willner and Lane (1977) took a different approach to the question of segregation of proteins destined for export and those for storage within the cell by injecting into *Xenopus* oocytes different messengers and following the distribution of their products in the various subcellular fractions containing intracellular membrane vesicles. Thus, when they examined the distribution of newly synthesized guinea pig milk proteins in the oocyte these were found to be enclosed within vesicles of endoplasmic reticulum membranes, as would be predicted by the "signal hypothesis" for intracellular movement of secreted proteins (Blobel and Dobberstein, 1975). On the other hand, newly synthesized vitellogenin, synthesized upon the injection of mRNA from estradiol-stimulated *Xenopus* liver (see below), was transferred to the vesicle fraction and then on to yolk platelets, where the protein is cleaved into phosvitin and lipovitellin (C. D. Lane, personal communication).

If the above results do not constitute definitive proof of a topological segregation of polysomes on membranes of the endoplasmic reticulum, the possibility that some function(s) other than secretion must also be served by a membrane–ribosome interaction is strengthened by the following correlations: (1) the widespread presence of membrane-bound polysomes in developing nonsecretory cells, i.e., brain, muscle, oocytes, etc.; (2) the enhanced proliferation of membrane–polysome complex in secretory cells switching to synthesis of intracellular proteins, as during growth or regeneration (see Tata, 1973). That one of these nonsecretory functions is to achieve a topological segregation can eventually be convincingly shown only by a combination of techniques of molecular biology and cell biology—for example, by combining cDNA probes for mRNA distribution and immunohistochemical localization of the corresponding polypeptide product. The ribosome–membrane interaction may also involve some other function, compatible with topological segregation, such as posttranslational modifications of the nascent polypeptide chain (see Section V, D).

C. TRANSLATION OF mRNAs FOR *Xenopus* VITELLOGENIN AND ALBUMIN IN *Xenopus* OOCYTES

We have already noted in work from Wallace's laboratory that the *Xenopus* ovary or the oocyte does not synthesize the egg-yolk platelet proteins (phosvitin and lipovitellin), which are entirely derived from circulating vitellogenin. Although *in vivo,* circulating vitellogenin is converted into phosvitin and lipovitellin in the ovary, it is degraded when injected into oocytes (Wallace and Jared, 1969; Wallace *et al.*, 1972; Dehn and Wallace, 1973). Berridge and Lane (1976) demonstrated that *Xenopus* liver mRNA for vitellogenin, when microinjected into *Xenopus* oocytes, not only is translated but the synthesized vitellogenin is cleaved into platelet phosvitin and lipovitellin. Lanclos and Hamilton (1975) also detected lipovitellin in oocytes after injection of total liver polyribosomes obtained from estradiol-treated frogs, and this was presumably derived from cleavage of newly synthesized vitellogenin.

The oocyte system has already proved to be a valuable living cell system for characterizing a number of eukaryotic messenger RNAs as well as throwing light on the posttranslational modifications of their products (Lane and Knowland, 1975). A general feature that has emerged from work on foreign mRNAs injected into *Xenopus* oocytes is the extraordinary stability of these messages and their continued translation at maximal rates for long periods of time. However, different messengers may be translated in the oocyte with different efficiencies, as Berridge and Lane (1976) found for the kinetics of the translation of *Xenopus* vitellogenin and albumin mRNA, which were injected in the same preparation. Whether or not such differences in rates of translation of vitellogenin mRNA and of other messengers are due to a relatively slow diffusion of an unusually large RNA is not known, but the phenomenon emphasizes the importance of accumulation and "translatability" of messenger RNAs when considering kinetics of induction of proteins, which may be particularly critical during development.

D. POSTTRANSLATIONAL MODIFICATIONS

Vitellogenin is extensively chemically modified soon after its synthesis and before it is secreted into the blood. The major modifications are the extensive phosphorylation of the 56% seryl residues of the phosvitin moiety, its glycosylation, and lipidation of the lipovitellin moiety. The intracellular site for the extensive posttranslational modifications of vitellogenin may be the membranes of the endoplasmic reticulum (see Clemens, 1974; Tata, 1976).

In the scheme shown in Fig. 15, it is suggested that the enzymes and substrates for phosphorylation, glycosylation, and lipidation are available only at the membrane site, so that modification of the polypeptide would begin during and immediately after translation on the rough endoplasmic reticulum. This process would continue throughout the vectorial movement and packaging of the protein in the Golgi apparatus prior to secretion. It could thus be argued that a coordinated proliferation of polyribosomes and membranes to which these are attached (Lewis *et al.*, 1976) after hormonal induction would ensure the rapid and correct modification of the newly synthesized vitellogenin. Very few reports have appeared on phosphorylation, glycosylation and lipidation of vitellogenin (Clem-

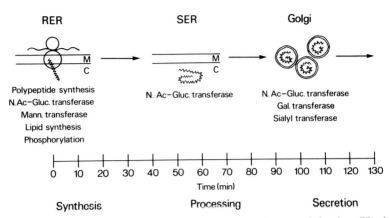

FIG. 15. Schematic representation of vectorial movement and posttranslational modification of vitellogenin synthesized on membrane-bound ribosomes through the smooth endoplasmic reticulum and the Golgi bodies before secretion into *Xenopus* blood. The location of enzymes involved in posttranslational modifications (phosphorylation, glycosylation, lipidation) in the different membrane components are indicated. RER, rough endoplasmic reticulum; SER, smooth endoplasmic reticulum; M, membrane; C, cisternal space of the endoplasmic reticulum; N.Ac-Gluc., *N*-acetylglycosamine; Mann., mannose; Gal., galactose. From Tata (1976).

ens, 1974; Follett and Redshaw, 1974; Smith *et al.,* 1978) and we still have much to learn about the details of the extensive posttranslational modifications that this protein undergoes before it is secreted.

Posttranslational modifications of vitellogenin are not merely a peculiarity of egg-yolk proteins, but have wider implications in cell biology. It is known that the enzymes or processes for posttranslational modifications of other proteins synthesized on membrane-bound ribosomes are also located in membranes of the endoplasmic reticulum, as, for example, the enzymes in the thyroid gland for iodination of nascent thyroglobulin, the enzyme responsible for the disulfide interchange in the maturation of ribonuclease, and the hydroxylation of proline in newly synthesized collagen (see Shore and Tata, 1977; Uy and Wold, 1977). It is indeed surprising that this aspect of the location in membranes of modification enzymes at the site of the synthesis of proteins, particularly those destined for secretion, has received scant attention. Since most, if not all, secreted proteins are modified after translation, the location of the posttranslational machinery in membranes may be the most important reason governing the synthesis of secreted proteins on membrane-bound ribosomes.

The derivation of yolk proteins from a larger precursor protein is also relevant to the current interest generated by findings that several important proteins, many of them hormones, are formed from larger precursors by proteolytic cleavage. These include the pituitary polypeptide complex ACTH/LPH/endorphin, insulin, parathyroid hormone, albumin, and collagen (Steiner *et al.,* 1972; Habener, 1976; Quinn *et al.,* 1975; Gallop and Paz, 1975; Roberts and Herbert, 1977).

What is unique about vitellogenin in this respect is not that it is the precursor of two totally different proteins, but that it is synthesized in one type of cell and cleaved in another. It may well happen that more such multicomponent protein precursors will be discovered in the future.

VI. Is There Translational Control of Vitellogenin and Albumin Synthesis?

The ease with which synthesis of massive amounts of a new protein can be reversibly induced in already differentiated and virtually nondividing cells, makes estradiol-induced vitellogenesis a system of choice for investigating possible specific translational control. We have tackled the question of selective control of translation of vitellogenin mRNA in the liver by comparing the difference between the kinetics of accumulation of translatable mRNA and the synthesis of the protein during primary and secondary induction of vitellogenin (Farmer *et al.*, 1978). As already mentioned (Fig. 3), the characteristic lag period between the administration of estradiol to male animals and the detection of circulating vitellogenin during primary induction is much reduced in previously treated animals exposed to the hormone for a second time. At the same time, the magnitude of the secondary response was greater, but often shorter-lived, than that of the primary response. When the rate of accumulation of mRNA, as quantitated in a reticulocyte cell-free translational system was compared with the appearance of immunoprecipitable polysomes actively engaged in synthesizing vitellogenin, functional vitellogenin mRNA appeared in the liver relatively rapidly and at about the same rate for both the primary and secondary responses (see Fig. 16). The kinetics of appearance of translatable mRNA did not match at later times during the primary and secondary responses, but it is the initial period of onset of the responses that is important. At this stage, one notices an absence of a strictly parallel correlation between the rate of mRNA synthesis and polysome formation during primary and secondary induction. A dissociation between translatable mRNA level and vitellogenin synthesis was, however, not observed by Baker and Shapiro (1977) when similar comparisons were made during primary induction. The difference between primary and secondary stimulation observed by Farmer *et al.* (1978) may thus be explained by the rate at which polyribosomes engaged in synthesizing vitellogenin became functional. Figure 16 also shows that at 35–40 days after the first injection of estradiol, when the synthesis of vitellogenin has ceased *in vivo* (see Figs. 3 and 4), there is virtually no (<4% of the maximum) translatable vitellogenin mRNA left in the cytoplasm. Thus, both the primary and secondary induction of vitellogenin are dependent on *de novo* transcription of the vitellogenin gene.

With the availability of complementary DNA probes, many investigators have now managed to obtain more precise estimates of the changes in the levels of vitellogenin messengers during primary and secondary induction in both birds

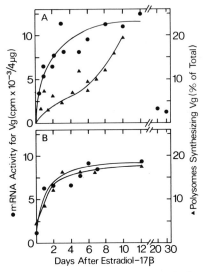

FIG. 16. Changes in levels of vitellogenin (Vg) mRNA and of polysomes engaged in its translation in liver of male *Xenopus* at different stages during (A) primary and (B) secondary responses to estradiol *in vivo*. The amount of functional messengers at different stages of primary and secondary responses was assayed in a reticulocyte cell-free system by immunoprecipitation of [³⁵S]methionine-labeled translation product, with antivitellogenin antibodies (●———●). Polysomes labeled *in vivo* and obtained at each stage of response to estradiol were immunoprecipitated with antivitellogenin antibody to quantitate the fraction engaged in the synthesis of vitellogenin (▲———▲). From Farmer *et al.* (1978).

and amphibians (Baker and Shapiro, 1977, 1978; Deeley *et al.*, 1977a,b; Jost *et al.*, 1978; Burns *et al.*, 1978; Ryffel *et al.*, 1977). In some of these studies, the rapid accumulation of mRNA has been correlated with the rate of synthesis of vitellogenin, as estimated by its appearance in circulation or in the tissue or medium of short-term organ cultures of liver taken from animals treated *in vivo*. The almost unanimous conclusion drawn is that the synthesis of vitellogenin during both primary and secondary responses is entirely a function of the level of messenger present at any given time, i.e., vitellogenesis is strictly under transcriptional control exerted by the hormone. The lag between the level of translatable vitellogenin mRNA and its mobilization into polysomes during the onset of the primary response, noticed by Farmer *et al.* (1978) (see Fig. 16), could not be detected by the determination of the number of mRNA sequences by hybridization assays. The discrepancy may, however, be more apparent than real and may stem from the vastly different sensitivities of the techniques used. Thus, the techniques of estimating levels of translatable mRNA and immunological quantitation of the fraction of polysomes engaged in synthesis of vitellogenin used by Farmer *et al.* (1978) are roughly comparable in their precision. On the other hand, hybridization with complementary DNA to measure messenger level is extraordinarily powerful, and its precision cannot be matched with the relatively crude method of measuring the accumulation of vitellogenin in the tissue, blood, or culture medium.

Whatever the real reason for the above discrepancy, one has to consider the possibility that some rate-limiting mechanism or factors essential for specific translation of vitellogenin messenger has to be established during the latent period preceding primary induction. Such a factor has to be relatively permanently "imprinted" so that secondary stimulation then involves only a replenishment of the mRNA formed during primary stimulation and that has been degraded. What component(s) of the translational machinery is involved is not certain, but from several indirect observations it seems most likely to be a combination of more than one underlying mechanism. The early studies by Clemens and Tata (1973) had already raised the possibility of the requirement for initiation or elongation factor(s). Other studies suggested the requirement for special tRNAs, especially in view of the high serine content of the phosvitin moiety (Mäenpää, 1972). Mäenpää and Bernfield (1975) also showed a preferential increase in a seryl-tRNA (AGU·AGC) in the nucleus and rough endoplasmic reticulum following estradiol injection in the rooster. Ultrastructural observations from our laboratory (Lewis et al., 1976; C. D. Green, personal communication) suggested that it may be necessary to establish a stable system of endoplasmic reticulum to preferentially facilitate both translation of vitellogenin mRNA and posttranslational modification of the nascent protein (see Sections V, B, D).

In our laboratory, we are now extending the above studies on the correlation between the formation and translation of vitellogenin mRNA to the converse situation—that of deinduction of albumin synthesis accompanying the induction of vitellogenin both in the whole animal and in culture (see Figs. 3, 4, and 6).

It is evident from Figs. 3 and 4 that the synthesis of albumin in vivo decreases following estradiol treatment, particularly after secondary hormonal exposure. When experiments similar to those carried out for vitellogenin (Fig. 16), namely, the comparison between the level of functional albumin mRNA and the fraction of polysomes actually engaged in the synthesis of albumin, a less clear-cut result was obtained. As can be seen from Fig. 17, there was a good deal of scatter of the values for both these parameters for albumin during the primary and secondary responses to estradiol. However, a decrease in the levels of mRNA and polysomes coding for albumin can be discerned. This result was verified by a more precise quantitative study of the levels of albumin-immunoprecipitable translation products during primary and secondary response (Fig. 18). It is evident from these data that a decrease in the synthesis of albumin does occur after estrogen treatment and that, although total translated protein levels are greater after secondary hormonal exposure, there is a more rapid and extensive deinduction of albumin synthesis during secondary response. Although it can be argued that part of the deinduction of albumin synthesis reflects a translational control mechanism, recent evidence from our laboratory suggests that a change in the tran-

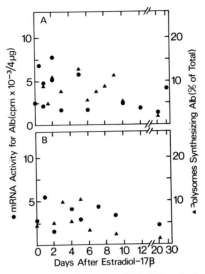

FIG. 17. Changes in levels of albumin (Alb) mRNA (●) and of polysomes engaged in its translation (▲) in *Xenopus* liver at different stages of (A) primary and (B) secondary responses to estradiol. The same samples of liver as those used in the experiments depicted in Fig. 16 were used, except that antialbumin antibodies replaced those directed against vitellogenin. From Farmer *et al.* (1978).

scriptional activity of the albumin gene may be of importance also in the estrogen response. This evidence is currently being extended by using cDNA hybridization to quantify the number of albumin mRNA sequences present at various times during primary and secondary exposure to estradiol.

VIII. Estradiol Receptors and Early Events in Vitellogenin Gene Expression

With the exception of the action of progesterone on amphibian egg maturation (see Baulieu *et al.*, 1978), it is generally accepted that all steroid hormones initiate their action by a "two-step" process by which the hormone first binds to a receptor in the target cell's cytoplasm and the hormone–receptor complex is then translocated into the nucleus to combine with "acceptor" sites on the chromatin (Jensen and De Sombre, 1973; O'Malley and Means, 1974). Although the initial event leading to vitellogenesis must be triggered off by an interaction between estradiol and a receptor in the liver, little is known about the nature of the receptor in bird or amphibian liver. The most likely reason for the paucity of information is that, unlike the estradiol receptor in tissues like the rat uterus or chick oviduct, the putative receptor in chicken or frog liver is extremely labile. Arias and Warren (1971) described a cytosol receptor for estradiol in chicken liver, but Mester and Baulieu (1972) and Lebeau *et al.* (1973) suggested that the

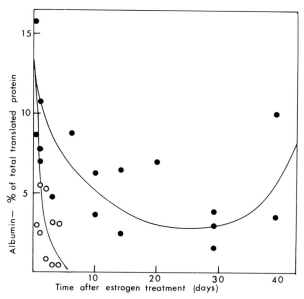

FIG. 18. Changes in levels of translatable albumin mRNA in *Xenopus* liver at different stages of primary and secondary responses to estradiol. Albumin mRNA levels during primary (●———●) and secondary (○———○) response were assayed in a rabbit reticulocyte cell-free protein-synthesizing system by immunoprecipitation of [^{35}S]methionine-labeled translation products with antibodies to albumin. Results are expressed as percentage of total [^{35}S]methionine incorporated into protein, which was recovered as radioactive vitellogenin.

hormone interacted directly with the nucleus without necessarily binding first to a cytosol component. In more recent studies estradiol was shown to bind directly to rooster liver chromatin with a high-affinity (K_d approx. $10^{-9} M$) and its interaction with cytosol proteins was weak (K_d approx. $10^{-6} M$) (Gschwendt and Kittstein, 1974; Gschwendt, 1975). For *Xenopus* liver the information is sparser. A recent report has described the presence in *Xenopus* liver of a protein of low molecular weight (~20,000), as determined by electrophoresis on polyacrylamide gels, which binds both estradiol and testosterone (Bergink and Wittliff, 1975). Wangh (personal communication) also detected estradiol binding sites in *Xenopus* liver cytosol, whose high affinity ($K_d \sim 1.3 \times 10^{-8} M$) is compatible with the induction of vitellogenesis *in vitro* by low concentrations ($10^{-10} M$ to $10^{-8} M$) of estradiol added to the culture medium (Wangh and Knowland, 1975; Green and Tata, 1976) (see Fig. 7). Undoubtedly, much work still has to be done before establishing a cytoplasm-to-nucleus translocation of hormone receptor as a prerequisite for the initiation of the chain of events leading to the full expression of the vitellogenin gene (Westley and Knowland, 1978).

Since a *de novo* transcription of the vitellogenin gene is the major action of estradiol, many investigators are now concentrating on the very early stages of induction following exposure of hepatocytes to the hormone. Eventually, much will depend on an accurate temporal analysis of the detection of nuclear receptor–hormone complex in the nucleus and the putative biochemical events triggered by the complex. For this reason, it will be essential to work with purified populations of hepatocytes, all of which are competent to respond to the hormone directly in tissue culture, rather than study whole animals. Nevertheless, it is most significant that, using the complementary DNA probe, Baker and Shapiro (1978) have detected newly transcribed vitellogenin mRNA sequences within 1 hour of the administration of estradiol to male *Xenopus*. It is generally accepted that one of the primary consequences of the nuclear receptor (or acceptor) when combined with steroid hormones that activate specific genes is to cause some change in the composition or structure of the chromatin of the target cell (Yamamoto and Alberts, 1976; Palmiter *et al.*, 1976; O'Malley *et al.*, 1977). This change may involve a covalent chemical modification of chromosomal proteins, such as phosphorylation, acetylation (Allfrey, 1977; Chiu and Hnilica, 1977), and/or an overall conformational change in the higher order of organization of chromatin (Yamamoto and Alberts, 1976). It is necessary to emphasize that the latter is a complex and not yet fully understood aspect of cell biology, so that our understanding of the mechanism of induction of vitellogenin by estradiol will have to await a more precise clarification of the significance of the organization of animal genes in the nucleus.

VIII. Conclusions

The important features of the induction of vitellogenesis are schematically summarized in Fig. 19, which also highlights the major problems that still have to be solved in order to integrate the different molecular responses of the hepatocyte stimulated by estradiol. Perhaps the most important question to be resolved is the characterization of the receptor(s) in the target cell and to link the hormone–receptor interaction with the activation of the vitellogenin gene. The possibility of inducing the whole physiological process directly in tissue cultures now makes it easier to attack this problem. Our knowledge of transcriptional events and their regulation is also relatively superficial. No doubt, the availability of a cloned cDNA probe to vitellogenin messenger RNA will help greatly in clarifying several questions concerning the activation of the vitellogenin gene, particularly during the early times after hormone administration, in the same way it has been possible to elucidate that concerning the ovalbumin gene in avian oviduct (see O'Malley *et al.*, this volume, Chapter 1). In particular, it would be important to verify whether the vitellogenin gene is completely "shut off" in the liver of an unstimulated male frog or chicken, or whether the gene is always transcribed at a low rate but the protein it codes for is not made, or whether or not the vitellogenin gene is at all transcribed in nontarget cells. The recent report of detection of tadpole and adult frog hemoglobin messenger sequences in *Xenopus*

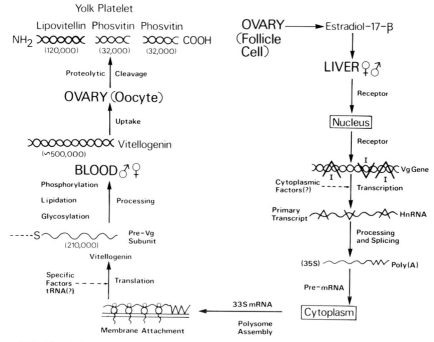

FIG. 19. Scheme summarizing the sequence of major events triggered by estradiol leading to the secretion of vitellogenin (Vg) into the blood of male or female *Xenopus* and the deposition of phosvitin and lipovitellin in egg-yolk platelets. Figures in parentheses refer to nominal size of RNA or protein. I, intervening sequences within the coding region of the gene; S, probable presence of the "signal" peptide in the primary translation product. See text for further details.

oocytes is of some considerable significance in this context (Perlman *et al.*, 1977).

The rapid advent of recombinant DNA and gene cloning technology now offers powerful molecular probes to study the regulation of transcription of the vitellogenin gene in isolated nuclei and subnuclear preparations. In a wider context, it is known that during differentiation the activation of specific genes is often accompanied by a concomitant deinduction of already expressed genes, but it has been difficult to quantitate this phenomenon at the molecular level (see Davidson, 1976). The coupled and reversible induction of vitellogenin and deinduction of albumin in hepatocytes offers a valuable "built-in control" when designing experiments to verify the specificity of detection of primary gene transcripts and the dynamics of their processing to nuclear precursors and ultimately to cytoplasmic messengers. It would also allow a better definition of the organization of expressed and unexpressed genes in different nuclear compartments of "active" and "inactive" chromatin.

Another facet of the problem of coupled induction and deinduction of specific genes is that very often one is dealing with well defined sets or families of genes. For example, during vitellogenesis estrogen not only induces vitellogenin synthesis, but also greatly stimulates that of other proteins made in the liver, particularly serum lipoproteins (Chan *et al.*, 1976) and vitamin-binding proteins that eventually accumulate in the yolk (Murthy and Adiga, 1978). Conversely, the deinduction of albumin synthesis is accompanied by a marked or total "shutoff" of the formation of 9 or 10 other serum proteins (L. J. Wangh, personal communication). Furthermore, glucocorticoid hormones and estrogen evoke a mutually antagonistic response in that glucocorticoids stimulate or suppress the synthesis of the same two sets of proteins in a reciprocal manner to that of estrogen. Could it be that this phenomenon is reflecting some unknown feature of organization of groups of genes in differentiated cells? The large size of the vitellogenin mRNA is also particularly suited to following the dynamics of synthesis and processing of the primary transcript bearing the pre-mRNA sequences.

Once the hormone has activated the gene and the mRNA accumulates in the cytoplasm, an unresolved question is to determine whether or not this messenger is selectively subjected to translational control. Two different lines of evidence presented above suggest that it is: (a) the preferential stimulation by cell sap of estrogenized male *Xenopus* liver of the synthesis of a vitellogenin-like protein by isolated polysomes; (b) the temporal dissociation between the rate of accumulation of vitellogenin message and the active polysomes engaged in synthesizing vitellogenin. Could there be a common mechanism underlying these two phenomena? An obvious explanation would be an "imprinting" of a different pattern of tRNAs (particularly seryl-tRNA) or initiation factors occurring at the onset of primary induction but which would be permanent or long-lasting so as not to be rate-limiting for the translation of new mRNA produced during secondary stimulation. This question can be directly tackled by analyzing liver cell sap for its ability to support vitellogenin translation at different stages of primary and secondary induction. Although mechanisms of specific translational control during development or adaptation have been previously proposed for other proteins (particularly for the initiation of synthesis of histones, tyrosine aminotransferase, myosin, ferritin, and hemoglobin), vitellogenesis is particularly well suited for finding a solution to this intriguing problem. Whatever the mechanism, from our current knowledge of regulation of translation of mRNA in eukaryotic cells, it is most likely that a number of separate steps in the translation process are integrated to facilitate the regulation of translation of specific messengers.

Being a secreted protein, vitellogenin is synthesized on membrane-bound ribosomes, which in itself is not unusual. But the fact that the extensive and diverse posttranslational modifications of vitellogenin (phosphorylation, glycosylation, lipidation) occur in the membranes of the rough endoplasmic reticulum and Golgi apparatus may mean that posttranslational modifications are a key determining factor accompanying vitellogenin synthesis on membrane-bound ribosomes. Much interest has also been generated recently around the posttranslational proteolytic cleavage of larger precursors of many secreted proteins and the multicomponent nature of vitellogenin lends itself particularly well to investigating this particular issue. What is unique about vitellogenin is that its cleavage does not occur in the cell in which it is synthesized, but that phosvitin and lipovitellin are produced in a remote tissue, the ovary. These considerations of posttranslational modifications make it imperative that we know more about the chemistry of vitellogenin; this would be particularly valuable when considering the evolutionary significance of this protein, which plays a central role in early embryonic development of all vertebrate and invertebrate egg-laying species.

Much of our knowledge of gene expression during development has been pieced together from information derived from a large number of experimental systems. The discrepancies one observes emphasize the drawback of assembling a composite picture derived from too many different developmental systems. It is unlikely that a single ideal system will be found that would enable us to integrate the diverse molecular and cellular processes involved in the control of differentiation. What we have attempted to emphasize in this chapter is how vitellogenesis offers a versatile model system for analyzing the multiple facets of hormonal regulation of specific gene expression.

ACKNOWLEDGMENTS

We are most grateful to Dr. S. R. Farmer for making available to us the data shown in Figs. 4 and 10.

REFERENCES

AB, G., Roskam, W. G., Dijkstra, J., Mulder, J., Willems, M., Van der Ende, A., and Gruber, M. (1976). *Biochim. Biophys. Acta* **454,** 67.

Allfrey, V. G. (1977). *In* "Chromatin and Chromosome Structure" (H. J. Li and R. Eckhardt, eds.), pp. 167–191. Academic Press, New York.

Ansari, A. Q., Dolphin, P. J., Lazier, C. B., Munday, K. A., and Akhtar, M. (1971). *Biochem. J.* **122,** 107.

Arias, F., and Warren, J. C. (1971). *Biochim. Biophys. Acta* **230,** 550.

Baker, H. J., and Shapiro, D. J. (1977). *J. Biol. Chem.* **252,** 8428.

Baker, H. J., and Shapiro, D. J. (1978). *J. Biol. Chem.* **253,** 4521.

Bast, R. E., Garfield, S. A., Gehrke, L., and Ilan, J. (1977). *Proc. Natl. Acad. Sci. U.S.A.* **74,** 3133.

Baulieu, E.-E., Godeau, F., Schorderet, M., and Schorderet-Slatkine, S. (1978). *Nature (London)* **275,** 593.

Bergink, E. W., and Wallace, R. A. (1974). *J. Biol. Chem.* **249,** 2897.

Bergink, E. W., and Wittliff, J. L. (1975). *Biochemistry* **14,** 3115.

Bergink, E. W., Wallace, R. A., Van den Berg, J. A., Bos, E. S., Gruber, M., and AB, G. (1974). *Am. Zool.* **14,** 1177.

Berridge, M. V., and Lane, C. D. (1976). *Cell* **8,** 283.

Berridge, M. V., Farmer, S. R., Green, C. D., Henshaw, E. C., and Tata, J. R. (1976). *Eur. J. Biochem.* **62**, 161.

Beuving, G., and Gruber, M., (1971). *Biochim. Biophys. Acta* **232**, 529.

Bieri-Boniot, F., Joss, H., and Dierks-Ventling, C. (1977). *FEBS Lett.* **81**, 91.

Blobel, G., and Dobberstein, B. (1975). *J. Cell Biol.* **67**, 835.

Bolivar, F., Rodriguez, R. L., Greene, P. J., Betlach, M. C., Heyneker, H. L., Boyer, H. W., Crosa, J. H., and Falkow, S. (1977). *Gene* **2**, 95.

Bownes, M., and Hames, B. D. (1977). *J. Exp. Zool.* **200**, 149.

Breathnach, R., Mandel, J. L., and Chambon, P. (1977). *Nature (London)* **270**, 314.

Brummett, A. R., and Dumont, J. N. (1977). *Dev. Biol.* **60**, 482.

Burns, A. T. H., Deeley, R. G., Gordon, J. I., Udell, D. S., Mullinix, K. P., and Goldberger, R. F. (1978). *Proc. Natl. Acad. Sci. U.S.A.* **75**, 1815.

Chan, L., Jackson, R. L., O'Malley, B. W., and Means, A. R. (1976). *J. Clin. Invest.* **58**, 368.

Chen, T. T., Strahlendorf, P. W., and Wyatt, G. R. (1978). *J. Biol. Chem.* **253**, 5325.

Chiu, J.-F., and Hnilica, L. S. (1977). *In* "Chromatin and Chromosome Structure" (H. J. Li and R. A. Eckhardt, eds.), pp. 193 254. Academic Press, New York.

Christmann, J. L., Grayson, M. J., and Huang, R. C. C. (1977). *Biochemistry* **16**, 3250.

Clemens, M. J. (1974). *Prog. Biophys. Mol. Biol.* **28**, 71.

Clemens, M. J., and Tata, J. R. (1973). *Eur. J. Biochem.* **33**, 71.

Clemens, M. J., Lofthouse, R., and Tata, J. R. (1975). *Biochem. J.* **250**, 2213.

Davidson, E. H. (1976). "Gene Activity in Early Development." Academic Press, New York.

Davidson, E. H., Klein, W. H., and Britten, R. J. (1977). *Dev. Biol.* **55**, 69.

Deeley, R. G., Mullinix, K. P., Wetekam, W., Kronenberg, H. M., Meyers, M., Eldridge, J. D., and Goldberger, R. F. (1975). *J. Biol. Chem.* **250**, 9060.

Deeley, R. G., Udell, D. S., Burns, A. T. H., Gordon, J. I., and Goldberger, R. F. (1977a). *J. Biol. Chem.* **252**, 7913.

Deeley, R. G., Gordon, J. I., Burns, A. T. H., Mullinix, K. P., Bina-Stein, M., and Goldberger, R. F. (1977b). *J. Biol. Chem.* **252**, 8310.

Dehn, P. F., and Wallace, R. A. (1973). *J. Cell. Biol.* **58**, 721.

Dolphin, P. J., Ansari, A. Q., Lazier, C. B., Munday, K. A., and Akhtar, M. (1971). *Biochem. J.* **124**, 751.

Farmer, S. R., Henshaw, E. C., Berridge, M. V., and Tata, J. R. (1978). *Nature (London)* **273**, 401.

Felber, B. K., Ryfell, G. U., and Weber, R. (1979). *Mol. Cell. Endocrinol.* **12**, 151.

Follett, B. K., and Redshaw, M. R. (1968). *J. Endocrinol.* **40**, 439.

Follett, B. K., and Redshaw, M. R. (1974). *In* "Physiology of the Amphibia" (B. Lofts, ed.), Vol. 2, pp. 219–308. Academic Press, New York.

Gallop, P. M., and Paz, M. A. (1975). *Physiol. Rev.* **55**, 418.

Gordon, J. I., Deeley, R. G., Burns, A. T. H., Patterson, B. M., Christmann, J. L., and Goldberger, R. F. (1977). *J. Biol. Chem.* **252**, 8320.

Green, C. D., and Tata, J. R. (1976). *Cell* **7**, 131.

Greengard, O., Gordon, M., Smith, M. A., and Acs, G. (1964). *J. Biol. Chem.* **239**, 2079.

Gruber, M., Bos., E. S., and AB, G. (1976). *Mol. Cell. Endocrinol.* **5**, 41.

Gschwendt, M. (1975). *Hoppe-Seyler's Z. Physiol. Chem.* **356**, 157.

Gschwendt, M., and Kittstein, W. (1974). *Biochim. Biophys. Acta* **361**, 84.

Habener, J. F. (1976). *Polypeptide Horm.: Mol. Cell. Aspects, Ciba Found. Symp.* No. 41, p. 197.

Jackson, R. L., Lin, H.-Y., Mao, J. T. S., Chan, L., and Means, A. R. (1977). *Endocrinology* **101**, 849.

Jailkhani, B. L., and Talwar, G. P. (1972a). *Nature (London), New Biol.* **236**, 239.

Jailkhani, B. L., and Talwar, G. P. (1972b). *Nature (London) New Biol.* **239**, 240.

Jensen, E. V., and De Sombre, E. R. (1973). *Science* **182**, 126.

Jost, J.-P., and Pehling, G. (1976). *Eur. J. Biochem.* **62**, 299.

Jost, J.-P., Keller, R., and Dierks-Ventling, C. (1973). *J. Biol. Chem.* **248**, 5262.

Jost, J.-P., Ohno, T., Panyim, S., and Schuersch, A. R. (1978). *Eur. J. Biochem.* **84,** 355.
Jost, J., Pehling, G., Ohno, T., and Cozens, P. (1978). *Nucleic Acids Res.* **5,** 4781.
Karasaki, S. (1963). *J. Cell Biol.* **18,** 135.
Kelly, T. J., and Telfer, W. H. (1977). *Dev. Biol.* **61,** 58.
King, R. J. B., and Mainwaring, W. I. P. (1974). "Steroid–Cell Interactions." Butterworth, London.
Koeppe, J. K., and Offengand, J. (1976). *In* "The Juvenile Hormones" (L. I. Gilbert, ed.), pp. 486–504. Plenum, New York.
Kunkel, J. G., and Pan, M. L. (1976). *J. Insect Physiol.* **22,** 809.
Lanclos, K. D., and Hamilton, T. H. (1975). *Proc. Natl. Acad. Sci. U.S.A.* **72,** 3934.
Lane, C. D., and Knowland, J. S. K. (1975). *In* "The Biochemistry of Animal Development" (R. Weber, ed.), Vol. 3, pp. 145–181. Academic Press, New York.
Lebeau, M.-C., Massol, N., and Baulieu, E.-E. (1973). *Eur. J. Biochem.* **36,** 294.
Lewin, B. (1975). *Cell* **4,** 11.
Lewis, J. A., and Tata, J. R. (1973). *J. Cell Sci.* **13,** 447.
Lewis, J. A., Clemens, M. J., and Tata, J. R. (1976). *Mol. Cell. Endocrinol.* **4,** 311.
McReynolds, L. A., Catterall, J. F., and O'Malley, B. W. (1977). *Gene* **2,** 217.
Mäenpää, P. H. (1972). *Biochem. Biophys. Res. Commun.* **47,** 971.
Mäenpää, P. H. (1976). *Biochem. Biophys. Res. Commun.* **72,** 347.
Mäenpää, P. H., and Bernfield, M. R. (1969). *Biochemistry* **8,** 4926.
Mäenpää, P. H., and Bernfield, M. R. (1975). *Biochemistry* **14,** 4820.
Maniatis, T., Kee, S. G., Efstratiadis, A., and Kafatos, F. C. (1976). *Cell* **8,** 163.
Mester, J., and Baulieu, E.-E. (1972). *Biochim. Biophys. Acta* **261,** 236.
Mullinix, K. P., Wetekam, W., Deeley, R. G., Gordon, J. J., Meyers, M., Kent, K. A., and Goldberger, R. F. (1976). *Proc. Natl. Acad. Sci. U.S.A.* **73,** 1442.
Murthy, U. S., and Adiga, P. R. (1978). *Biochim. Biophys. Acta* **538,** 364.
Nierlich, D. P., Rutter, W. J., and Fox, C. F., eds. (1976). "Molecular Mechanisms in the Control of Gene Expression." Academic Press, New York.
Ohlendorf, D. H., Barbarash, G. H., Trout, A., Kent, C., and Banaszak, L. J. (1977). *J. Biol. Chem.* **252,** 7992.
Ohlendorf, D. H., Wren, R. F., and Banaszak, L. J. (1978). *Nature (London)* **272,** 28.
O'Malley, B. W., and Means, A. R. (1974). *Science* **183,** 610.
O'Malley, B. W., Towle, H. C., and Schwartz, R. J. (1977). *Annu. Rev. Genet.* **11,** 239.
Palade, G. E. (1975). *Science* **189,** 347.
Palmiter, R. D. (1975). *Cell* **4,** 189.
Palmiter, R. D., Moore, P. B., Mulvihill, E. R., and Emtage, S. (1976). *Cell* **8,** 557.
Pan, M. L., Bell, W. J., and Telfer, W. H. (1969). *Science* **165,** 393.
Panyim, S., Ohno, T., and Jost, J.-P. (1978). *Nucl. Acids Res.* **5,** 1353.
Penning, T. M., Merry, A. H., Munday, K. A., and Akhtar, M. (1977). *Biochem. J.* **162,** 157.
Perlman, S. M., Ford, P. J., and Rosbash, M. M. (1977). *Proc. Natl. Acad. Sci. U.S.A.* **74,** 3835.
Quinn, P. S., Gamble, M., and Judah, J. D. (1975). *Biochem. J.* **146,** 389.
Rabbitts, T. H. (1976). *Nature (London)* **260,** 22.
Redshaw, M. R., and Follett, B. K. (1971). *Biochem. J.* **124,** 759.
Roberts, J. L., and Herbert, E. (1977). *Proc. Natl. Acad. Sci. U.S.A.* **74,** 5300.
Roskam, W. G., Tichelaar, W., Schirm, J., Gruber, M., and AB, G. (1976a). *Biochim. Biophys. Acta* **435,** 82.
Roskam, W. G., Gruber, M., and AB, G. (1976b). *Biochim. Biophys. Acta* **435,** 91.
Rougeon, F., and Mach, B. (1976). *Proc. Natl. Acad. Sci. U.S.A.* **73,** 3418.
Ryffel, G. U. (1978). *Mol. Cell. Endocrinol.* **12,** 237.
Ryffel, G. U., Wahli, W., and Weber, R. (1977). *Cell* **11,** 213.
Schimke, R. T., McKnight, G. S., Shapiro, D. J., Sullivan, D., and Palacios, R. (1975). *Recent Prog. Horm. Res.* **31,** 175.

Schjeide, O. A., and Lai, G. G. B. (1970). In "Cell Differentiation" (O. A. Schjeide and J. de Vellis, eds.), pp. 447–475. Van Nostrand-Reinhold, Princeton, New Jersey.

Schuetz, A. W., Hollinger, T. G., Wallace, R. A., and Samson, D. A. (1977). Dev. Biol. 58, 428.

Shapiro, D. J., and Baker, H. J. (1977). J. Biol. Chem. 252, 5244.

Shapiro, D. J., Baker, H. J., and Stitt, D. T. (1976). J. Biol. Chem. 251, 3105.

Shore, G. C., and Tata, J. R. (1977). Biochim. Biophys. Acta 472, 197.

Skipper, J. K., and Hamilton, T. H. (1977). Proc. Natl. Acad. Sci. U.S.A. 74, 2384.

Smith, D. F., Penning, T. M., Ansari, A. Q., Munday, K. A., and Akhtar, M. (1978). Biochem. J. 174, 353.

Smith, D. F., Searle, P. F., and Williams, J. G. (1979). Nucleic Acids Res. 6, 487.

Stanchfield, J. E., and Yager, J. P. (1977). J. Cell. Biol. Abstr. No. HM 382.

Steiner, D. F., Kemmler, W., Clark, J. L., Oyer, P. E., and Rubenstein, A. H. (1972). Handb. Physiol. Sect. 7, Vol. 1, p. 175.

Tata, J. R. (1970). In "The Biochemical Actions of Hormones" (G. Litwack, ed.), Vol. 1, pp. 89–133. Academic Press, New York.

Tata, J. R. (1973). Karolinska Symp. Res. Methods Reprod. Endocrinol. 6th Symp., p. 192.

Tata, J. R. (1976). Cell 9, 1.

Tata, J. R. (1978). In "Hormones and Cell Regulation" (J. Dumont, and J. Nunez, eds.), Vol. 2, pp. 37–54. Elsevier/North-Holland, Amsterdam.

Tata, J. R., and Baker, B. (1974). Exp. Cell Res. 83, 125.

Tata, J. R., and Baker, B. (1975). Biochem. J. 150, 345.

Tata, J. R., and Baker, B. (1978). J. Mol. Biol. 118, 249.

Tilghman, S. M., Tiemeier, D. C., Polsky, F., Edgell, M. H., Seidman, J. G., Leder, A., Enquist, L. W., Norman, B., and Leder, P. (1977). Proc. Natl. Acad. Sci. U.S.A. 74, 4406.

Tilghman, S. M., Tiemeier, D. C., Seidman, J. G., Peterlin, B. M., Sullivan, M., Maizel, J. V., and Leder, P. (1978a). Proc. Natl. Acad. Sci. U.S.A. 75, 725.

Tilghman, S. M., Curtis, P. J., Tiemeier, D. C., Leder, P., and Weismann, C. (1978b). Proc. Natl. Acad. Sci. U.S.A. 75, 1309.

Uy, R., and Wold, F. (1977). Science 198, 890.

Wachsmuth, E. D., and Jost, J.-P. (1976). Biochim. Biophys. Acta, 437, 454.

Wahli, W., Dawid, I. B., Wyler, T., Jaggi, R. B., Weber, R., and Ryffel, G. U. (1979). Cell 16, 535.

Wahli, W., Wyler, T., Weber, R., and Ryffel, G. U. (1976). Eur. J. Biochem. 66, 457.

Wahli, W., Wyler, T., Weber, R., and Ryffel, G. U. (1978). Eur. J. Biochem. 86, 225.

Wallace, R. A. (1963). Biochim. Biophys. Acta 74, 505.

Wallace, R. A. (1965). Anal. Biochem. 11, 297.

Wallace, R. A. (1970). Biochim. Biophys. Acta 215, 176.

Wallace, R. A., and Jared, D. W. (1968a). Science 160, 91.

Wallace, R. A., and Jared, D. W. (1968b). Can. J. Biochem. 46, 953.

Wallace, R. A., and Jared, D. W. (1969). Dev. Biol. 19, 498.

Wallace, R. A., and Jared, D. W. (1976). J. Cell Biol. 69, 345.

Wallace, R. A., Nickol, J. M., Ho, T., and Jared, D. W. (1972). Dev. Biol. 29, 225.

Wangh, L. J., and Knowland, J. (1975). Proc. Natl. Acad. Sci. U.S.A. 72, 3172.

Wangh, L. J., and Osborne, J. A. (1979). Cell (in press).

Weckler, C., and Gschwendt, M. (1976). FEBS Lett. 65, 220.

Westley, B., and Knowland, J. (1978). Cell 15, 367.

Wetekam, W., Mullinix, K. P., Deeley, R. G., Kronenberg, H. M., Eldridge, J. D., Meyers, M., and Goldberger, R. F. (1975). Proc. Natl. Acad. Sci. U.S.A. 72, 3364.

Wittliff, J. L., and Kenney, F. T. (1972a). Biochim. Biophys. Acta 269, 485.

Wittliff, J. L., and Kenney, F. T. (1972b). Biochim. Biophys. Acta 269, 493.

Yamamoto, K. R., and Alberts, B. M. (1976). Annu. Rev. Biochem. 45, 721.

Zehavi-Willner, T., and Lane, C. (1977). Cell 11, 683.

DISCUSSION

H. Seo: I would like to present data on the effect of estrogen on prolactin synthesis in male rats, which is similar to the observed effect of estrogen on vitellogenin synthesis. Figure A shows the

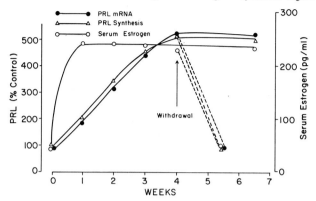

FIG. A. Effect of chronic estrogen stimulation on prolactin (PRL) synthesis and prolactin mRNA.

effect of chronic stimulation on prolactin synthesis and prolactin mRNA. Estrogen treatment was done by *in vivo* implantation of an estrogen pellet subcutaneously. We measured prolactin mRNA in total RNA extracted from pituitary both by cell-free translation or hybridization to complementary DNA to prolactin mRNA. Endogenous PRL synthesis was measured by pulse labeling of the pituitary *in vitro*. As shown in Fig. A, prolactin mRNA and prolactin synthesis increased in parallel in terms of 1-week intervals. In this chronic stimulation, there is no distinguishable difference in the appearance of prolactin mRNA and endogenous prolactin synthesis. When the estrogen pellet was removed after

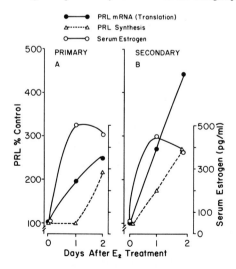

FIG. B. Comparative effects of primary and secondary estrogen stimulation on prolactin (PRL) synthesis and prolactin mRNA.

prolactin synthesis and mRNA plateaued (4 weeks), it took about 2 weeks for these parameters to return to the basal levels. The secondary stimulation shown in Fig. B was applied to these animal groups.

If you compare the primary stimulation in which animals did not experience any estrogen stimulation to the secondary stimulation, the induction of prolactin mRNA is more rapid and of greater magnitude than in secondary stimulation. Note that serum estrogen level (O——O) was almost identical in primary (left) and secondary (right) stimulation. Prolactin mRNA (●——●) was measured by both translation and hybridization. As Dr. Tata mentioned, in vitellogenin mRNA, prolactin mRNA measured by hybridization completely coincide with mRNA activity measured by translation. Thus, at least accumulation prolactin mRNA by estrogen is a translatable (functional) *in vitro* system.

The most interesting phenomenon observed was the lack of synthesis in primary stimulation in spite of the fact that prolactin mRNA is translatable, as Dr. Tata depicted in vitellogenin synthesis. We observed always about 24 hours' lag in the stimulation of endogenous synthesis of prolactin. But in secondary stimulation, there is no such lag. In our system, a prolactin cell might be differentiated from nonfunctional cells by estrogen stimulation; also the multiplication of the cell must be considered. Thus, it is difficult to elucidate the mechanism of estrogen action and different responses between primary and secondary stimulation.

I would like to ask one question: Is the difference in response between primary and secondary stimulation in vitellogenin synthesis caused by preferential differentiation in the cell, like endoplasmic reticulum, or by the difference in the receptor site for estrogen?

J. Tata: I cannot answer your question directly, but we know that once you stimulate the proliferation of endoplasmic reticulum by up to 3- to 5-fold, its level is maintained for several months. What disappears rapidly is the message for vitellogenin. Why this is so, I don't know.

C. Lazier: Terrell Hamilton and I have recently done some work on the estrogen receptor in *Xenopus* livers and have found that after estrogen injection there is an enormous increase in a high-affinity nuclear receptor, just as in the chicken. I expect that there will be much more done on this soon.

Your proposed experiments injecting receptor into the oocyte are very interesting; even if you can get pure receptor for the experiments, you still may not be able to turn on the vitellogenin gene. An analogy here is found in the developing chick embryo, where at day 12 of development the nuclear estrogen receptor can be increased by giving exogenous estradiol, but vitellogenin production is not turned on until day 15. It would be very nice to know what elements at the time are involved in turning on the gene.

J. R. Tata: I would like to congratulate you for looking at receptors in the embryonic system. The oocyte injection experiment will answer the kind of questions you have raised, because if you find that you have something like a receptor in embryonic chick liver, but without a vitellogenic response, then one can ask if this is really the functional receptor. I think that your recent experiments on embryonic livers are very exciting and tell us a lot about acquisition of competence to respond to steriod hormones.

C. Lazier: It certainly would be nice to know if that day 12 high-affinity estradiol-binding protein is really a receptor. I must admit, we certainly do not know that.

J. E. Rall: How about the nonhistone proteins? Are you worried about them as everyone seemed to be a few years ago?

J. R. Tata: I did not want to go into this, but obviously when one talks about a gene, one is always simplifying. The gene as you know is packaged in nucleosomes and there is a complex architecture built around it; we have yet to understand in molecular terms what this packaging of genes really means in terms of regulation, and the question that you are asking is whether or not there is some non-histone protein regulator that recognizes the right sequences that reprograms the genetic apparatus. The answer is that we do not know.

W. Odell: I have a question about the oocyte endocytotic uptake of vitellogenin. Is this a specific recognition step; can you substitute other proteins for the vitellogenin? If it is specific, is the process inducible or modifiable? Is it hormone related?

J. R. Tata: That has all been done by Wallace and Dumont's groups recently. The uptake is due to endopinocytosis, and there must be something on the oocyte surface that recognizes vitellogenin, which is very specific. As to the question of hormonal regulation, it is certainly not dependent on estrogen, but it may be on progesterone, because progesterone is required for maturation and progesterone interestingly acts on the surface of the oocyte. It is not clear, however, whether one really needs progesterone for some general maturation function or specifically to take up vitellogenin. What is also interesting is that only if one has added vitellogenin to oocytes, and it has been taken up by endopinocytosis, will the vitellogenin be correctly processed and inserted into the crystalline platelet, but if one injects vitellogenin into the oocyte, then it is very rapidly degraded and one never sees any of it appearing in the platelet. This suggests that vitellogenin picks up something either on or near the surface of the oocyte, which then allows it to be properly handled and segregated from lysosomal or degradative elements.

T. G. Muldoon: My question concerns your observation that glucocorticoids cause in serum proteins a marked increase that can be largely eliminated by estrogens. I was not sure of the temporal sequence here, but do you feel that this is a deinduction of newly induced proteins or is there perhaps some antagonism between the hormones at a different level, possibly even at receptor binding interactions?

J. R. Tata: We have not done all the permutations, simply because it was not our main purpose. In general, dexamethasone or glucocorticoids will prevent or diminish the induction of vitellogenin if added as you set up the culture. This work has been done by Larry Wangh.

E. H. Frieden: Since my brother is not at this meeting, I will ask a question that he might ask if he were here, unless indeed he already knows the answer—namely, does the capacity to respond with vitellogenin synthesis occur in the tadpole liver? Have you done *in vitro* studies with this material?

J. R. Tata: The answer is yes. John Knowland has recently done experiments very analogous to what Catherine Lazier has recently published, showing that the tadpole liver at an early stage responds to estrogen by making vitellogenin.

K. Sterling: I am glad that you got the thyroid hormone in your last answer. My question concerns a small point about the 5-day lag between the primary and secondary estradiol inductions. Now if I have understood it correctly, the lag seemed attributable to mobilization of mRNA onto active polysomes. I was not certain whether you were determining that by cDNA hybridization studies, or were doing it with translation in another system, such as rabbit reticulocyte lysate; this seemed a rather critical point at the end of the talk. Could you enlighten me please?

J. R. Tata: That particular experiment was done as follows. One makes polyribosomes from one aliquot of liver cells and extracts total RNA from the other. The total RNA is translated in a heterologous system (rabbit reticulocyte or wheat germ), and in the other half the polysomes are assayed by immunoprecipitation, which gives the fraction of total polysomes that are engaged in making vitellogenin. And so the dissociation you saw in the primary induction (Fig. 16) was that the amount of messenger accumulates very rapidly, but, for some unknown reason, the translation or the mobilization of the message into active polysomes does not keep pace during primary response but does so during secondary response.

K. Sterling: Then the rate of transcription is the same in both the primary and secondary induction. This is fascinating and most informative.

J. R. Tata: Yes, this has been looked at now by several laboratories. The answer is the same—namely, that there is not much difference in kinetics of transcription, as judged by hybridization assays, for both primary and secondary induction.

J. E. Rall: You seem to more than imply that it is endoplasmic reticulum that has been built up and has not been degraded. You are sure that it is not ribosomes in cells that accumulate?

J. R. Tata: I chose the endoplasmic reticulum as a possible explanation for a lag in translation during primary response as just one of many mechanisms. If I may digress into a very general topic of translational control, it will turn out to be a combination of all kinds of regulations that are integrated, so that translational control is the sum total of a large number of inputs. The reason I chose endoplasmic reticulum is to raise the possibility that the processing of nascent polypeptide might turn out to be very important in determining the rate of translation. For example, it has been shown recently that slowing down of hydroxylation of proline in collagen can very drastically reduce the rate of translation of the message. On the other hand, we also know that there are cytosolic factors that specifically enhance translation of vitellogenin in a homologous cell-free system, including tRNAs. But you are right, there must also be elements linked to the ribosomes that are allowing them to handle certain messages very efficiently.

D. Nelson: I would like to suggest a mechanism by which dexamethasone may be producing some of the effects described by Dr. Tata. We have become very interested in the effects of corticosteriods upon membranes, particularly upon the phospholipid composition of various membranes. In association with Dr. Darrell K. Murray and Dr. Ann Ruhmann-Wennhold, we have obtained data indicating that when one incubates epididymal fat cells with $8 \times 10^{-8} M$ dexamethasone very significant changes in the composition of the fat cell occur. As shown in Table A, this treatment of fat cells produces significant changes in the sphingomyelin content of isolated fat cell ghosts, but no statistically significant changes in the other phospholipids present in large enough quantity to measure. We are not certain of the mechanisms involved but have preliminary information indicating that synthesis of phospholipids in these cells is being affected by the dexamethasone. We suggest that many of the permissive actions of corticosteroids may be mediated by changes in the composition of cellular membranes that may effect fluidity and then responsivity to receptors or the activity of membrane-bound enzymes.

J. R. Tata: I agree with you completely. In fact it is very useful that you showed this table, because it relates to what Gordon Tomkins used to call pleiotypic effects, or the metabolic code.

B. Katzenellenbogen: How efficient is your induction of vitellogenin *in vitro* versus *in vivo*? I ask this in part because you mention that vitellogenin production is dependent upon continuous exposure to hormone.

J. R. Tata: It is difficult to answer that question. Roughly, it is anywhere from one-half to one-fourth as efficient as in a whole animal.

B. Katzenellenbogen: But if you quantitate vitellogenin messenger RNA molecules per cell, how does that compare *in vitro* and *in vivo*?

J. R. Tata: Anywhere from 20% to 50% from what you would see in a whole animal.

B. Katzenellenbogen: I would like to inquire further about the dexamethasone effect. I wonder if you or Dr. Lazier have any information as to whether this effect may be mediated by changes in estrogen receptor populations?

TABLE A

Effect of Dexamethasone on Phospholipid Content of Epididymal Fat Cell Ghosts Obtained from Intact Rats[a]

Phospholipids	Control	Dexamethasone	P
Sphingomyelin	1.029 ± 0.127	1.221 ± 0.18	<0.025
Phosphatidylethanolamine	2.047 ± 0.114	2.106 ± 0.161	>0.5
Phosphatidylcholine	4.804 ± 0.361	5.277 ± 0.192	>0.2
Phosphatidylserine and phosphatidylinositol[b]	0.448 ± 0.168	0.598 ± 0.224	>0.4

[a] Phosphorus and protein were measured in ghosts from intact rat fat cells which had been incubated for 3 hours with and without $8 \times 10^{-8} M$ dexamethasone. Each value represents mean $\pm$ SE from 7 experiments expressed as micrograms of phosphorus per milligram of protein.

[b] For this group, $n = 4$.

J. R. Tata: I don't know. That is a very interesting thought.

H. Schwartz: With reference to your comments on the variety of responses that the same hormone elicits from different tissues, I am sure you are aware that the responses to thyroid hormone that we measure vary not only from tissue to tissue. In fact, the same tissue from various species will show a different response profile. This suggests the presence of a very complex system for regulation of genomic expression. May I ask whether you see in your ability to stimulate vitellogenin synthesis in the male an argument against the proposal that differentiation is the result of irreversible repression of portions of the genome?

J. R. Tata: As to the first point, we moved to vitellogenin because we could not find any protein that was not made in the absence of thyroid hormone (even in the tadpole) and which was made in its presence.

The second question relates to what Bert O'Malley alluded to [this volume, Chapter 1], namely, that there is nothing magical about "turning on" or "turning off" a gene by a hormone. If the cell has the recognition mechanism, such as the receptor, then, if the hormone can set it in the right conformation, it will do whatever it has to do. I would like to emphasize that I know of no hormone-induced system of the kind we have been discussing that is irreversible.

Thyroid Hormone Receptors and Responses

John D. Baxter, Norman L. Eberhardt, James W. Apriletti,
Lorin K. Johnson, Robert D. Ivarie, Beth S. Schachter,
Julie A. Morris, Peter H. Seeburg, Howard M. Goodman,
Keith R. Latham, Jon R. Polansky, and Joseph A. Martial

Howard Hughes Medical Institute Laboratories and the Endocrine Research Division of the Department of Medicine, the Metabolic Research Unit, and the Department of Biochemistry and Biophysics, University of California, San Francisco, California

I. Introduction

Thyroid hormones regulate selected aspects of differentiation and development in a number of species and are important for the regulation of metabolic homeostasis in the adult (Wolff and Wolff, 1964). In man and rat, thyroxine (T_4) is the major hormone produced by the gland (Ingbar and Woeber, 1974). A smaller amount of the more active triiodothyronine (T_3) is produced. However, most of this hormone arises from monodeiodination of T_4 in the peripheral tissues. Other iodothyronines are also produced by the gland and by metabolism. However, the general consensus at present is that T_3 accounts for most of the thyromimetic activity (for discussion, see Surks and Oppenheimer, 1978). The numerous effects of these hormones have been extensively studied (for review, see Oppenheimer and Dillmann, 1978; Samuels, 1978; Latham *et al.*, 1978). Over the years, several models for the mechanism of action of these hormones have been proposed. Nevertheless, many details of the molecular mechanism of thyroid human action are lacking.

Three recent developments have provided a better means for a detailed analysis of the molecular mechanism of thyroid hormone action. First, specific receptors for these hormones have been detected in the nuclei of target tissues (Oppenheimer *et al.*, 1972; Oppenheimer and Dillman, 1978). Second, systems in cell culture have been described that respond to thyroid hormones (Samuels *et al.*, 1973; Samuels, 1978). Third, two specific mRNAs, those for α_{2u}-globulin (Kurtz *et al.*, 1976) and growth hormone (discussed below) have been found to be under thyroid hormone control, and in some tissues total RNA synthesis can be affected by thyroid hormones (Tata and Widnell, 1966; DeGroot *et al.*, 1977; Dillman *et al.*, 1978). The data with receptors and RNA have focused attention on the nucleus as one site for thyroid hormone action. It is not clear at present, however, that the nucleus is the only site where the hormones exert their effects (Goldfine *et al.*, 1975; Segal and Gordon, 1977; Sterling *et al.*, 1978).

The nuclear receptors are of additional interest because they appear to be intrinsic nonhistone chromosomal proteins (Surks et al., 1973; DeGroot et al., 1974; Latham et al., 1978; Charles et al., 1975). Despite the considerable focus on the role of nonhistone chromosomal proteins as one important element in regulation of gene activity, there has been little progress in the identification of the proteins responsible for the regulation of specific genes. Thus, the thyroid hormone receptors represent a unique example to date in which such a nonhistone chromosomal protein has been identified. An understanding of the function of these proteins may therefore relate generally to the regulation of chromatin function.

In addition to the recent development of potential systems for understanding the molecular biology of thyroid hormone action, the study of particular gene products under thyroid hormone control has provided a link between the biochemical actions and physiological effects. For instance, the observation by Edelman and his collaborators that thyroid hormones induce the sodium-potassium-activated ATPase may explain in part thyroid hormone-controlled thermogenesis (Edelman and Ismail-Beigi, 1974). The simultaneous discovery by Tsai et al. (1977) and Williams et al. (1977) that thyroid hormones regulate the β-adrenergic receptors may help to understand how T_3 stimulates the cardiovascular system. In fact, it is possible that control of a very few gene products can explain many of the diverse influences of thyroid hormones. Two additional products, hyaluronidase and growth hormone, that may be of importance are discussed below.

During the past 4 years we have been studying the cellular actions of thyroid hormones. The cultured pituitary cells first shown to be responsive to T_3 by Samuels and co-workers (1973) have been employed in the following ways: (1) to understand the role of metabolites in thyroid hormone action; (2) to investigate the relations between receptor occupancy and the hormone response; (3) to examine the regulation of a specific mRNA (that for growth hormone) by thyroid hormone; (4) to probe the early influences of thyroid hormone on chromatin structure and the distribution of receptors in chromatin; (5) to understand the complexity of the thyroid hormone response; and (6) to study several gene products under thyroid hormone control. Finally, cultured pituitary cells and liver (from which a larger quantity of material can be obtained) have been used to begin to purify and characterize the receptors. These endeavors are described in this communication.

II. Responses to Thyroid Hormones in Cultured Cells

Cultured rat pituitary tumor cells synthesize growth hormone and prolactin, and the production of these hormones can be regulated by several classes of hormones including T_3 (Yosumura et al., 1966; Tashjian et al., 1968, 1970; Bancroft et al., 1969; Kohler et al., 1969; Dannies and Tashjian, 1973a,b; Tsai and Samuels, 1974; Yu *et al.*, 1977; Martial *et al.*, 1977a,b; Shapiro *et al.*, 1978). Growth hormone and prolactin are secreted into the medium within minutes after their synthesis (Bancroft *et al.*, 1969). There is little degradation of them in either cells or medium; thus, measurements of the production of these hormones generally reflect the rates of their synthesis (Dannies and Tashjian, 1973a). There are several sublines of these cells; these differ in their growth characteristics and in their production of the two polypeptide hormones (Dannies and Tashjian, 1973b). We confirmed the earlier observations by Samuels *et al.* (1977) that GH_1 cells respond to thyroid hormones by a stimulation of glucose oxidation and growth hormone production (Papavasiliou *et al.*, 1977). We found that GH_3 and GC cells are affected by T_3 (Martial *et al.*, 1977a,b; Ivarie *et al.*, 1979). Finally, Perrone and Hinkle (1978) reported that the receptors for, and cellular sensitivity to, the thyrotropin-releasing hormone (TRH) are regulated by T_3 in GH_3 cells. The GH_3 and GC sublines have certain advantages over GH_1 cells; of particular usefulness is that, in contrast to GH_1 cells, they have been propagated in either suspension or monolayer culture. GC cells do not produce prolactin, but make large amounts of growth hormone (Bancroft *et al.*, 1973). They have been particularly useful for purification of growth hormone mRNA. GH_3 cells make both growth hormone and prolactin (Dannies and Tashjian, 1973a,b); their morphology is more constant and they adhere more strongly to surfaces than do GC cells (Ivarie *et al.*, 1979).

In order to reproducibly examine effects of thyroid hormones in GH cells, it has been important to employ conditions in which control cells are not exposed to thyroid hormone. As emphasized earlier by Samuels *et al.* (1973), most commercial serum used for tissue culture contains thyroid hormone, so that some inductive effect will be present in the absence of added hormone. This problem was bypassed with the use of serum from a thyroidectomized calf.

Figure 1 shows an analysis by polyacrylamide gel electrophoresis of the proteins synthesized by GC cells before and after their transfer from medium containing normal calf serum to that containing serum from a thyroidectomized calf. This transfer results in a major and selective decrease in growth hormone production by the cells.

Since serum contains variable amounts of growth factors and hormones it does not constitute the ideal medium for defining the requirements for biological responses. Consequently, we have employed a serum substitute-containing medium whose composition is precisely defined. This medium, originally described by Bauer *et al.* (1976), does not contain any proteins; it contains macromolecules, such as methyl cellulose and protamine sulfate, vitamins, lipids, and metal ions. We have used it as described by Bauer *et al.* (1976) except that insulin, thyroxine, and hydrocortisone are ordinarily omitted. Figure 2 shows the kinetics of deinduction of growth hormone production by GC cells after their transfer to serum substitute-containing medium. Like the case with medium containing serum from a thyroidectomized calf, the half-life of decrease

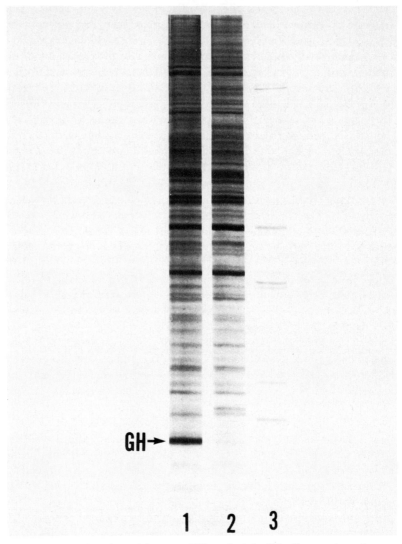

FIG. 1.   Deinduction of growth hormone (GH) synthesis by GC cells grown in medium containing serum from a thyroidectomized calf. Shown are autoradiograms after sodium dodecyl sulfate–
polyacrylamide gel electrophoresis of the [^{35}S]methionine pulse-labeled cellular proteins extracted
from GC cells. Lane 1: Proteins from cells grown in complete medium. Lane 2: Proteins from cells
grown in hypothyroid medium. Lane 3: Bacteriophage T4 proteins used as molecular weight markers.
Reprinted from Martial *et al.* (1977b).

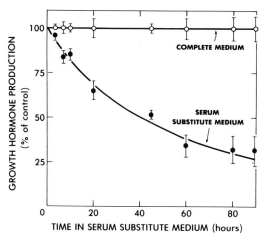

FIG. 2. Kinetics of deinduction of growth hormone synthesis by GC cells in serum substitute-containing medium. GC cells were grown in complete medium (○) for 48 hours, and a portion of them was transferred to serum substitute-containing medium (●). Growth hormone levels were measured by radioimmunoassay. Reprinted from Schachter *et al.* (1979).

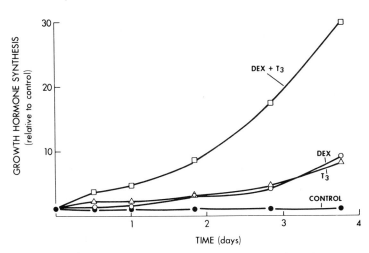

FIG. 3. Kinetics of the glucocorticoid and thyroid hormone mediated induction of growth hormone production by GC cells grown in serum substitute-containing medium (Bauer *et al.*, 1976). The cells had been maintained in this medium in the absence of hormones for 4 days prior to the experiment. Growth hormone synthesis was measured by radioimmunoassay at the indicated times. Control cells (●), 10 nM triiodothyronine (T$_3$) (△), 1 μM dexamethasone (○), or 10 nM triiodothyronine (T$_3$) plus 1 mg of dexamethasone (□).

of growth hormone production is approximately 48 hours. This probably reflects the half-life of growth hormone mRNA. In Fig. 3 are shown the kinetics of induction of growth hormone production by the cells after they have been cultured in serum substitute-containing medium for 6 days followed by addition of glucocorticoids, thyroid hormone, or both hormones simultaneously. As indicated, the cells respond to either hormone and the two hormones in combination show synergistic effects. Of note is that growth hormone production continues to increase after 4 days upon readdition of the hormones. This suggests that the half-life of whatever is being induced is relatively long (Berlin and Schimke, 1965). Since GC cells rapidly secrete the newly synthesized growth hormone, these data imply that it is the growth hormone mRNA that is relatively long-lived.

Figure 4 shows an analysis by sodium dodecyl sulfate (SDS)–polyacrylamide gel electrophoresis of the proteins synthesized by the cells at different times after their transfer to serum substitute-containing medium. In this case, the cells were exposed to $[^{35}S]$methionine prior to harvest and application of cell extracts to the gels. It is apparent from these studies that the deinduction is specific for growth hormone. This is the only protein detectable by this technique whose rate of synthesis is affected by the transfer. Thus, cells grown in serum substitute-containing medium continue to produce most of their proteins at relative rates similar to that achieved in normal medium. Therefore, these conditions allow for hormone action to be studied in highly defined media. The usefulness of this in understanding the interrelationships between T_3, glucocorticoids, and insulin is discussed below.

A. THYROID HORMONE REGULATION OF THE CELL SURFACE

In studies of GH_1 cells (Polansky et al., 1978a), we noted that T_3 alters the morphologic appearance of the cells. The hormone-treated cells appeared to show more distinct cell boundaries than the controls and tended to form aggregate colonies. Electron micrographs of such hormone-treated and control cells are shown in Fig. 5. Cells maintained in the absence of T_3 showed much less distinct cell borders and were evenly spread; by contrast, the cells exposed to T_3 have numerous microvilli. The effect is not due merely to differences in cell density, and it can be observed in confluent cultures in the absence of an effect on growth. The effect can be observed at the same hormone concentrations (1–5 nM) required for eliciting other T_3 effects in these cells. From 48 to 72 hours of exposure to T_3 are required before the surface effect is observed. Therefore, it is possible that it is due to induction of some protein, and it could be due to a process mediated through the nuclear receptor. Whatever the exact mechanisms, these findings suggest that thyroid hormones can regulate the structure of the cell surface. Since cellular differentiation includes changes in cell surface morphol-

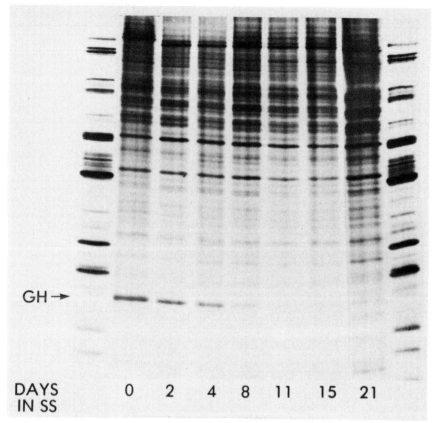

GH →

DAYS   0   2   4   8   11   15   21
IN SS

FIG. 4. Deinduction of growth hormone (GH) synthesis by GC cells grown in serum substitute-containing medium. Shown are autoradiograms after sodium dodecyl sulfate–polyacrylamide gel electrophoresis of the [^{35}S]methionine pulse-labeled cellular proteins extracted from GC cells grown in complete medium (0 days) or in serum substitute-containing medium (SS) for the days indicated (Schachter *et al.*, 1979).

ogy, the idea that thyroid hormones may influence differentiation through cell surface effects such as this one deserves further consideration.

B. REGULATION OF HYALURONIDASE BY THYROID HORMONE

Tissue hyaluronidase is an endoglycosidase that cleaves hyaluronic acid into smaller oligosaccharides (Toole, 1976). Although the role of hyaluronic acid in cell metabolism is not entirely understood, it is known that there are orderly changes in the quantity of this glycosaminoglycan in different developing tissues (Toole, 1973; Polansky *et al.*, 1974). For each tissue examined, there is more hyaluronic acid in rapidly proliferating tissues and less of it as division ceases

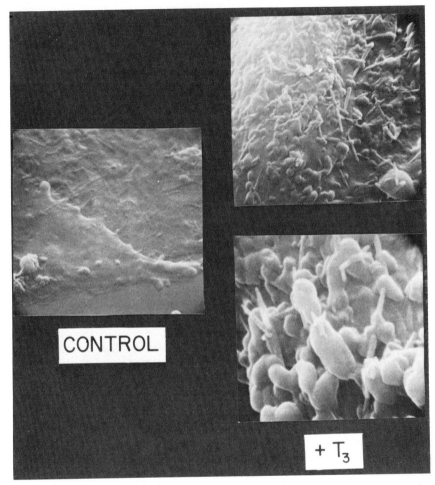

FIG. 5.   Influence of thyroid hormones on GC_1 cell surface morphology. Shown are scanning electron micrographs of control and triiodothyronine (T_3)-treated GH_1 cells. Cells were grown in hypothyroid media for 4 days; half of the cells were exposed to 5 nM T_3 for 4 additional days. Medium was changed at daily intervals. The cells were originally plated at confluency to inhibit hormone effects on cell division. Control cells left are shown at 8000 × and T_3-treated cells are shown at 8000 × (top right) and 20,000 × (bottom right). Data from Polansky *et al.* (1978a).

and more differentiated functions of mature tissues become manifest. In most cases, the enzyme hyaluronidase is induced in a time sequence corresponding to the enzymic removal of hyaluronic acid in developing tissues. Thus, the hypothesis is considered that hyaluronic acid is one of the factors that is necessary for cells to proliferate and exhibit a more dedifferentiated state, whereas hyaluronidase is a signal for differentiation. The relationship of thyroid hormone and hyaluronidase became apparent with the studies of Polansky and Toole

(1976), who found that in thyroid hormone-induced differentiation of the tadpole there is a decrease in hyaluronic acid levels and an increase in hyaluronidase levels. This observation raised the possibility that thyroid hormone could be regulating the levels of the enzyme and thereby influencing the development of the tadpole. Unfortunately, in systems such as this it is difficult to distinguish causally related events from associated ones. For instance, the increase in hyaluronidase could also be secondary to some other influence that affected the cells. In addition it has been difficult to study this enzyme because it has never been detected in a stable line of cultured cells. A further suggestion that thyroid hormones regulate glycosaminoglycan metabolism comes from studies indicating that in myxedematous tissues from subjects with hypothyroidism there is an increased accumulation of hyaluronic acid (Schiller et al., 1962).

Because of these questions and the fact that cultured pituitary cells respond to thyroid hormones, we examined whether these cells also contain hyaluronidase. Endoglycosidase activity characteristic of this enzyme could be measured by techniques that distinguish contributions from exoglycosidases as demonstrated by an analysis of degradation products and the use of D-saccharolactone, a specific inhibitor of the exoglycosidase β-glucuronidase (Polansky et al., 1978b). Treatment of GH_1 cells with T_3 increased the activity of this enzyme 2- to 3-fold by 48–72 hours. The kinetics of this induction are shown in Fig. 6. As shown in Fig. 7, induction of hyaluronidase activity occurs under conditions where there is a minimal effect on cell growth. In this case, the fold induction of hyaluronidase activity is as great as that of glucose oxidation or growth hormone production. These data suggest that thyroid hormones can regulate hyaluronidase activity, possibly by a primary mechanism; this mechanism could account for the

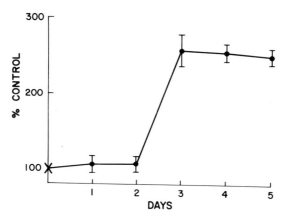

FIG. 6.   Kinetics of thyroid hormone-mediated induction of hyaluronidase activity. Cells plated at confluency were transferred to hypothyroid medium and then exposed to 5 nM triiodothyronine for 1–5 days. Medium was changed daily. Hyaluronidase activities are expressed as percent of control values of cells that received no hormone treatment. Data from Polansky et al. (1978b).

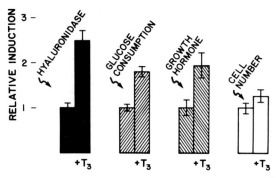

FIG. 7. Relative thyroid hormone-mediated induction of hyaluronidase activity, glucose consumption, and growth hormone production in GH$_1$ cells after 4 days in culture. Cells were grown as described in the legend to Fig. 5. Growth hormone and glucose consumption were measured between days 3 and 4, and cell number and hyaluronidase activities were determined at the end of day 4. T$_3$, triiodothyronine. Data from Polansky et al. (1978b).

increased levels of hyaluronic acid in thyroid hormone deficiency and for the decrease in thyroid hormone-induced metamorphosis in the tadpole. Based on these observations, the hypothesis should be considered that the regulation of this enzyme is one of the key ways in which thyroid hormone influences differentiation.

C. ROLE OF METABOLISM IN THYROID HORMONE ACTION

As mentioned earlier, the major product of the thyroid gland, thyroxine (T$_4$), may be considered a prohormone, since it is monodeiodinated in the peripheral tissues to T$_3$ which is the most active natural thyroid hormone and under normal circumstances occupies most of the thyroid hormone receptor sites (Surks and Oppenheimer, 1978). However, thyroxine can be monodeiodinated in the inner ring instead of the outer ring, resulting in 3,3′,5′-triiodothyronine, reverse T$_3$ (Bravermen et al., 1970; Fisher et al., 1972; Schwartz et al., 1971; Chopra et al., 1975a,b). In some circumstances (e.g., severe illness, starvation, hepatic disease), the production of reverse T$_3$ can exceed that of T$_3$ itself (Chopra et al., 1975b). The literature on reverse T$_3$ has largely given conflicting results. Some have proposed that this substance is actually an antihormone; others reported that it was inactive, and yet others suggested that it may be a weak agonist (for discussion and references, see Papavasiliou et al., 1977).

The cultured pituitary cells provide a useful system to examine the biological activity of reverse T$_3$. It was found that this metabolite was indeed active and could also bind to the thyroid hormone receptor (Fig. 8) (Papavasiliou et al., 1977). Its affinity for the receptor measured in cell-free and intact cell (Fig. 8)

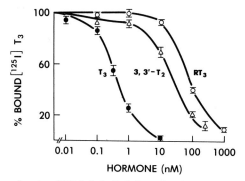

FIG. 8.   Inhibition of nuclear ^{125}I-labeled triiodothyronine (T_3) binding by unlabeled T_3, reverse T_3 $(3,3',5'\text{-}T_3)$, and $3,3'$-diiodothyronine $(3,3'\text{-}T_2)$ in GC cells grown in serum substitute-containing medium. Reprinted from Papavasiliou *et al.* (1977).

conditions was found to be 0.5 and 0.1%, respectively, that of T_3. Given adequate dosages, reverse T_3 elicits responses as great as T_3 or T_4 and acts as a weak agonist. We additionally found, however, that if cells were incubated with reverse T_3, most of the cellular hormone was present as $3,3'$-diiodothyronine $(3,3'\text{-}T_2)$ (Papavasiliou *et al.*, 1977), a monodeiodination product of reverse T_3. The latter also binds to the receptor about 5-fold more avidly than reverse T_3 (Fig. 8), and itself is a full agonist (Papavasiliou *et al.*, 1977). Thus, reverse T_3 may be considered to be a prohormone, and most of its actions may be due to the $3,3'\text{-}T_2$ that is generated from it. In spite of the fact that these two compounds are agonists, we calculate on the basis of these activities and the blood levels reported in humans (assuming human and rat receptors to have similar affinities for the hormones) that, in most of the states in which there is excess reverse T_3 or $3,3'\text{-}T_2$ production, these substances still contribute very little to thyroid hormone action. Thus, when there is a switch *in vivo* from T_3 to reverse T_3 production, the effect is mainly one that tends to reduce the active thyroid hormone pool.

Two additional points concerning reverse T_3 and $3,3'\text{-}T_2$ deserve emphasis. First, most preparations of these compounds are contaminated with other active hormones (for discussion, see Papavasiliou *et al.*, 1977). Because the affinity of reverse T_3 for the receptor is so low relative to potential contaminants, such as triac, tetrac, T_4, and T_3, the presence of very low levels of these contaminants can lead to erroneous results. This is probably the case with reverse T_3 but not $3,3'\text{-}T_2$ in our earlier studies (Latham *et al.*, 1976), but significant contamination was probably not a problem in the later studies (Papavasiliou *et al.*, 1977). Second, reverse T_3 binds to plasma proteins more avidly than $3,3'\text{-}T_2$ (Snyder *et al.*, 1976). Thus, at equal concentrations in plasma, a higher proportion of $3,3'\text{-}T_2$ than of reverse T_3 is available for binding to the receptors.

D. INFLUENCE BY THYROID HORMONES ON THE CELLULAR SENSITIVITY TO OTHER HORMONES

There are numerous examples in endocrinology of synergistic and antagonist influences of hormone combinations (for review, see Baxter and MacLeod, 1978; Granner, 1978). In parallel with the studies of thyroid hormone action, we investigated and found in GC cells (Martial *et al.*, 1977a), in confirmation of earlier findings with GH₃ cells (Bancroft *et al.*, 1969; Kohler *et al.*, 1969; Tsai and Samuels, 1974; Yu *et al.*, 1977), that growth hormone production can be regulated by glucocorticoid hormones. We found with GC cells (Martial *et al.*, 1977b), as did Samuels *et al.* (1977) with GH₁ cells, that when glucocorticoids were added to cultures that had been maintained for several days in thyroidectomized-calf serum there was no or negligible induction of growth hormone (Fig. 9). By contrast, thyroid hormone alone did readily induce growth hormone production under these conditions. When glucocorticoids and thyroid hormones were given together, there was a synergistic effect. Thus, under these conditions, the capability of glucocorticoids to regulate growth hormone production may be controlled by thyroid hormone; whereas glucocorticoids are not required for thyroid hormone action, they enhance the effect. These observations also suggest that there are certain differences in the mechanism by which thyroid and glucocorticoid hormones control expression of the growth hormone gene.

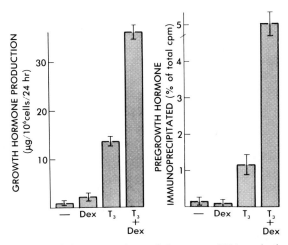

FIG. 9.   Effect on growth hormone and growth hormone mRNA production in GC cells by glucocorticoid and thyroid hormones. GC cells grown for 5 days in hypothyroid medium supplemented with thyroidectomized calf serum were stimulated for 50 hours by triiodothyronine (T₃; 10 n*M*), dexamethasone (Dex; 1 μ*M*), both hormones, or no hormones. *Left:* Levels of growth hormone production as measured by radioimmunoassay. *Right:* Levels of growth hormone mRNA as measured by cell-free translation and immunoprecipitation. Reprinted from Martial *et al.* (1977b).

Quite different results have been obtained in more recent studies with the use of serum substitute-containing medium. As shown in Fig. 3, in cells maintained in serum substitute-containing medium without added hormones, glucocorticoids increase the production of growth hormone in the absence of T_3. An explanation in part for this surprising result emerged with the finding that, when insulin at high concentrations was added to the cultures, the ability of glucocorticoids to increase growth hormone production was impaired (Schachter *et al.*, 1979; Ivarie *et al.*, 1979). Under these circumstances, T_3 and dexamethasone were synergistic in the presence or in the absence of insulin (Fig. 10). In these studies high concentrations of insulin have been employed. Therefore it is not possible to know from these data whether insulin is acting through its own receptors or through those for some of the other polypeptide hormones, somatomedin or other growth factors, that it can occupy with less affinity (for review see Van Wyck *et al.*, 1973; Rechler and Nissley, 1977; Rechler *et al.*, 1977; Baxter and MacLeod, 1978). Irrespective of the mechanism of the insulin effect, these studies suggest that insulin or other factors present in serum can have a negative effect on the ability of glucocorticoids to regulate expression of the growth hormone gene. T_3 can operate in spite of this influence; additionally, it can almost completely reverse the negative influence of insulin on glucocorticoid action.

E. SPECIFICITY OF THE HORMONAL RESPONSES IN CULTURED RAT PITUITARY TUMOR CELLS

That thyroid hormones affect a number of selected cellular responses has been discussed above. These observations do not provide a measure, however, of the total number of cellular processes, functions, and genes (or gene products) under hormonal control. Nevertheless, in GH_3 cells thyroid hormones do not alter total cellular protein or RNA synthesis in spite of the fact that they do promote cellular growth (Samuels *et al.*, 1973). One approach toward measuring the complexity of the thyroid hormone response involved nucleic acid hybridization experiments (Fig. 11) (Martial *et al.*, 1977a). A complementary DNA probe (cDNA) synthesized by reverse transcription of total poly(A)$^+$ RNA from hormone-treated cells was hybridized to RNA from control and thyroid hormone-treated cells. The early kinetics of hybridization of the probe to each RNA preparation was identical. These data indicated that the hormone did not induce any RNA species that constituted a significant percentage (e.g., more than 5–10%) of the total polyadenylated RNA population.

Recently, Ivarie and O'Farrell (1978) have established an approach that measures more precisely a substantial subpopulation (10–15%) of the number of expressed gene products whose rates of synthesis are affected by a hormone. In brief, hormonally stimulated and unstimulated cells are pulsed for a short time with a radioactive amino acid (e.g., [^{35}S]methionine), and the cellular proteins are separated by high resolution two-dimensional gel electrophoresis (O'Farrell,

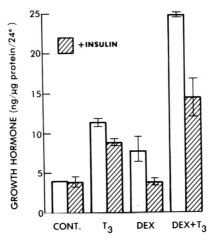

FIG. 10. Influence of insulin on the stimulation of growth hormone synthesis in GH₃ cells by glucocorticoid and thyroid hormones. Cells were grown for 4 days in serum substitute-containing medium devoid of added hormone (Bauer *et al.*, 1976). Half of the cells were activated in the presence of insulin (240 units/ml). After 48 hours the medium was replaced and either triiodothyronine (T₃; 0.1 n*M*), dexamethasone (DEX; 100 n*M*), both hormones, or neither hormone was added. Cells were cultured for an additional 40 hours prior to determination of growth hormone levels by radioimmunoassay. Reprinted from Schachter *et al.* (1979).

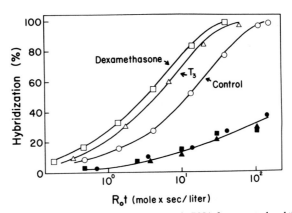

FIG. 11. Kinetics of hybridization of total cytoplasmic RNA from control and thyroid hormone- and glucocorticoid hormone-treated GC cells with cDNA from total poly(A)⁺ cellular RNA (filled symbols) or with cDNA highly enriched for sequences complementary to growth hormone mRNA (open symbols). Cells were grown in medium supplemented with thyroidectomized calf serum containing low levels of thyroid hormone and were treated with additional triiodothyronine (T₃; 10 n*M*) or with dexamethasone (1 μ*M*) for 4 days prior to isolation of total cytoplasmic RNA. The cDNAs were hybridized with total cytoplasmic RNA from control (○, ●), T₃-treated (△, ▲), and dexamethasone-treated (□, ■) cells. Reprinted from Martial *et al.* (1977b).

1975; O'Farrell *et al.*, 1977). The labeled proteins are detected by autoradiography, and the intensity of each spot in the untreated cell pattern is compared to the spot's intensity in the treated cell pattern. Because the labeling time is kept short (15–30 minutes) and the gels can resolve over a thousand individual proteins, the method amounts to a simultaneous measurement of the rate of synthesis of over a thousand specific gene products. Both inductions and repressions are readily detected, as are potential charge modifications of proteins (e.g., phosphorylation, glycosylation, acetylation).

Figure 12 illustrates an experiment using two-dimensional gel electrophoresis to measure alterations in the synthetic rates of individual proteins in GH_3 cells following thyroid hormone and dexamethasone treatment. GH_3 cells were grown for several days in serum-containing medium and then deinduced in thyroid hormone- and glucocorticoid-free serum substitute-containing medium for 2 days. After deinduction, T_3 and dexamethasone alone or in combination were added for an additional 2 days, at which time cells were labeled for 30 minutes with [^{35}S]methionine and the cellular proteins were subjected to two-dimensional "NEPHGE" gel electrophoresis (O'Farrell *et al.*, 1977). Insulin was present throughout the experiment. Shown in Fig. 12 are regions of the final autoradiograms containing three proteins under thyroid hormone and glucocorticoid control in GH_3 cells: growth hormone (gh), prolactin (prl), and p16 (an unidentified protein of about 16,000 MW). Growth hormone and prolactin were identified in the total pattern by specific immunoprecipitation from a labeled cell extract and coelectrophoresis of the precipitated protein with a labeled spot in the cell extract following two-dimensional electrophoresis (Ivarie *et al.*, 1979). As can be seen in Fig. 12, T_3 alone induces growth hormone and p16 synthesis but does not alter prolactin synthesis. In contrast, dexamethasone by itself has no effect on the synthesis of growth hormone and p16, but does substantially repress the synthesis of prolactin. In combination with T_3, dexamethasone can induce the synthesis of growth hormone and p16 to levels significantly higher than T_3 by itself. From these data it is clear that the influence of T_3 on the sensitivity of GH_3 cells to glucocorticoids is not limited to growth hormone but includes the protein p16. Furthermore, the dexamethasone-mediated inhibition of prolactin synthesis in the absence of T_3 demonstrates that glucocorticoids can function in these cells without an absolute requirement for thyroid hormones. Although the results are preliminary, a few other gene products in GH_3 cells appear to be induced by dexamethasone alone. This idea is also supported by the studies of Samuels *et al.* (1978), who recently reported that T_3 does not control the ability of glucocorticoids to induce glutamine synthetase. Thus, it is likely that both induction and repression of specific protein synthesis by glucocorticoids can occur in the absence of T_3. If these two hormones regulate specific gene transcription in GH_3 cells, these observations suggest that hormonally sensitive genes are quite different from each other.

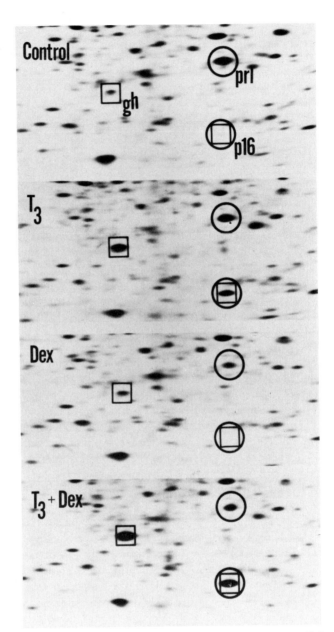

FIG. 12. Alterations in the rates of synthesis of three polypeptides in GH₃ cells in response to thyroid and glucocorticoid hormones measured by two-dimensional gel electrophoresis. Shown are autoradiograms of regions containing growth hormone (gh, square), prolactin (prl, circle), and p16 (unidentified protein of molecular weight 16,000, enclosed in a box and circle). GH₃ cells were

F. REGULATION OF SPECIFIC MESSENGER RNAs BY THYROID HORMONES

The cultured pituitary cells have been useful to examine the thyroid hormone regulation of specific mRNAs. Several years ago Bancroft *et al.* (1973) detected growth hormone mRNA by cell-free translation. We have used this approach to quantitate hormonally regulated changes in growth hormone mRNA activity by measuring the amount of pregrowth hormone (the primary translation product of this mRNA) (Sussman *et al.*, 1976) that is synthesized in the translation system in response to added RNA (Martial *et al.*, 1977a,b). The amount of pregrowth hormone produced is quantitated by first binding it to antiserum directed against rat growth hormone and then precipitating the complexes with staphylococci (SAC). Fortunately, our antiserum to rat growth hormone does react with pregrowth hormone. We found with the use of this assay that thyroid and glucocorticoid hormones did stimulate increases in growth hormone mRNA (Figs. 9 and 13). In the experiment shown in Fig. 13, serum containing a small amount of T_3 was present in the medium to which the hormones were added (Martial *et al.*, 1977a). Thus, in this case the fold stimulation by additional T_3 was less than in the experiment shown in Fig. 9. This endogenous T_3 also allowed for a glucocorticoid response in the absence of additional T_3.

That thyroid (and glucocorticoid) hormones increase growth hormone mRNA was also studied by nucleic acid hybridization techniques. Growth hormone mRNA was purified to about 70% homogeneity (Martial *et al.*, 1977a) as documented by analysis of the cDNA by restriction endonuclease cleavage and subsequent sequence analysis of the products (Seeburg *et al.*, 1977b). cDNA was then prepared from this mRNA. The cDNA was further enriched for sequences complementary to growth hormone mRNA by hybridizing it back to its poly(A)$^+$ RNA template and isolating the material that hybridized more rapidly. Figure 11 shows the hybridization kinetics when this cDNA probe was mixed with RNA from the hormone-treated and control cells. The hybridization kinetics were more rapid with RNA from thyroid or glucocorticoid hormone-treated cells than with RNA from control cells. Further, the increase in mRNA levels calculated from the hybridization kinetics was identical to the increase of growth hormone production as measured by radioimmunoassay and to the increase in growth hormone mRNA activity as assayed by cell-free translation (Fig. 13). Therefore, it appears that the induction of growth hormone production by thyroid and

---

grown in serum substitute-containing medium free of triiodothyronine (T_3) and dexamethasone (Dex) for 2 days prior to the addition of 10 nM T_3, 1 μM dexamethasone, or both hormones. After 48 hours, cells were pulse-labeled with [^{35}S]methionine and cell protein extracts were subjected to two-dimensional electrophoresis (O'Farrell *et al.*, 1977). The basic end of the first dimension is on the left, and the acidic on the right. Equal amounts of radioactivity were electrophoresed for each sample. Data from Ivarie *et al.* (1979).

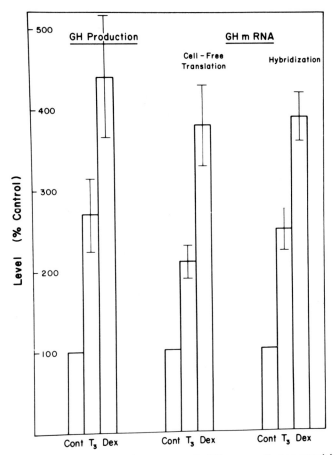

FIG. 13.   Comparisons of the thyroid and glucocorticoid hormone effect on growth hormone and growth hormone mRNA levels in GC cells. Cells were grown in medium supplemented with thyroidectomized calf serum containing low levels of thyroid hormone. After 48–72 hours, medium was replaced with fresh hypothyroid medium containing 10 nM triiodothyronine (T$_3$) 1 μM dexamethasone (DEX), or neither hormone. Growth hormone was measured by radioimmunoassay, and growth hormone mRNA was measured by cell-free translation or cDNA–RNA hybridization. Data from Martial *et al.* (1977a).

glucocorticoid hormones is due to an increase in growth hormone mRNA. Some of the findings with cell-free translation were also obtained by Seo *et al.* (1977) and by Samuels *et al.* (1978).

   The complexity of the response at the mRNA level was also examined. The cell-free products synthesized in response to mRNA from control and hormone-treated cells were electrophoresed on polyacrylamide gels (Martial *et al.*, 1977b) as shown in Fig. 14. The band corresponding to pregrowth hormone was much larger in the sample from reactions with RNA from cells induced with either T$_3$

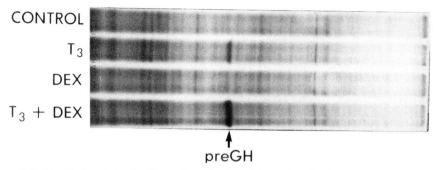

CONTROL

T₃

DEX

T₃ + DEX

preGH

FIG. 14. Sodium dodecyl sulfate–polyacrylamide gel electrophoresis of the cell-free synthesized products made in response to poly(A)$^+$ RNA from control and hormone-treated GH cells. (T₃, triiodothyronine; DEX, dexamethasone). Reprinted from Martial *et al.* (1977b).

or T_3 plus dexamethasone than in the reactions with RNA from control cells. By contrast, no other consistent mRNA changes were detected. Thus, most of the mRNAs detectable by cell-free translation are not affected by T_3. This finding further supports the view that the thyroid hormone response is highly specific and is directed only at a subset of the expressed genes of the cell.

To understand how thyroid hormone regulates growth hormone mRNA levels, it must be known whether T_3 affects synthesis, degradation, or processing of the mRNA or its precursor. It may also be helpful to know the structure of the growth hormone gene itself. Some progress has been made toward these ends. We have recently been successful in cloning cDNA complementary to growth hormone mRNA (Seeburg *et al.*, 1977a). It is hoped that this cloned DNA can be used as a probe in DNA-excess hybridization reactions to examine more directly growth hormone mRNA synthesis by the cells and in cell-free transcription experiments. Such DNA may also help with the isolation of the growth hormone gene from the natural DNA and with the cell-free reconstitution of a hormonally regulated gene.

The structure of a growth hormone mRNA as determined by sequence analysis of the cDNA and of the cloned DNA (Seeburg *et al.*, 1977a) is shown in Fig. 15. It contains about 800 bases; there are approximately 50 bases in the 5′ noncoding region and 150 bases between the stop codon and the poly(A) segment. An examination of this structure also provided a prediction of the amino acid sequence of the signal peptide portion of pregrowth hormone and of the portions of rat growth hormone for which amino acid sequence data were not available. There is some selectivity in the choice of codons; this is largely due to a high preference for G over A and C over U for the third position of the triplet codon. The reasons for this G-C preference are unknown; it may result in a more stable conformation of the gene in the natural DNA (as G-C pairing is tighter than A-T pairing) or be due to some preference for certain tRNAs used for translating growth hormone mRNA. There is at least one sequence in the 3′ noncoding

```
                                           -26
                                           Met Ala Ala Asp Ser Gln Thr Pro Trp Leu Leu Thr Phe Ser Leu Leu Cys Leu Leu
5'---(UUCAAACGUCGGUCC)GUGGACAGAUCACUGAGUGGCG AUG GCU GCA GAC UCU CAG ACU CCC UGG CUC CUG ACC UUC AGC CUG CUG UGC CUG CUG
                                            1                                                                    20

Trp Pro Gln Glu Ala Gly Ala Phe Pro Ala Met Pro Leu Ser Ser Leu Phe Ala Asn Ala Val Leu Arg Ala Gln His Leu His Gln Leu
UGG CCU CAA GAG GCU GGU GCU UUU CCU GCC AUG CCC UUG UCC AGU CUG UUU GCC AAU GCU GUG CUC CGA GCG CAG CAC CUC CAC CAG CUG
                                100                                                                             50

Ala Ala Asp Thr Tyr Lys Glu Phe Glu Arg Thr Tyr Ile Pro Glu Gly Gln Arg Tyr Ser Ile Gln Asn Thr Gln Val Ala Phe Cys Phe
GCU GCU GAC ACC UAC AAA GAG UUC GAG CGU ACC UAC AUC CCA GAG GGA CAG CGC UAC UCC AUC CAG AAU ACC CAG GUG GCC UUC UGC UUC
       150                           40                           200

Ser Glu Thr Ile Pro Ala Pro Thr Gly Lys Asn Glu Ala Gln Gln Lys Ser Asp Leu Glu Leu Leu Arg Ile Ser Leu Leu Leu Ile Gln
UCA GAG ACC AUC CCA GCC CCC ACU GGC AAG AAU GAG GCC CAG CAG AAG UCU GAC CUG GAG CUG CUG CGC AUC UCG CUG CUG CUC AUC CAG
                60                           250                           80

Ser Trp Leu Gly Pro Leu Gln Phe Leu Ser Arg Val Phe Thr Asn Ser Leu Val Phe Gly Thr Ser Asp Arg Val Tyr Glu Lys Leu Lys
UCA UGG CUG GGG CCC CUC CAG UUC CUG UCG CGA GUC UUC ACC AAU AGC CUG GUC UUU GGC ACC UCG GAC CGC GUC UAU GAG AAG CUG AAG
                         350                           100                        400

Asp Leu Glu Glu Gly Ile Gln Ala Leu Met Arg Glu Leu Glu Asp Gly Thr Pro Arg Ala Gly Gln Ile Leu Lys Gln Thr Tyr Asp Lys
GAC CUG GAA GAA GGC AUC CAG GCU CUG AUG CGG GAG CUG GAA GAC GGC ACC CCC CGG GCU GGG CAG AUC CUC AAG CAG AUC UAC GAC AAG
       120                           450                           140

Phe Asp Ala Asn Met Arg Ser Asp Asp Ala Leu Leu Lys Asn Tyr Gly Leu Leu Ser Cys Phe Arg Lys Asp Leu His Lys Ala Glu Thr
UUU GAC GCC AAC AUG CGC AGC GAC GAU GCU CUG CUG AAG AAC UAU GGG CUG CUC UCC UGC UUC CGC AAG GAC CUG CAC AAG GCA GAG ACC
                         550                           160                           500

Tyr Leu Arg Val Met Lys Cys Arg Arg Phe Ala Glu Ser Cys Ala Phe
UAC CUG CGG GUC AUG AAG UGU CGG CGC UUC GCG GAA AGC UGU GCU UUC UAG  GCACACACUGGUCGUCUCUGCGGCACUCCCCCGUACCCCCUGUACU
       180                           600                                              650

CUGGCAACUGCCACCCUACACUUUGUCCUAAUAAAAUUAAUGAUGCAUCAUAUC  poly (A) ---3'
700                                                      750
```

FIG. 15. Nucleotide sequence of rat growth hormone mRNA and amino acid sequence of rat pregrowth hormone. The nucleotide sequence was deduced from the sequence of fragments of single-stranded cDNA prepared from rat growth hormone mRNA and from cloned cDNA. Reprinted from Seeburg et al. (1977a).

portion which consists of stretches of C's on either side of a GUUA sequence that resembles palindrome-like structures present in the 3'-noncoding portion of human growth hormone (Seeburg *et al.*, 1979) and human chorionic somatomammotropin (placental lactogen) mRNAs (Shine *et al.*, 1977; Seeburg *et al.*, 1977b). It is possible that these structures play some regulatory role as well, but there is as yet no information on this point. Whereas the distal portion of the 3' untranslated region is rich in A and U (73%), 30 of the first 64 nucleotides following the termination codon are C's, dominantly occurring in stretches of 4, 5, or 6 residues. Such asymmetric distribution of purines and pyrimidines is known to influence the secondary structure of the DNA (Thiele *et al.*, 1973) and could therefore be of regulatory importance.

The sequences of rat growth hormone have also been linked in phase with those of the β-lactamase gene of plasmid pBR322 that confers bacterial resistance to ampicillin (Seeburg *et al.*, 1978). Plasmids containing this new gene do synthesize a protein the size of the expected β-lactamase–growth hormone fusion product; this protein reacts specifically with antiserum to rat growth hormone. Thus, it appears that the structural sequences of the rat growth hormone gene can be efficiently and faithfully replicated, transcribed, and translated in bacteria.

G. EARLY EFFECTS OF THYROID HORMONES ON CHROMATIN STRUCTURE: A POSSIBLE CLUE TO THE MECHANISM OF HORMONAL INFLUENCE ON mRNA LEVELS

A key and as yet unanswered question is what receptor property, stimulated by the hormone–receptor interaction, is responsible for the thyroid hormone-directed effects on the expression of specific genes. The receptors could be located at distinct loci in chromatin (e.g., at specific "operators") analogous to the case with certain bacterial regulatory proteins (for review, see Zubay, 1974). The binding of the ligand to the protein could then influence gene expression by stoichiometric mechanisms similarly to the way that some of the bacterial operons are regulated. Alternatively, the interaction of the hormone with the receptor could induce a structural alteration in chromatin either by directly affecting chromatin conformation in certain regions or by modifying chromosomal proteins through direct or indirect receptor actions on nuclear enzymic processes such as phosphorylation, acetylation, or ADP-ribosylation (for review, see Johnson *et al.*, 1978). In this case, the sites of receptor action could be the substrate for the modification. The T_3-induced changes could be extensive, in which case influences on the expression of specific genes might arise through elements distal to the site of the hormone–receptor interaction, e.g., programmed responses that depend upon the state of cellular differentiation. In this case, the hormonal effect on chromatin at many sites would not result in extensive influences on gene expression.

With steroid hormones there is a gross change in the capacity of chromatin to bind bacterial RNA polymerase (for review, see Manwaring, 1976; Johnson *et al.*, 1979; Spelsberg and Cox, 1976) as judged by the number of sites at which these polymerases can initiate transcription on chromatin from hormone-treated cells. It must be emphasized that these studies do not provide any information about the transcription of specific genes, since the bacterial polymerase is not known to transcribe mammalian chromatin with the same fidelity as the endogenous polymerases (Steggles *et al.*, 1974; Wilson *et al.*, 1975). The modification in response to glucocorticoids (Johnson and Baxter, 1978) involves such large changes in the capacity for polymerase binding (the capacity can increase by several hundred thousand sites per cell, a 50% increase) that models such as those proposing that one receptor stimulates the binding of one polymerase molecule (Buller *et al.*, 1976) do not explain the effect. Further, with glucocorticoids, the conditions in which the cells are cultured can actually result in the hormone either reducing or increasing the chromatin's capacity to bind the bacterial enzyme (Johnson *et al.*, 1978). These latter findings suggest that a reversible modification reaction rather than a direct receptor-mediated alteration in chromatin structure may explain this effect.

We have used this assay to determine if thyroid hormone can also have a detectable influence on chromatin structure. Figure 16 shows the bacterial RNA polymerase binding (as reflected by the amount of RNA synthesis) in chromatin isolated from thyroid hormone-treated (24 hours) and control cells. These experiments were performed under conditions where there is no reinitiation of RNA synthesis (Johnson and Baxter, 1978) so that RNA synthesis adequately reflects RNA polymerase binding. There is a marked increase in the capacity of the

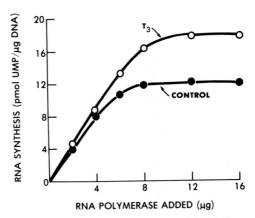

FIG. 16. Effect of thyroid hormones on GH_3 cell chromatin binding and initiation sites for *Escherichia coli* RNA polymerase. GH_3 cells grown in medium containing hypothyroid serum were exposed for 24 hours to 10 n*M* T_3. Chromatin was then prepared from control (●) and treated (○) cells and titrated with increasing concentrations of *E. coli* RNA polymerase as described by Johnson and Baxter (1978). Elongation of the RNA chains is performed in the presence of rifampicin to inhibit reinitiation.

chromatin from T_3-treated cells to bind the bacterial enzyme. This change has also been observed within 60 minutes of giving the hormone (data not shown). The hormone increases the number of new binding sites by about 50% (from 10^6 to 1.5×10^6/cell). This increase largely exceeds the number of T_3 receptors in the nucleus (around 8000/cell; Samuels $et\ al.$, 1973). Thus, like the case with glucocorticoids, each T_3–receptor interaction does not simply stimulate the binding of one polymerase molecule. The mechanism of this T_3 influence on chromatin is not known, as is the question of whether it is causally related to the influences on growth hormone mRNA. Nevertheless, the data suggest that T_3 can rapidly alter chromatin structure. Thus, it may be helpful to understand in more detail the nature of this rapid T_3-mediated influence.

   To obtain an independent index of whether thyroid hormone does induce some change in chromatin, we have examined the influence of T_3 on the proteins of chromatin by two-dimensional gel electrophoresis as discussed above. For these gels, the nonequilibrium method of O'Farrell $et\ al.$ (1977), which allows a better detection of the more basic proteins, was used. The proteins shown in Fig. 17 are largely nonhistones; the histones are not clearly observed in these gels. Although the general pattern of proteins is similar, there are differences between the two gels in the intensity of several of the spots. Since the radioactive amino acid was exposed to the cells for a prolonged period, hormone-induced changes on the relative abundance of proteins can be detected. The experiments designed in this

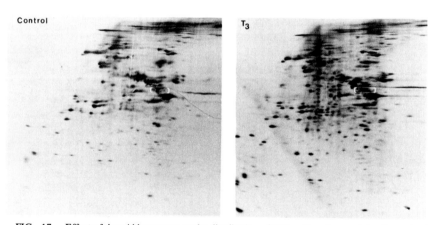

FIG. 17.   Effect of thyroid hormones on the distribution of GH_3 cell nuclear proteins determined by two-dimensional gel electrophoresis. GH_3 cells grown in medium containing hypothyroid serum were induced for 24 hours with 10 nM triiodothyronine (T_3) in the presence of 50 μCi of [^{35}S]-methionine per milliliter. Nuclei prepared from control and treated cells were solubilized in the isoelectric focusing buffer of O'Farrell (1975), and the proteins were fractionated by the electrophoresis procedure of O'Farrell $et\ al.$ (1977). Autoradiograms are of gels exposed to Kodak No Screen X-ray film for 10 days. The acidic end of the gradient is on the right, and the sodium dodecyl sulfate dimension runs high molecular weight (top) to low molecular weight (bottom). Some of the more obvious differences are outlined by boxes.

way, unlike the case with the rapid pulse of radiolabeled amino acid, does not provide information about the rate of synthesis of the proteins. These findings suggest that the hormone has in some way altered the distribution of the chromatin proteins. Taken together these experiments support the idea that the hormone can influence chromatin structure.

III. Nuclear Receptors for Thyroid Hormones

A. GENERAL CHARACTERISTICS OF THE INTRANUCLEAR THYROID HORMONE RECEPTOR

Thyroid hormone receptors have been found in the nuclei of nearly all mammalian tissues (for review, see Oppenheimer et al., 1976; Latham et al., 1978; Samuels, 1978; Oppenheimer and Dillmann, 1978), but are not found in certain lower species, such as Drosophila (Charles et al., 1975), that are not known to respond to these hormones. Receptors are found in the nucleus in equal amounts whether or not the cells or tissues have been previously exposed to the hormone (Spindler et al., 1975; DeGroot et al., 1976; Oppenheimer et al., 1975; Bernal et al., 1978). Therefore, the thyroid hormone receptors differ from the steroid hormone receptors whose binding to chromatin is dependent on the hormone. A number of lines of evidence implicate a role for these proteins in thyroid hormone action (for review, see Oppenheimer et al., 1976; Latham et al., 1978; Samuels, 1978; Oppenheimer and Dillmann, 1978).

Of importance is an excellent correlation between the binding of T_3, T_4, and a large number of other iodothyronine analogs to these receptors and the analog's biological potency (Koerner et al., 1975; Jorgensen et al., 1974, 1976; Papavasiliou et al., 1977). Receptor proteins can be solubilized from nuclei, and they have an apparent molecular weight of 50,000–70,000 (Surks et al., 1973; Latham et al., 1978). The receptors appear to be somewhat asymmetric, but less so than the steroid hormone receptors (Latham et al., 1976). These proteins behave as if they are predominantly acidic (Surks et al., 1973; Latham et al., 1976) although, as emphasized later, they may associate with histones.

B. THE RECEPTOR AS AN INTRINSIC CHROMOSOMAL AND DNA-BINDING PROTEIN

When nuclei are fractionated, all the detectable receptors are found in association with the chromatin (Spindler et al., 1975; Charles et al., 1975; Latham et al., 1978). Additional support for the idea that the receptor is an intrinsic chromosomal protein comes from cross-linking studies (Charles et al., 1975). Formaldehyde treatment of chromatin fixes histones and a small proportion of the acidic proteins to the DNA, but does not fix randomly chosen proteins (Doenecke and McCarthy, 1975). Since T_3 has a reactive amino group, we studied the question of whether this cross-linking agent could fix the hormone bound to the receptor and the receptor to chromatin. After formaldehyde treatment of nuclei containing T_3-bound receptors, and subsequent centrifugation of the material in cesium chloride, radioactively labeled T_3 did sediment with the DNA (Fig. 18). By this "diagnostic criterion" the receptor does indeed appear to be intrinsic to chromatin.

Studies of fractionated chromatin were also performed (Charles *et al.*, 1975). When chromatin containing bound T_3 was hydrodynamically sheared and sedimented on glycerol gradients, the bound T_3 was preferentially concentrated in the more slowly sedimenting chromatin that contains a lower ratio of protein to DNA (Fig. 19) and all of the binding capacity for bacterial RNA polymerase (Fig. 20). Interestingly, the distribution of receptors paralleled that of the endogenous RNA polymerase II (Fig. 19), another nonhistone protein known to be involved in mRNA synthesis. Chromatin containing bound T_3 was also fractionated by a brief treatment with DNase II (Levy and Baxter, 1976). This preferen-

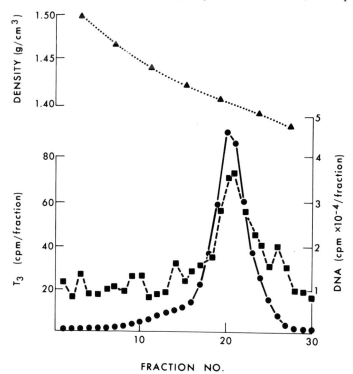

FIG. 18. ▲ .... ▲, Cesium chloride equilibrium density gradient centrifugation of formaldehyde-fixed HeLa cell chromatin containing specifically bound ^{125}I-labeled triiodothyronine (T_3). DNA content (●) was measured by [^{3}H]thymidine uptake *in vivo*. Specifically bound [^{125}I]T_3 is indicated by the squares (■). Reprinted from Charles *et al.* (1975).

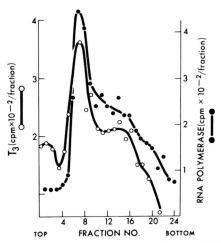

FIG. 19.   Distribution of thyroid hormone receptor and endogenous RNA polymerase activity in fractionated HeLa chromatin. HeLa chromatin was sheared hydrodynamically and separated by sucrose gradient sedimentation. Reprinted from Charles *et al.* (1975).

tially releases chromatin fragments containing nascent RNA chains. The released fragments (''active chromatin'') are also enriched in specific gene sequences that are actively transcribed (Gottesfeld *et al.*, 1974). Approximately 10% of the DNA of the specifically bound hormone was released by the nuclease treatment (Levy and Baxter, 1976). Thus, these studies (which have been questioned by

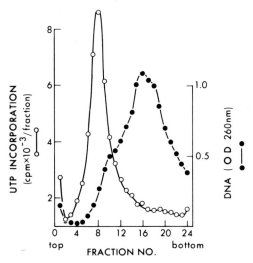

FIG. 20.   Distribution of DNA (●) and template activity (○) as measured by [³H]UTP incorporation of fractionated HeLa chromatin. Chromatin was hydrodynamically sheared and fractionated by sucrose gradient sedimentation. Data from Charles *et al.* (1975).

Samuels *et al.*, 1977) do not provide any indication that the receptors are preferentially concentrated on chromatin segments being transcribed. The receptors could be concentrated on control regions outside the DNA segments being transcribed, and therefore not be released by the nuclease. Alternatively, the findings of a roughly similar concentration of receptors in actively transcribed and inactive chromatin fragments could indicate that the receptors are extensively distributed in both active and inactive chromatin.

The finding of an association of the receptor with the more DNA-enriched fractions of chromatin as well as the general knowledge that the receptors may act at the level of the gene prompted us to explore the possibility that the receptor is a DNA-binding protein. This was found to be the case. T_3–receptor complexes in crude nuclear extracts bind to purified DNA (MacLeod and Baxter, 1975, 1976). We were not able to detect DNA binding of cytosol T_3 binding proteins; nor were we able to detect DNA binding of T_3–plasma protein complexes (MacLeod and Baxter, 1975, and unpublished observations). The latter point is of interest, since it has been recently postulated that thyroid hormone-binding prealbumin (TBPA) contains a DNA-binding site (Blake and Oatley, 1977). The receptors bind to double- and single-stranded DNA; they bind weakly to RNA and bind less avidly to synthetic polynucleotides than to natural DNA (MacLeod and Baxter, 1976). Binding by prokaryotic and eukaryotic DNA is similar (MacLeod and Baxter, 1976). These observations indicate that there is some selectivity in the receptor's association for DNA and argue against the possibility that high-affinity association of receptors with RNA explains their localization in chromatin. When increasing concentrations of receptors are incubated with DNA, many more receptors can be bound by DNA than are associated with the nucleus (MacLeod and Baxter, 1976). Thus, the capacity of the DNA for binding the receptor is very large. This finding and the observation that prokaryotic and eukaryotic double-stranded DNA binds receptors with equal avidity could imply that there is extensive nonspecific association of the receptors with DNA. In these studies no evidence for sequence-specific DNA binding was obtained, although this cannot be excluded. Whereas these data indicate that the receptor or some receptor-associated protein is a DNA-binding protein, it is not clear from these studies with crude receptor-containing preparations, whether the receptor itself or a protein associated with it is binding to DNA. This point is of relevance in considering the studies below, which suggest that histones may play a role in the maintenance of receptor integrity.

C. GENERATION OF A FORM OF THE RECEPTOR WITH ALTERED BINDING SPECIFICITY: IMPLICATIONS FOR THE INTERRELATIONSHIPS WITH OTHER T_3 BINDING PROTEINS

During the course of purification of the thyroid hormone receptor, we found that T_3 binding activity in the solubilized preparations was lost (Latham *et al.*,

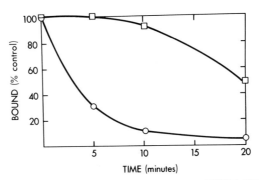

FIG. 21.   Kinetic analysis of the effect of heat on the binding of [^{125}I]T$_3$ (○) and [^{125}I]T$_4$ (□) by the thyroid hormone receptor solubilized from purified rat liver nuclei. The nuclear extract was heated at 50°C for the indicated times, cooled to 4°C, and centrifuged at 15,000 *g* for 10 minutes. The supernatants were assayed for [^{125}I]T$_4$ binding activity as previously described (Latham *et al.*, 1976). T$_3$, triiodothyronine; T$_4$, thyroxine. Reprinted from Eberhardt *et al.* (1979a).

1976; Eberhardt *et al.*, 1979a). Surprisingly, in these same preparations, there was not an associated loss of T$_4$ binding activity. This type of selective loss of T$_3$ binding activity could also be obtained by heating a crude extract (Fig. 21), lowering the pH of a crude extract, or aging partially purified preparations (Eberhardt *et al.*, 1979a). Even a Sephadex G-100 filtration step results in a selective loss of T$_3$ binding activity in the included fractions where receptors elute (Eberhardt *et al.*, 1979b).

Ordinarily, such a finding would suggest that there was present in the preparation a stable protein that bound T$_4$ but not T$_3$, and a labile protein that binds T$_3$ but not T$_4$. However, this is not the case. Thus, in the original nuclear extract there was an identical number of T$_3$ and T$_4$ binding sites (Fig. 22) (Latham *et al.*,

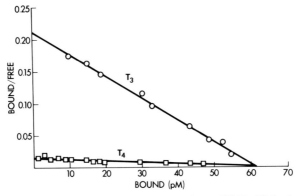

FIG. 22.   Scatchard analysis of the binding of [^{125}I]T$_3$ (○) and [^{125}I]T$_4$ (□) by the nuclear thyroid hormone receptor (data from N. L. Eberhardt, previously unpublished). Isolation and assay of the solubilized receptor was performed as previously described (Latham *et al.*, 1976).

1976) and all the radiolabeled T_4 binding was more avidly blocked by non-radioactive T_3 than by T_4 (Fig. 23). These data imply that the T_4 binding in this case was by sites that actually have a higher affinity for T_3 (Latham et al., 1976; Eberhardt et al., 1979a) (Fig. 23). Similarly, all the T_3 binding was avidly blocked by either T_3 or T_4, and T_3 was the more effective competitor (Eberhardt et al., 1979a). The binding of either T_3 or T_4 was also inhibited by iodoacetamide, and the inhibition constant was identical in the case of T_3 and T_4 (Eberhardt et al., 1979a). All these experiments indicated that in the starting material T_3 and T_4 were binding to the same protein(s). Thus, the observation that there was a loss of T_3 binding activity without any loss of T_4 binding activity suggested that either the receptor's hormonal binding specificity was changing or else there was a loss of one binding species and generation of another. The latter possibility seemed unlikely for several reasons, including the fact that such a generation would have to be quantitatively and kinetically coupled with the loss of T_3 binding activity (Fig. 21).

The nature of the binding activity before and after heating was studied in greater detail (Eberhardt et al., 1979a). Scatchard analysis of the T_3 and T_4 activity in the nuclear extract following heating at 50°C for 10 minutes indicated that the T_4 binding affinity and site concentration for binding to the receptor is so low that the affinity and capacity cannot be accurately measured with [^{125}I]T_3. Figure 23 shows the competition for radiolabeled T_4 binding by unlabeled T_4 and T_3 in the extract after the heat treatment. As expected, T_4 binding exhibits a similar ability to inhibit its own binding before and after heating. By contrast, whereas in the initial extract all the T_4 binding is more avidly inhibited by T_3, the ability of T_3 to inhibit T_4 binding after the heating has been reduced by a factor of about 1000. These studies indicate, therefore, that the heating has markedly reduced the receptor's affinity for T_3 without affecting its T_4 binding affinity.

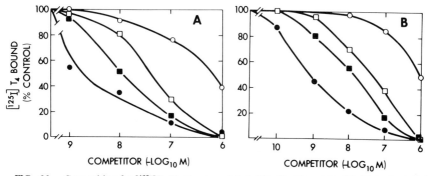

FIG. 23.   Competition for [^{125}I]T_4 binding by unlabeled T_3 (○, ●) and T_4 (□, ■) in the initial nuclear extracts (solid symbols) and in an extract heated at 50°C for 10 minutes (filled symbols). The extracts in (A) and (B) were obtained from rat liver nuclei and GH_3 cell nuclei, respectively. Assays were performed according to Latham et al. (1976). Reprinted from Eberhardt et al. (1979a).

The question can be raised whether the capability of generating a form of the receptor with altered binding specificity is unique for liver, the source of receptors used for the data shown thus far, or is more general. To test this possibility, we examined receptors solubilized from cultured pituitary (GH) cells (Eberhardt *et al.*, 1979a). The findings were identical to the case with liver. Figure 23 shows that in the initial extract in which the concentration of high-affinity T_3 and T_4 binding sites are identical (Samuels and Tsai, 1973), T_3 inhibits [^{125}I]T_4 binding more avidly than does T_4. Again, this indicates that T_4 is binding to a protein(s) that actually has a higher affinity for T_3. After heating there is no change in the number of T_4 binding sites or the activity of T_4 as a competitor. By contrast, the activity of T_3 as a competitor has decreased by 1000-fold. Thus, the receptors from diverse sources can undergo this change in their binding properties.

A model to explain the observed changes in the binding activity in solubilized preparations containing thyroid hormone receptors is shown in Fig. 24. The intact receptor that recognizes T_3, T_4, and other analogs in proportion to their biological activity is here designated "holo" receptor. Influences during purification, pH, and heating a crude extract favor a conversion of the receptor to the form, here designated as "core" receptor, with an altered binding specificity.

The most striking property of the "core" receptor is that it resembles certain other thyroid hormone-binding proteins that have a higher affinity for T_4 than T_3. The altered form of the receptor in particular is similar to thyroid hormone-binding prealbumin (TBPA) (Ferguson *et al.*, 1975), which, as mentioned

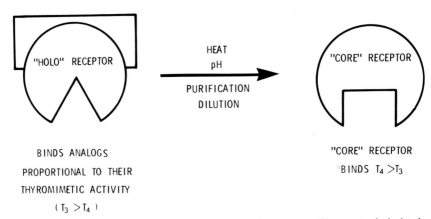

FIG. 24. Schematic model of the thyroid hormone nuclear receptor. The receptor is depicted as consisting of subunits—a "factor" and a "core" subunit, which possesses the thyroid hormone binding site and binds T_4 more avidly than T_3. Interaction of the "factor" with the "core" subunit forms the "holo" receptor which binds the biologically potent T_3 more avidly than T_4. Heat, pH, dilution, and purification affect dissociation of the subunits, which results in a loss of T_3 binding activity. Since the "core" receptor binds T_4 more avidly than T_3, it may be related to other thyroid hormone-binding proteins (e.g., thyroid hormone-binding prealbumin) that possess a similar hormone binding specificity.

earlier, also contains a putative DNA binding site. The finding that the receptor can be converted to a form that has a binding specificity similar to TBPA therefore raises the question of whether the receptor has a greater similarity to some of these other thyroid hormone-binding proteins than has been previously appreciated. For example, these two proteins could have evolved from the same ancestral gene. Alternatively, receptors and TBPA could have common subunits that are differentiated by posttranslational processing, such as glycosylation, proteolysis, or other covalent modifications or associations with other factors. The finding that the receptor can be converted to a form with an altered hormone binding specificity also indicates that the criterion of hormone binding specificity cannot be used to differentiate some fundamental binding unit of the receptor from other proteins.

D. A PROTEIN(S) FROM CHROMATIN CAPABLE OF RECONSTITUTING HIGH-AFFINITY T_3 BINDING ACTIVITY

The finding that certain manipulations could quantitatively alter the receptors led us to search for conditions to reconstitute the original hormone-binding specificity. The alteration in binding activity could be generated by irreversible processes such as proteolysis; however, it seemed equally plausible that a small ligand or a macromolecule might be responsible for maintaining the receptor in a conformation in which it binds T_3 more avidly than T_4. We were able to reconstitute high-affinity T_3 binding activity by adding fractions from an extract of chromatin to receptor-containing fractions that had lost T_3 binding activity (Fig. 25) (Eberhardt et al., 1979b). For these experiments a receptor-containing

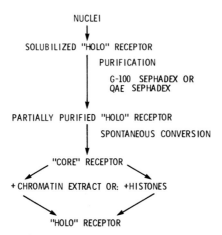

FIG. 25. Experimental scheme utilized for the reconstitution of the "holo" receptor from the "core" receptor. After partial purification of the receptor-containing nuclear extract, there is a spontaneous generation of the "core" receptor. The "holo" receptor is then regenerated by the addition of a heat-treated chromatin extract or purified histones.

crude nuclear extract was filtered over Sephadex G-100. The major form of the receptor elutes in the included volume of the column (Fig. 26, Latham *et al.*, 1976). After the filtration, T_3 binding activity in this included fraction is spontaneously lost without a loss of T_4 binding activity. Other materials are then added to this fraction in order to study factors required for the reconstitution of binding activity. Figure 26 shows the effect on T_3 binding activity upon addition to the included column fractions of a chromatin extract which was heat-treated to destroy endogenous T_3 binding activity.

This experimental approach was based upon the reasoning that potential factors that influenced the receptor's hormonal binding specificity might be relatively heat stable. In this case, the heat treatment (60°C for 10 minutes) was greater than that usually employed to obtain selective loss of T_3 binding activity. This reduced but did not abolish endogenous hormone binding; this background binding was subtracted from the total binding for determination of the profile shown in Fig. 26. As indicated, the heated chromatin extract specifically stimulated T_3 binding activity in the included fractions that had lost such activity; it did not stimulate binding in other column fractions. Shown in Fig. 27 (left) is a Scatchard analysis of the T_3 and T_4 binding in the G-100 Sephadex-included fraction before and after adding the heat-treated extract. The reconstitution increased the number of high-affinity T_3 binding sites; there was no increase in

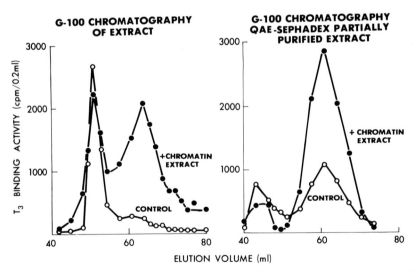

FIG. 26.   Regeneration of ^{125}I-labeled triiodothyronine ($[^{125}I]T_3$) binding activity by the G-100 Sephadex-included receptor fraction from the initial nuclear extract (left) or from a QAE-Sephadex partially purified extract (right) in the presence (●) or the absence (○) of the heat-treated chromatin extract. Aliquots of the initial or partially purified extracts were filtered over G-100 Sephadex. $[^{125}I]T_3$ binding activity in each fraction was then assayed (Latham *et al.*, 1976) in the presence or the absence of the heat-treated chromatin extract. Residual binding of $[^{125}I]T_3$ by the heated chromatin extract has been subtracted from the data. Reprinted from Eberhardt *et al.* (1979b).

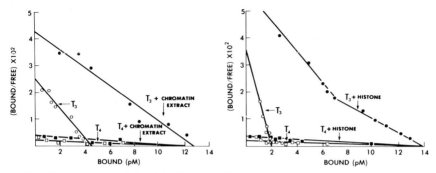

FIG. 27.   Scatchard analysis of the binding of [^{125}I]T$_3$ (○, ●) and [^{125}I]T$_4$ (□, ■) by the G-100 Sephadex-included receptor fraction (open symbols) and influence of the presence of the heat-treated chromatin extract (left, filled symbols) and purified histones (right, filled symbols). Assays were performed according to Latham *et al.* (1976), and the data have been corrected for the residual [^{125}I]T$_3$ or [^{125}I]T$_4$ binding by the heated chromatin extract or histone fractions. Reprinted from Eberhardt *et al.* (1979b).

the number of sites that bind T$_4$. Thus, there is selective restoration of the T$_3$ binding activity, which had been previously lost.

The factor present in the heated extract responsible for the reconstitution of T$_3$ binding activity appears to be a protein (Eberhardt *et al.,* 1979b). First, when trypsin is added, followed by trypsin inhibitor, to either the G-100 Sephadex-included fraction or the heated chromatin extract, the reconstitution is abolished. Simultaneous addition of trypsin and trypsin inhibitor to either component of the reconstituted mixture does not cause such an inhibition of the restimulation. Second, the reconstitution is insensitive to DNase or RNase. It cannot be mimicked by the addition of randomly chosen acidic or basic proteins, such as ovalbumin, poly-L-lysine, lysozyme, or cytochrome *c*. Also, it cannot be mimicked by the addition of DNA, RNA, or several micromolecular monovalent or divalent ions. These data imply that there is a protein–protein interaction responsible for reconstitution of the high-affinity T$_3$ binding activity of the receptor. These studies led us to investigate in more detail the protein components of chromatin responsible for reconstitution of the receptor's ability to bind hormones in proportion to their biological activity.

E. STIMULATION OF HIGH-AFFINITY T$_3$ BINDING ACTIVITY BY HISTONES (EBERHARDT *et al.,* 1979b)

In studies of the isoelectric focusing behavior of the receptor, we found that the binding activity focused with acidic and basic isoelectric points. With increased isoelectric focusing time, the proportion of receptors that focused with the more basic isoelectric point disappeared. These observations suggested that receptors are possibly associated with more basic components of chromatin.

Consequently, we were led to ask if the reconstitution of high-affinity T_3 binding can be obtained with histones; this was found to be the case. As shown in Fig. 28, the addition of histones to the G-100 Sephadex-included fractions that had lost high-affinity T_3 binding activity caused a marked stimulation of T_3 binding activity. Activity was stimulated best by a mixture of core histones (H_{2A} + H_{2B} + H_3 + H_4). Histone H_1 and total histones have less influence. Also, shown in Fig. 28 is that lysozyme is without effect. In Fig. 27 (right) are shown Scatchard analyses of the T_3 and T_4 binding before and after addition of core histones. Like the case with the heat-treated chromatin extract (Fig. 27, left), there was a marked stimulation of high affinity T_4 binding activity. Thus, addition of histones results in reconstitution of the receptor with the original binding properties. Again, it is unlikely that a new hormone-binding species has appeared, because T_4 binding is unaffected.

The spontaneous loss of T_3 binding activity in the G-100 Sephadex-included fractions is dependent on the extent of dilution of the sample. This is indicated in Fig. 29, which shows the results from a number of studies in which for each data point the quantity of high-affinity T_3 and T_4 binding sites is analyzed by the Scatchard technique. In the most concentrated preparations (higher protein concentration), there is no spontaneous loss of T_3 binding activity and the concentration of high-affinity T_3 and T_4 binding sites is the same. As the sample is diluted, high-affinity T_3 binding activity is selectively lost, whereas T_4 binding activity is maintained. These data suggest that an association–dissociation phenomenon

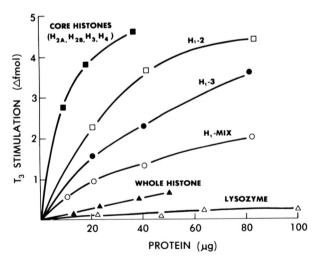

FIG. 28. Reconstitution of [^{125}I]T_3 binding activity in the G-100 Sephadex included receptor fraction by core histones (■) (H_{2A} + H_{2B} + H_3 + H_4) purified H_1 subfractions (□, ●) (gift from R. D. Cole, Berkeley, California), a mixture of H_1 subfractions (○) (5% perchloric acid extract of whole histone), whole histone (▲) and lysozyme (△). Assays were performed as described in the legend to Fig. 27. Reprinted from Eberhardt *et al.* (1979b).

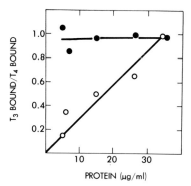

FIG. 29. Dependence of the ratio of high-affinity [^{125}I]T$_3$ and [^{125}I]T$_4$ binding capacities on the protein concentrations of the G-100 Sephadex-included receptor fractions in the absence (○) and the presence (●) of histones (50 μg/ml). Assays were performed as described in the legend to Fig. 27 except that the amount of the included receptor fraction was varied. Each of the data points represents the extrapolated binding capacity from individual Scatchard analyses as in Fig. 27. Reprinted from Eberhardt *et al.* (1979b).

participates in the selective loss. As also shown, when histones are added the high-affinity T$_3$ binding capacity is selectively stimulated. Noteworthy is that the quantity of high-affinity T$_3$ binding sites is stimulated to a level that equals, but does not exceed, the number of T$_4$ binding sites.

The above observations therefore suggest that thyroid hormone receptors interact with histones or a histonelike species in order to maintain their high-affinity T$_3$ binding activity. These findings are summarized in the model shown in Fig. 30. The "core" receptor which binds T$_4$ more avidly than T$_3$ is synthesized in the cytosol. Upon association with histones or a histonelike species in chromatin the "core" receptor is converted to the "holo" receptor which binds the biologically active T$_3$ more avidly than T$_4$. Since the "core" receptor binds T$_3$ weakly, this model may explain the inability to detect receptors in the cytoplasm. This model contrasts with models of steroid hormone action. Thus, in the case of steroids the binding of the hormone increases the receptor's affinity for chromatin, whereas with the thyroid hormone receptor, the binding of the receptor ("core" receptor) to chromatin increases its affinity for the biologically active T$_3$. In addition to their theoretical interest these findings have been adventitiously exploited for purification of the receptor (discussed below).

The idea that histones have an influence on the thyroid hormone receptor should also be considered in a general context. The thyroid hormone receptor represents a unique case in which an intrinsic chromosomal protein known to regulate the expression of specific genes has been identified. The suggestion that histones are important for the function of this protein implies that histones play a role in the maintenance of the functional integrity of regulatory proteins in addition to their role in DNA packaging (for review, see Elgin and Weintraub,

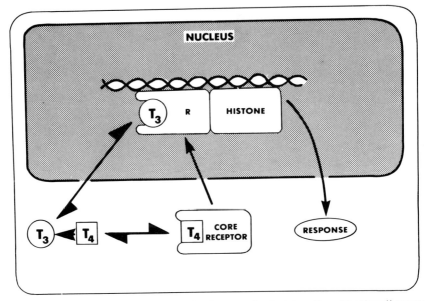

FIG. 30. Model of thyroid hormone action incorporating the interaction of the "core" receptor with histones. The "core" receptor, which binds thyroxine (T_4) more avidly than triiodothyronine (T_3), is synthesized in the cytosol; after association with histones or a histonelike species in chromatin, it is converted to the "holo" receptor, which recognizes thyroid hormones in relation to their thyromimetic potencies. Upon association with the biologically active T_3, an unknown series of events occurs, which leads to increased levels of specific mRNA molecules in the cytoplasm. Subsequent translation of the mRNAs results in synthesis of specific proteins that mediate the hormone's responses.

1975; Felsenfeld, 1978). Interactions of histones with the receptor may also be of importance for the regulation of genetic expression.

F. AFFINITY CHROMATOGRAPHY PURIFICATION OF THYROID HORMONE RECEPTORS

Purification of the thyroid hormone receptors is important for understanding the details of their actions. For example, purified preparations will facilitate studies of receptor interactions with DNA and histones. If the receptor possesses enzymic properties, these can be unambiguously studied only with purified preparations. Finally, purified receptors will be required for the reconstitution of a thyroid hormone-regulated gene. Initial attempts at conventional purification procedures (Latham *et al.*, 1976) suggested that it would be advantageous to use more powerful techniques for large-scale purification of these binding proteins, since up to 50,000-fold purification may be required. Affinity chromotography is one such technique, and this has now been used with some success.

G. PREPARATION OF AFFINITY SUPPORT MATRICES AND EXAMINATION OF THEIR PROPERTIES

Extensive studies of the structural requirements for thyroid hormone binding to the receptors (Jorgensen *et al.*, 1974, 1976) suggested that the amino moiety of T_3 would be the best group to modify in the preparation of affinity support matrices. These studies indicated that the 4' hydroxyl and carboxyl groups of T_3 were involved in the binding reaction, but that loss of the amino function (e.g., in deaminated analogs like triac) did not decrease binding to the receptor. We consequently prepared a series of amino-substituted thyroid hormone analogs according to the scheme shown in Fig. 31. D- and L-triiodothyronine-derived "dimers" and "monomers" were prepared by reaction of D-T_3 or L-T_3 with the diactivated succinimide esters of either glutaric or pimelic acid (Anderson *et al.*, 1964). The ability of T_3 receptors to bind these derivatives is shown in Fig. 32. Confirming earlier reports (Oppenheimer *et al.*, 1973), L-T_3 binds to the receptor more avidly than does D-T_3. Also, L-T_4 binds with a somewhat lower affinity

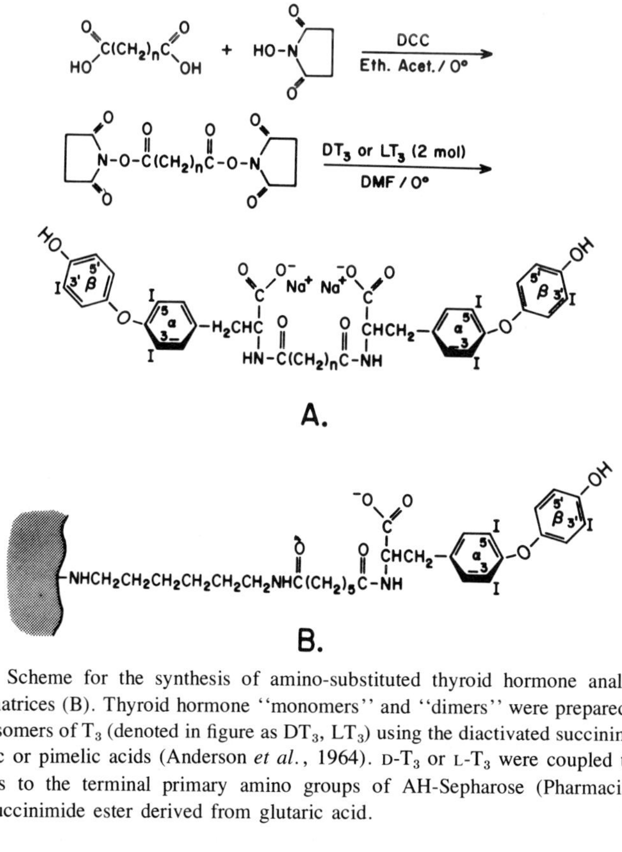

FIG. 31. Scheme for the synthesis of amino-substituted thyroid hormone analogs (A) and affinity gel matrices (B). Thyroid hormone "monomers" and "dimers" were prepared from the D- and L-stereoisomers of T_3 (denoted in figure as DT$_3$, LT$_3$) using the diactivated succinimide esters of either glutaric or pimelic acids (Anderson *et al.*, 1964). D-T_3 or L-T_3 were coupled through their amino groups to the terminal primary amino groups of AH-Sepharose (Pharmacia) using the diactivated succinimide ester derived from glutaric acid.

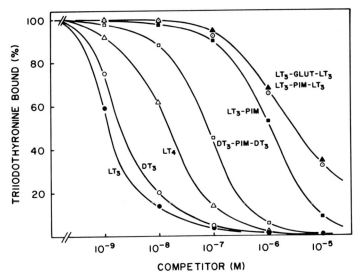

FIG. 32. Competition for [^{125}I]T$_3$ binding in the nuclear extract (Latham *et al.*, 1976) by unlabeled T$_3$ (●), D-T$_3$ (DT$_3$, ○), T$_4$ (△), D-T$_3$ pimelate dimer (□), L-T$_3$ (LT$_3$) pimelate monomer (■), L-T$_3$ pimelate dimer (⊙), and L-T$_3$ glutarate dimer (▲). Assays were performed as described (Latham *et al.*, 1979).

than either of the T$_3$ isomers. The amino-substituted derivatives tested can competitively inhibit the binding of T$_3$ by the receptors, but substitution of the bulky group at this position diminishes their effectiveness. Surprisingly, in contrast to the parent hormones, T$_3$ and T$_4$, we found that the D-substituted derivatives bind to the receptor more tightly than do the L-substituted derivatives. These seemingly paradoxical results might be explained by the model shown in Fig. 33. For L-T$_3$ the amino group decreases the binding interaction either by unfavorable charge interactions (as indicated in Fig. 33) or by unfavorable steric interactions. This could explain the relatively higher affinities of deaminated hormone analogs, such as triac, for the receptor (Oppenheimer *et al.*, 1973). In the case of D-T$_3$, either the charge interactions (Fig. 33) or steric interactions are more unfavorable than for L-T$_3$, thereby leading to a relative decrease in the binding affinity of D-T$_3$ for the receptor (Oppenheimer *et al.*, 1973). However, when a bulky substituent is coupled to the amino groups, there may be greater steric hindrance when the molecule is in the L than in the D configuration. Thus, the affinity of the D-T$_3$ derivative is higher than that of the L-T$_3$ derivative.

After demonstrating that amino-substituted derivatives could bind to the receptors, the chemical techniques used to produce such derivatives were employed for preparation of thyroid hormone-substituted affinity gels (Fig. 31B). Figures 34 and 35 show that these affinity gels can remove T$_3$ binding activity from a crude nuclear extract. As predicted from the competition studies (Fig. 32), Fig.

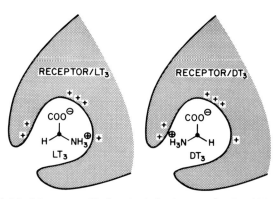

FIG. 33. Model of the receptor binding site indicating receptor–thyroid hormone interactions. Normally, L-T_3 (LT$_3$) binds to the binding site with a higher affinity than D-T_3 (DT$_3$). Substitution of a bulky substituent on the amino group, however, reverses the stereospecificity of this interaction such that D-T_3 derivatives bind with a higher affinity than L-T_3 derivatives. Since deaminated thyroid hormone analogs bind with equal or greater avidity to the receptor than the parent hormones (Oppenheimer et al., 1973), the interaction of the amino group with the receptor is viewed as a relatively negative interaction (shown here as a change interaction) for the L-T_3 itself. D-T_3 binds with lower affinity than L-T_3 owing to steric restriction and/or increased negative charge interactions (shown on the right). Substitution of the amino group increases steric restriction; however, in this case there is a marked preference for the D-T_3 derivative owing either to more favorable charge and/or to steric interactions. From Latham et al. (1979).

34 demonstrates that the D-T_3-substituted gel preparations are more efficient in removing T_3 binding activity than are the L-T_3 preparations. As shown in Fig. 35, gels prepared from T_4 or reverse T_3 were less effective in removing the T_3 receptors. Thus, the receptor adsorption efficiency of the various affinity matrices parallels the binding affinity of the thyroid hormone analog utilized in the synthesis of the matrices. Figure 35 also demonstrates that an unsubstituted gel is ineffective in removing T_3 binding activity. As indicated in Fig. 36, progressive increases in the concentration of T_3 added to the crude extract during the adsorption reaction effectively block the adsorption of the receptors by the T_3 affinity matrix. All these data, taken together, indicate that the adsorption of the T_3 receptor by the affinity gels is biospecific, i.e., is the result of binding of the receptor to the hormone attached to the gel, rather than nonspecific uptake, such as by ionic binding.

H. ELUTION OF RECEPTORS FROM THE AFFINITY MATRIX (RING et al., 1975; LATHAM et al., 1979; APRILETTI et al., 1979)

Having developed conditions for effective adsorption of receptors by the affinity gels, we determined conditions for elution of these binding proteins. We earlier found that receptors could be eluted specifically by adding free [^{125}I]T_3 (Ring et al., 1975). However, the yields of recovered receptor were low. After

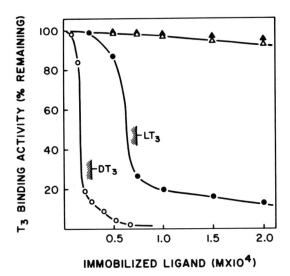

FIG. 34. Binding of the thyroid hormone receptor by affinity matrices containing D-triiodthyronine (DT$_3$, ○) or L-T$_3$ (LT$_3$, ●). The affinity matrices containing equivalent concentrations of bound ligand were incubated with nuclear extracts for 2 hours at 22°C, and the gel was removed by filtration. The filtrate was assayed for [^{125}I]T$_3$ binding activity as previously described (Latham *et al.*, 1976). To control for leakage of ligand from the affinity matrices, the matrix was incubated with buffer only for 2 hours at 22°C. After filtration of the matrix, an aliquot of the nuclear extract was added to the filtrate and [^{125}I]T$_3$ binding activity was determined as above (L-T$_3$ matrix, ▲; D-T$_3$ matrix, △). Reprinted from Latham *et al.* (1979).

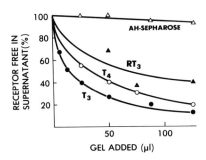

FIG. 35. Receptor adsorption by various affinity supports, L-triiodothyronine (●), L-thyroxine (○), and reverse T$_3$ (▲), were coupled to AH-Sepharose via the diactivated succinimide ester of glutaric acid, yielding gels containing 1.5 m*M* bound hormone in each case. Uncoupled AH-Sepharose (△) was used as a control. Receptor was adsorbed to these gels by adding 1 ml of rat liver nuclear extract (Latham *et al.*, 1976) to the indicated bed volume of gel suspended in 0.25 ml of buffer. After incubation for 2 hours at 22°C with continuous agitation, the gel was removed by centrifugation and the supernatant was assayed for [^{125}I]T$_3$ binding activity. Reprinted from Latham *et al.* (1979).

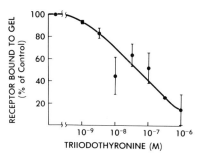

FIG. 36. Blockage of receptor adsorption to the L-triiodothyronine (L-T$_3$) affinity matrix by free T$_3$. L-T$_3$ affinity gel (5 μl bed volume), 200 μl of nuclear extract, and various concentrations of free T$_3$ were mixed in a total volume of 250 μl. After incubation for 2 hours at 22°C with continuous agitation, the gel was removed by centrifugation, and free T$_3$ was removed from the supernatant by filtration over G-25 Sephadex. The filtrate was assayed for [^{125}I]T$_3$ binding activity as described (Latham et al., 1976). As a control, a parallel set of reactions was performed in which the T$_3$ affinity gel was omitted from the initial incubation. Reprinted from Latham et al. (1979).

examination of a number of variables, the scheme for purification shown in Fig. 37 was adopted. Three factors were considered to be of particular importance for elution.

First, it was found, as can be predicted (Latham et al., 1979), that recovery of receptors from the affinity gels is dependent on the concentration of counter-ligand (T$_3$). In the [^{125}I]T$_3$ binding assays there is specific (displaced with unlabeled T$_3$) and nonspecific (not displaced with unlabeled T$_3$) binding. Whereas the former is saturated at low T$_3$ concentrations, the latter increases linearly with increasing ligand concentrations. Therefore, the ratio of nonspecific to specific binding increases with increasing [^{125}I]T$_3$ concentrations so that, above a concentration of 0.1 μM (lower than required for optimal elution with the gels obtained), the nonspecific binding is so large that specific binding cannot

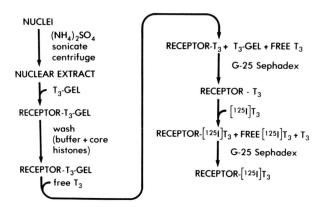

FIG. 37. Scheme for the affinity-chromatography purification of the nuclear thyroid hormone receptor (see the text).

be accurately measured. Consequently, the procedures were modified (Fig. 37) to elute with high concentrations of nonradiolabeled counterligand (10 μM T_3); excess free T_3 is then removed by Sephadex G-25 filtration of the eluted material. The quantity of receptors is then measured by an exchange assay in which the nonradioactive T_3 is displaced by incubation of the samples with [^{125}I]T_3. In experiments with crude extract, incubation for 3 hours at 22°C followed by gel filtration at 0°C resulted in greater than 90% exchange.

The second consideration for successful elution of adsorbed receptors relates to the earlier findings that high-affinity T_3 binding activity is stabilized by histones or histonelike factors (Figs. 27–29). We therefore asked whether the presence of purified histones in the buffers used to wash the columns and to elute receptors from them would improve the yield. In the absence of histones in the wash and elution buffers, the recovery of receptor from the affinity columns was usually 1–5%. By including histones (at 50–200 μg/ml) in the wash and elution buffers, the receptor recovery increased to 15–20%.

The third factor of major importance for eluting receptors is ionic strength. There is substantial nonspecific binding of proteins to the column at low ionic strengths. Much of this can be eliminated by binding the receptor to the column at high ionic strength (ionic strength = 0.6) and then washing it with a histone-containing high-salt (ionic strength = 0.9) buffer. The elution is performed in a low-salt buffer (ionic strength = 0.3), which minimizes release of any remaining nonspecific binding proteins.

Some binding characteristics of the affinity-purified material have been examined. In preliminary experiments, the affinity-purified receptor behaves identically to crude receptor when chromagraphed on either Sephadex G-100 or DEAE-Sephadex (data not shown). Figure 38 shows the hormone-binding activities of the affinity-purified material. T_3 has the greatest capability for competing with radiolabeled T_3 for binding to the affinity purified receptor. The highly potent isopropyl T_2 also has a high affinity for these purified receptors. T_4 has a

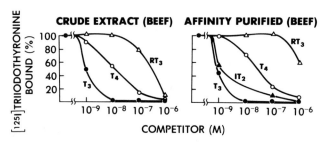

FIG. 38. Competition for [^{125}I]T_3 binding in nuclear extracts and affinity-purified receptor preparations. Standard binding reactions containing 1 nM [^{125}I]T_3 and either beef nuclear extract or nuclear extract that had been purified by affinity chromatography were performed with various concentrations of competing unlabeled triiodothyronine (T_3, ●), thyroxine (○), reverse T_3 (△), or 3'-isopropyl T_2 (▲).

slightly lower affinity, and reverse T_3 has a much lower affinity. This rank order of binding potency parallels that of the original receptor preparations and provides strong evidence that the purified material is indeed the thyroid hormone receptor. It is important that this study, along with the finding that the non-radioactive T_3 bound to the eluted receptors can be exchanged by $[^{125}I]T_3$, also demonstrated that the affinity-purified material reversibly binds the hormones. This property therefore permits a detailed study of the binding characteristics of the receptor in a purer form.

Owing to the presence of added histones, the actual purification achieved by this procedure is not yet known. In many preparations, the total measured protein concentration equals that of the added histones. Including the histones in the calculation, the purification by affinity chromatography is approximately 200-fold. Therefore, excluding the histones, the actual purification must be much higher than this value. These studies indicate that techniques of affinity chromatography can be applied to the purification of thyroid hormone receptors.

IV. Summary and Conclusions

These studies have focused on several aspects of thyroid hormone action. Specific responses to these hormones have been investigated in cell culture, and several elements, including receptors and the growth hormone gene sequences whose expression is regulated by these hormones, have been examined.

A. THE BIOLOGY OF THYROID HORMONE ACTION IN CULTURED PITUITARY CELLS

The actions of reverse T_3 and $3,3'$-T_2 were examined because the conversion of T_4 to these iodothyronines is frequently favored over T_3 production. In cultured pituitary cells, reverse T_3 and $3,3'$-T_2 are full thyroid hormone agonists, but bind more weakly than T_3 or T_4 to the nuclear receptors. Therefore, these would have to be present in the circulation at free concentrations 100-fold above those of T_3 to elicit effects as great as T_3. As this rarely occurs, it is unlikely that these metabolites have quantitatively important actions when there is a shift from T_3 to reverse T_3 production. Reverse T_3 may serve as a prohormone, as it is rapidly converted to the more active $3,3'$-T_2.

Confirming earlier studies, we found that growth hormone production is increased by thyroid hormone. This regulation is due to a modulation of growth hormone mRNA levels by the hormone. Thus, thyroid hormones may regulate gene expression by affecting transcription or processing of precursor mRNAs. DNA complementary to growth hormone mRNA has been cloned and its structure determined; these results may facilitate efforts for cell-free reconstitution of a thyroid hormone-responsive gene.

Thyroid hormone was found to regulate hyaluronidase levels in GH_1 cells.

These findings are of interest in considering developmental actions of these hormones, as levels of hyaluronidase change in thyroid hormone-induced metamorphosis of the tadpole, and changes in its substrate, hyaluronic acid, are associated with differentiation. Thus, the hypothesis that certain developmental actions of thyroid hormone are mediated through the regulation of hyaluronidase should be considered. Regulation of this enzyme may also explain how myxedematous tissues are formed in the hypothyroid state; the known increase in tissue levels of hyaluronic acid in myxedematous tissues may be a consequence of a decrease in hyaluronidase due to lack of thyroid hormone.

T_3 was also found to be capable of regulating the cell surface of GH_1 cells. There were numerous microvilli on the surface of T_3-treated cells, but not of control cells. At least 24 hours are required for detection of a clear influence. Thus, the effect could be due to the induction of protein(s) that mediates it.

Thyroid hormone was found to regulate the cellular sensitivity to glucocorticoids. In cells cultured in medium supplemented with serum free of thyroid hormone, glucocorticoids negligibly induce production of growth hormone or growth hormone mRNA. By contrast, the steroid produced a marked effect on these parameters when T_3 was present. Interestingly, this effect may in part be due to a T_3-regulated inhibition of a negative influence by factors in serum. Thus, when cells were cultured in hormone-free serum substitute-containing medium, glucocorticoids could induce growth hormone production.

The complexity of the thyroid hormone response in terms of the number of mRNAs and proteins regulated was investigated in several ways. Of these, an analysis with the use of two-dimensional gel electrophoresis of extracts from control and T_3-treated cells that have been pulse labeled with [35S]methionine provides the most sensitive index; a comparison of the relative intensities of spots on autoradiographs of the gels of extracts from hormone-treated and control cells provides an index of the relative rates of synthesis of up to 1500 proteins, possibly 10% of the expressed genes of the cells. With GH_3 cells, less than 0.5% of the detectable proteins were consistently affected by T_3, indicating that the thyroid hormone response is highly specific and restricted to a small subset of the expressed genes of the cells. Therefore, the hormone appears to elicit its diverse influences by regulating a very few key gene products. For instance, the induction of the β-adrenegic receptor, Na^+/K^+ ATPase, the thyroid-releasing hormone receptor, growth hormone, and hyaluronidase may to some extent explain physiological effects of thyroid hormone, respectively, on the cardiovascular system, thermogenesis, feedback inhibition of thyroid-stimulating hormone release, growth, and differentiation.

With the use of two-dimensional gel electrophoresis it was also found that the ability of glucocorticoids to regulate the synthesis of at least one protein other than growth hormone was also affected by T_3. Nevertheless, the influence of glucocorticoids on the synthesis of prolactin was unaffected by T_3. Thus, the two classes of hormones have independent but overlapping domains of control, and the thyroid hormone influence on glucocorticoid hormone action is restricted to a subset of the genes whose expression is affected by the steroid.

B. THYROID HORMONE RECEPTORS

The thyroid hormone receptor is unique in that it is an intrinsic chromosomal nonhistone protein known to be involved in regulation of the expression of specific genes. Thus, it is of interest for generally understanding the regulation of chromatin activity. These receptors, unlike those for steroid hormones, are bound to chromatin in the absence or the presence of thyroid hormone. They can be solubilized from chromatin and can (alone or through proteins associated with them) bind to DNA. In hydrodynamically sheared chromatin, the receptors follow a distribution similar to that of RNA polymerase II, being preferentially localized in fractions with a lower protein to DNA ratio. They do not appear to be concentrated in chromatin fractions enriched for gene fragments being actively transcribed.

Progress has been made toward purification of these proteins after their solubilization from chromatin. Our findings to date suggest that affinity chromatography can be used for large-scale purification of these receptors. Affinity support matrices containing covalently bound T_3 were prepared that biospecifically adsorbed the receptor. The finding that these derivatives of T_3 that contain bulky substituents on the amino group retain receptor binding activity supports the idea that T_3 binds to the receptor in a manner analogous to thyroid hormone-binding prealbumin (TBPA) with the phenolic hydroxyl placed deep in a pocket and the amino group on the outside. Elution of the adsorbed receptor in reasonable yields has been achieved with the use of a counterligand (T_3). It is important that the purified receptors maintain their capability of reversibly binding the hormone, so that it should be possible to study the effect of the hormone on the receptor in the more purified preparations.

The receptor was found to undergo a change during purification in which it spontaneously and selectively lost its capability for high-affinity T_3 binding but its affinity for binding T_4 did not change. This conversion also occurs after heating a crude receptor-containing nuclear extract, by lowering the pH and by diluting partially purified preparations. Several lines of evidence indicate that the observed changes were not due to a selective loss of a T_3 binding species that does not bind T_4. The finding that a form of the receptor with altered hormonal binding specificity, designated as "core" receptor, can be generated indicates that the criterion of binding specificity (e.g., higher affinity for T_3 than for T_4) cannot be used to distinguish certain forms of the receptors from other binding species. Of interest is that TBPA and other thyroid hormone-binding proteins also bind T_4 more avidly than T_3. Thus, the receptor may be more closely related to proteins such as TBPA than has been previously apparent.

We also found that high-affinity T_3 binding activity could be reconstituted.

Purified core histones or a protease-sensitive, relatively heat-stable factor isolated from chromatin, when added to preparations of "core" receptors, resulted in a recovery of high-affinity T_3 binding activity. Other basic proteins, such as cytochrome c, poly-L-lysine, and lysozyme, were ineffective, as were ovalbumin, DNA, RNA, and several ions. The core histones ($H_{2A} + H_{2B} + H_3 + H_4$) were more effective than histone H_1 or total histones. These observations suggest that histones, or a histonelike species in chromatin, confer on the receptors their capability for high-affinity T_3 binding. Thus, histones may be involved in maintenance of the functional integrity of the acidic regulatory proteins in addition to their role in DNA packaging.

C. RAPID EFFECTS OF THYROID HORMONES ON CHROMATIN

In studies related to the possible influence of the hormone–receptor interaction on chromatin, we found that the chromatin's capability to bind bacterial RNA polymerase was increased by 50%. Although this assay does not provide information about transcription of specific genes within the time of giving T_3 to GC cells, the experiments indicate that the chromatin is rapidly altered by the hormone. This concept was supported by additional studies; chromosomal proteins were radioactively labeled by incubating the cells with [^{35}S]methionine and examined by two-dimensional gel electrophoresis. There were several changes in the relative content of these proteins after such cells were exposed to T_3.

D. GENERAL MODEL FOR THYROID HORMONE ACTION

The working hypothesis for the mechanism of thyroid hormone action depicted in Figs. 30 and 39 may be helpful for designing further experiments. The hormone (mainly T_4 or T_3) enters the cell where it can be metabolized. Several metabolites of thyroxine (T_4), such as T_3, 3,3'-T_2, reverse T_3, triac, and tetrac, have biological and receptor-binding activity, but quantitatively T_3 is the most important hormone *in vivo*. The mechanism of entry is unknown, but this does not appear to limit the hormones' accessibility to the receptors. Thyroid hormone-binding proteins are also present in the cytoplasm of the cell and associate with the hormones, but there is no direct evidence that any of these play any obligatory role in the hormone binding to nuclear receptors believed to mediate certain actions of these hormones. There could be direct actions of the hormones at extranuclear sites, but the hormones do appear to elicit certain actions by binding directly to nuclear receptors.

There exists a form of the receptor that does not recognize the active hormones proportional to their biological activity, which binds T_4 more avidly than T_3. This may be the form that is present in the cytosol; it associates with the histones in

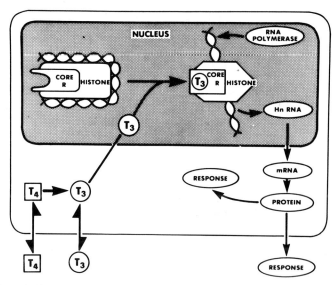

FIG. 39. Working model for the mechanism of thyroid hormone action in a responsive cell. Thyroid hormones enter the cell by as yet unknown mechanisms and may be metabolized as is shown for the conversion of T_4 to the biologically active T_3. After association of T_3 with the "holo" receptor ("core" receptor plus histones), there is a structural change in chromatin which influences the transcription of specific genes. Subsequent to transcription, processing of precursor forms of RNA may occur, yielding the mature mRNA. Translation of the mRNA results in the synthesis of proteins whose effects may be expressed intracellularly or extracellularly (e.g., growth hormone).

chromatin (and possibly with the DNA as well). These interactions localize the receptors in chromatin and also confer on them their capability of binding T_3 with high affinity. This model for thyroid hormone action contrasts with the case of steroid hormones. Whereas the chromatin stimulates the capability of the thyroid hormone-receptor ("core" receptor) to bind the hormone, steroids stimulate the binding of their receptors to chromatin. The findings further suggest a role for histones in regulating the activity of regulatory chromosomal proteins.

Shortly after the interaction of thyroid hormone with the receptor, there is a major increase (by 50%) in the chromatin's capacity to bind bacterial RNA polymerase and the distribution of chromatin proteins is altered. These data suggest that the hormone rapidly (and perhaps extensively) modifies chromatin in some way. These influences nevertheless are transmitted into effects only on the expression of a small subset of the cellular genes. The hormone in some cases also affects the ability of other hormones (glucocorticoids) to regulate the levels of specific mRNAs, such as that for growth hormone. Presumably, elements of chromatin distal to the hormone–receptor interaction account for the highly specific thyroid hormone response.

ACKNOWLEDGMENTS

This work was supported by NIH Grants AM18878, AM19997, GM25549, and CA20346 and NSF Grant PCM771432. J. W. Apriletti is a recipient of an NIH postdoctoral fellowship AM05863, and Beth Schachter was supported by a fellowship from the American Cancer Society No. ACS-CA-J334.

REFERENCES

Anderson, G. W., Zimmerman, J. E., and Callahan, F. M. (1964). *J. Am. Chem. Soc.* **86,** 1839.

Apriletti, J. W., Eberhardt, N. L., Latham, K. R., and Baxter, J. D. (1979). Submitted for publication.

Bancroft, F. C. (1973). *Endocrinology* **92,** 1014.

Bancroft, F. C., Levine, L., and Tashjian, A. H. (1969). *J. Cell Biol.* **43,** 432.

Bancroft, F. C., Wu, G.-J., and Zubay, G. (1973). *Proc. Natl. Acad. Sci. U.S.A.* **70,** 3646.

Bauer, R. F., Arthur, L. O., and Fine, D. L. (1976). *In Vitro,* **12,** 558–563.

Baxter, J. D., and MacLeod, K. M. (1979). *In* "Duncan's Diseases of Metabolism" (P. Bondy and L. Rosenburg, eds.). Saunders, Philadelphia, Pennsylvania. In press.

Berlin, C. M., and Schimke, R. T. (1965). *Mol. Pharmacol.* **1,** 149.

Bernal, J., Coleoni, A. H., and DeGroot, L. J. (1978). *Endocrinology* **102,** 403.

Blake, C. C. F., and Oatley, S. J. (1977). *Nature (London)* **268,** 115.

Braverman, L. E., Ingbar, S. H., and Sterling, K. (1970). *J. Clin. Invest.* **49,** 855.

Buller, R., Schwartz, R., Schrader, W., and O'Malley, B. W. (1976). *J. Biol. Chem.* **251,** 5178.

Charles, M. A., Ryffel, G. N., Obinata, M., McCarthy, B. J., and Baxter, J. D. (1975). *Proc. Natl. Acad. Sci. U.S.A.* **72,** 1787.

Chopra, I. J., Sack, J., and Fisher, D. A. (1975a). *In* "Perinatal Physiology and Disease" (D. A. Fisher and G. N. Burrow, eds.), pp. 33–48. Raven, New York.

Chopra, I. J., Chopra, U., Smith, R., Roa, M., and Solomon, D. H. (1975b). *J. Clin. Endocrinol. Metab.* **41,** 1043.

Dannies, P. S., and Tashjian, A. H., Jr. (1973a). *J. Biol. Chem.* **248,** 6174.

Dannies, P. S., and Tashjian, A. H., Jr. (1973b). *In* "Tissue Culture: Methods and Applications" (P. P. Kruse, Jr. and M. K. Patterson, Jr., eds.), pp. 561–569. Academic Press, New York.

DeGroot, L. J., Refetoff, S., Strausser, J., and Barsano, C. (1974). *Proc. Natl. Acad. Sci. U.S.A.* **71,** 4042.

DeGroot, L. J., Torresani, J., Carrayon, P., and Tirard, A. (1976). *Acta Endocrinol.* **83,** 293.

DeGroot, L. J., Rue, P., Robertson, M., Bernal, J., and Sherberg, N. (1977). *Endocrinology* **101,** 1690.

Dillmann, W. H., Mendecki, J., Koerner, D., Schwartz, H. L., and Oppenheimer, J. H. (1978). *Endocrinology* **102,** 568.

Doenecke, D., and McCarthy, B. J. (1975). *Biochemistry* **14,** 1366.

Eberhardt, N. L., Ring, J. C., Latham, K. R., and Baxter, J. D. (1979a). *J. Biol. Chem.* In press.

Eberhardt, N. L., Latham, K. R., Johnson, L. K., Ring, J. C., Apriletti, J. W., Kitsis, R., and Baxter, J. D. (1979b). Submitted for publication.

Edelman, I. S., and Ismail-Beigi, F. (1974). *Recent Prog. Horm. Res.* **30,** 325.

Elgin, S. C. R., and Weintraub, H. (1975). *Annu. Rev. Biochem.* **44,** 725.

Felsenfeld, G. (1978). *Nature (London)* **271,** 115.

Ferguson, R. N., Edelhoch, H., Saroff, H. A., and Robbins, J. (1975). *Biochemistry* **14,** 282.

Fisher, D. A., Chopra, I. J., and Dussault, T. H. (1972). *Endocrinology* **91,** 1141.

Goldfine, I. D., Simons, C. G., Smith, G. J., and Ingbar, S. H. (1975). *Endocrinology* **96,** 1030.

Gottesfeld, J. M., Garrard, W. T., Bagi, G., Wilson, R. F., and Bonner, J. (1974). *Proc. Natl. Acad. Sci. U.S.A.* **71,** 2193.

Granner, D. K. (1979). *In* "Glucocorticoid Hormone Action" (J. D. Baxter and G. G. Rousseau, eds.) Springer-Verlag, Heidelberg. In press.

Ingbar, S. H., and Woeber, K. A. (1974). *In* "Textbook of Endocrinology" (R. H. Williams, ed.), pp. 95–227. Saunders, Philadelphia, Pennsylvania.

Ivarie, R. D., and O'Farrell, P. H. (1978). *Cell* **13,** 41.

Ivarie, R. D., Morris, J. A., and Baxter, J. D. (1979). In preparation.

Johnson, L. K., and Baxter, J. D. (1978). *J. Biol. Chem.* **253,** 1991.

Johnson, L. K., Baxter, J. D., and Rousseau, G. G. (1978). *In* "Glucocorticoid Hormone Action" (J. D. Baxter and G. G. Rousseau, eds.). Springer-Verlag, Heidelberg. In press.

Johnson, L. K., Lan, N. C., and Baxter, J. D. (1979). *J. Biol. Chem.* In press.

Jorgensen, E. C., Murray, W. J., and Block, P., Jr. (1974). *J. Med. Chem.* **17,** 434.

Jorgensen, E. C., Bolger, M. B., and Dietrich, S. W. (1976). *Proc. Int. Congr. Endocrinol. 5th, Excerpta Med. Found. Int. Congr. Ser.* **402,** 117.

Koerner, D., Schwartz, H. L., Surks, M. I., Oppenheimer, J. H., and Jorgensen, E. C. (1975). *J. Biol. Chem.* **250,** 6417.

Kohler, P. O., Frohman, L. A., Bridson, W. E., Vanha-Pertulla, T., and Hammond, J. M. (1969). *Science* **166,** 633.

Kurtz, D. T., Sippel, A. E., and Feigelson, P. (1976). *Biochemistry* **15,** 1031.

Latham, K. R., Ring, J. C., and Baxter, J. D. (1976). *J. Biol. Chem.* **251,** 7388.

Latham, K. R., MacLeod, K. M., Papavasiliou, S. S., Martial, J. A., Seeburg, P. H., Goodman, H. M., and Baxter, J. D. (1978). *In* "Receptors and Hormone Action" (B. W. O'Malley and L. Birnbaumer, eds.), Vol. 3, pp. 76–100. Academic Press, New York.

Latham, K. R., Apriletti, J. W., Eberhardt, N. L., and Baxter, J. D. (1979). Submitted for publication.

Levy, B. W., and Baxter, J. D. (1976). *Biochem. Biophys. Res. Commun.* **68,** 1045.

MacLeod, K. M., and Baxter, J. D. (1975). *Biochem. Biophys. Res. Commun.* **62,** 577.

MacLeod, K. M., and Baxter, J. D. (1976). *J. Biol. Chem.* **251,** 7380.

Manwaring, W. I. P. (1976). *In* "The Mechanism of Action of Androgens," pp. 95–96. Springer-Verlag, Berlin and New York.

Martial, J. A., Baxter, J. D., Goodman, H. M., and Seeburg, P. H. (1977a). *Proc. Natl. Acad. Sci. U.S.A.* **74,** 1816.

Martial, J. A., Seeburg, P. H., Guenzi, D., Goodman, H. M., and Baxter, J. D. (1977b). *Proc. Natl. Acad. Sci. U.S.A.* **74,** 4293.

O'Farrell, P. H. (1975). *J. Biol. Chem.* **250,** 4007.

O'Farrell, P. Z., Goodman, H. M., and O'Farrell, P. H. (1977). *Cell* **12,** 1133.

Oppenheimer, J. H., and Dillmann, W. H. (1978). *In* "Receptors and Hormone Action" (B. W. O'Malley and L. Birnbaumer, eds.), Vol. 3, pp. 1–34. Academic Press, New York.

Oppenheimer, J. H., Koerner, D., Schwartz, H. L., and Surks, M. I. (1972). *J. Clin. Endocrinol. Metab.* **35,** 330.

Oppenheimer, J. H., Schwartz, H. L., Dillmann, W. H., and Surks, M. I. (1973). *Biochem. Biophys. Res. Commun.* **55,** 544.

Oppenheimer, J. H., Schwartz, H. L., and Surks, M. I. (1975). *Endocrinol. Res. Commun.* **2,** 309.

Oppenheimer, J. H., Schwartz, H. L., Surks, M. I., Koerner, D., and Dillmann, W. H. (1976). *Recent Prog. Horm. Res.* **32,** 529.

Papavasiliou, S. S., Martial, J. A., Latham, K. R., and Baxter, J. D. (1977). *J. Clin. Invest.* **60,** 1230.

Perrone, M. H., and Hinkle, P. M. (1978). *J. Biol. Chem.* **253,** 5168.

Polansky, J. R., and Toole, B. P. (1976). *Develop. Biol.* **53,** 30.

Polansky, J. R., Toole, B. P., and Gross, J. (1974). *Science* **183,** 862.

Polansky, J. R., Corbett, G., and Baxter, J. D. (1978a). Submitted for publication.

Polansky, J. R., Johnson, L., Papavasiliou, S., and Baxter, J. D. (1978b). Submitted for publication.

Rechler, M. M., and Nissley, S. P. (1977). *Nature (London)* **270**, 665.

Rechler, M. M., Podskalny, J. M., and Nissley, S. P. (1977). *J. Biol. Chem.* **252**, 3898.

Ring, J. C., Latham, K. R., and Baxter, J. D. (1975). *Program 57th Annu. Meet. Endocrine Soc., Endocrinology* **96**, Suppl., 117.

Samuels, H. H. (1978). *In* "Receptors and Hormone Action" (B. W. O'Malley and L. Birnbaumer, eds.), Vol. 3, pp. 35–74. Academic Press, New York.

Samuels, H. H., and Tsai, J. S. (1973). *Proc. Natl. Acad. Sci. U.S.A.* **70**, 3488.

Samuels, H. H., Tsai, J. S., and Cintron, R. (1973). *Science* **181**, 1253.

Samuels, H. H., Stanley, F., and Shapiro, L. E. (1977). *J. Biol. Chem.* **252**, 6052.

Samuels, H. H., Klein, D., Stanley, F., and Casanova, J. (1978). *J. Biochem.* **253**, 5895–5898.

Schachter, B. S., Martial, J. A., and Baxter, J. D. (1979). Submitted for publication.

Schiller, S., Slover, G. A., and Dorfman, A. (1962). *Biochim. Biophys. Acta* **58**, 27.

Schwartz, H. L., Surks, M. I., and Oppenheimer, J. H. (1971). *J. Clin. Invest.* **50**, 1124.

Seeburg, P. H., Shine, J., Martial, J. A., Ulrich, A., Baxter, J. D., and Goodman, H. M. (1977a). *Cell* **12**, 157.

Seeburg, P. H., Shine, J., Martial, J. A., Baxter, J. D., and Goodman, H. M. (1977b). *Nature (London)* **270**, 486.

Seeburg, P. H., Shine, J., Martial, J. A., Ivarie, R. D., Morris, J. A., Ulrich, A., Baxter, J. D., and Goodman, H. M. (1978). *Nature (London)* **276**, 795.

Seeburg, P. H., Shine, J., Martial, J. A., Baxter, J. D., and Goodman, H. M. (1979). In preparation.

Segal, J., and Gordon, A. (1977). *Endocrinology* **101**, 150.

Seo, H., Vassart, G., Brocas, H., and Refetoff, S. (1977). *Proc. Natl. Acad. Sci. U.S.A.* **74**, 2054.

Shapiro, L. E., Samuels, H. H., and Yaffe, B. H. (1978). *Proc. Natl. Acad. Sci. U.S.A.* **75**, 45.

Shine, J., Seeburg, P. H., Martial, J. A., Baxter, J. D., and Goodman, H. M. (1977). *Nature (London)* **270**, 494.

Snyder, S. M., Cavalier, R. R., Goldfine, I. D., Ingbar, S. H., and Jorgensen, E. C. (1976). *J. Biol. Chem.* **251**, 6489.

Spelsburg, T., and Cox, R. (1976). *Biochim. Biophys. Acta* **435**, 376.

Spindler, B. J., MacLeod, K. M., Ring, J., and Baxter, J. D. (1975). *J. Biol. Chem.* **250**, 4113.

Steggles, A. W., Wilson, G. N., Kantor, J. A., Picciano, D. J., Falvey, A. K., and Anderson, W. F. (1974). *Proc. Natl. Acad. Sci. U.S.A.* **71**, 1219.

Sterling, K., Lazarus, J. H., Milch, P. O., Sakurada, T., and Brenner, M. A. (1978). *Science* **201**, 1126.

Surks, M. I., and Oppenheimer, J. H. (1978). *J. Clin. Invest.* **60**, 555.

Surks, M. I., Koerner, D., Dillmann, W., and Oppenheimer, J. H. (1973). *J. Biol. Chem.* **248**, 7066.

Sussman, P. M., Tushinski, R. J., and Bancroft, F. C. (1976). *Proc. Natl. Acad. Sci. U.S.A.* **73**, 29.

Tashjian, A. H., Jr., Yasumora, Y., Levine, L., Sato, G. H., and Parker, M. L. (1968). *Endocrinology* **82**, 342.

Tashjian, A. H., Jr., Bancroft, S. C., and Levine, L. (1970). *J. Cell Biol.* **47**, 61–70.

Tata, J. R., and Widnell, C. C. (1966). *Biochem. J.* **98**, 604.

Thiele, D., Sarocchi, M.-T., Guschlbauer, W., Lazius, A., and Mark, C. (1973). *Mol. Biol. Rep.* **1**, 155.

Toole, B. P. (1973). *Am. Zool.* **13**, 1061.

Toole, B. P. (1976). *In* "Neuronal Recognition (S. Barondes, ed.), pp. 275–323. Plenum, New York.

Tsai, J. S., and Chen, A. (1977). *Clin. Res.* **25**, 303A.

Tsai, J. S., and Samuels, H. H. (1974). *Biochem. Biophys. Res. Commun.* **59**, 420.

Van Wyck, J. J., Underwood, L. E., Lister, R. C., and Marshall, R. N. (1973). *Am. J. Dis. Child.* **126,** 705.

Williams, L. T., Lefkowitz, R. J., Watanabe, A. M., Hathaway, D. R., and Besch, H. R., Jr. (1977). *J. Biol. Chem.* **252,** 2787.

Wilson, G. N., Steggles, A. W., Kantor, J. A., Nienhuis, A. W., and Anderson, W. F. (1975). *J. Biol. Chem.* **250,** 8604.

Wolff, E. C., and Wolff, J. (1964). *In* "The Thyroid Gland" (R. Pitt-Rivers and W. R. Trotter, eds.), Vol. 1, pp. 237–282. Butterworth, London.

Yosumura, Y., Tashjian, A. H., Jr., and Sato, G. (1966). *Science* **154,** 1186.

Yu, L. Y., Tushinski, R. J., and Bancroft, F. C. (1977). *J. Biol. Chem.* **252,** 3870.

Zubay, G. (1974). *Annu. Rev. Genet.* **7,** 267.

DISCUSSION

S. W. Spaulding: I was very interested by your comment that the cytoplasmic binding proteins, which we looked at a number of years ago, may be converted into "nuclear receptors" in the presence of a histone. Did you purify the cytoplasmic binder, add it to histone, and show that it then does go into the nucleus?

J. Baxter: No. We have obtained some stimulation of T_3 binding in preliminary studies in which histones were added to cytosol. However, all the T_4 binding proteins are not converted to species that bind T_3 more avidly. Thus, we do not know the answer to your question, but agree that it is an interesting topic worth further study.

M. Sherman: We have shown that the steroid receptors in cytosols from four target organs are converted to small steroid-binding fragments, called meroreceptors, and that this conversion is prevented by leupeptin, a bacterial protease inhibitor [*Fed. Proc., Fed. Am. Soc. Exp. Biol.* **37,** 167 (1978)].

As the conditions you used to convert the holoreceptor to the core receptor in your system are similar to those that promote the cleavage of steroid receptors, I wonder if you have tested the effects of leupeptin or any other protease inhibitors on that conversion.

J. Baxter: When we initially found the loss of T_3-binding activity, the possibility that this was the result of proteolysis was considered. To date, this possibility has not been excluded. However, one argument against it is that the lost binding activity could be reconstituted by the addition of certain other protein-containing fractions.

M. Sherman: The fact that you can reconstitute the holoreceptor does not prove that the core receptor was not formed by proteolysis. An analogous situation was described by Haber and Anfinsen, who demonstrated the regeneration of ribonuclease activity of combining the two fragments formed by subtilisin treatment of the enzyme [*J. Biol. Chem.* **236,** 422 (1961)].

J. Baxter: I agree.

H. Schwartz: L. J. DeGroot has shown the leakage of the T_3 receptors from the isolated nuclei in his incubation system, and typically he finds that the receptors that have leached have a higher affinity for T_3 than those in the nucleus. Have you looked at the same system to see whether hidden in that pool are the core receptors, since I interpret Fig. 30 to suggest an equilibrium of the nucleus. Am I correct?

J. Baxter: We assume that the core receptors are in equilibrium with the chromatin, but we do not know enough about the nature of that equilibrium to answer your question. I suspect that under the conditions of DeGroot and co-workers, there is a leakage of holoreceptors, just as in the case where we solubilize holoreceptors from chromatin.

C. A. Snipes: Have you found the depletion of the nuclear receptor upon stimulation by T_3 that has been reported by H. H. Samuels, F. Stanley, and L. E. Shapiro [*Proc. Natl. Acad. Sci. U.S.A.* **73,** 388 (1976)]? They proposed that the receptor was a repressor, as the induction of growth hormone synthesis by T_3 correlated better with receptor depletion than with hormone binding.

J. Baxter: We have not looked at that in cultured pituitary cells. We found, as have other groups, that in rat liver the receptor levels are identical in euthyroid and thyroidectomized animals. We obtained some suggestive but preliminary data that in hyperthyroid animals there may be a slightly lower level of receptors.

C. A. Snipes: That was cultured rat pituitary tumor cells that they were studying.

J. Baxter: That is correct.

B. O'Malley: Since this is probably the last discussion in which we'll be speaking of recombinant DNA technology, it might be worth emphasizing a couple of points relating to current work that may have immense application to future medical therapy. A number of recent successes have occurred in which mRNA has been used to make DS-cDNAs which have subsequently been expressed in bacteria. In the last couple of months, growth hormone (your laboratory), ovalbumin, somatostatin, insulin have all been synthesized in bacteria. We are likely to see now an avalanche of these proteins produced in bacteria and, it is hoped, new sources for scarce proteins beneficial for medical therapy. The work of the Riggs and Boyer groups in synthesizing the human insulin gene from nucleotides inserting it into bacteria and getting it expressed in bacteria is particularly exciting. Finally, a point that may have one of the largest impacts on medicine relates to the field of gene replacement therapy. This is something that is not coming this year or next year, but that will be available in the 1980s. Having the ability to purify mRNAs for given proteins, synthesize CS-cDNA probes, and purify the natural genes, there is an irrepressible desire to attempt to place these genes back into cells and to attempt to get them to function. As we know, a large number of pediatric diseases are due to defects in single genes. Work on gene replacement in cells could be very important to curative therapy for such illnesses. At present, experiments are being carried out in which natural gene segments are being linked to nontransforming pieces of SV40 DNA and inserted into animal cells in culture. Although such technology could not be applied to humans for some years, it will probably be available sometime in the 1980s.

D. K. Biswas: My comments regard the use of a well characterized cDNA probe in the understanding of cellular regulatory mechanisms in eukaryotes. Dr. Baxter has already mentioned that rat pituitary tumor cell strains in culture produce along with growth hormone large amounts of prolactin. We have been trying to isolate and characterize the prolactin cDNA probe for the study of regulation of prolactin gene expression in these cells. With the permission of the chairman and the speaker I am going to present here today some of the results of such an attempt for the isolation and characterization of prolactin cDNA.

The scheme of our experimental approach for the isolation of prolactin cDNA is described in Fig. A. Rat pituitary tumor cells, which produce large amounts of prolactin, designated here as PRL^+ strain, contain prolactin-specific mRNA among the total translatable mRNA population, whereas the PRL^- (prolactin nonproducing cells) do not contain the translatable prolactin mRNA. We exploited these properties of these two GH-cell strains (rat pituitary tumor cells) to isolate the prolactin-specific cDNA. When cDNA is prepared from total polysomal mRNA of PRL^+ strain in the presence of viral reverse transcriptase and subsequently hybridized with total polysomal mRNA isolated from PRL^- strain under conditions permitting complete reassociation of complementary sequences of DNA and RNA molecules, almost all the cDNA molecules form double-stranded cDNA/mRNA hybrids, except the prolactin cDNA. The latter, i.e., the single-stranded prolactin cDNA, is then separated from cDNA/mRNA hybrids by fractionation on a hydroxyapatite column.

We have also isolated simultaneously prolactin-specific mRNA by exploiting the same properties of these two cell strains by adopting scheme 2, as shown in Fig. A. Scheme 1 (Fig. A) leads to the isolation of prolactin-specific cDNA whereas Scheme 2 leads to that of prolactin-specific mRNA. For reasons, that I will not be able to go into in detail, we feel that isolation of both cDNA and prolactin-specific mRNA is essential for the characterization of a $cDNA_{PRL}^-$ probe. In the case of

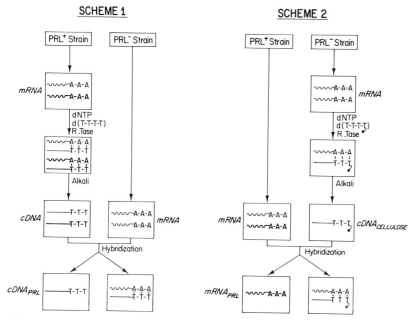

FIG. A.   Schemes for experimental approach for the isolation of prolactin-specific cDNA (Scheme 1) and prolactin-specific mRNA (Scheme 2).

prolactin-specific mRNA isolation as described in Scheme 2 (Fig. A) cellulose-bound cDNA from the total polysomal mRNA isolated from PRL⁻ strain is prepared, and total polysomal mRNA isolated from PRL⁺ strain is hybridized with matrix-bound cDNA. Unhybridized PRL-specific mRNA passed through the cDNA cellulose column. This fraction when tested in a cell-free translation system has been found to be enriched for prolactin mRNA.

We have characterized the cDNA$_{PRL}$ isolated by adopting the procedure described in Scheme 1 (Fig. A) by alkaline sucrose gradient centrifugation, by polyacrylamide gel electrophoretic analysis, and by studying the reassociation kinetics with polysomal RNA isolated from PRL⁺ and PRL⁻ strains. The reassociation kinetics of cDNA$_{PRL}$ with total polysomal RNA isolated from PRL⁺ strain and with that isolated from PRL⁻ strains is shown in Fig. B. As evident from the results presented in Fig. B, cDNA$_{PRL}$ hybridized rapidly with RNA isolated from PRL⁺ strain with pseudo first-order kinetics whereas it did not reassociate with RNA isolated from PRL⁻ strain even though hybridization is permitted to reach completion by incubation for 60 hours. Further characterization of this cDNA$_{PRL}$ probe by studying the reassociation kinetics with mRNA$_{PRL}$ fraction isolated by the procedure described in Scheme 2 of Fig. A is currently in progress.

R. Levine: Dr. O'Malley discussed some of the work being done on the bacterial translation of peptide hormones. For completeness sake, I want to report to you that Drs. Itakura and Riggs at the City of Hope, who produced human somatostatin in January 1978, have now successfully completed the expression of human insulin in *Escherichia coli* by techniques very similar to those they used for somatostatin. The A and the B chains were obtained separately and then reconstituted into free insulin with a yield of about 10%. The paper will appear soon.

H. W. Dickerman: I would like to make a comment about the comparison of the steroid receptors with the T$_3$ and T$_4$ receptors; they are not quite so different. In our laboratory we have been studying the binding of estradiol cytosol receptors in the mouse uterus and the mouse kidney to

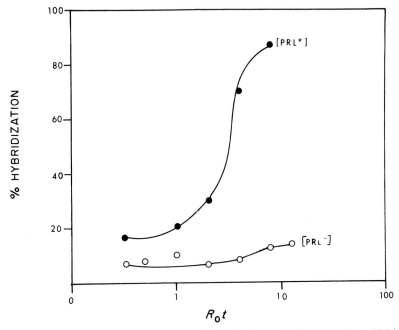

FIG. B.   Reassociation kinetics of $cDNA_{PRL}$ with total polysomal RNA isolated from PRL^+ and PRL^- strains.

oligodeoxythymidylate cellulose, and under those circumstances we too find an optimum binding at isotonic KCl; in other words there is little or no binding at low ionic strength and an optimum is reached at $0.15 M$ KCl. Furthermore, when using oligo(dT) in the purification of the estradiol cytosol receptors, we lose the ability to rebind to oligo(dT) after elution with $0.4 M$ KCl, but this rebinding can be facilitated by a heat-stable protein that is of cytosolic origin; this activity can be mimicked to some extent by histone, but apparently not as well. Histones are not quantitatively as efficient, yet it sounds a little bit like your histone story in that the heat-stable protein facilitates rebinding of estradiol receptors to a DNA-like model compound, and the stability of the receptors seems to be improved with the protein.

J. Baxter: I think that your point is well taken. In our studies, the histones appear to be regulating the specificity of ligand recognition by the receptor rather than the stability of the protein. Further, it is worth reemphasizing that, in the case of thyroid receptors, the chromatin stimulates the binding of the hormone to the receptor whereas with the steroid systems, the hormone stimulates the binding of the receptor to chromatin.

K. Sterling: Your analog binding, as that of others of the nuclear investigators, does not correspond well with physiological activity in that your 3'-isopropyl-3,5-diiodothyronine (IT_2) which in humans and rodents *in vivo* is at least 3–5 times as active as the native hormone, T_3, is bound, if anything, less well in your data. I want you to account for that.

J. Baxter: In liver, IT_2 is of equal potency to T_3 in terms of receptor binding, and Oppenheimer *et al.* (1973), found it to be 2.4-fold as potent as T_3 in binding to cardiac receptors. We have not tested the effect of IT_2 in GH cells. Dietrich and co-workers [S. W. Dietrich, M. B. Bolger, P. A. Kollman, and E. C. Jorgensen, *J. Med. Chem.* **20**, 863 (1977)] found that the activity of IT_2 in the rat antigoiter assay was 1.4-fold that of T_3, in reasonable agreement with the binding data. Of course, to precisely relate binding data with *in vivo* biological activity, it is important also to consider the relative rates of metabolism of the analogs.

K. Sterling: Other intracellular binders, not in the nucleus, show IT_2 binding of the order of a decade of five times as high as T_3. One report from your own institution was unmentioned—that is, the plasma membrane receptor of Ira Goldfine. Do you not believe it?

J. Baxter: I did not intend to comprehensively review the literature on thyroid hormone action or on other thyroid hormone-binding proteins. This presentation was intended mostly to be a survey of the work that we have done. I did not say or mean to imply that the nucleus is the only site of thyroid hormone action or that some of the binding activity you mention is unimportant.

K. Sterling: The last point, however, is that I have to confess some skepticism and confusion about your "core receptor." I have heard a little about this work, some via Chicago and even Marseilles, where Torresani, and later DeGroot, have had serious troubles in attempting to purify nuclear T_3 binding proteins. In fact, J. Torresani specifically refers to the difficulties with affinity chromatography [*Biochem. Biophys. Res. Commun.* **81**, 147 (1978)].

Now what worries me is that you have added material back to the heat-denatured "core" receptor, and whether the added material be a chromatin extract or a histone, this may raise some serious problems. In line with what Dr. Schwartz alluded to, we know about DeGroot's evidence that the receptor leaks out of nuclei, which are, indeed, rather leaky [*Endocrinology* **100**, 648 (1977)]. Therefore, it is easy for this receptor to get it into any chromatin extract or even, I would venture, into the histone fraction. Therefore, I would certainly reserve the *caveat* that what you may be adding back might contain some of this very real and potent nuclear chromatin receptor. Have you considered and excluded that? Have you tested it carefully before addition to your heat-denatured so-called "core"?

J. Baxter: Yes, these controls are done as part of every experiment. The cleanest example is with the histone stimulation; the histones themselves have no detectable specific hormone-binding activity. In the other cases, where an extract of chromatin is added to core receptors, we start with material that did contain receptors. In these cases the extract is heated to destroy the endogenous T_3 binding activity. There is sometimes a small amount of residual T_3 binding activity and, if present, this is subtracted in the final calculations.

J. R. Tata: Regarding experiments that you might not have had time to mention: (1) If the T_3 receptor in the nucleus is present in the same amount whether or not the cells have been exposed to T_3, then would you not expect to get some effect by adding T_3 directly to the nuclei? (2) Have you done the experiments of the type Weintraub and Axel have reported for ovalbumin and globin—that if a given gene is transcribed actively, then it is more sensitive to digestion by DNase? Did you try to see whether growth hormone gene is more sensitive to digestion after adding T_3 to the cells or directly to nuclei?

J. Baxter: We have initiated these types of studies, but the progress to date is not such that we can draw any conclusions.

J. Geller: I was intrigued by your concept of conversion of a "holo" receptor into a core receptor. I wonder if your *in vitro* conditions for this to occur might be likely to occur spontaneously *in vivo* as well. There is a clinical condition in which the conversion of T_4 and T_3 is turned "off," the so-called low T_3 syndrome. This occurs in acute febrile conditions and chronic disease, and I wonder whether conversion to a "core" receptor might occur *in vivo* when T_4 is more available than T_3 for binding to cell nuclei. Do you have any data on that or any speculation?

J. Baxter: I agree that these are very interesting questions, but we have not done any experiments to get any information about them.

O. P. Ganda: I was interested in your studies with insulin on the inducing effects of T_3 and glucocorticoids. You showed that insulin had no effect on the inducing effect of T_3, but caused a pronounced inhibition of the glucocorticoid effect. What was the concentration of the insulin used, since this could have important clinical implications? Did you perform a dose-response relationship?

J. Baxter: The insulin concentrations used in these experiments are quite high, and we have not done dose-response curves. As you are aware, insulin at high concentrations can have actions mediated through the receptors for other classes of hormones, such as the somatomedins. Therefore, we do not know whether the effects of insulin we observed are due to actions of this hormone through insulin receptors or through other types of receptors.

C. Monder: You described interactions between corticosteroids and triiodothyronine which led to the induction of growth hormone. Evidently, the two hormones interact in a synergistic manner. You interpreted this to mean that the T_3 amplifies the effect of glucocorticoids in the production of growth hormone. You suggested that there is a sequence of events that occur, initiated by T_3 and subsequently acted upon by glucocorticoids. Glucocorticoids and other hormones also interact synergistically in other systems—for example, in the induction of liver tyrosine aminotransferase. This enzyme is increased much more in the presence of cortisol and glucagon or cyclic AMP together with either one individually. This has been interpreted to indicate that the glucocorticoids cause an increase in mRNA, which is then translated by the other hormones. The sequence of interactions in your system is inconsistent with this interpretation. How do you interpret the interactions that you see?

J. Baxter: First, I think that you did interpret my statement correctly. Thyroid hormone does appear to amplify glucocorticoid hormone action, but from our data it also appears that glucocorticoids amplify thyroid hormone action. Our data do not distinguish whether there are sequential or simultaneous reactions that are participating in the synergism. The data do imply in this case that both hormones regulate at the mRNA level. The example you give concerning the synergistic glucocorticoid and cAMP effects on tyrosine aminotransferase (TAT) is noteworthy. It was once thought that the synergism was due to the fact that glucocorticoids induce TAT mRNA and that cAMP then stimulated its translation. However, recent studies by Fiegelson and co-workers and by Granner and co-workers suggest that both classes of ligands act to regulate the mRNA.

J. Kowal: Were your experiments concerning the hormone effects in tissue culture done in serum-free medium? If not, how did you remove endogenous hormones?

J. Baxter: The experiments with insulin were performed in a serum-free medium that contains a serum substitute. The medium contains vitamins, protamine, cellulose, amino acids, and other chemicals (see Bauer *et al.*, 1976) but it is protein-free.

J. Kowal: In your two-dimensional chromatograms, by eyeballing it several of us noticed spots that are notably lighter with hormone treatment. Are they being studied?

J. Baxter: Was that the second two-dimensional gel (Fig. 17) or the first (Fig. 12)?

J. Kowal: The first.

J. Baxter: In the portion of the gel shown (Fig. 12), the only spots that are consistently affected are circled. There are other occasional changes, but these are not reproducible. When the entire gels are examined there are a small number of other reproducible changes and, as said, these reflect less than 1% of the detectable proteins.

B. Robaire: Could you give a bit more detail on the temperatures and pH changes needed for the conversion of "holo" to "core" receptor. Is this a reversible process? Can you convert one form of the receptor to the other (back and forth) going up and down the temperatures?

J. Baxter: In answer to the first question regarding the conditions for stimulating the conversion of holoreceptors to core receptors, the experiments shown reflect the effect of heating at 50°C. The conversion will occur in a few minutes at 50°C; at 37°C it will occur much more slowly. Conversion also occurs with dilution, even at 0°C, and it is easier to achieve with this manipulation in the more purified preparations. Conversion can occur on storage at 0°C in some of the purified preparations, but this is minimal at 0°C in the crude nuclear extracts. It appears that the more acidic pH (e.g., ca. 6.0) promotes the conversion. Concerning the reversion of core receptors to holoreceptors it appears, in preliminary experiments, that this can be achieved by raising back the pH after initially lowering it. With the temperature conversion to core receptors there is no evidence for spontaneous reconversion to holoreceptors.

In the preparations of core receptor generated from the gel-filtered fraction, there can be complete reconversion to core receptors if the fractions are concentrated, as, for example, by dialysis. In fact, after initial Sephadex chromatography, the extent of generation of core receptors depends on the extent of dilution of the sample.

J. E. Rall: I presume you really mean a sort of analogy with prealbumin rather than implying anything closer, because prealbumin as you well know, is extraordinarily resistant to denaturation. It is a very sturdy protein compared to your rather delicate flower.

J. Baxter: Our "core" receptors appear to be relatively stable proteins. It is the holoreceptor that is delicate unless the environment is precisely manipulated.

S. Cohen: I have one objection and one question. The objection I want to make is to the use of the term steroid. Steroid means different things to different people. To an estrologist it means one, to an andrologist it means another, and to an internist it means still another. I think we should be a little bit more specific, rather than use the general term steroid. The question concerns your comment that dexamethasone (which is not really a hormone, but a synthetic product with a hormonelike action), potentiates the formation of receptor and growth hormone. Now, since the glucocorticoids tend to inhibit the action of estrogens, do estrogens inhibit the action of glucocorticoids?

J. Baxter: We have not looked at the effects of estrogens in this system. Incidentally, estrogens can, at high dosage, act as antiglucocorticoids in some systems by interactions with the glucocorticoid receptor. Regarding the term "steroid," I feel that it should be used to designate substances that are classified as steroids. This is a precise usage and it should be learned by anyone who must deal with steroids.

T. Landefeld: With regard to the first set of two-dimensional gels, were the changes in proteins based only on qualitative examination or did you also quantify these? If so, what percentage of total proteins synthesized did prolactin or growth hormone represent in response to the T_3 treatment?

J. Baxter: Growth hormone production in the presence and in the absence of hormones has been quantified, but not by the two-dimensional gel approach. The latter allows an estimation of relative differences in the rate of synthesis of various proteins. Since the specific activities of most of the proteins detectable by the gel are not known, it is difficult to obtain absolute estimates from the gels. We have quantified prolactin and growth hormone production with standard radioimmunoassay approaches. Growth hormone levels can drop to undetectable, and with the GC cells that produce it at the highest rate, synthesis of the hormone can get up to perhaps 2% of the total cellular protein synthesis. We have not made precise measurements in the case of prolactin.

T. Landefeld: Also, I am curious as to what percentage of the total protein being synthesized you are able to pick up from the gels. This becomes very important when identifying changes in individual proteins in response to the hormone treatment—not so much with major proteins, such as growth hormone, but more so with proteins that are present in much lesser amounts. These and prolactin may, in fact, be changing in response to the hormone, but owing to the sensitivity, you are unable to identify them.

J. Baxter: It appears in the case of those proteins that have been measured by independent assays, such as growth hormone and prolactin in these cells and tyrosine aminotransferase in cultured hepatoma cells, that differences of 1.5-fold can readily be detected.

T. Landefeld: You do, of course, have the possibility of both the radioautography and the stable protein stains, so that you have a little better.

J. Baxter: Yes, any of these major proteins could in the end be quantified.

M. Siperstein: Your insulin-inhibiting effect on growth hormone induction in the defined media suggests that the inhibition of serum by this effect might be due to insulin or an insulinlike factor. The obvious question is whether you have used serum from a pancreatectomized animal?

J. Baxter: No, we have not.

Circular Dichroism of Pituitary Hormones

Thomas A. Bewley

Hormone Research Laboratory, University of California, San Francisco, California

I. Introduction

It is intended herein to acquaint the reader with the basic principles of the physicochemical technique known as circular dichroism (CD),[1] and to illustrate with specific examples how this measurement may be used to gain further insight into questions that would be of interest to the experimental endocrinologist. Although a fair number of investigators have made highly significant contributions to endocrinology, in part through the use of CD measurements, it remains a relatively specialized technique and is therefore, understandably, not readily familiar to most workers in this field.

Discussion of the principles of the technique will necessarily be brief and somewhat oversimplified. Indeed, a thorough quantum mechanical examination of the origins of optical activity and the design of instruments to measure this property by either ORD or CD would not be relevant. The reader whose interest is sufficiently piqued by this chapter will find references within the text that examine these points more completely. In addition, this chapter deals only with selected examples from the field of polypeptide and protein hormones. An introduction to the vast and highly rewarding application of ORD and CD to the study of steroid hormones may be found elsewhere (Djerassi, 1960; Crabbé, 1972).

PRINCIPLES OF CIRCULAR DICHROISM

Circular dichroism is one of several specialized types of spectrophotometry. In contrast to the more familiar type of spectrophotometry in which one measures the amount of ordinary, unpolarized light absorbed by a specific amount of

---

[1]Abbreviations used: CD, circular dichroism; ORD, optical rotatory dispersion; hGH, human pituitary growth hormone; HCS, human chorionic somatomammotropin; bGH, bovine pituitary growth hormone; oGH, ovine pituitary growth hormone; oPr, ovine pituitary prolactin; cPr, camel pituitary prolactin; pPr, porcine pituitary prolactin; PL-hGH, plasmin-modified hGH; oLH (ICSH), ovine pituitary lutropin; FSH, pituitary follitropin; TSH, pituitary thyrotropin; DTT, dithiothreitol; T.D.M., transition dipole moment; UV, ultraviolet.

sample, CD measures the amounts of *circular polarized* light absorbed by a test substance. In ordinary spectrophotometry *all* absorbing chromophores produce absorption bands with characteristic wavelength maxima and molar extinction coefficients. However, because of the polarized nature of the light used in CD measurements, only those chromophores that are optically active (i.e., exhibit optical rotation, the ability to rotate the plane of polarized light) produce CD bands. These bands also occur at characteristic wavelengths and with characteristic intensities (rotational strengths) that are formally analogous to extinction coefficients. It is this fundamental selectivity for optically active transitions that distinguishes CD from ordinary absorption spectrophotometry and also provides the fundamental link between CD spectra and optical rotation in the form of ORD spectra. In fact, CD and ORD spectra are, in principle, totally equivalent. The Kronig–Kramers transforms (Kronig, 1926; Kramers, 1927) provide algorithms with which modern computers can generate CD data from ORD data and vice versa. However, with the advent of extremely sensitive commercial dichrographs, the somewhat older technique of ORD is receding into the background. This stems largely from the intrinsically greater experimental potential for CD to resolve and identify closely spaced optically active absorption bands.

Figure 1 presents a schematic optical path for a typical circular dichrograph. At far left, the light source (usually a high-pressure xenon arc) produces an intense continuum of radiation from about 900 nm down to approximately 170 nm. This unpolarized radiation is first collimated and then dispersed by a grating or prism monochromator into essentially monochromatic light. The monochromatic light is then linearly polarized by passage through a Rochon prism. At this point the instrument is identical to a spectropolarimeter, and by measuring the sample's ability to rotate the plane of polarization of the beam, as a function of the beam's wavelength, we could generate an ORD spectrum. However, the measurement of CD requires the presence of an additional element to further modify the light beam before it reaches the sample. This device is the electrooptic modulator (E.O.M.). As shown schematically in Fig. 1, this component resolves the linearly polarized beam into two equally intense, circularly polarized beams—one whose electric vector is rotating clockwise (as seen when looking into the oncoming beam), called the *right circularly polarized* beam, and the other whose electric vector is rotating anticlockwise, or the *left circularly polarized* beam. The E.O.M.[2] produces alternating bursts of these two types of light, usually several hundred to several thousand times a second, which then pass through the sample cell and to a photomultiplier (P.M.), which measures their individual intensities as a function of wavelength. In effect (though not actually), the instrument produces two complete absorption spectra, one in right

---

[2]The design and operation of the E.O.M. in the form of a Pockels cell may be found in Beychok (1967), or, in the form of a piezooptical (photoelastic) modulator, in Kemp (1969).

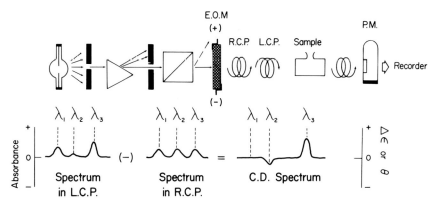

FIG. 1. Schematic optical path of a typical circular dichrograph (top line). E.O.M. electrooptic modulator; R.C.P., right circularly polarized beam; L.C.P., left circularly polarized beam; P.M., photomultiplier. The lower line presents a schematic representation of the generation of a circular dichroism spectrum by subtraction of the spectrum in R.C.P. from the spectrum in L.C.P. The differences in the two polarized spectra are greatly exaggerated.

and one in left circularly polarized light. These two spectra are also represented schematically in Fig. 1.

As shown in Fig. 1, the test substance contains three isolated absorption bands centered at λ_1, λ_2, and λ_3. These absorption bands might arise from electronic transitions in three separate chromophores. In the next phase of the instrument's operation, the spectrum taken with right circularly polarized light is electronically subtracted from the spectrum taken in left circularly polarized light. The resulting "difference spectrum" is then displayed graphically. Thus, a CD spectrum may be defined as the difference spectrum generated by subtracting the absorption spectrum taken with right circularly polarized light from the absorption spectrum taken with left circularly polarized light. The choice of subtracting right from left is arbitrary but is conventionally used so that CD and ORD data will be consistent. The point is that for optically *inactive* transitions, the molar extinction coefficients for right and left circularly polarized light are always equal, and therefore subtraction always leads to a complete cancellation of these bands in the resultant CD spectrum. This is exemplified by the transition at λ_1 in Fig. 1, which does not appear at all in the CD spectrum. However, for optically active transitions, the extinction coefficients for right and left circularly polarized light will not be equal (differing typically by only one part per 10^3 to 10^5), and subtraction will always leave a net remainder, which is the CD band for that transition. Thus, unlike ordinary spectrophotometry, which produces only positive absorption bands, CD bands may be either positive or negative, although in general, they will appear at the same wavelength maxima as the ordinary absorption bands. For example, between 250 and 280 nm, the ordinary aromatic absorption spectra of L- and D-tyrosine are indistinguishable. In contrast, the aromatic CD spectrum of L-tyrosine is generally positive[3] while that of D-tyrosine in the same solvent will be a negative mirror image (see Fig. 3). In this way CD spectra can be seen to give more information about the geometry of the chromophore than do ordinary spectra. In Fig. 1 the optically active transition of λ_3 produces a positive CD band while the optically active transition at λ_2 produces a negative CD band. It is worth noting that the ordinary absorption spectrum of the hypothetical sample in Fig. 1 would be the *average* of the two spectra in right and left circularly polarized light and therefore would display three positive bands.

In general, CD spectra are published in either of two types of units. The choice is usually dictated by the type of instrument used. Some machines are designed to display directly the difference in extinction coefficient ($\Delta E = E_L - E_R$) where E_L and E_R are the extinction coefficients for the two circularly polarized beams. Other instruments plot the spectra in terms of *ellipticity* [θ]. This results from the fact that optically active transitions convert the two circularly polarized beams into one *elliptically* polarized beam, the ellipticity of which is directly proportional to the molar extinction coefficient difference for the two circularly polarized beams. Both types of spectra are identical in appearance, differing only in their units. A simple, linear relationship ([θ] = 3300 ΔE), in which [θ] is in ellipticity units (deg cm^2, decimole^{-1}), can be used to interconvert the two types of units.

It may be seen that CD, ORD, and ordinary absorption are intimately related phenomena, all arising from the absorption of electromagnetic radiation by matter. Polypeptide and protein hormones contain a number of chromophoric groups capable of absorbing light in the measurable region of the spectrum. Specifically, these include the aromatic rings of the phenylalanine, tyrosine, and tryptophan side chains, the disulfide bonds, and the carbonyl groups of the amide bonds. All these groups give ordinary absorption bands, which are fairly familiar (with the possible exception of disulfide bonds) to most protein enthusiasts. As stated above, only those absorption bands that are optically active will also give CD bands. It remains then to describe the origins of optical activity for these chromophoric groups.

In elementary organic chemistry courses, optical activity (also referred to as chirality) is associated most often with the asymmetric carbon, i.e., a carbon atom covalently linked to four *different* substituents. This geometry produces an asymmetric electrostatic field around the carbon atom, and it is this asymmetric field's interaction with the asymmetric electric and magnetic fields of the right and left circularly polarized beams that ultimately produces the well known

---

[3]The sign of the aromatic CD band cannot be inferred from the chirality of the α-carbon alone. These bands are highly solvent and conformation dependent, as well as being dependent on the *configuration* of the α-carbon.

optical activity of these atoms. Thus, asymmetry and optical activity are related. Since all natural proteins are polymerized from optically active amino acids (with the exception of glycine which is incapable of optical activity), it is easy to see that the asymmetric α-carbons are the basic source of most of the optical activity of these molecules. Other forms of geometric asymmetry can also be imposed onto the peptide chain giving rise to additional sources of optical activity.

1. Amide Bond

The carbonyl group of the amide bond undergoes two major electronic transitions; the $n \rightarrow \pi^*$ and $\pi \rightarrow \pi^*$. Because of the close juxtaposition of this chromophoric group to the asymmetric α-carbons, electronic coupling produces an asymmetry in these normally symmetrical transitions rendering them optically active. Thus, even randomly coiled polypeptides will show CD bands associated with the $n \rightarrow \pi^*$ and $\pi \rightarrow \pi^*$ carbonyl transitions between 190 and 210 nm. If, in addition, the polypeptide chain is also *coiled* into a helical structure, the additional asymmetry of the helix[4] will further enhance the optical activity of the carbonyl groups. In the commonly observed α-helix the carbonyls also act as a group, producing what is termed an *exciton* band, whose optical activity is quite intense and characteristic. Thus, the right-hand α-helix can be identified by the presence of two intense negative CD bands near 221 nm ($n \rightarrow \pi^*$) and 209 nm ($\pi \rightarrow \pi^*$). A third, very intense, positive CD band ($\pi \rightarrow \pi^*$) can also be seen near 190 nm. Figure 2 presents the CD spectra of a randomly coiled polypeptide as well as spectra of completely α-helical and completely β-structured polypeptides. It is evident from the figure that these three conformational forms display readily identifiable CD patterns. Since the far-UV CD spectrum[5] of a globular protein is, to a reasonably good first approximation, the weighted sum of the spectra for these three conformational types, one is able, in principle, to resolve the overall spectrum into these three components and determine the contribution, and therefore the contents of each (Greenfield and Fasman, 1969; Chen *et al.*, 1974). It is for this reason that the far-UV CD spectrum, which is dominated by the amide bond absorption, is generally conceded to reflect the *secondary structure* of the polypeptide or protein.

2. Aromatic Chromophores

The side chain of phenylalanine, tyrosine, and tryptophan residues all produce absorption bands in the near-UV, between 250 and 300 nm. Again, because of close spatial connection to the asymmetric α-carbons, these normally symmetrical $\pi \rightarrow \pi^*$ transitions pick up varying degrees of asymmetry, and therefore optical activity. Figure 3 shows the CD spectra of *N*-acetyl-L-tyrosine ethyl ester

---

[4] All helical structures are intrinsically asymmetric, being either right- or left-handed screws.
[5] In the following "far-UV" will refer to wavelengths below 250 nm; "near-UV" will refer to wavelengths above 250 nm.

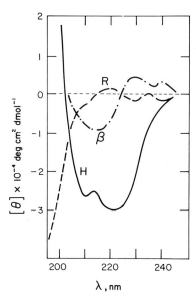

FIG. 2.   Circular dichroism of the α-helix (H), β, and random coil (R) forms. Modified from Chen *et al.* (1974).

and *N*-acetyl-D-tyrosine ethyl ester. It is evident that the aromatic transitions of the two isomers produce mirror-image CD spectra that reflect the mirror-image configurations of their respective α-carbons. The racemic, DL, mixture produces a signal indistinguishable from the base line because of cancellation of the positive and negative bands. In free amino acids or simple derivatives the aromatic rings of these side chains enjoy nearly free rotation about the α–β carbon bonds. As shown in Fig. 4 for phenylalanine, the electronic transition dipole moment[6] of the $\pi \rightarrow \pi^*$ transition rotates with the ring, sweeping out a symmetrical cone in space. Despite this symmetry, weak electronic coupling between the α-carbons and the T.D.M. field produces a very small $\pi \rightarrow \pi^*$ CD signal. If, however, the aromatic rings are sterically hindered from rotation by the close approach of other groups (such as in the case of aromatic amino acids buried within the hydrophobic interior of globular proteins), a much greater degree of asymmetry will be "seen" by the nonrotating aromatic T.D.M., and the resultant CD of the $\pi \rightarrow \pi^*$ transition will become quite intense. Thus, one can follow the denaturation of a protein by the fading or complete loss of its aromatic transitions as the side chains become free to rotate with the breaking up of the local conformation. Similarly, the refolding of a protein can be followed by noting the appearance of intense CD bands in the aromatic region of the spectrum.

[6]The transition dipole moment is a vector quantity that describes the intensity and direction of the electric field generated by the electron during its excitation.

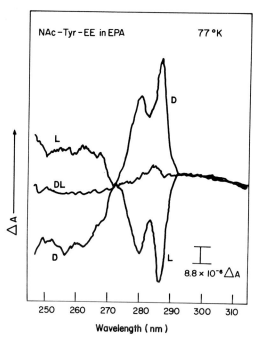

FIG. 3.   Circular dichroism spectra of 32 mM N-acetyl-L-tyrosine ethyl ester and 32 mM N-acetyl-D-tyrosine ethyl ester in ethyl ether–isopentane–ethanol (5:5:2, v:v:v) at 77°K. The base line (DL) is 32 mM N-acetyl-DL-tyrosine ethyl ester. Scale is in Δ-absorbance units. Modified from Horwitz *et al.* (1970).

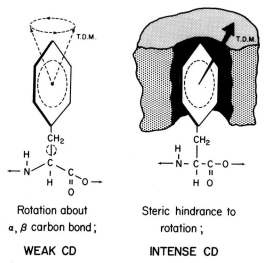

FIG. 4.   Schematic representation of a phenylalanine residue freely exposed to the external solvent (left) and buried within the interior of a protein (right).

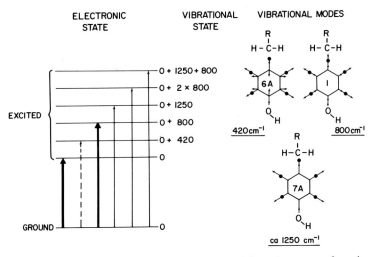

FIG. 5. Transitions resolved in the circular dichroism and absorption spectra of tyrosine derivatives. The (0–0) and (0 + 800 cm^{-1}) transitions are very intense. The (0 + 420 cm^{-1}) transition is very weak. The (0 + 1250) and (0 + 1250 + 800 cm^{-1}) bands may include several transitions in addition to the one shown. Modified from Horwitz et al. (1970).

Another property of aromatic transitions should be mentioned which is also very useful. In these transitions one can easily resolve the spectrum to include the vibrational modes of the excited electronic state. Depending on how the various atoms of the aromatic rings are vibrating at the instant of absorption, the quantum energy, and therefore the wavelength maximum for that molecule, will vary. The drawings on the right side of Fig. 5 show three of the most common "vibrational modes" of tyrosine near room temperature. These vibrational modes have sufficiently different energies in the excited state that they can be resolved into separate peaks with modern instrumentation. The transition from the ground state to the first excited state without vibrational energy is termed the (0–0) transition.[7] In aqueous solvents at room temperature, only a portion of the population of tyrosine molecules will be in this state at any instant. The absorption band for this (0–0) transition will occur near 283 nm. This transition is shown as the heavy arrow at far left in Fig. 5. Under the same conditions, a much larger portion of the remaining tyrosines will be in vibrational mode 1. This mode is more energetic and absorbs a more energetic photon, i.e., one of lower (bluer) wavelength. The energy difference is equivalent to 800 cm^{-1}, which in this region of the spectrum is equal to about 6 nm. Therefore, the absorption peak of these molecules will be at 283 (−) 6 = 277 nm. Because the majority of the molecules are in this mode at any instant, the (0 + 800 cm^{-1}) transition will be more intense (higher peak height) than the (0–0) transition. This is symbolized in

[7]The vibrational modes in the ground state are too close energetically to be resolved, and so the ground state is generally considered to be in a "0" vibrational mode.

Fig. 5 as the very heavy arrow, third from the left. Under the stated conditions, the third most heavily populated state will be the $(0 + 2 \times 800 \text{ cm}^{-1})$ mode, which is a harmonic overtone of the $(0 + 800 \text{ cm}^{-1})$ mode. This peak will appear at $[283 - (2 \times 6)] = 271$ nm. Because only about 10% or less of the tyrosines are in this state, this transition will usually appear only as a shoulder, 6 nm to the blue of the major peak and 12 nm to the blue of the first peak. The rest of the tyrosines are distributed into a multitude of additional vibrational modes and overtones. None of these are sufficiently populated to produce observable peaks, but serve to broaden the observable bands.

The asymmetry of the basic transition, described above, also holds for the vibrational modes; so each will also give a distinct CD band. In Fig. 3 the (0–0) transition is seen as a positive peak at 286 nm and the $(0 + 800 \text{ cm}^{-1})$ transition appears faithfully 6 nm to the blue at 280 nm. Figure 3 serves to demonstrate two additional phenomena. This spectrum was taken at 77°K rather than at room temperature. At this temperature the distribution of molecules into the various vibrational modes is quite different than at room temperature, most of them being devoid of vibrational energy under these cold conditions. Therefore, the (0–0) transition is the most intense; the $(0 + 2 \times 800 \text{ cm}^{-1})$ transition is not even visible as a shoulder. In addition, this spectrum was taken not in an aqueous solvent, but in a very nonpolar solvent composed of ethyl ether–isopentane–ethanol (5:5:2, v:v:v). The energy of the (0–0) transition of tyrosine is highly solvent dependent, appearing at lower wavelengths in aqueous media and at higher wavelengths in nonpolar media. Notice that although the position of the maximum of the (0–0) transition varies with solvent polarity (Table I), the *spacing* of the predominant vibronic modes (i.e., 800 cm^{-1}) remains constant (Fig. 3). Thus, the vibronic peaks will always appear at 6 or 2×6 nm toward the blue of the (0–0) transition, regardless of the position of the (0–0) transition maximum. Since the energy increments for phenylalanine and tryptophan vibra-

TABLE I

Effect of Solvent on the Position of the (0–0) Transition of Tyrosine Derivatives at 77°K[a]

Compound[b]	Solvent[c]	(0–0) Position (nm)
NAc-Y-Tyr EE	THF-D	287.8
NAc-L-TYR EE	EPA	287.2
L-Tyr EE	EPA	286.6
NAc-L-Tyr A	M-G	286.5
L-Tyr	W-G	282.6

[a] Modified from Horwitz *et al.* (1970).

[b] NAc-L-Tyr EE, *N*-acetyl-L-tyrosine ethyl ester; L-Tyr EE, L-tyrosine ethyl ester; NAc-L-Tyr A, *N*-acetyl-L-tyrosine amide; L-Tyr, L-tyrosine.

[c] THF-D, tetrahydrofuran–diglyme, 5:1, v:v; EPA, ethyl ether–isopentane–ethanol, 5:5:2, v:v:v; M-G, methanol–glycerol, 9:1, v:v; W–G, water–glycerol, 1:1, v:v.

tional modes are somewhat different than for tyrosine, the ≈6 nm spacing can sometimes be used to identify the bands originating from tyrosyl residues, while the positions of the maxima on the wavelenth axis can be used to estimate the relative polarity or nonpolarity of the immediate environments of these side chains. A thorough review of the CD of aromatic side chains may be found in Beychok (1966, 1967) and Strickland (1974).

It is for the reasons outlined above and others similar to them that the near-UV CD is generally assumed to provide information about the *tertiary* structure of the protein, and in some cases the *quaternary* structure. Examples of such interpretations will be given below.

3. Disulfide Bonds

Most globular proteins contain internal covalent cross-links in the form of disulfide bonds (cystine residues). There is relatively free rotation about the disulfide bond in simple compounds, such as dimethyl disulfide. However, more highly substituted versions, including the free amino acid cystine, experience a considerable steric hindrance to rotation, amounting to as much as 3–10 kcal/mol (Winnewisser *et al.*, 1968). Because of this high barrier to internal rotation, most disulfides, including those found in polypeptides and proteins, exist in only one of two possible rotational isomeric forms. These two geometries are shown in Fig. 6. The two bonds joining R_1 and R_2 to the sulfur atoms, along with the disulfide bond itself, define two planes whose relative orientation can be described conveniently by the dihedral angle (ϕ) between them. In most disulfides this angle is close to ±90°. In the case of proteins, R_1 and R_2 will not be equivalent, and the two rotamer forms will be intrinsically asymmetric. This asymmetry is preserved by the nonrotating nature of the S—S bond. Accordingly, the electronic transitions of the disulfide bonds, which produce weak absorption bands between 250 and 300 nm, are also capable of optical activity.

From studies carried out on small disulfide-containing compounds (Carmac and Neubert, 1967; Dodson and Nelson, 1968; Coleman and Blout, 1968; Ito and Takagi, 1970; Casey and Martin, 1972; Ludescher and Schwyzer, 1971; Nagara-

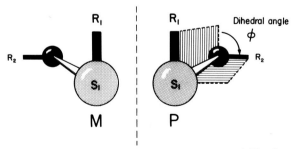

FIG. 6.   The two possible rotational conformers of the disulfide bond. They have been tentatively named the M (minus) and P (plus) forms according to the helicity rule of Cahn *et al.* (1966).

jan and Woody, 1973), it is now known that the disulfide produces very broad, weak CD bands, devoid of vibrational structure. The maxima of these bands appear anywhere between 250 and 300 nm, depending on the value of the dihedral angle. It is also known that in many cases the sign of the disulfide CD band can be used to determine the chirality or rotamer form of the bond in question.

At present, little is known about the contributions of disulfide bonds to the total optical activity of the larger globular proteins. The relatively low content of these chromophores and their characteristically weak CD bands, devoid of vibrational fine structure, make their recognition and direct measurement in such materials very difficult. In many instances it has been assumed that their contribution is negligible, although in others where the disulfide content is unusually high and/or the aromatic chromophore content is low, this is known not to be the case (Horwitz et al., 1970; Breslow, 1970; Bewley et al., 1972a, 1974; Puett, 1972; Menendez-Botet and Breslow, 1975; Holladay and Puett, 1975).

Having completed this brief description of CD, this is perhaps a good point to interject the following, quite legitimate, question: Why pursue these CD studies? An X-ray crystallographic study would provide an enormously more detailed picture of the structures of the hormones. As stated, the point is completely valid. However, there are several other points to be considered. First, with the notable exceptions of insulin (Blundell et al., 1971a,b) and glucagon (Sasaki et al., 1975) very few polypeptide or protein hormones, and none of the pituitary hormones, have provided crystals of X-ray quality. This is probably a technical difficulty, and such crystals will possibly be available in the near future. There is a second more important point, however, which is perhaps not just a technical problem. Although a crystallographic picture of these hormones would undoubtedly provide an enormous amount of important information, it might prove very difficult or impossible to confidently extrapolate this basically "static" information to include the more *dynamic* properties, such as the interactions between hormones and antibodies, or hormones and receptors, which we wish most to understand and ultimately control. Investigation of the dynamic properties of these interactions will almost certainly involve studies under solution conditions. It is in these types of studies where techniques such as CD will reach their full potential. The true understanding of hormone action will, of course, come from a condensation of information from all types of studies including crystallographic, conformations in solution, and the various biological studies. Thus X-ray and CD studies are adjunct to one another rather than competitive or redundant in helping to understand biological systems.

II. Static Studies

The most recent flurry of generalized interest in CD studies followed the reports of Holzwarth (1964) and Holzwarth and Doty (1965) that the α-helix could be readily recognized and quantitatively estimated in polypeptides and proteins by this method. Eventually, it was recognized that certain aspects of the tertiary structures of proteins could also be investigated through CD measurements of the much weaker side-chain transitions appearing in the near-UV region (Beychok, 1966, 1967; Strickland, 1974). All these studies were basically static in nature, in that they nearly always involved measurements under defined conditions in which the proteins were not undergoing any time-dependent changes in structure. The results were generally interpreted in terms of the so-called *native* structure of the protein, or occasionally, in terms of a partially or totally denatured, but nevertheless static, molecular form.

In accordance, the earliest studies of protein hormones utilizing CD were also static in nature. In the following description, these results have been arranged on the basis of increasing molecular organization rather than on a chronological scale. It is not intended that this be an exhaustive review of the literature, but rather, examples of CD studies that might serve to acquaint the general reader with the potentials for this type of investigation.

A. SECONDARY STRUCTURE

The folding of a polypeptide chain into an orderly, repetitive, and intrinsically stable geometry, in which the amide bond elements of each amino acid residue are in definable positions with relation to the residues that immediately precede and follow it within the sequence, is termed the *secondary structure* of the molecule. The most common types of secondary structure are the α-helix and the various extended β-forms (for a review of these structures see, e.g., Dickerson and Geis, 1969), and the β-turn (Venkatachalam, 1968). If none of these conformations can be demonstrated, the protein is said to be a *random coil*, devoid of secondary structure.

1. β-Lipotropin and β-Endorphin

It is usually conceded that most polypeptides of fewer than 100 residues that are not internally cross-linked by disulfide bonds will not contain appreciable amounts of secondary structure (particularly α-helix) in aqueous solvents. At high concentrations some polypeptides may occasionally show evidence of intermolecular association and the formation of concentration dependent, interchain β-sheet. However, for molecules that carry out their biological function at the very low concentrations typical of hormones, it is questionable whether such induced secondary structures are of physiological relevance.

Recent reports from several laboratories on the effect of nonpolar solvents on the secondary structure of β-lipotropin (St. Pierre *et al.*, 1976; Makarov *et al.*, 1976; Yang *et al.*, 1977) and β-endorphin (Gráf *et al.*, 1977; Bayley *et al.*, 1977; Yang *et al.*, 1977) suggest, however, that some induced secondary structures may be of considerable physiological importance. Figure 7 demonstrates how the

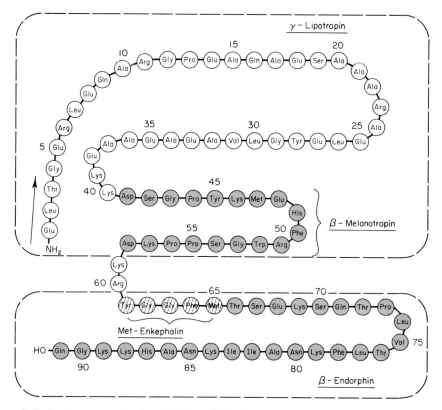

FIG. 7. Structures of bovine β-MSH, γ-LPH, Met-enkephalin, and β-endorphin, contained within the amino acid sequence of ovine β-LPH. Taken from Li (1978a).

31-residue endogenous opiatelike peptide, known as β-endorphin (Li and Chung, 1976), is contained as the carboxyl-terminal portion of the 91-residue pituitary hormone, β-lipotropin (Li *et al.*, 1965, 1966b; Gráf and Li, 1973). Figure 8 shows the far-UV CD spectra of ovine β-lipotropin and camel β-endorphin (Yang *et al.*, 1977). In water at pH 5.9, the absence of two negative maxima near 222 and 210 nm, characteristic of the α-helix, and the appearance of a large negative band near 200 nm suggest that the structure of both molecules is nonperiodic, although very small amounts (<5%) of helix and/or β-form cannot be completely ruled out. The two polypeptides appear to be completely denatured in 6 *M* guanidine hydrochloride. In contrast, it is apparent that both molecules, in either methanol or sodium dodecyl sulfate (NaDodSO₄) solutions, pick up an appreciable amount of α-helical structure, amounting to approximately 50% of the polypeptide backbone. Other nonpolar additives or solvents, such as dioxane (St. Pierre *et al.*, 1976), trifluoroethanol (Gráf *et al.*, 1977), and ethanol (Makarov *et al.*, 1976), have also been reported to produce the same effect.

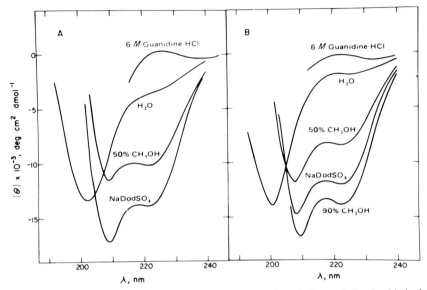

FIG. 8.   Circular dichroism spectra of (A) ovine β-lipotropin and (B) camel β-endorphin in the far-UV region. NaDodSO$_4$, sodium dodecyl sulfate. Taken from Yang *et al.* (1977).

Removal of the excess NaDodSO$_4$ does not reverse the effect, suggesting that the new helical conformation is stabilized by the formation of a very tight complex between the NaDodSO$_4$ and the polypeptide. The stoichiometry of this complex is presently unknown. It is tempting to speculate that it is the nonpolar hydrocarbon chain of the NaDodSO$_4$ that is largely responsible for the increase in helical content while the complex between the NaDodSO$_4$ and the peptide chain is strongly stabilized by salt bridges formed from the sulfate group and the net positive charge on these basic polypeptides.

Additional investigation might prove these preliminary observations to be of considerable interest to the endocrinologist. This stems from the demonstration that cerebroside sulfate may be an obligatory and active component of the opiate receptor in brain tissue (Loh *et al.*, 1975, 1977). The close chemical similarity between NaDodSO$_4$ and cerebroside sulfate is shown in Fig. 9. Since it has also been demonstrated that β-endorphin probably produces its action through the same opiate receptor (Loh *et al.*, 1976; Cox *et al.*, 1976), it is extremely tempting to further speculate that it may be the cerebroside sulfate component of the opiate receptor that first binds a random-coil form of the circulating β-endorphin and then proceeds to *induce* it into a more rigid conformation by the formation of the α-helix. Perhaps it is only the helical form that is then topochemically competent to trigger the opiate action. This suggests the general hypothesis that the small polypeptide hormones, which appear to lack organized topochemical structures in free solution, might be *induced* into active con-

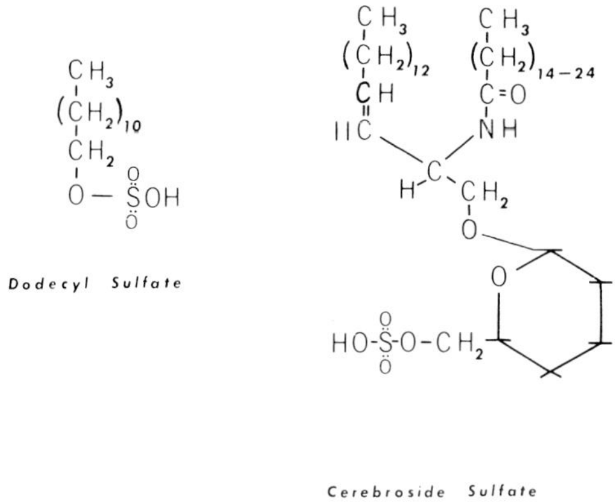

FIG. 9.   Chemical structures of dodecyl and cerebroside sulfates.

formations as a result of binding to a receptor complex. The "conforming" of the hormone molecule might well be the subsequent step in such hormone–receptor interactions, following the initial binding.

Thus, although the study described above is exclusively static in nature, if the speculations turn out to have any basis in fact, they might ultimately prove to be of value in understanding one of the more important dynamic aspects of the hormone.

2. Lutropin

Lutropin, a glycoprotein hormone isolated from the pituitary gland, and also known as luteinizing hormone (LH) or interstitial cell-stimulating hormone (ICSH), provides another example of how static CD studies have suggested interesting possibilities with regard to the more dynamic properties of the molecule.

The three pituitary glycoprotein hormones, lutropin, follitropin, and thyrotropin, as well as the placental glycoprotein, human chorionic gonadotropin, are all composed of two, nonidentical subunits designated α and β (Papkoff and Samy, 1967; De La Llosa and Jutisz, 1969; Lamkin et al., 1970; Liao and Pierce, 1970; Swaminathan and Bahl, 1970; Morgan and Canfield, 1971). The α-subunits of these hormones appear to be either identical or nearly so in primary structure (Liu et al., 1972; Sairam et al., 1972a,b; Pierce et al., 1971b; Liao and Pierce, 1971; Sairam and Li, 1973; Bahl et al., 1972). Hormonal specificity resides in the β-subunit. Although the isolated subunits are essentially devoid of biological activity, the recombination of β-subunits with any of the four α-subunits results in a regeneration of the biological activity characteristic of the β-subunit (Papkoff and Samy, 1967; De La Llosa and Jutisz, 1969; Papkoff and Ekblad, 1970; Liao and Pierce, 1970; Pierce et al., 1971a).

The far-UV CD spectra of ovine lutropin, its isolated subunits, and the

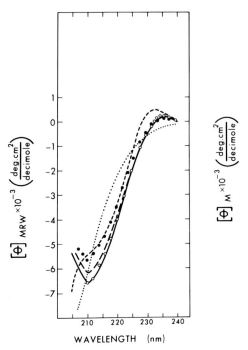

WAVELENGTH   (nm)

FIG. 10.   Amide bond circular dichroism spectra of interstitial cell-stimulating hormone (ICSH) (----) and the reassociated molecule (○) in 0.1 M phosphate buffer, pH 6.0; ICSH (-- --), the reassociated molecule (●), the α subunit (– – –), and the β subunit ($\cdots$) in 0.1 M Tris-phosphate–5% dioxane buffer (pH 7.5). Protein concentrations were between 0.5 and 1.0 mg/ml. Data are expressed as mean residue ellipticities. Taken from Bewley et al. (1972a).

recombinant molecule are shown in Fig. 10 (Bewley et al., 1972a). It is evident that the native molecule and the recombinant exhibit essentially the same spectra in either solvent[8] with a negative maximum near 210 nm. In contrast, the two isolated subunits do not exhibit this peak. There is no evidence for α-helix or extensive β-structures in any of the molecules. The spectra in Fig. 10 are essentially equivalent to spectra published by other investigators (Jirgensons and Ward, 1970; Pernollet and Garnier, 1971; Holladay and Puett, 1975). Holladay and Puett (1975) have interpreted the 210 nm peak as arising from the amide bonds existing in the N-acetylhexosamine groups. It can clearly be seen that the CD of the intact or recombinant molecules is *not* the molar sum of the CD of the two subunits. This demonstrates that a considerable conformational change occurs on either dissociation or reassociation of the molecule. This con-

[8]Owing to aggregation of the β-subunit in purely aqueous solvents, 5% (v/v) dioxane had to be added. All spectra were taken in both purely aqueous and the dioxane-containing solvents. The dioxane had no significant effect on the CD of the intact, recombinant, or α-subunit spectra.

formational change is described more fully in terms of the tertiary structure and its dynamic properties in Sections II,B,1 and III,A.

3. Growth and Lactogenic Hormones

The far-UV CD of pituitary growth and lactogenic hormones can conveniently be grouped together, since these are the only pituitary hormones yet isolated that show any appreciable amount of ordered secondary structure in aqueous solutions. Moreover, they appear to contain approximately the same amount of secondary structure in the form of the α-helix. The fact that they are all so similar is not surprising, since they are known to contain extensive regions of homology in amino acid sequence (Bewley and Li, 1970a; Niall et al., 1971; Sherwood et al., 1971; Bewley et al., 1972c). It is quite evident that these two types of hormones have evolved from a common ancestor. This fundamental relatedness is reflected in overall similarities in primary, secondary, and tertiary structures, and in some instances (most notably hGH), extends to the overlapping of biological activities (Li, 1968).

The human placental protein, variously known as human chorionic somatomammotropin (HCS), or human placental lactogen (hPL), has also been included owing to its well known structural relatedness to hGH (Li, 1972; Niall, 1972; Li et al., 1973a).

All these hormones are simple proteins containing 191–199 amino acids (Li et al., 1966a, 1970, 1973a,b; Li, 1972, 1973; Niall, 1972). The growth hormones are internally cross-linked with two disulfide bonds, one forming a small loop near the carboxyl terminus and one forming a large internal loop. The lactogenic hormones (prolactins) appear to contain two disulfides homologous to those in the growth hormones, plus a third forming a small loop near the amino terminus.

To begin with, we shall adopt the following assumption: the so-called "native" structures of these molecules may be satisfactorily approximated by solutions in 0.1 M Tris-Cl buffer (pH 8.2). The actual choice of buffer or pH is somewhat arbitrary, but we have found this to be a good compromise, allowing sufficient solubility (1–2 mg/ml), without engendering too much aggregation or ionization of titratable groups, compared to what might be presumed to be a more physiological pH of 7.4. The only real exception to this is bGH, which exists almost totally as a dimer under these conditions (Dellacha et al., 1968; Bewley and Li, 1972b).

Figure 11 shows the CD spectra at pH 8.2 of several pituitary growth hormones and prolactins in the region dominated by amide bond absorption (Bewley and Li, 1971, 1972a,b, 1975; Bewley, unpublished results). All these spectra display the two negative bands at 221 and 209 nm that are characteristic of the α-helix. Indeed, the helix contents of all seven proteins, estimated as described by Bewley et al. (1969), are quite close, ranging from 45 ± 5% for HCS to 55 ± 5% for hGH and oPr. However, as shown in Fig. 11, the spectra can be divided into two distinct groups. In (A), the $n \rightarrow \pi^*$ helix band at 221 nm is always

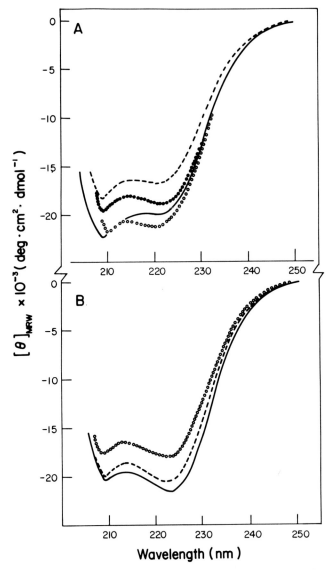

FIG. 11.   Circular dichroism spectra in the region dominated by amide bond absorption of: (A) hGH (----), HCS (---), pGH (○ ○ ○), bGH (●●●), and (B) oPr (——), pPr (---), and cPr (○ ○ ○). All spectra were taken in 0.1 *M* Tris–Cl buffer (pH 8.2).

somewhat less intense than the $\pi \rightarrow \pi^*$ band at 209 nm. This is reversed in (B), where the $n \rightarrow \pi^*$ band is somewhat more intense than the $\pi \rightarrow \pi^*$. Moreover, in (B) the $n \rightarrow \pi^*$ band is always slightly red-shifted to 223 nm compared to 221 nm in (A). No shift occurs in the band at 209 nm. This has suggested (Bewley and Li, 1972a) that the spectra in (B) contain additional sources of intense, negative optical activity not found in (A), but which are not resolved owing to the very intense bands of the α-helix. These might include a more intense negative β-structure band centered between 215 and 220 nm, or more intense far-UV bands from the aromatic chromophores. At present the source is unknown. Surprisingly, all members of group (A) are growth hormones (or related in sequence to growth hormones) whereas all the examples in (B) are prolactins. Indeed, the far-UV spectrum alone is sufficient to decide whether an unknown sample is related to growth hormone or prolactin, at least within these species. It remains to be seen whether this grouping can be extended to include other growth hormones and prolactins from different species. Notice also that the grouping is not so much related to the biological activity of the molecule as to similarities in primary structure. Thus, HCS, whose amino acid sequence is very close to that of hGH, is a potent lactogenic hormone, but a relatively poor promoter of growth (Li, 1970).

Although the origin of this spectral difference is not known at present, it most probably arises from conformational differences between the prolactins and the growth hormones, rather than from a simple difference in chromophore content. As shown in Fig. 12, when the CD of these molecules is taken in 0.1 M glycine–HCl buffer (pH 3.6)[9], the spectra are very close to identical, *all* showing the pattern characteristic of the "native" growth hormones. In fact, the prolactins can be titrated back and forth between pH 8.2 and 3.6 indefinitely, with the CD oscillating reversibly between the two forms shown in Figs. 11B and 12. Similar titrations of the growth hormones causes very little change in their far-UV CD. The α-helix contents of all these proteins at pH 3.6 range from 50 $\pm$ 5% to 55 $\pm$ 5%. Clearly, none of these molecules are appreciably denatured at this pH. This stable and nearly ubiquitous α-helix content may therefore be thought of as the architectural "core" of *all* these structurally related molecules, much as steel girders provide the architectural core of most modern buildings. The extra optical component in the spectra of the native prolactins represents an additional architectural element, or detail, not found in the native growth hormone structures. Obviously, it would be impossible to confidently identify any of these molecules on the basis of the pH 3.6 spectra alone. Even the structural class to which the molecule belongs could not be inferred. Essentially equivalent spectra have been reported elsewhere for hGH (Aloj and Edelhoch, 1972;

---

[9]The choice of 0.1 M glycine-HCl at pH 3.6 was not arbitrary. It is under these conditions that bGH (as well as all the others shown) exists in the monomeric form (Dellacha *et al.*, 1968; Bewley and Li, 1972b).

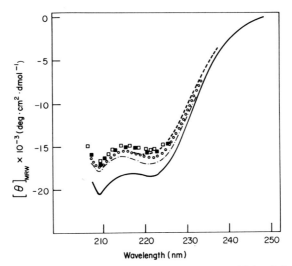

FIG. 12.   Circular dichroism spectra in the region dominated by amide bond absorption of: hGH (——), HCS (– – –), bGH (○ ○ ○), oPr (– · – ·), pPr (■ ■), and cPr (□ □). All spectra were taken in 0.1 M glycine–HCl buffer (pH 3.6).

Holladay *et al.*, 1974), bGH (Edelhoch and Lippoldt, 1970; Holladay *et al.*, 1974; Chen and Sonenberg, 1977; Hara *et al.*, 1978), and HCS (Aloj and Edelhoch, 1971).

B. TERTIARY STRUCTURES

Just as the far-UV CD spectra are generally interpreted in terms of secondary structure, the near-UV CD is known to reflect the conformations and local environments of the side-chain and disulfide chromophores, and in doing so, gives some limited information regarding the tertiary and quaternary structures of the molecules in question (Beychok, 1966, 1967; Strickland, 1974).

1. Lutropin

In Section II,A,2 the far-UV CD spectra of ovine lutropin (oLH) and its subunits were described. The spectrum of intact oLH was found not to be the sum of the spectra of its two subunits, indicating the presence of a reversible conformational change occurring upon dissociation or reassociation.

Figure 13 presents the near-UV CD spectra of oLH and its subunits in 0.1 M Tris-PO$_4$ buffer (pH 7.5), which also contains 5% dioxane to solubilize the β-subunit (Bewley *et al.*, 1974). The spectrum of the native hormone is dominated by a broad negative envelope between 315 and 248 nm. The α-subunit shows no dichroism above 298 nm, only a weak, broad positive envelope, centered near 273 nm and extending to 245 nm, being visible. The β-subunit

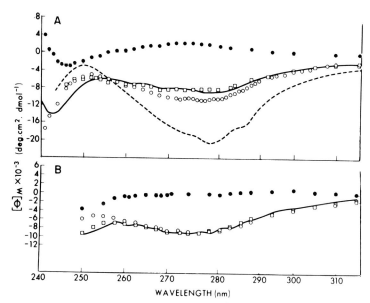

FIG. 13.   (A) Circular dichroism (CD) spectra at pH 7.5 of LH (----), LH-α ($\bullet$--$\bullet$), LH-β (O——O), LH in 5.4 M guanidine hydrochloride (□ □), and the graphical sum of the α and β subunit spectra (——). (B) CD spectra at pH 2.15 of LH-α ($\bullet$—$\bullet$), LH-β (O—O), the graphical sum of the α and β subunit spectra (——), and the spectra of either an equimolar mixture of α and β subunits or native LH after 2–3 hours at pH 2.15 (□——□). All spectra were taken at 27°C, and protein concentrations were less than 1.0 mg/ml. Taken from Bewley *et al.* (1974).

displays a similar weak, broad, negative envelope between 300 and 245 nm, centered near 275 nm. Both subunit spectra are essentially featureless, containing no convincing vibrational fine structure.

Since these molecules contain no tryptophan (Papkoff *et al.*, 1971) and their CD shows none of the bands typical of phenylalanine residues (Horwitz *et al.*, 1969), it can be assumed that the chromophores giving rise to these spectra are primarily tyrosine residues and disulfide bonds. The spectra of the two subunits have the broad, featureless character expected of disulfide dichroism (Beychok, 1966, 1967; Horwitz *et al.*, 1970). The unusually high disulfide content of these molecules and the relative signs and strengths of the subunit CD suggests that they are probably the sum of several separate disulfide CD bands, each arising from an individual disulfide bond, which may have a positive or a negative sign. Thus, each represents largely the *net* dichroism of its constituent disulfides. Apparently, in the isolated subunits, the tyrosine side chains are free to rotate in the aqueous solvent, reducing their average asymmetry so that they display little or no characteristic dichroism.

The spectra in Fig. 13 are presented as molar ellipticities. Accordingly, the CD of oLH *should* be the graphical sum of the spectra of the two subunits. Clearly it is not. From this it is obvious that some conformational change does occur upon dissociation, in agreement with the far-UV data shown previously. Figure 13 further demonstrates that a CD spectrum for oLH *can* be generated, which is very close to the graphical sum of the two subunit spectra. This is achieved by dissolving the intact hormone in either 5 *M* guanidine–HCl or 0.1 *M* glycine–HCl at pH 2.15 and waiting a bit. Under either condition, the intact hormone dissociates into a noninteracting, equimolar mixture of the two subunits, whose CD *is* the sum of the isolated subunit spectra.

An understanding of at least part of the conformational change occurring upon dissociation comes from the following observations. The most distinguishing features of the CD of the intact hormone are the pronounced shoulder near 287–288 nm, the negative maximum near 280–281 nm, and the slight shoulder near 273–274 nm. From the absence of tryptophan and the known characteristics of disulfide CD bands, the negative shoulder at 287–288 nm can confidently be assigned to one or more tyrosine residues. Moreover, this negative band may be more precisely assigned to the (0–0) transition of tyrosine, since the CD spectrum shows no evidence of any lower-energy (higher-wavelength) peaks. From the data presented in Table I, it is evident that the phenolic ring(s) giving rise to this band are in a relatively hydrophobic local environment. We can test this assignment by application of the known spectral properties of tyrosine. If the (0–0) transition lies at 287–288 nm, then we can predict the presence of a slightly more intense negative vibronic band 6 nm to the blue, at 281–282 nm, and a third, less intense negative vibronic overtone band $2 \times 6 = 12$ nm farther into the blue, at 275–276 nm. Tyrosines exposed to an aqueous solvent would produce a less intense family of three bands at 283, 277, and 270.5 nm. These two families of tyrosyl bands are depicted in Fig. 14 along with a hypothetical broad disulfide CD band. The solid line in Fig. 14 is the CD of intact oLH. It is clear that the oLH spectrum is a composite of the disulfide CD plus the three bands originating from tyrosines buried in a hydrophobic environment. Even fairly large errors in the hypothetical disulfide CD would not alter this interpretation. Thus, both the increased intensity of the tyrosyl bands in the intact hormone, which are virtually invisible in a summation of the subunit spectra, and their position on the wavelength axis can be meaningfully interpreted. In Section III,A, covering dynamic measurements, it will be shown that oLH can be reversibly dissociated and reassociated and that this change in quaternary structure is accompanied by the reversible exposure and reburying of these same tyrosyl groups.

Unfortunately, at present it is not possible to estimate from the CD spectra alone how many tyrosine residues are buried in the intact hormone and become exposed on dissociation. It may be mentioned, however, that in either the native or recombined molecules, two tyrosyl groups are completely unreactive toward tetranitromethane and hence buried in the native structure, these being Tyr-21 in the α-subunit and Tyr-59 in the β-subunit (Sairam *et al.*, 1972c). In contrast *all*

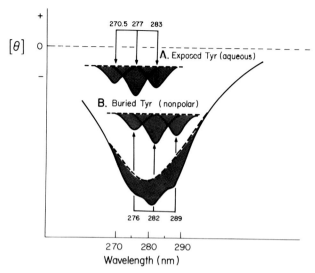

FIG. 14. Resolution of the near-UV circular dichroism of oLH (——) into a hypothetical disulfide band (– – –) and a family of three bands representing either exposed (A) or buried (B) nonpolar tyrosines.

the tryosyl groups in the isolated subunits are quantitatively reactive to tetranitromethane, indicating them to be completely exposed to the external solvent in agreement with the CD spectra.

In the example given above, static CD studies have again suggested properties that might eventually be exploited in studying a more dynamic aspect of the hormone: What happens during biosynthesis of these subunit proteins? Can the appearance of biological activity be correlated with a recognizable physical event? This point will be explored further in Section III,A.

2. Growth and Lactogenic Hormones

In Section II,A,3 static studies of the far-UV CD of several growth and lactogenic hormones demonstrated that they all contained a similar secondary structural core consisting of about 50% α-helix. The prolactins were shown to contain an additional element, whose exact nature remains uncertain, but which nevertheless seems characteristic of those lactogenic hormones isolated from the limited number of mammalian species shown in Figs. 11 and 12. These fundamental structural "cores" appear to be highly conserved during the evolution of the hormones and were likened to the architectural steel cores of modern buildings.

Static studies of the near-UV CD of these molecules provide some insight into their tertiary structures. Figure 15 presents the near-UV CD spectra of hGH and oPr (Bewley and Li, 1972a), bGH (Bewley and Li, 1972b), and HCS (Bewley

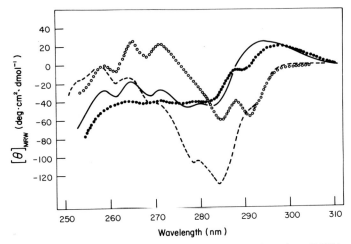

FIG. 15.   Circular dichroism spectra in the region of side-chain absorption of hGH (——), HCS
(– – –), bGH (ooo), and oPR (●●●). All spectra were taken in 0.1 *M* Tris-Cl buffer (pH 8.2).

and Li, 1971). Similar spectra have been published for hGH by Aloj and
Edelhoch (1971) and Holladay *et al.* (1974); for bGH by Edelhoch and Lippoldt
(1970) and Holladay *et al.* (1974); and for HCS by Aloj and Edelhoch (1972).
The near-UV spectrum of pPr is not shown in Fig. 15 but is quite similar to that
of oPr (Bewley and Li, 1975). The spectrum of oGH is almost identical to that of
bGH (Bewley and Li, 1972b; Holladay *et al.*, 1974).

   One is immediately struck by the fact that these near-UV spectra are all
different and distinctive in contrast to the far-UV spectra. The prolactins and
growth hormones cannot be split into two separate groups on the basis of these
spectral patterns. In fact, the two spectra showing the greatest similarities are
hGH and oPr. Since pPr has a spectrum related to oPr, one might attempt a
grouping of lactogenic hormones with hGH, oPr, and pPr. However, HCS is as
potent a lactogenic hormone as hGH (Li, 1970). Unfortunately, the CD spectrum
of HCS is very different from the other three. This is further complicated by the
fact that the near-UV CD of rat growth hormone is reported to be very similar to
the HCS spectrum (Holladay *et al.*, 1974).

   Apparently, although the structural cores of all these molecules have been
highly conserved, the tertiary structures are quite characteristic for each. Naturally, in cases like oGH and bGH, which differ by only one amino acid (Gráf and
Li, 1974), the spectral differences are minimal. If we extend our analogy with
architecture, the tertiary structures of these molecules might be thought of as the
"fine details" of the architectural plan including the outer surface details like the
type, number, and placement of windows and doors. In the hormones these
surface details define the topochemical properties of the molecule, which in turn
probably control or give specificity to such important features as antigen–

antibody reactions and interactions with receptors. Thus, the differences in these near-UV CD spectra may well arise from the same structural features that also produce the well known species and biological specificities of these proteins.

At present we are unable to translate most of these near-UV spectra into specific details of the tertiary structures in question. This is partly due to their complexity, which makes resolution into individual bands very difficult. From studies with model compounds (Strickland, 1974) the dichroism above 290 nm can be assigned to tryptophan residues; that between 270 and 288 nm is mostly due to tyrosines, although both tryptophan and disulfide bonds can also contribute in this region. The two small, negative peaks near 269 and 261 nm, seen in the spectra of the growth hormones and HCS can be assigned to phenylalanine. These bands are either very weak or absent from the spectra of oPr and pPr, but this may be due to cancellation of both positive and negative phenylalanine peaks in these molecules.

Holladay et al. (1974) have attempted a computer-assisted resolution of the CD spectra of hGH, bGH, oGH, and rat growth hormone. One of the difficulties encountered in this type of approach is a general lack of information regarding the contribution of the two disulfide bonds to the total CD of these molecules. In their study, Holladay et al. (1974) assumed that this contribution was negligible. Previously, Bewley and Li (1970b) had published the CD spectra of native, fully reduced, and reoxidized hGH. These spectra are shown in Figs. 16 and 17. From Fig. 16 it is evident that reduction of the two disulfides in hGH has no effect on the secondary structure of the molecule. However, Fig. 17 demonstrates that reduction does cause a change in the near-UV CD spectrum. This difference amounts to a gradually increasing loss of negative dichroism, beginning at about 293 nm, reaching a maximum difference around 265–270 nm, the curves for the native and reduced proteins gradually reconverging again below 245 nm. Reoxidation of the reduced hormone completely reverses all changes in the spectrum. It was suggested (Bewley and Li, 1970b) that, since the secondary structure and all the CD band systems for tryptophan, tyrosine, and phenylalanine seemed to be present in the reduced protein, perhaps this difference in the two CD spectra did not represent a conformational change, but, instead, was due to a loss of the intrinsic dichroism of the two disulfide bonds. The difference between the two spectra could then be equated with the *sum* of the CD contributions from the two bonds. In 1970 there was very little precedent for such an assignment, most changes in CD being interpreted as a conformational difference rather than a simple loss of an optically active chromophore, and so the question remained open.

Adjunct to a study of a modified form of hGH (PL-hGH) produced by removal of the hexapeptide comprising residues 135 through 140, brought about by digestion with the enzyme plasmin (Li and Gráf, 1974), procedures were developed that allowed the quantitative and selective reduction and carbamidomethylation of the carboxyl-terminal disulfide in PL-hGH (Li and Bew-

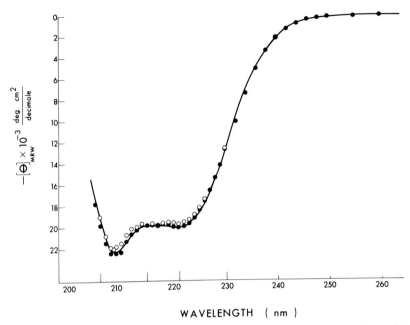

FIG. 16.   Far-UV circular dichroism spectra of native (——), reoxidized (●●), and reduced (○○) human growth hormone in $0.1\,M$ Tris-Cl buffer, pH 8.2. The values for the reoxidized protein are the means of three preparations. The standard error of the means are shown as vertical bars at selected wavelengths above the abscissa. Values for the reduced protein are the means of two preparations. Taken from Bewley and Li (1970b).

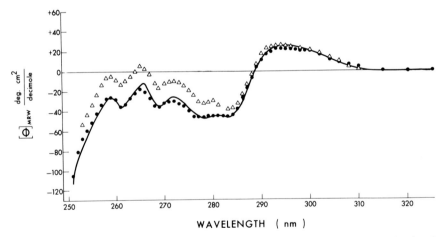

FIG. 17.   Near-UV circular dichroism spectra of native (——), reoxidized (●●), and reduced (△△) human growth hormone in $0.1\,M$ Tris-Cl buffer, pH 8.2. Each point represents the mean of two determinations. Taken from Bewley and Li (1970b).

ley, 1976a; Bewley, 1977a). Under other conditions, both disulfides in PL-hGH could be reduced and carbamidomethylated. The PL-hGH, and both the partially and fully reduced-carbamidomethylated derivatives have been reported to retain full biological and immunological activities (Lewis *et al.*, 1972; Mills *et al.*, 1973; Yadley and Chrambach, 1973; Li and Gráf, 1974; Clarke *et al.*, 1974; Reagan *et al.*, 1975; Li and Bewley, 1976a).

Figure 18A shows the near-UV CD spectrum of PL-hGH compared with the

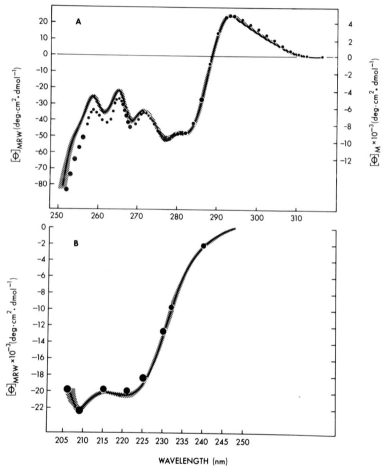

FIG. 18. Circular dichroism spectra in the region of side-chain absorption (A) and the region dominated by amide bond absorption (B) of PL-hGH (—-) and hGH (○) in 0.1 *M* Tris–Cl buffer, pH 8.2. In (A) the spectrum of PL-hGH is the mean of ten separate spectra using three preparations of the protein. The shaded area represents the standard error of the mean for these spectra as a function of wavelength. Similarly, the diameter of the circles represents the standard error of the mean for seven spectra of hGH. In (B) three spectra were used for PL-hGH and four for hGH. Taken from Bewley (1977a).

spectrum of native hGH. Except for very small differences above 289 nm and below 266 nm, it can be seen that the two spectra are essentially identical. The positive, asymmetric band above 289 nm has been assigned to transitions arising from the tryptophan-86 residue (Bewley *et al.*, 1972b; Bewley and Li, 1972a; Aloj and Edelhoch, 1972; Holladay *et al.*, 1974). The negative bands at 282 and 277 nm have been assigned predominantly to tyrosine residues, the two negative bands at 269 and 261 nm being assigned to phenylalanine (Bewley *et al.*, 1972b; Bewley and Li, 1972a; Aloj and Edelhoch, 1972; Holladay *et al.*, 1974). The same assignments may be applied to the spectrum of PL-hGH. From Fig. 18B, it can be seen that, in the region dominated by amide bond absorption, PL-hGH and hGH again display the same CD. The content of secondary structure in PL-hGH is estimated at 55 ± 5% excess right-hand α-helix, as also reported for hGH (Bewley *et al.*, 1969). The near equality of these two spectra, and the retention of full biopotencies by the modified protein, may be presumed to reflect the near-conformational identity of PL-hGH and hGH.

The near-UV spectrum of PL-hGH after 2×10^3 seconds in the presence of a 2.5 molar excess of reducing agent (DTT) over total disulfide content in the protein, is presented in Fig. 19. This figure also shows the spectrum of PL-hGH for comparison. Under these conditions it is known that the carboxyl-terminal disulfide linking half-cystine 182 and half-cystine 189 has been selectively and quantitatively reduced to the dithiol form (Bewley, 1977a). The far-UV spectrum

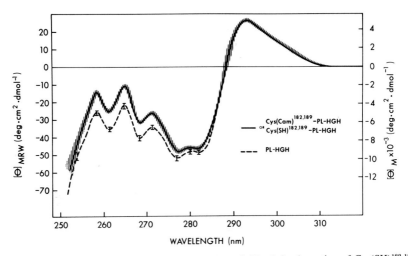

FIG. 19.   Circular dichroism spectra in the region of side-chain absorption of Cys(SH)[182,189]-PL-hGH (——). Spectra of the reduced form were taken after 2×10^3 seconds in the presence of a 2.5 molar excess of DTT; the shaded area represents the standard error of the mean for four preparations. The standard error of the mean for the PL-hGH (———) spectrum is the same as in Fig. 18A, but shown here as vertical bars. The spectrum of Cys(Cam)[182,189]-PL-hGH is identical with that of Cys(SH)[182,189]-PL-hGH. Taken from Bewley (1977a).

of the reduced protein (not shown) is identical to that of PL-hGH and/or hGH. Notice the similarity between these two spectra and those in Fig. 17. Again, the difference consists of a gradually increasing loss of negative dichroism beginning at ≈290 nm, maximizing around 260 nm, with the spectra reconverging below 245 nm. Reoxidation of the partially reduced protein completely returns the spectrum to that of PL-hGH. Blocking of the thiol groups with iodoacetamide to form the carbamidomethyl derivative provides a permanently modified hormone whose CD is identical to the partially reduced form. As stated above, this derivative is fully active biologically and immunologically (Li and Bewley, 1976a). The maintenance of these activities, along with the retention of all the secondary structure and aromatic maxima, argues for few, if any, conformational differences between the two forms. Graphical subtraction of the spectrum of the partially reduced protein from that of PL-hGH produces the "difference" CD band shown in Fig. 20B. This broad, featureless band is almost identical to the

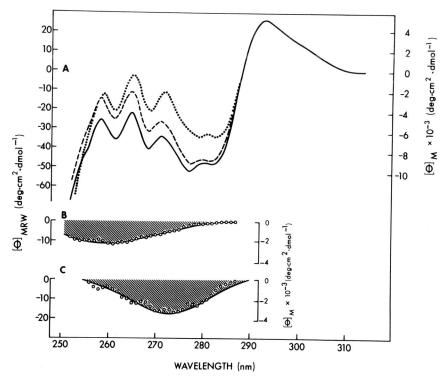

FIG. 20.   (A) Circular dichroism (CD) spectra in the region of side-chain absorption of PL-hGH (——), Cys(Cam)[182,189]-PL-hGH (–––), and Cys(Cam)[53,165,182,189]-PL-hGH (●). (B) The CD band generated by subtracting the spectrum of Cys(Cam)[182,189]-PL-hGH from that of PL-hGH. (C) The CD band generated by subtracting the spectrum of Cys(Cam)[53,165,182,189]-PL-hGH from that of Cys(Cam)[182,189]-PL-hGH. Taken from Bewley (1977a).

near-UV CD of L-cystine (Coleman and Blout, 1968; Ito and Takagi, 1970; Yamashiro *et al.*, 1975). Accordingly, it has been proposed (Bewley, 1977a) that this band (Fig. 20B) represents the intrinsic optical activity of the carboxyl-terminal disulfide linking half-cystines 182 and 189 in PL-hGH.

Reduction of the second disulfide bond in PL-hGH, linking half-cystines 53 and 165, requires a 25 molar excess of DTT for at least 6 hours (Bewley, 1977a). The carboxyl-terminal disulfide is, of course, also cleaved under these conditions to provide a fully reduced protein. After carbamidomethylation with iodo-acetamide, the tetra-*S*-carbamidomethyl-PL-hGH does not immediately dissociate[10] and is in fact quite stable and fully active biologically if stored in the cold or frozen in solution (Li and Bewley, 1976a; Bewley, 1977a). Figure 20A displays the near-UV CD spectrum of this fully reduced-carbamidomethylated derivative along with the spectra of the partially reduced-carbamidomethylated and "native" PL-hGH. Subtraction of this spectrum from that of the partially reduced carbamidomethylated protein produces the second broad, featureless band between 290 and 250 nm shown in Fig. 20C. Again, the far-UV spectrum of the fully modified protein is identical to that of PL-hGH, and reoxidation of the fully reduced hormone repairs all CD changes, returning to the spectrum of PL-hGH. The "difference" CD shown in Fig. 20C has been assigned to the contribution of the disulfide bond linking half-cystines 53 and 165 to the total optical activity of PL-hGH (Bewley, 1977a). It is of interest that the maximum of this band is red-shifted, relative to the carboxyl-terminal disulfide band, to 272–274 nm. This difference can be ascribed to unequal dihedral angles for the two disulfide bonds. It remains to be seen if the two disulfides in hGH have similar CD contributions to those in PL-hGH.[11]

Highly selective reductions of the homologous, carboxyl-terminal disulfide bonds in bGH (Gráf *et al.*, 1975) and HCS (Li, 1970; Neri *et al.*, 1973; Breuer, 1969) have also been reported. Figure 21 shows both the near and far-UV CD spectra of native and partially reduced HCS (Bewley, 1977b). This figure also contains CD data on the partially reduced-carbamidomethylated, partially reduced-carboxymethylated, and partially reduced-reoxidized HCS. From Fig. 21C, it is evident that none of these chemical modifications of the disulfide bond linking half-cystines 182 and 189 produce any significant effects on the secondary structure of the molecule. It can be seen from Fig. 21A that, although the near-UV CD of HCS is quite unlike that of hGH of PL-hGH, the *difference* between the CD of the native or reoxidized protein and of the partially reduced or partially reduced-alkylated derivatives, is very nearly the same as for native and

---

[10]The disulfide linking half-cystines 53 and 165 is the only covalent link holding the amino-terminal 134 residue fragment to the 51-residue carboxyl-terminal fragment in PL-hGH. The dissociation and reassociation of these fragments is discussed in Section III,B.

[11]Unfortunately, strictly selective reduction of only one bond in hGH is very difficult if not impossible to achieve (Bewley, unpublished results). Accordingly, only the *sum* of the two disulfide CD bands can be measured with any accuracy.

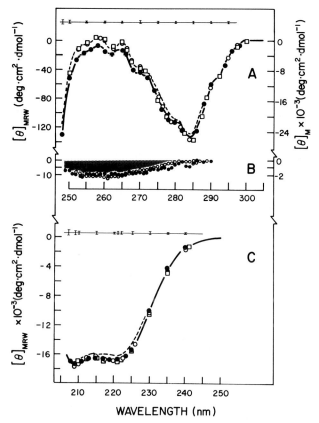

FIG. 21.   Circular dichroism (CD) spectra of native HCS (—), partially reduced HCS (- - -), partially reduced-carbamidomethylated HCS (□), partially reduced-carboxymethylated HCS (○). and reoxidized HCS (●), in the region of side-chain absorption (A) and amide bond absorption (C). For the native protein, the mean of seven spectra is shown, and the mean of four spectra appears for the partially reduced protein. The standard errors of the mean for the partially reduced protein are shown at selected wavelengths on separate abscissas above the appropriate portion of the spectrum. The standard errors of the mean for the native hormone are not shown, but are equal to or slightly smaller than those shown for the partially reduced form, at all wavelengths. The points depicting the derivatives are taken from individual spectra and are not mean values. In (B) the difference spectrum (●) obtained by subtracting the spectrum of the partially reduced protein from that of the native hormone is coplotted with a similar difference spectrum for PL-hGH (○) taken from Bewley (1977a). The standard error at the negative maximum of the difference spectrum in (B) appears above in the shaded region as a vertical bar at 260.5 nm. Note the change of scale in the ordinates for A and B. Taken from Bewley (1977b).

partially reduced PL-hGH. This difference is shown in Fig. 21B coplotted with
the data on PL-hGH from Fig. 20B. It appears that these two disulfide bonds,
forming cross-linked loops that are identical in amino acid sequence, are also
essentially identical in their contributions to the total optical activities of their
respective parent molecules.

Figure 22 shows similar data obtained from reduction of the homologous, but
nonidentical, carboxyl-terminal disulfide in bGH (Bewley, 1977b). Note that the
secondary structure (Fig. 22C) is not altered by partial reduction. Again, although bGH exhibits a completely different near-UV CD pattern from PL-hGH
or HCS, the difference (Fig. 22B) between the native and partially reduced forms

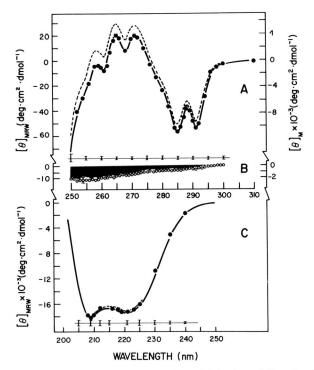

FIG. 22.   Circular dichroism (CD) spectra of native BGH (——), partially reduced BGH (– – –),
and reoxidized BGH (●), in the region of side-chain absorption (A) and amide bond absorption (C).
For both the native and partially reduced protein, the mean of three experiments is shown. The
standard errors of the mean for the partially reduced hormone are presented at selected wavelengths
on separate abscissas below the appropriate portion of the spectrum. The standard errors for the native
protein are essentially as shown for the partially reduced form. The points representing the reoxidized
protein are from a single spectrum and do not constitute mean values. In (B), the difference spectrum
(○) obtained by subtracting the spectrum of the partially reduced protein from that of the native
hormone is depicted. The standard error at the negative maximum in (B) appears as a vertical bar at
254 nm. Taken from Bewley (1977b).

is very similar to those found for the latter molecules. The contributions of the carboxyl-terminal disulfides in PL-hGH, bGH, HCS, and a synthetic undecapeptide (Yamashiro et al., 1975) representing the homologous carboxyl-terminal disulfide in oPR are summarized in Table II.

It is hoped that this type of basically static CD study will eventually aid in a complete resolution of the CD spectra of these molecules into individual bands, assignable to specific chromaphores and ultimately translatable into meaningful descriptions of some of the details in the tertiary structures of these proteins. In turn, this information will be used to gain greater insights into the more important dynamic properties of the hormones.

III. Dynamic Studies

In contrast to the static studies described above, this section contains examples of the use of CD to follow selected dynamic properties of protein hormones. Since a single scan of an entire CD spectrum requires from 20 to 90 minutes, it is not always possible to follow the changing CD of a compound during a rapid reaction. Often, the spectra can be taken only before the reaction starts, and again after it is completed. Nevertheless, some limited dynamic information can sometimes be obtained by following a single key wavelength as a function of time. In other cases, the reaction may be so slow, or can be slowed down to such an extent, that successive complete spectra may be obtained with sufficient accuracy. In the following, examples of both single-wavelength and slow-reaction procedures will be discussed.

TABLE II

Estimated Contribution of the Carboxyl-Terminal Disulfide Bonds in PL-hGH, HCS, bGH, and oPr to the Total Optical Activity of the Parent Protein

| Protein | Disulfide linking ½-cystines A and B | | λ_{max} (nm) | $[\theta]M$ (deg cm² dmol⁻¹) | Δ^a (nm) |
	A	B			
PL-hGH[b]	182	189	258–260	-2100 ± 120^c	16–18
HCS	182	189	258–260	-2100 ± 160	16–18
bGH	182	189	252–255	-2200 ± 210	24–26
oPr[d]	191	199	260–262	-1350	24–26

[a] Half-bandwidth in nanometer, measured at $1/e$ of the maximum ordinate.

[b] Taken from Bewley (1977a).

[c] The uncertainty in these ellipticities has been calculated as the square root of the sum of squares of the standard errors taken from the circular dichroism spectra of the native and partially reduced hormones at λ_{max}. No estimate available in the case of oPr.

[d] From Yamashiro et al. (1975). Taken from Bewley (1977b).

A. LUTROPIN

In Sections II,A,2 and II,B,1, it was shown that oLH can be dissociated by treatment with acid or denaturants to produce a noninteracting mixture of its biologically impotent subunits. It was also noted that this reaction could be reversed at neutral pH, allowing recombination (complementation) to a fully active native-type hormone. The dissociation and complementation were shown to be accompanied by a reversible conformational change involving the transfer of two tyrosines, one in each subunit, from exposure to the aqueous solvent in the free subunits, to a sterically hindered, hydrophobic environment in the native or recombinant proteins.

In an attempt to gain further understanding of the kinetics of these events, a dynamic CD study of the dissociation–complementation reaction was carried out. Since both reactions occur too rapidly for reliable complete spectra to be obtained, it was decided to follow the time course of the ellipticity at 280 nm. This wavelength was chosen because it is the position of greatest spectral change and lies on the peak of the $(0 + 800 \text{ cm}^{-1})$ transition of the buried tyrosines. Thus, the time course of ellipticity at this wavelength should give some idea of the kinetics of exposure and reburying of the tyrosyl groups.

Figure 23 (Bewley *et al.*, 1974) shows the near-UV CD of oLH at pH 7.5. It

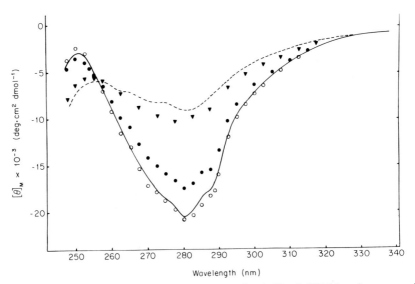

FIG. 23.   CD spectra of ovine LH in 0.1 *M* Tris-phosphate buffer of pH 7.5 (——), same sample 48 hours after titrating to pH 3.61 (▼▼), and 48 hours after titrating back to pH 7.50 (●●). The graphical sum of the CD spectra of the isolated subunits is shown as a dashed line (---). The spectrum of the purified, reassociated lutropin is shown as open circles (○○). The reassociated LH was measured at 1.0 mg/ml; all other spectra were taken at a protein concentration of 9.45 mg/ml. Taken from Bewley *et al.* (1974).

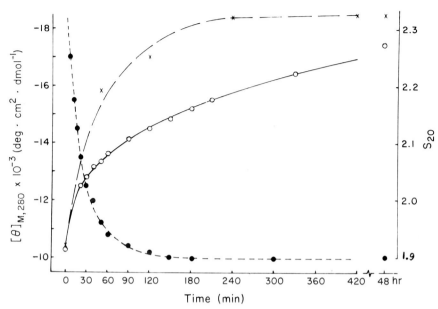

FIG. 24.   The dissociation and reassociation of ovine LH at 27°C and a protein concentration of 9.45 mg/ml in 0.1 M Tris-phosphate buffer. The loss of ellipticity at 280 nm after titrating from pH 7.50 to 3.61 (●---●), the regain of the same ellipticity on titrating back to pH 7.50 (○——○), and the increase in sedimentation velocity after titrations from pH 3.61 to 7.50 (x--x). Taken from Bewley *et al.* (1974).

can be seen that after titration of the sample to pH 3.61 there is a marked loss of negative ellipticity. In fact, after 48 hours at pH 3.61 the spectrum is essentially that of a noninteracting, equimolar mixture of subunits, demonstrating nearly complete dissociation. Figure 24 (Bewley *et al.*, 1974) shows the rate of loss of dichroism at 280 nm. The dissociation is seen to be quite rapid, reaching completion in about 2.5 hours at this pH. Sedimentation velocity analyses of this same sample exhibited a drop in the sedimentation coefficient from 2.54 at pH 7.5 to 1.94 at pH 3.61, further demonstrating essentially complete dissociation.

After establishing that the sample had dissociated, it was retitrated back to pH 7.5, and the ellipticity at 280 nm and the sedimentation coefficient were again followed. It may be seen from Fig. 24 that the sedimentation coefficient rapidly increased to a steady value of 2.32 in about 4 hours. In sharp contrast, the repair of the dichroism at 280 nm was considerably slower, taking nearly 24 hours to reach a stable value. The final sedimentation and ellipticity values suggested that about 80% complementation had occurred. Exclusion chromatography of the reaction mixture demonstrated that, indeed, approximately 80% of the material eluted at the position of intact oLH, with a minor higher molecular weight peak, and a minor lower molecular weight peak. The major peak was examined and proved to have the CD spectrum, sedimentation coefficient, and 50–60% of the biological activity[12] of native oLH. The near-UV CD spectrum of this purified recombinant is also shown in Fig. 23.

Consideration of these data discloses some interesting aspects concerning the dynamics of the reassociation reaction. It is obvious that titration from pH 3.61 to pH 7.5 does not immediately reverse the conformational changes that have occurred during the previous dissociation reaction. Nevertheless, the two subunits are able to recognize one another despite their partially denatured state. The β-subunit is well known for its tendency to self-association at neutral pH (Bewley et al., 1972a, 1974). Despite this, the α-subunit is able to compete effectively to form a stable 30,000-dalton α–β complex. It is assumed that the small amount of high molecular weight material in the final reaction mixture is an aggregate of the β-subunit, while the minor, small molecular weight component represents uncomplexed, excess α-subunit (Bewley et al., 1974). It is especially noteworthy that the return of the average mass to a 30,000-dalton complex occurs much faster than the repair of the CD. Apparently, formation of the α–β complex, and final annealing of the conformation, including reburying of the two tyrosine side chains, are completely separate reactions. Since the three pituitary glycoprotein hormones LH, FSH, and TSH all contain identical, or nearly identical, α-subunits, it has been proposed, as outlined in Section II,A,2, that hormonal specificity resides in the three differing β-subunits. From the results described above, it might be further speculated that, after formation of the initial α–β complex, the subsequent conformational adjustments depend on the exact nature of the β-subunit. The three homologous β-subunits will produce three slightly different conformational variants, each with its own characteristic biological specificity.

Figure 25 presents a schematic version of these reactions. The recombinant has been labeled ICSH' because of the failure of most of these complemented samples to reattain full biological activity. The source of this problem is presently unknown and will require further investigation.

The advantage of this type of dynamic study is its ability to separate kinetically distinct phases in an overall protein–protein interaction. In the instance described above, this additional kind of information may ultimately be of importance in understanding the biosynthesis and source of specificity for these hormones.

B. PLASMIN-MODIFIED hGH (PL-hGH)

Static studies, presented in Sections II,A,3 and II,B,2, have outlined evidence demonstrating near-conformational identity between native hGH, and PL-hGH, which is produced from hGH by limited digestion with human plasmin, resulting in the loss of the hexapeptide comprising residues 135–140. It was also noted

---

[12]Measured by the ovarian ascorbic acid depletion test (Parlow, 1961).

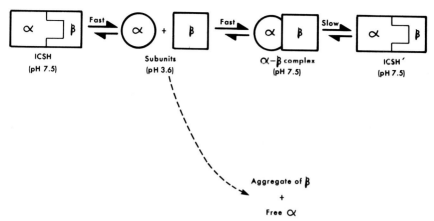

FIG. 25. Proposed scheme for the dissociation and reassociation of ovine interstitial cell-stimulating hormone (oICSH, oLH) and its susubunits. Taken from Bewley *et al.* (1974).

that both of the disulfide bonds in PL-hGH could be reduced and car-bamidomethylated, either selectively or together, also without any gross change in conformation. The CD changes brought about by the reduction were assigned to the intrinsic dichroism of the disulfide bonds, which was lost owing to the chemical removal of these chromophores. The resultant molecule, tetra-*S*-carbamidomethylated-PL-hGH, lacks any covalent link between its 134-residue amino-terminal fragment (hGH-1–134) and its 51-residue carboxyl-terminal fragment (hGH-141–191). Despite this, the derivative is fully active biologically (Reagan *et al.*, 1975; Li and Bewley, 1976a; Kostyo *et al.*, 1976) and completely stable to dissociation in slightly alkaline solution when either frozen or kept at 2°C for periods of up to 3 months.

However, if incubated at 25 ± 2°C, the modified hormone undergoes a slow dissociation. This reaction is so slow that it has been possible to follow it by both repeated exclusion chromatography and repeated complete CD spectra (Li and Bewley, 1976a; Bewley and Li, 1978).

Although initial experiments clearly demonstrated the possibility of performing highly selective reductions of the two disulfides in PL-hGH, it had not been determined which was the more labile of the two bonds. It was decided that this problem could be conveniently solved simultaneously with a study of the kinetics of dissociation of the two fragments. Figure 26 presents the logic of this experiment. First, the most labile disulfide was reduced and blocked with [1-^{14}C]carbamidomethyl groups. After repurification of the now radioactively labeled protein, the second disulfide was reduced and blocked with "cold" carbamidomethyl groups. The fully modified protein was again purified by exclusion chromatography on Sephadex G-100 in 90% yield and exhibited a specific radioactivity of 2.9 μCi/μmol. This undissociated, monomeric product was then allowed to dissociate spontaneously at room temperature in 0.1 *M*

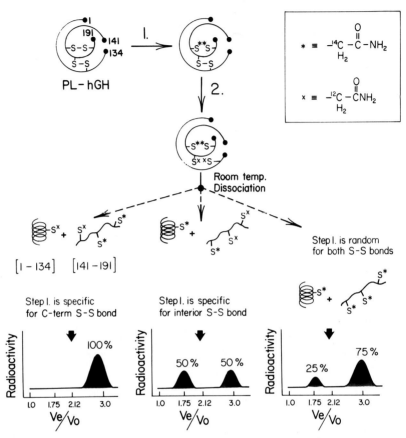

FIG. 26.   Reaction scheme for selective modification of the two disulfide bonds in PL-hGH. The lower half of this figure describes the three possible distributions of radioactivity on exclusion chromatography (Sephadex G-100) of the fully dissociated molecule, depending on the degree and order of selectivity of the first reduction–carbamidomethylation.

Tris–Cl, pH 8.2. At regular intervals, small aliquots of the dissociating mixture were submitted to exclusion chromatography on Sephadex G-100. CD spectra of the mixture were also taken at intervals.

Preliminary experiments had established that the modified protein would ultimately dissociate to the extent of at least 95%, producing a monomeric form of the small carboxyl-terminal fragment eluting at a V_e/V_o ratio of 3.08, and a trimeric form of the larger amino-terminal fragment, eluting at $V_e/V_o = 1.75$ (Li and Bewley, 1976a). The intact hormone was known to elute at a $V_e/V_o = 2.12$. As shown in Fig. 26, three possibilities existed for the distribution of radioactivity in the chromatogram of the dissociated hormone. If it was the carboxyl-terminal disulfide linking half-cystines 182 and 189 which reduced first, then all the radioactivity would appear in the carboxyl-terminal fragment at $V_e/V_0 = 3.08$. In contrast, if it was the disulfide linking half-cystines 53 and 165 which were most reactive, then half the radioactivity would appear at $V_e/V_0 = 3.08$ and half at $V_e/V_0 = 1.75$, attached to cysteine-53 in the amino-terminal trimer. On the off chance that the reductions were actually random rather than selective, the radioactivity would be evenly distributed among all four half-cystines, producing a chromatogram with one-fourth of the radioactivity at $V_e/V_0 = 1.75$ and three-fourths at $V_e/V_0 = 3.0$.

Figure 27 shows the radioactivity profile for successive chromatograms during the dissociation. There is a slow, progressive transfer of virtually all (98%) the radioactivity from $V_e/V_0 = 2.12$ (intact protein) to $V_e/V_0 = 3.08$ (free amino-terminal fragment). After 500–600 hours, the chromatograms are all equivalent. It is clear from Fig. 27 that it was the carboxyl-terminal disulfide which was modified first. The complete absence of radioactivity at $V_e/V_0 = 1.75$ attests to the remarkable selectivity of the first-stage reduction–carbamidomethylation. From the kinetic standpoint, the extent of dissociation at any time is simply the percentage of the total radioactivity appearing at $V_e/V_0 = 3.08$.

Since the amino-terminal fragment contains the sole tryptophan at position 86, the indole fluorescence of this side chain can be used to selectively follow this fragment's behavior on these same chromatograms. The superposition of both radioactivity and indole fluorescence, of course, identifies the intact molecule. Figure 28 shows the exact same chromatograms as Fig. 27 except that the profile of indole fluorescence at 340 nm has been added. It is evident that the trimeric form of the amino-terminal fragment begins to appear at $V_e/V_0 = 1.75$ only *after* 80–90 hours of incubation, a time period during which approximately 30% of the molecules have dissociated. Obviously, the trimerization of this fragment is an even slower reaction than the dissociation itself. Monomeric and dimeric forms of this fragment cannot be convincingly resolved from the intact protein on this column. Figure 28 also demonstrates that there is a gradual loss of total fluorescence due to quenching of the indole emission in the trimer form.

Because the dissociation reaction is so very slow, it is possible to record intermittent, complete CD spectra with considerable accuracy. Figure 29 presents a series of such spectra taken during the dissociation. The positive, asymmetric band above 290 nm, which has been assigned to the tryptophan-86 residue, is lost, being gradually replaced by a much stronger negative band at 298 nm. From model compound studies this negative band may also be assigned to tryptophan-86 (Strickland, 1974). It should be noted that no discernible changes occur in the positive band until after 40–50 hours, although approximately 20% of the protein dissociates in this time period. Kinetically, this is similar to the appearance of indole fluorescence at $V_e/V_0 = 1.75$. Thus, we can kinetically equate the appearance of the negative indole CD at 298 nm with the trimerization of the amino-terminal fragment, rather than with the dissociation itself. Very

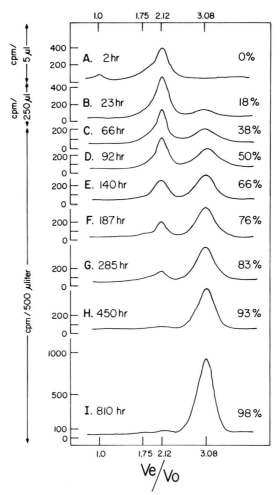

FIG. 27. Exclusion chromatography of the dissociating tetra-S-carbamidomethyl-PL-hGH mixture on Sephadex G-100. The times of incubation are shown above each chromatogram at the position of V_o. The extent of dissociation obtained from the integrated radioactivity profile appears above each chromatogram at the far right. In curve A, 2 mg of protein were applied to the column; in curves B through H approximately 50 μg total protein were applied, and in curve I approximately 100 μg total protein were applied. In all chromatograms radioactivity is shown as a solid line (———). Taken from Bewley and Li (1978).

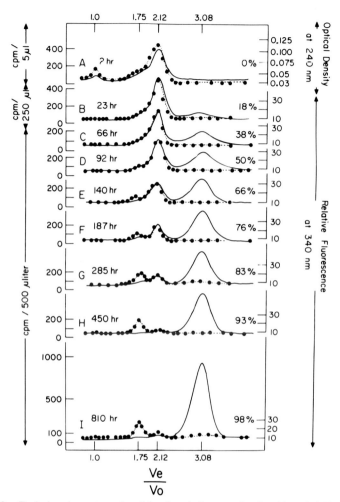

FIG. 28.   Exclusion chromatography of the dissociating tetra-*S*-carbamidomethyl-PL-hGH mixture on Sephadex G-100. The times of incubation are shown above each chromatogram at the position of V_0. The extent of dissociation obtained from the integrated radioactivity profile appears above each chromatogram at the far right. In curve A, 2 mg of protein were applied to the column; in curves B through H, approximately 50 μg total protein were applied; and in curve I, approximately 100 μg total protein were applied. In all chromatograms radioactivity is shown as a solid line (——); the filled circles (●) represent optical density in A and relative fluorescence in B through H.

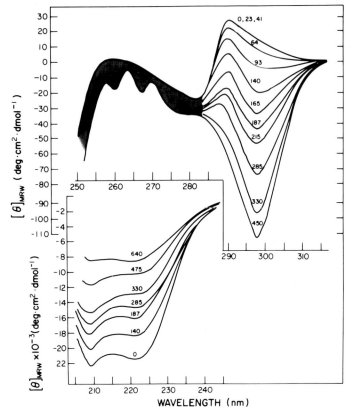

FIG. 29. Circular dichroism spectra of the dissociating tetra-S-carbamidomethyl-PL-hGH mixture at various times in the region of side-chain absorption (A) and the region of amide bond absorption (B). The duration (hours) of incubation is indicated above each spectrum. Taken from Bewley and Li (1978).

little change can be seen at any time in the tyrosine and phenylalanine bands between 289 nm and 250 nm, although there is a general tendency for these bands to weaken in intensity during the incubation.

In contrast, a very significant change occurs below 250 nm in the region dominated by amide bond absorption (Fig. 29). The two negative bands at 221 and 209 nm, characteristic of the 55 ± 5% α-helix in hGH or PL-hGH, are progressively lost. A stable state is reached after ≈500 hours, corresponding to an average helical content of 30–35% for the entire mixture (when calculated as though still intact). The rates of dissociation, loss of indole fluorescence, and change in the CD at 298 and 221 nm are shown in Fig. 30.

The CD spectra of the amino-terminal trimer and the carboxyl-terminal monomer which have been purified by rechromatography on Sephadex G-100 are presented in Fig. 31. The carboxyl-terminal fragment exhibits no discernible

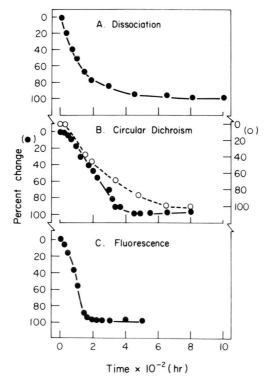

FIG. 30. The rates of change of measured parameters as a function of time during dissociation of tetra-S-carbamidomethyl-PL-hGH. Each parameter is expressed as a percentage of the total change in terminal fragment at $V_e/V_o = 3.08$. In (B) the rates of change in the ellipticity at 298 nm (●——●) and 221 nm (○---○) are shown. In (C) the rate of change in fluorescence emission at 340 nm (excitation at 294 nm) is presented. Taken from Bewley and Li (1978).

bands in the region of side-chain absorption and no evidence of any ordered form of secondary structure in the region dominated by amide bond absorption. The trimeric amino-terminal fragment, however, shows a very intense negative band at 298 nm, which has been assigned to the Trp-86 residue. In addition, this fragment exhibits very intense negative bands at 221 and 209 nm, characteristic of the α-helix. This far-UV spectrum (Fig. 31B) is very similar to that of native hGH or intact tetra-S-carbamidomethyl-PL-hGH, representing approximately 55 ± 5% α-helix in the trimer form of the fragment. This corresponds to an average of 75 α-helical residues. Native hGH (Bewley et al., 1969) or intact tetra-S-carbamidomethyl-PL-hGH (Li and Bewley, 1976a) is also reported to contain 55% α-helix, or about 105 α-helical residues. Since the rate of loss of the 30 or so residues of α-helix corresponds kinetically with the formation of amino-terminal trimer, rather than with the liberation of the random-coil carboxyl-terminal fragment, it may tentatively be concluded that nearly all the α-helix in

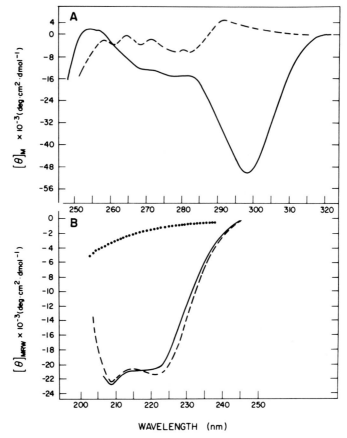

FIG. 31. Circular dichroism spectra of the purified amino-terminal fragment (———) and the purified carboxyl-terminal fragment (· · ·) in the region of side-chain absorption (A) and the region dominated by amide bond absorption (B). The CD spectrum of undissociated tetra-S-carbamidomethyl-PL-hGH (– – –) is added for comparison. Taken from Bewley and Li (1978).

the intact tetra-S-carbamidomethylated-PL-hGH, and probably in native hGH itself, must be contained within the first 134 residues.

Figure 32 shows the elution pattern of the dissociated mixture (1.9 mg total protein in 2.0 ml) after 1025 hours at $25° ± 2°C$. When the peak tube of the trimer form is incubated for 24 hours at $25° ± 2°C$ (concentration = 0.4 mg/ml) and then rechromatographed, a purified trimer is recovered in good yield (Fig. 32D).

The small amount of intact hormone that always remains at $V_e/V_o = 2.12$ could have arisen for several reasons: because of incomplete cleavage of the peptide backbone during the plasmin digestion, incomplete reduction or alkylation of the second disulfide bond, or both. In contrast to these mechanisms, the presence of

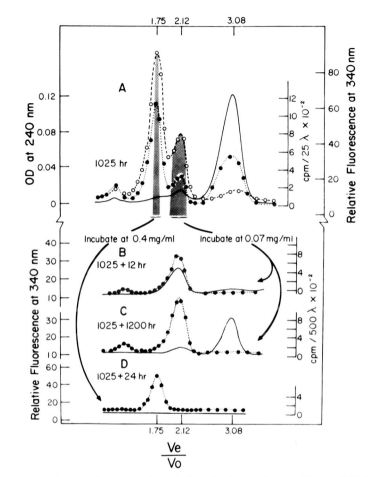

FIG. 32. Exclusion chromatography of dissociated tetra-S-carbamidomethyl-PL-hGH on Sephadex G-100. In (A) the final chromatogram after 1025 hours of incubation is shown. Approximately 1 mg of total protein was applied to the column. The peak representing intact protein ($V_e/V_0 =$ 2.12) was concentrated by ultrafiltration to 0.07 mg of total protein per milliliter. One aliquot of this concentrate was rechromatographed after an additional 12 hours (B) and a second aliquot was allowed to incubate for 1200 additional hours before rechromatography (C). In (D) the peak tube of the amino-terminal fragment ($V_e/V_0 = 1.75$, concentration = 0.4 mg/ml) was directly rechromatographed after 24 additional hours of incubation. All incubations were carried out at 25° ± 2°C. In all chromatograms radioactivity is shown as a solid line (———), optical density as open circles (○---○), and relative fluorescence as filled circles (●····●). Taken from Bewley and Li (1978).

this form might represent an equilibrium state between the intact and the dissociated molecules.

If the 2–3% intact form ($V_e/V_o = 2.12$) from Fig. 32A is pooled and concentrated approximately 2-fold to 0.070 mg/ml by ultrafiltration, essentially no radioactivity can be detected in the filtrate from a PM-10 membrane (Amicon Inc.). Since this membrane is highly permeable to free carboxyl-terminal fragment, it would appear that this material is indeed an undissociated form. Immediate rechromatography of this pooled material also demonstrates it to be intact (Fig. 32B). However, after incubation at this relatively low concentration (0.07 mg/ml) for extended periods, the intact protein further dissociates to an extent of 90–95% (Fig. 32C). It should be noted that in contrast to the incubations carried out at higher concentrations, the amino-terminal fragment now elutes at a potition ($V_e/V_o = 2.10$–2.12) indicating a monomer or possible dimer form, with no evidence of trimer formation. Any attempt to concentrate it by lyophilization or ultrafiltration results only in trimer and more highly aggregated forms. Figure 32A,C clearly demonstrates that this is indeed an equilibrium state since the remaining intact sample will itself spontaneously dissociate further when separated from the fragments, reestablishing the equilibrium. If we assume the overall reaction to be an equilibrium between intact, monomeric, and trimeric forms as shown in Fig. 33, an equilibrium constant at $25° \pm 2°C$ may be calculated from the molar concentrations of these three components. These concentrations may be computed from the known starting concentration of the intact form and the degree of dissociation at equilibrium taken from the elution pattern of radioactivity. Thus, the equilibrium constant is found to be 1.77 mol/liter, corresponding to a standard free energy of dissociation of -340 cal/mol at $25° \pm 2°C$. Again it can be seen how dynamic CD studies, coupled with other dynamic approaches, can be used to "dissect" a complex protein–protein interaction into individual, recognizable physical events. Further use of the information gained in this way is outlined below.

At much the same time that the experiments described above relating to the spontaneous dissociation of tetra-S-carbamidomethylated-PL-hGH were being carried out, other experiments were being successfully performed in which purified samples of the same carbamidomethylated-PL-hGH fragments were

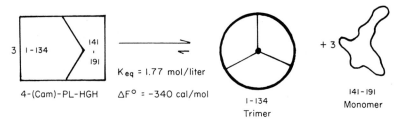

FIG. 33.   Schematic diagram of the equilibrium state for tetra-S-carbamidomethylated-PL-hGH at room temperature in a purely aqueous solvent.

remixed under appropriate conditions and found to spontaneously recombine by noncovalent interaction (complementation) to produce a fully active recombinant molecule in 25% yield (Li and Bewley, 1976a,b; Li et al., 1976). These experiments included the use of a fully synthetic carboxyl-terminal fragment complementing with the natural amino-terminal fragment (Li et al., 1977). In the complementation experiments, the incubations were carried out at 2°C rather than at 25°C, and it was initially assumed that it was this difference in tempera-ture that was responsible for the apparent shift in the equilibrium, allowing spontaneous complementation rather than spontaneous dissociation. Figure 34A shows the elution pattern of a typical complementation mixture. Peak IV repre-sents the intact monomeric form of the tetra-S-carbamidomethyl-PL-hGH re-combinant. Rechromatography of this peak (Fig. 34B) demonstrates that it runs true with only a slight degree of dissociation in 24 hours. Figure 35 presents the CD spectrum of the purified recombinant compared with the spectra of intact and dissociated samples. It is evident that the recombinant is conformationally identical to the intact form. The complete repair of the positive tryptophan band above 290 nm, and the α-helical bands below 250 nm, is especially noteworthy. The recombinant was found to be fully active biologically and immunologically (Li and Bewley, 1976b; Li et al., 1976, 1977).

However, transfer of a fully dissociated sample of tetra-S-carbamidomethylated-PL-hGH from room temperature to 2°C for as long as 2000 hours produced no discernible complementation (Bewley, unpublished results). This seemed to present a dilemma in which the existence of both a spontaneous

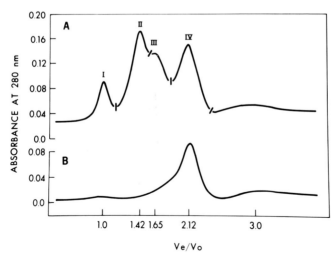

FIG. 34. Exclusion chromatography of the complementation mixture on a Sephadex G-100 column (1.5 × 58 cm) in 0.1 M Tris–Cl buffer at pH 8.2 (A). Fraction IV was concentrated by ultrafiltration and rechromatographed as shown (B). Taken from Li et al. (1977).

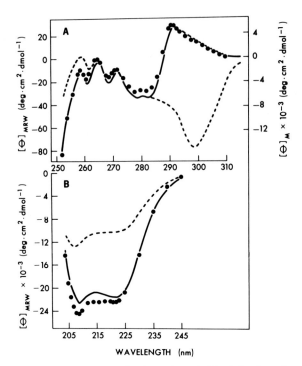

FIG. 35. Circular dichroism spectra in the region of side-chain absorption (A) and amide bond absorption (B). Undissociated Cys(Cam)[53,165,182,189]-PL-hGH (——); dissociated Cys(Cam[53,165,182,189]-PL-hGH (---); the purified recombinant (●●●). Taken from Li et al. (1977).

dissociation and spontaneous complementation violated the second law of thermodynamics.

After a somewhat uncomfortable period of confusion over this situation, it was noted that in all the dissociation experiments, 0.02% NaN$_3$ had routinely been used as a bacteriostat. In contrast, all the complementation experiments contained 2% (v/v) n-butanol for the same purpose. It was decided to test the effect of nonpolar additives on reversing the equilibrium point of the reaction. Since the carboxyl-terminal fragment existed as a random-coil monomer, and the trimer form of the amino-terminal fragment most probably returns to the monomer form before complementation can occur, it seemed reasonable to try the nonpolar solvents first on the trimer form by itself. This trimer was prepared as described by Li and Gráf (1974), rather than by spontaneous dissociation. Trimer prepared in this way is identical to the spontaneously formed trimer except that the negative 298 nm tryptophan band is not as intense (Li and Bewley, 1976a).

Figure 36 shows the effect on the near-UV CD spectra of the amino-terminal trimer, brought about by the addition of 1%, 2%, and 3% (v/v) of n-butanol. The major effect is a nearly complete loss of the negative indole band at 298 nm.

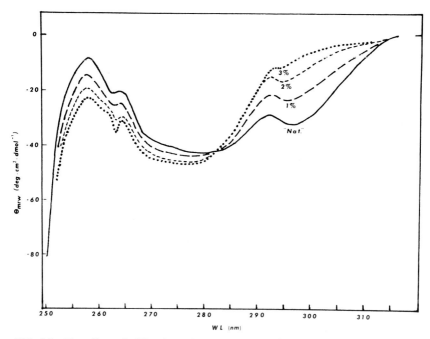

FIG. 36.   The effect of adding increasing amounts (%, v/v) of n-butanol on the side-chain circular dichroism of the amino-terminal fragment. The "Nat" symbolizes the spectrum in the Tris–Cl buffer alone. The percentage (v/v) of n-butanol is shown below each spectrum.

There is no measurable effect on the strong α-helix bands below 250 nm, indicating that the butanol does not affect the secondary structure at all. Chromatography of the butanol-treated fragment also demonstrates that the nonpolar solvent does not produce any appreciable dissociation of the trimer form.

In order to establish whether this was a specific or a general effect, ethanol was also tried. Figure 37 presents the effect on the CD spectra of this same fragment when treated with increasing amounts of ethanol. Again, there is no effect on the secondary structure or state of aggregation of the fragment. It appears that in terms of the indole dichroism at 298 nm, the addition of ethanol is equivalent to n-butanol, although it requires higher concentrations to produce the same quantitative change in conformation. Presumably this reflects the difference in nonpolarity of the two alcohols. Although these additives do not affect the state of aggregation of the trimer, it is obvious that they produce some changes in the tertiary structure. It seemed reasonable to next try test complementations to see whether the carboxyl-terminal fragment could now affect dissociation of the pretreated trimer through complementation. In addition, an improved method (Li, 1978b) for solubilizing the carboxyl-terminal fragment was employed.

Figure 38 demonstrates that after pretreatment of the amino-terminal fragment with 10% (v/v) ethanol, addition of 0.5 equivalent of solubilized carboxyl-

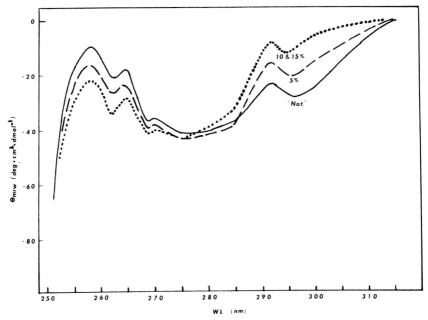

FIG. 37. The effect of adding increasing amounts (%, v/v) of ethanol on the side-chain circular dichroism of the amino-terminal fragment. The "Nat" symbolizes the spectrum in the Tris–Cl buffer alone. The percentage (v/v) of ethanol is shown below each spectrum.

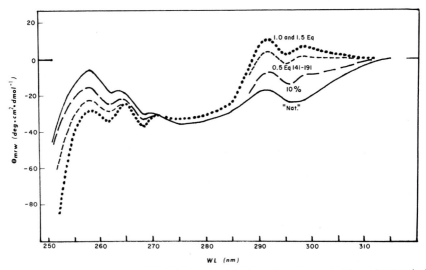

FIG. 38. The effect on the side-chain circular dichroism of pretreatment of the amino-terminal fragment with 10% (v/v) ethanol, followed by addition of 0.5, 1.0, and 1.5 equivalents of the carboxyl-terminal fragment dissolved in dilute NaOH. The "Nat" symbolizes the amino-terminal fragment in the Tris–Cl buffer only.

terminal fragment will produce additional changes in the CD spectrum. The indole dichroism at 298 nm moves to the positive side, more like the intact hormone, and there is a considerable increase in the α-helix content of the mixture (not shown). Addition of a second half-equivalent of carboxyl-terminal fragment produces further changes, the indole dichroism now being fully positive, along with a continued increase in α-helix content. These changes occur very quickly at 27°C, being complete in less than 5 minutes. No significant changes occur on addition of a third half-equivalent. Exclusion chromatography on Sephadex G-100 (Fig. 39) of a one-to-one equivalent mixture, prepared by pretreatment in 10% ethanol, demonstrates about 50% complementation, the rest appearing as high molecular weight aggregates. Larger-scale studies will be required for full characterization of the complemented molecule.

It is evident that the equilibrium position of the dissociation reaction can be changed, leading to approximately 50% recombination by the addition of small amounts of nonpolar solvents, such as n-butanol or ethanol. The evidence indicates that the affect of these mixed solvents is almost wholly on the tertiary structure of the amino-terminal trimer with little or no affect on the secondary structure or state of aggregation of this fragment. It also appears that the complementation is very rapid in comparison to the dissociation. The achievement of 50% complementation in the 10% ethanol experiment is a considerable improvement over previously published results (Li and Bewley, 1976a; Li et al., 1977) reporting 25% yield. Similar improved yields have recently been reported for complementations involving synthetic analogs of the carboxyl-terminal hGH fragment (Li et al., 1978), and a fragment prepared from HCS (Li, 1978b) with the hGH amino-terminal fragment.

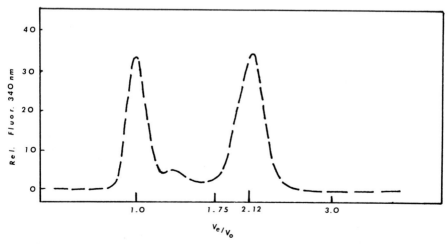

FIG. 39. Exclusion chromatography of approximately 50 μg of a one-to-one equivalent complementation mixture in which the amino-terminal fragment had first been pretreated with 10% (v/v) ethanol.

The dissociation and complementation of the PL-hGH fragment is schematically summarized in Fig. 40. The left-hand side shows the overall dissociation equilibrium to produce the unreactive trimer. Here, the trimer is characterized as "tight," indicating a highly organized, stable structure as evidenced by the very intense negative indole CD band at 298 nm (Fig. 31). The three asterisks symbolize that, in this form, the indole rings in each monomer unit have highly similar or identical environments. Treatment of this "tight" trimer either with 25% (v/v) ethanol or lyophilization from 20% acetic acid, produces the "loose" trimer, with a slightly more disorganized conformation as evidenced by the weaker negative indole CD (Figs. 36–38) and symbolized by the more random placement of the asterisks. This "loose" trimer can be reconverted back into the "tight" form by the sequential dialysis scheme indicated (Bewley, unpublished results). Further treatment of the "loose" trimer with a nonpolar solvent and addition of the carboxyl-terminal fragment allows complementation to occur,

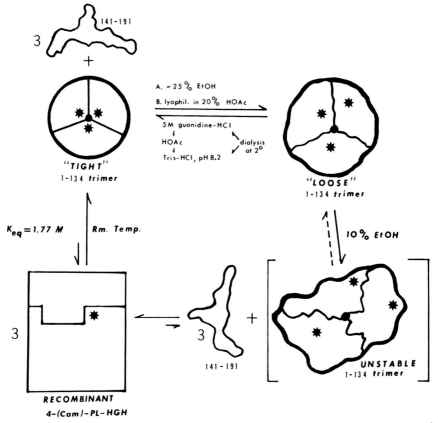

FIG. 40. Schematic diagram of reactions involving the dissociation and complementation of tetra-S-carbamidomethyl-PL-hGH. For explanation, see text.

producing a fully active recombinant whose conformation is identical by CD measurements to the starting intact tetra-S-carbamidomethyl-PL-hGH.

It can be seen how an improved understanding of these complex protein–protein interactions has been aided by following the CD spectra of the reaction mixtures. It is hoped that additional studies of this nature will lead to improved methods of producing, following, and controlling such reactions, with eventual extensions into hormone–receptor interactions.

ACKNOWLEDGMENTS

The author wishes to express his deep gratitude to Professor C. H. Li, who has so generously supported and encouraged his work in this field over the past thirteen years. Experimental work cited in this review was supported in part by grants GM-2907 and AM-6097 and the Hormone Research Foundation (to C. H. Li). Other portions of the work described herein, as well as the writing of the manuscript, were supported in part by a grant to C. H. Li and T. A. Bewley from the National Institutes of Health (AM-18677).

REFERENCES

Aloj, S. M., and Edelhoch, H. (1971). *J. Biol. Chem.* **246,** 5047.
Aloj, S. M., and Edelhoch, H. (1972). *J. Biol. Chem.* **247,** 1146.
Bahl, O. P., Carlsen, R. B., Bellisario, R., and Swaminathan, N. (1972). *Biochem. Biophys. Res. Commun.* **48,** 416.
Bayley, P., Snell, C., and Smyth, D. (1977). *Biochem. Soc. Meeting,* March 1977, University of Aberdeen, Abstract No. 16.
Bewley, T. A. (1977a). *Biochemistry* **16,** 209.
Bewley, T. A. (1977b). *Biochemistry* **16,** 4408.
Bewley, T. A., and Li, C. H. (1970a). *Science* **168,** 1361.
Bewley, T. A., and Li, C. H. (1970b). *Arch. Biochem. Biophys.* **138,** 338.
Bewley, T. A., and Li, C. H. (1971). *Arch. Biochem. Biophys.* **144,** 589.
Bewley, T. A., and Li, C. H. (1972a). *Biochemistry* **11,** 884.
Bewley, T. A., and Li, C. H. (1972b). *Biochemistry* **11,** 927.
Bewley, T. A., and Li, C. H. (1975). *Arch. Biochem. Biophys.* **167,** 80.
Bewley, T. A., and Li, C. H. (1978). *Biochemistry* **17,** 3315.
Bewley, T. A., Brovetto-Cruz, J., and Li, C. H. (1969). *Biochemistry* **8,** 4701.
Bewley, T. A., Sairam, M. R., and Li, C. H. (1972a). *Biochemistry* **11,** 932.
Bewley, T. A., Kawauchi, H., and Li, C. H. (1972b). *Biochemistry* **11,** 4179.
Bewley, T. A., Dixon, J. S., and Li, C. H. (1972c). *Int. J. Pept. Protein Res.* **4,** 281.
Bewley, T. A., Sairam, M. R., and Li, C. H. (1974). *Arch. Biochem. Biophys.* **163,** 625.
Beychok, S. (1966). *Science* **154,** 1288.
Beychok, S. (1967). *In* "Poly-α-amino Acids" (G. D. Fasman, ed.), Vol. 1, Chapter 7. Dekker, New York.
Blundell, T. L., Dodson, G. G., Dodson, E. J., Hodgkin, D. C., and Vijayan, M. (1971a). *Recent Prog. Horm. Res.* **27,** 1.
Blundell, T. L., Cutfield, J. F., Cutfield, S. M., Dodson, E. J., Dodson, G. G., Hodgkin, D. C., Mercola, D. A. and Vijayan, M. (1971b). *Nature (London)* **231,** 506.
Breslow, E. (1970). *Proc. Natl. Acad. Sci. U.S.A.* **67,** 493.
Breuer, C. B. (1969). *Endocrinology* **85,** 989.

Cahn, R. S., Ingold, C., and Prelog, V. (1966). *Angew. Chem. Int. Ed. Engl.* **5**, 385.

Carmac, M., and Neubert, L. A. (1967). *J. Am. Chem. Soc.* **89**, 7134.

Casey, J. P., and Martin, R. B. (1972). *J. Am. Chem. Soc.* **94**, 6141.

Chen, C.-J. H., and Sonnenberg, M. (1977). *Biochemistry* **16**, 2110.

Chen, Y.-H., Yang, J.-T., and Chau, K.-H. (1974). *Biochemistry* **13**, 3350.

Clarke, W. C., Hayashida, T., and Li, C. H. (1974). *Arch. Biochem. Biophys.* **164**, 571.

Coleman, D. L., and Blout, E. R. (1968). *J. Am. Chem. Soc.* **90**, 2405.

Cox, B. M., Goldstein, A., and Li, C. H. (1976). *Proc. Natl. Acad. Sci. U.S.A.* **73**, 1821.

Crabbé, P. (1972). *In* "ORD and CD in Chemistry and Biochemistry" (P. Crabbé, ed.), p. 1. Academic Press, New York.

De La Llosa, P., and Jutisz, M. (1969). *Biochim. Biophys. Acta* **181**, 426.

Dellacha, J. M., Santomé, J. A., and Paladini, A. C. (1968). *Ann. N. Y. Acad. Sci.* **148**, 313.

Dickerson, R. E., and Geis, I. (1969). *In* "The Structure and Action of Proteins" Benjamin, New York.

Djerassi, C. (1960). *In* "Optical Rotatory Dispersion." McGraw-Hill, New York.

Dodson, R. M., and Nelson, V. C. (1968). *J. Org. Chem.* **33**, 3966.

Edelhoch, H., and Lippoldt, R. E. (1970). *J. Biol. Chem.* **245**, 4199.

Gráf, L., and Li, C. H. (1973). *Biochem. Biophys. Res. Commun.* **53**, 1304.

Gráf, L., and Li, C. H. (1974). *Biochem. Biophys. Res. Commun.* **56**, 168.

Gráf, L., Li, C. H., and Bewley, T. A. (1975). *Int. J. Pept. Protein Res.* **7**, 467.

Gráf, L., Cseh, G., Barát, E., Ronai, A. Z., Székely, J. I., Kanessey, A., and Bajusz, S. (1977). *Ann. N. Y. Acad. Sci.* **297**, 63.

Greenfield, N., and Fasman, G. D. (1969). *Biochemistry* **8**, 4108.

Hara, K., Chen, C.-J. H., and Sonnenberg, M. (1978). *Biochemistry* **17**, 550.

Holladay, L. A., and Puett, D. (1975). *Arch. Biochem. Biophys.* **171**, 708.

Holladay, L. A., Hammonds, R. G., and Puett, D. (1974). *Biochemistry* **13**, 1653.

Holzwarth, G. (1964). Ph.D. Dissertation, Harvard Univ., Cambridge, Massachusetts.

Holzwarth, G., and Doty, P. (1965). *J. Am. Chem. Soc.* **87**, 218.

Horwitz, J., Strickland, E. H., and Billups, C. (1969). *J. Am. Chem. Soc.* **91**, 184.

Horwitz, J., Strickland, E. H., and Billups, C. (1970). *J. Am. Chem. Soc.* **92**, 2119.

Ito, N., and Takagi, T. (1970). *Biochim. Biophys. Acta* **221**, 430.

Jirgensons, B., and Ward, D. N. (1970). *Tex. Rep. Biol. Med.* **28**, 553.

Kemp, J. C. (1969). *J. Opt. Soc. Am.* **59**, 950.

Kostyo, J. L., Mills, J. B., Reagan, C. R., Rudman, D., and Wilhelmi, A. E. (1976). *Excerpta Med. Found. Int. Congr. Ser.* **381**, 33.

Kramers, H. A. (1927). *Atti. Congr. Int. Fisici. Como* **2**, 545.

Kronig, R. D. (1926). *J. Opt. Soc. Am.* **12**, 547.

Lamkin, W. M., Fujino, M., Mayfield, J. D., Holcomb, G. N., and Ward, D. N. (1970). *Biochim. Biophys. Acta* **214**, 290.

Lewis, U. J., Singh, R. N. P., and Seavey, B. K. (1972). *In* "Prolactin and Carcinogenesis" (A. R. Boyns and K. Griffiths, eds.), pp. 4–12. Alpha Omega Alpha Publ. Co., Cardiff, Wales.

Li, C. H. (1968). *Perspect. Biol. Med.* **11**, 498.

Li, C. H. (1970). *Ann. Sclavo* **12**, 651.

Li, C. H. (1972). *Proc. Am. Philos. Soc.* **116**, 365.

Li, C. H. (1973). *J. Int. Res. Commun.* **1**, 19.

Li, C. H. (1976). *Int. J. Pept. Protein Res.* **8**, 205.

Li, C. H. (1978a). *Perspect. Biol. Med.* **21**, 447.

Li, C. H. (1978b). *Proc. Natl. Acad. Sci. U.S.A.* **75**, 1700.

Li, C. H. and Bewley, T. A. (1976a). *Excerpta Med. Found. Int. Congr. Ser.* **381**, 85.

Li, C. H., and Bewley, T. A. (1976b). *Proc. Natl. Acad. Sci. U.S.A.* **73**, 1476.

Li, C. H., and Chung, D., (1976). *Proc. Natl. Acad. Sci. U.S.A.* **73**, 1145.

Li, C. H., and Gráf, L. (1974). *Proc. Natl. Acad. Sci. U.S.A.* **71**, 1197.

Li, C. H., Barnafi, L., Chrétien, M., and Chung, D. (1965). *Nature (London)* **208,** 1093.
Li, C. H., Liu, W. K., and Dixon, J. S. (1966a). *J. Am. Chem. Soc.* **88,** 2050.
Li, C. H., Barnafi, L., Chrétien, M., and Chung, D. (1966b). *Excerpta Med. Found. Int. Congr. Ser.* **112,** 349.
Li, C. H., Dixon, J. S., Lo, T.-B., Schmidt, K. D., and Pankov, Y. A. (1970). *Arch. Biochem. Biophys.* **141,** 705.
Li, C. H., Dixon, J. S., and Chung, D. (1973a). *Arch. Biochem. Biophys.* **155,** 95.
Li, C. H., Gordon, D., and Knorr, J. (1973b). *Arch. Biochem. Biophys.* **156,** 493.
Li, C. H., Hayashida, T., Doneen, B. A., and Rao, J. A. (1976). *Proc. Natl. Acad. Sci. U.S.A.* **73,** 3463.
Li, C. H., Bewley, T. A., Blake, J., and Hayashida, T. (1977). *Proc. Natl. Acad. Sci. U.S.A.* **74,** 1016.
Li, C. H., Blake, J., and Hayashida, T. (1978). *Biochem. Biophys. Res. Commun.* **82,** 217.
Liao, T. H., and Pierce, J. G. (1970). *J. Biol. Chem.* **245,** 3275.
Liao, T. H., and Pierce, J. G. (1971). *J. Biol. Chem.* **246,** 850.
Liu, W.-K., Nahm, H. S., Sweeney, C. M., Lamkin, W. M., Baker, H. N., and Ward, D. N. (1972). *J. Biol. Chem.* **247,** 4351.
Loh, H. H., Cho, T. M., Wu, Y. C., and Way, E. L. (1975). *Life Sci.* **14,** 2231.
Loh, H. H., Tseng, L. F., Wei, E., and Li, C. H. (1976). *Proc. Natl. Acad. Sci. U.S.A.* **73,** 2895.
Loh, H. H., Cho, T. M., Wu, Y. C., Harris, R. A., and Way, E. L. (1977). *Life Sci.* **16,** 1811.
Ludescher, U., and Schwyzer, R. (1971). *Helv. Chim. Acta* **54,** 1637.
Makarov, A. A., Esipova, N. A., Pankov, Y. A., Brishkousky, B. A., Lobachev, U. M., and Sukhomudrenko, A. G. (1976). *Mol. Biol. (Moscow)* **10,** 704.
Menendez-Botet, C. J., and Breslow, E. (1975). *Biochemistry* **14,** 3825.
Mills, J. B., Reagan, C. R., Rudman, D., Kostyo, J. L., Zachariah, P., and Wilhelmi, A. E. (1973). *J. Clin. Invest.* **52,** 2941.
Morgan, F. J., and Canfield, R. E. (1971). *Endocrinology* **88,** 1045.
Nagarajan, R., and Woody, R. W. (1973). *J. Am. Chem. Soc.* **95,** 7212.
Neri, P., Arezzini, C., Botti, R., Cocola, F., and Tarli, P., (1973). *Biochim. Biophys. Acta* **322,** 88.
Niall, H. D. (1972). *Prolactin Carcinog. Proc. Tenovus Workshop, 4th,* p. 13.
Niall, H. D., Hogan, M. L., Sauer, R., Rosenblum, I. Y., and Greenwood, R. C. (1971). *Proc. Natl. Acad. Sci. U.S.A.* **68,** 866.
Papkoff, H., and Ekblad, M. (1970). *Biochem. Biophys. Res. Commun.* **40,** 614.
Papkoff, H., and Samy, T. S. A. (1967). *Biochim. Biophys. Acta* **147,** 175.
Papkoff, H., Sairam, M. R., and Li, C. H. (1971). *J. Am. Chem. Soc.* **93,** 1531.
Parlow, A. F. (1961). *In* "Human Pituitary Gonadotropins" (A. Albert, ed.), pp. 300–310, Thomas, Springfield, Illinois.
Pernollet, J. C., and Garnier, J. (1971). *FEBS Lett.* **18,** 189.
Pierce, J. G., Liao, T. H., Carlsen, R. B., and Reimo, T. (1971a). *J. Biol. Chem.* **246,** 866.
Pierce, J. G., Bahl, O. P., Cornell, J. S., and Swaminathan, N. (1971b). *J. Biol. Chem.* **246,** 2321.
Puett, D. (1972). *Biochemistry* **11,** 1980.
Reagan, C. R., Mills, J. B., Kostyo, J. L., and Wilhelmi, A. E. (1975). *Proc. Natl. Acad. Sci. U.S.A.* **72,** 1684.
Sairam, M. R., and Li, C. H. (1973). *Biochem. Biophys. Res. Commun.* **51,** 336.
Sairam, M. R., Papkoff, H., and Li, C. H. (1972a). *Arch. Biochem. Biophys.* **153,** 554.
Sairam, M. R., Papkoff, H., and Li, C. H. (1972b). *Biochem. Biophys. Res. Commun.* **48,** 530.
Sairam, M. R., Papkoff, H., and Li, C. H. (1972c). *Biochim. Biophys. Acta* **278,** 421.
Sasaki, K., Dockerill, S., Adamiak, D. A., Tickle, I. J., and Blundell, T. (1975). *Nature (London)* **257,** 751.
Sherwood, L. M., Handwerger, S., McLaurin, W. D., and Lanner, M. (1971). *Nature (London), New Biol.* **233,** 59.
St.-Pierre, S., Gilardeau, C., and Chrétien, M. (1976). *Can. J. Biochem.* **54,** 992.

Strickland, E. H. (1974). *C.R.C. Crit. Rev. Biochem.* **2**, 113.

Swaminathan, N., and Bahl, O. P. (1970). *Biochem. Biophys. Res. Commun.* **40**, 422.

Venkatachalam, C. M. (1968). *Biopolymers* **6**, 1425.

Winnewisser, G., Winnewisser, N., and Gordy, W. (1968). *J. Chem. Phys.* **49**, 3465.

Yadley, R. A., and Chrambach, A. (1973). *Endocrinology* **93**, 858.

Yamashiro, D., Rigbi, M., Bewley, T. A., and Li, C. H. (1975). *Int. J. Pept. Protein Res.* **7**, 389.

Yang, J.-T., Bewley, T. A., Chen, G. C., and Li, C. H. (1977). *Proc. Natl. Acad. Sci. U.S.A.* **74**, 3235.

DISCUSSION

D. N. Ward: In circular dichroism you are measuring effects at a very narrow wavelength. In the older ORD, or optical rotatory dispersion, which was mainly used before 1964, you measure perturbations that spread out over the whole wavelength spectrum. Do you think there is any possibility of obtaining more structural information from combinations of these two methods?

T. A. Bewley: Yes, I think that is a very good question. As you have indicated, CD came into vogue, and in doing so it pushed ORD almost completely out of the picture because CD is capable of looking much more selectively at these transitions. The problem is that carbohydrates do not show transitions that can be seen in the CD because those transitions lie below 180 nm. Therefore, they do not show up with commercial instruments. This means that, for instance, in the case of the glycoprotein hormones, we can look at the polypeptide chain and say that it completely repairs or does not, but we cannot look at the carbohydrate portion except those residues that you yourself have shown are N-acetylated. These have a legitimate amide bond that is dichroic, as shown by David Puett and his colleagues. I am sure he is correct. What we would like to do is go backward in history a bit and resurrect ORD, as we would like to look at sugars as we refold the LH. We know how long it takes to produce the right molecular weight and how long it takes to put the polypeptide chain back in its place. We know how long it takes to put the two buried tyrosine residues back into their place, but we do not yet know at what rate the sugars refold. For this type of study, ORD may be useful.

B. F. Rice: This is a beautiful exposition on those conformational changes, and I wonder whether anyone else has any data on the opposite end of this business, and this receptor for polypeptide hormone; is this even amenable to this type of examination?

T. A. Bewley: I would be the first to shout EUREKA if handed a beaker of 0.1 *M* receptors. However, one problem is that, first of all, there is no highly purified receptor preparation that we can measure. The other problem is that the receptors presumably have very large molecular weights. They would probably tend to scatter light a great deal, and CD spectra are badly distorted by any sample that scatters light. Until complete solubilization of the receptor can be produced, without dismembering it, it is going to be a rough job; but we have hope.

T. F. Davies: Regarding your recombination studies with placental lactogens and growth hormone, why have you chosen human placental lactogen, when ovine placental lactogen is most active as one of the most human growth hormone receptors?

T. A. Bewley: Professor Li had human placental lactogen on hand from earlier studies and our laboratory has not yet prepared any ovine placental lactogen, but I agree that is an important molecule to try. Stay with us, we'll get to it.

K. Sterling: Your presentation was most enjoyable, and at times it was reminiscent of Charles Tanford. What I missed is the Cotton effect. Could you show us that on one of your slides?

T. A. Bewley: The Cotton effect is the effect that is measured by optical rotatory dispersion rather than circular dichroism. Here is a graph [sketch on blackboard] with the wavelength across the bottom. In ordinary optical density, we have an absorption band, in a Gaussian shape, which is always positive. Next, we have a CD band, which may be either positive or negative depending on the local geometry, but the wavelength maximum would be the same. Now, if we were to measure optical rotation as a function of wavelength, this would give a Cotton effect. The optical rotation will start here, it will rise, then go through zero at the wavelength maximum. It will then go down, and stretch asymptotically to infinity in both directions. The shape of this curve is the Cotton effect. Actually that is why Dr. Ward was talking about measuring the optical rotation of the sugars. We cannot see them because their transitions lie very far into the ultraviolet, but because ORD curves extend to infinity, we can see the presence of the sugars by looking in the near ultraviolet.

E. H. Frieden: This may have been implicit in what you said at the end, but if it was I missed it. Have you tried hybridization experiments with growth hormones of various species? If so, what about the biological properties of the hybrids?

T. A. Bewley: It was implied that we were hoping to do this in the future; to create fragments of growth hormones from various species and build hybrids using the complementation reaction and following the process with CD. So far we just have not had time to do that many variations yet. We have used nothing natural other than HCS, and Dr. Li chose it first because it is so similar in sequence. There are only 23 or so amino acids that are different, and only seven of those are nonconservative replacements, yet there is a big difference in the biological profile. We hope in time to be able to use other pieces from other species.

T. Landefeld: I have a similar type of question in regard to the glycoprotein hormones. Have you looked at any of the other glycoprotein hormones, or perhaps, hybrid molecules made from the alphas and betas of those hormones, to see whether or not they have similar spectra? In other words, would you expect that, if you took alphas that are identical or very similar and put them with betas to make hybrid molecules, to see a spectrum that would look similar to that for the original intact hormone? For example, a follicle-stimulating hormone (FSH) hybrid consisting of an alpha from LH and a beta from FSH?

T. A. Bewley: We have looked at ovine FSH, pregnant mare serum gonadotropin (PMSG), and ovine LH. The point is that all of these have differences in their CD spectra. FSH does not look exactly like LH: it has a similar type of spectrum, but is recognizably different. PMSG is again different from either one of those two. I expect that each one of these different alpha–beta complexes, although the alpha portion is the same or very similar, will have a different conformer when it is finally melded together, and it will be these differences that will show in the CD and are also responsible for the specificity of action.

T. Landefeld: So, in other words, do the various alpha subunits show similar spectra and the beta subunits different ones?

T. A. Bewley: I have not done that particular experiment, but it is another one I'll try to do.

L. S. Jacobs: I am curious about your statements regarding the biological activities of the recombinants, since in the hands of some investigators, the biological activity of plasmin digests may not be exactly equivalent to that of native hormone, but rather increased by as much as severalfold. When you say that full biological activity was recovered, do you mean full with respect to that of the plasmin digest, or full with respect to undigested hormone?

T. A. Bewley: It means "full" in respect to native human growth hormone. When we used plasmin in our laboratory, Li and Gráf showed that only a hexapeptide is removed. The resulting molecule has full activity related to native growth hormone. Other investigators have found samples of plasmin that apparently will remove 12 residues, rather than 6. That molecule appears to have increased activity relative to native growth hormone, which I suspect is due to its being more stable. It is imploded rather than exploded.

L. S. Jacobs: Has the crop sac-stimulating activity of the hybrid molecules been examined as well as their growth-promoting activity?

T. A. Bewley: My recollection is that they are equivalent. They go back to the same as native growth hormone—not increased.

W. L. Duax: As a crystallographer, I would like to comment on the relevance of data from crystal structure determinations to the dynamics of molecular behavior *in vitro* and *in vivo*. By looking at different crystal forms or complexes of the same compound, one may learn about molecular flexibility or the existence of conformational isomers that will also be present in solution. For instance, two crystal forms of insulin (the 2-zinc and the 4-zinc complexes) illustrate an interesting conformational flexibility in the B chain. Eight residues on one terminus of the B chain that are in a linear conformation in 2-zinc insulin are found to be helical in 4-zinc insulin. This transition can be brought about through adjustment of pH and can be reversibly effected in the solid state. Structural data of this nature, obtained in the solid state complement your data on change in protein conformation in solution as a function of pH.

My impression has been that in solution more than one conformer of a given molecule may be present and that spectral measurements are a statistically weighted average of the spectra of the individual conformers. To what extent do you feel that a given CD spectrum represents a unique conformation of a protein molecule?

T. A. Bewley: First, let me say that I did not mean to pan crystallography at all. The two studies, crystallography and CD are adjunct to one another. I fully agree. Now, as to the question of conformers, of course you are quite right. The CD looks at the time-average conformation of the entire population of molecules. Some of them may be vibrating a little bit, others are moving through wide conformational limits, but the time-average may be the same. So we have to be very careful when we interpret these spectra. We may find two molecules that have the same CD, but are not the same in terms of the stability of their conformations. For instance, one may be digested by proteolytic enzymes much faster than the other.

M. M. Grumbach: I wish to comment on the question of the biologic activity and immunoreactivity of modified and recombinant hGH preparations. Our group has had a long-standing collaboration with Dr. C. H. Li and Dr. Bewley, who have provided the hGH preparations and through much extra effort have characterized their purity. By comparing the manner in which radioligand binding of highly purified monomeric native hGH in several defined immunoassays and receptor assays is affected (1) by tetra-S-carbamoylmethylated plasmin modified hGH (RCAM-Pl-hGH); (2) by an hGH recombinant of the natural amino-terminal fragment Cys(Cam)^{53}-hGH (1–134) with a synthetic carboxy-terminal fragment Cys(Cam)^{165,182,189}-hGH (141–191); and (3) by the recombinant resulting from the noncovalent complementation of the reduced carbamoylmethylated 134-residue amino-terminal fragment of hGH with the reduced Cys(Cam)^{51} residue of hCS, Burstein, Kaplan, and I have attempted to obtain information on the structural conformation of the displacing species and structure–function relationships of the hGH molecule. The hGH recombinant with the natural carboxyl fragment and the recombinant with the synthetic carboxyl fragment reacted in 7 immunoassay systems and 2 receptor assay systems in a similar manner and with comparable potency to its naturally occurring analog as well as to the native hormone. While these preparations had comparable or greater immunoreactivity than native hGH in a monospecific hGH radioimmunoassay (RIA), they had only 20–25% of the radioreceptor activity. The RCAM-PL-hGH, while exhibiting comparable immunoreactivity to native hGH, had reduced radioreceptor activity even though it is reported to exhibit augmented activity in the rat tibia assay. The hGH (1–134) fragment and hGH (141–191) fragment did not displace native hGH in the radioreceptor assay or RIA. These studies suggested that subtle alterations in molecular conformation could be detected by this approach. Further, the determinants for hepatic growth hormone receptor binding and for lactogenic receptor binding appear to be on the amino-terminal fragment; similarly the antigenic determinants for a monospecific anti-hGH serum also are on the amino-terminal fragment.

L. S. Jacobs: Some time ago, we examined the radioreceptor assay activity of plasmin-digested human growth hormone which had been reported by Dr. U. J. Lewis and his associates to have enhanced growth hormone and prolactin bioactivity. In both the pregnant rabbit liver and the pregnant rat liver assay systems, these preparations had substantially less activity than that of the native hormone. I have no fully satisfactory explanation for these results, although I probably should note that the lyophilized preparations we tested were not freshly prepared.

T. A. Bewley: I have no explanation for that either. I have never looked at the CD or the stability of those preparations.

G. Baumann: I may have an explanation. We have looked at some of Chrambach's plasmin-digested hGH which exhibits enhanced activity and lacks a dodecapeptide in the large disulfide loop *in vivo* in man. The metabolic clearance rate of the cleaved, more active form, appeared to be slower *in vivo* whereas, as Dr. Jacobs said, in receptor assays the cleaved forms have virtually identical binding activity when compared with intact hGH. Thus, it may be slower *in vivo* metabolism which is responsible for the enhanced bioactivity.

T. A. Bewley: That is a very interesting result. I am glad to hear that, because I had talked to Andreas about it and suggested that all we can think of was that it has a longer half-life and that is the reason for its increased activity—not that it is more efficient with the receptor.

J. M. McKenzie: I wonder if you would care to speculate, probably excessively, for a moment. TSH and thyroid-stimulating antibody of Graves' disease stimulate the thyroid in a virtually identical fashion. Although the immunoglobulin has a much larger molecular weight than has TSH you can cut it down, and the FAb fragment of about 50,000 molecular weight has qualitatively the same action on the thyroid. If you were to get TSH and this Fab fragment purified and in solution, would you expect their CD spectra to be similar, if they were acting on the identical receptor?

T. A. Bewley: I cannot say yes to that. For instance, morphine and β-endorphin act on the same receptor, but certainly will not have the same CD spectra. I am going to leave it at that.

H. Keutmann: With regard to the solvent studies, you emphasized at the outset that extensive formation of α-helix is favored in the presence of methanol, but later it appeared that butanol and ethanol had less effect on secondary structure. Is this simply a result of different concentrations used, or is there some rule of thumb concerning the different alcohols and their effects on far-UV vs. near-UV changes?

T. A. Bewley: In the first instances we were using relatively large amounts of alcohol, higher concentrations, on flexible peptides. In the second instance, we are using very small amounts of alcohol on fairly rigid peptides, so there is much less effect in the second case than in the first.

M. C. Rao: I wonder whether you have done any studies with iodinated hormones to see whether or not they exhibited an altered CD profile.

T. A. Bewley: I know of one example that I have looked at with Dr. Kawauchi, and that is ovine prolactin. When ovine prolactin is iodianted it seems to have a supraactive tyrosine: tyrosine 44. This tyrosine diiodinates, not monoiodinates. I presume that when it is iodinated for radioimmunoassay the same thing happens. This modification changes the CD of the iodinated protein, and we do not know quite what this means. We think it means a conformational change after iodination.

C. Monder: A substantial amount of literature has accumulated on the conformational analysis of proteins and peptides by nuclear magnetic resonance. A number of systems have been dealt with in great detail, for example, in the studies of Roderick Walter with vasopressin, oxytoxin, and related peptides. Do circular dichroism and NMR yield the same kinds of information? If they do, how do the results of the two kinds of studies compare with each other?

T. A. Bewley: In general, the CD studies will look at smaller portions of the protein. With NMR, one can, in principle, look at all the protons. CD can only look at those residues that absorb light. This includes tryptophan, tyrosine, phenylalanine, and, of course, the amide and disulfide bonds. CD cannot look at the side chains of leucine, alanine, or lysine, for example. NMR can look at everything. Of course the trouble is that when you do the NMR of a globular protein, you get everything.

Receptor-Mediated Uptake of Lipoprotein-Cholesterol and Its Utilization for Steroid Synthesis in the Adrenal Cortex

MICHAEL S. BROWN, PETRI T. KOVANEN, AND JOSEPH L. GOLDSTEIN

Departments of Molecular Genetics and Internal Medicine,
University of Texas Health Science Center at Dallas,
Dallas, Texas

I. Introduction

A. EVIDENCE THAT ADRENAL STEROIDS ARE DERIVED FROM PLASMA CHOLESTEROL

In 1945, Bloch fed isotopic cholesterol to a pregnant woman and isolated labeled pregenanediol from her urine, thus establishing that steroid hormones are derived from cholesterol (Bloch, 1945). In the succeeding 10 years, the major pathways for this conversion were elucidated, largely through studies of perfused bovine adrenal cortex. The latter studies were reviewed at a Laurentian Hormone Conference by Hechter *et al.* (1951). A major question then remained: How did the adrenal gland obtain the cholesterol that it used for steroid hormone synthesis?

In a classic experiment, Morris and Chaikoff (1959) fed [^{14}C]cholesterol to rats and found that the specific activity of adrenal cholesterol became equal to that of plasma. These data created the strong likelihood that the bulk of adrenal cholesterol in the rat was derived not from synthesis *in situ,* but rather by means of uptake from plasma cholesterol. Subsequently, Dexter, Fishman, and Ney (1970) showed that the uptake of [^{3}H]cholesterol from plasma into adrenal cortex was enhanced by adrenocorticotropin (ACTH) in rats. Finally, in a series of complex isotopics studies, Borkowski and co-workers (1970, 1972a,b) presented evidence that the bulk of adrenal cholesterol in humans is derived from plasma cholesterol.

Despite the overwhelming evidence that plasma cholesterol can gain access to the adrenal gland and the further suggestion that the uptake process might be regulated, few experiments were conducted to determine whether some type of specific uptake mechanism was involved. The possibility that such a specific uptake mechanism might exist was raised by the discovery in 1974 that cultured mammalian cells possess a cell surface receptor that facilitates the uptake of cholesterol carried in plasma lipoproteins (Brown and Goldstein, 1974; Goldstein

215

and Brown, 1974). This lipoprotein uptake process was originally delineated in cultured human fibroblasts, which were shown to obtain all their cholesterol from the receptor-mediated uptake of one specific plasma lipoprotein, called low-density lipoprotein (LDL). In this paper, we briefly review the earlier studies of the LDL receptor in fibroblasts and then present the evidence that a similar receptor plays a key role in steroid synthesis in adrenocortical cells.

B. PLASMA LDL

Figure 1 shows a model of LDL, which is the major cholesterol-carrying lipoprotein in human plasma. The bulk of the cholesterol carried in LDL is located in an apolar core that contains approximately 1600 molecules of choles-terol per lipoprotein particle. Each molecule of cholesterol in this core is ester-ified with a long-chain fatty acid, the most abundant of which is linoleate. Surrounding this cholesteryl ester core is a polar coat consisting of phos-pholipids, relatively small amounts of free cholesterol, and a protein called apoprotein B (Jackson *et al.*, 1976; Kane, 1977). The structure of apoprotein B has not been elucidated, owing to its frustrating tendency to aggregate when it is delipidated. However, a growing body of evidence suggests that apoprotein B is composed of multiple identical subunits, each having a molecular weight of 25,000–35,000. Seven to ten of these subunits are associated to form a chain of approximately 240,000 daltons, and two such chains are present in each LDL particle. The nature of the chemical link between the apoprotein B monomers that form the two chains is not yet known (Bradley *et al.*, 1978; Deutsch *et al.*, 1978; Kuehl *et al.*, 1977).

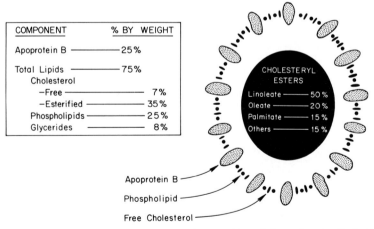

COMPONENT	% BY WEIGHT
Apoprotein B	25%
Total Lipids	75%
Cholesterol	
—Free	7%
—Esterified	35%
Phospholipids	25%
Glycerides	8%

CHOLESTERYL ESTERS

Linoleate	50%
Oleate	20%
Palmitate	15%
Others	15%

Apoprotein B
Phospholipid
Free Cholesterol

FIG. 1.   Schematic diagram of the structure and composition of plasma low-density lipoprotein (LDL). Plasma LDL is depicted as a lipoprotein particle composed of an apolar core of esterified cholesterol that is surrounded by a polar coat composed of phospholipid, free cholesterol, and apoprotein B.

C. THE LDL RECEPTOR PATHWAY IN HUMAN FIBROBLASTS

Inasmuch as the bulk of the cholesterol in LDL is esterified, fibroblasts must have some way to hydrolyze these cholesteryl esters if they are to obtain the free cholesterol needed for membrane synthesis. The sequence of reactions by which LDL is taken up by the cells and its cholesteryl esters hydrolyzed has been called the LDL receptor pathway (Brown and Goldstein, 1976; Goldstein and Brown, 1976, 1977). As shown in Fig. 2, the critical component of this pathway is a cell surface receptor that specifically binds the apoprotein component of LDL (Brown and Goldstein, 1974; Goldstein *et al.*, 1976; Mahley *et al.*, 1977; Shireman *et al.*, 1977; Steinberg *et al.*, 1978). In fibroblasts these receptors are located in discrete segments of the plasma membrane called coated pits (Anderson *et al.*, 1976, 1977). Approximately once every 5 minutes, each coated pit invaginates into the cell and pinches off to form a coated vesicle that carries the receptor-bound LDL to lysosomes. Within the lysosomes, the protein component of LDL is hydrolyzed (Goldstein and Brown, 1974; Goldstein *et al.*, 1975a), the cholesteryl esters of LDL are cleaved by an acid lipase, and the resultant free cholesterol is transported from the lysosome into the cellular compartment (Brown *et al.*, 1975a,c; Goldstein, *et al.*, 1975b). In fibroblasts this free cholesterol is used primarily for membrane synthesis (Brown *et al.*, 1975c).

The cholesterol derived from LDL also serves as the mediating agent for three

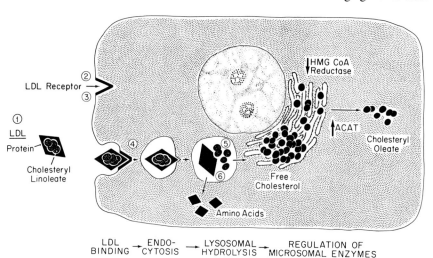

FIG. 2. Sequential steps in the low-density lipoprotein (LDL) receptor pathway. Numbers indicate the sites at which mutations have been identified in human cells: (1) abetalipoproteinemia; (2) familial hypercholesterolemia, receptor-negative; (3) familial hypercholesterolemia, receptor-defective; (4) familial hypercholesterolemia, internalization defect; (5) Wolman's disease; and (6) cholesteryl ester storage disease. HMG CoA reductase denotes 3-hydroxy-3-methylglutaryl coenzyme A reductase; ACAT denotes acyl-CoA: cholesterol acyltransferase. From Brown and Goldstein (1976).

regulatory actions that stabilize its intracellular concentration. First, the incoming cholesterol suppresses the activity of 3-hydroxy-3-methylglutaryl coenzyme A reductase (HMG-CoA reductase), the rate-controlling enzyme of cholesterol biosynthesis (Brown *et al.*, 1973, 1974). Second, the free cholesterol activates a microsomal acyl-coenzyme A:cholesteryl acyltransferase (ACAT), which esterifies any excess free cholesterol that is generated from LDL so that it can be stored as cholesteryl ester droplets (Goldstein *et al.*, 1974; Brown *et al.*, 1975b). Finally, the free cholesterol derived from LDL suppresses the synthesis of LDL receptors, thus preventing an overaccumulation of cholesterol (Brown and Goldstein, 1975).

An important concept arising from studies of the LDL pathway in human fibroblasts was that the receptor is specific for LDL; thus, under normal circumstances, LDL is the only lipoprotein that supplies cholesterol for cell growth. The other major cholesterol-carrying lipoprotein in human plasma is high-density lipoprotein (HDL), which contains two major proteins, apoproteins A-I and A-II. HDL does not bind to the LDL receptor and thus is not able to satisfy the cholesterol requirements of fibroblasts (Brown *et al.*, 1975c; Mahley *et al.*, 1977). In certain animals that are fed large amounts of cholesterol, a new lipoprotein, called HDL_c, accumulates in plasma (Mahley, 1978). Although this lipoprotein does not contain apoprotein B, it contains a protein with similar properties called the arginine-rich protein or apoprotein E. Because the arginine-rich protein can also bind to the LDL receptor, HDL_c can deliver cholesterol to fibroblasts just as can LDL (Bersot *et al.*, 1976; Mahley *et al.*, 1977; Mahley, 1978). HDL_c may be of importance in pathologic states; however, it has not been shown to occur in appreciable amounts in normal plasma, and hence its role in normal physiology is presently uncertain.

That the LDL receptor pathway is not limited to fibroblasts was established by the demonstration that LDL receptors were active in a variety of human cell types in culture, including arterial smooth muscle cells (Albers and Bierman, 1976; Brown *et al.*, 1977) and lymphoblasts (Ho *et al.*, 1976b). Moreover, this receptor pathway has been demonstrated in fibroblast lines from several other animal species, including mice, hamsters, swine, and monkeys (for review, see Goldstein and Brown, 1976, 1977). Finally, freshly isolated human lymphocytes have been shown to satisfy their cholesterol requirements by taking up LDL through the receptor pathway, suggesting that this receptor functions in cells in the human body (Ho *et al.*, 1976a, 1977; Bilheimer *et al.*, 1978).

The physiologic importance of the LDL receptor pathway became apparent when it was found that a series of allelic mutations in the gene specifying the LDL receptor causes familial hypercholesterolemia, one of the most common single gene-determined disorders affecting man (Brown and Goldstein, 1974, 1979). In heterozygotes with this disease, the number of functional receptors is reduced by one-half, the efficiency of degradation of LDL in the body is reduced by 50%, and the lipoprotein accumulates in plasma to levels of 2- to 3-fold above normal, with the result that myocardial infarctions occur early in middle age. In patients with the homozygous form of this disease, LDL receptors are either absent or markedly reduced, the efficiency of LDL degradation is severely impaired, the lipoprotein accumulates to massive levels in plasma, and severe atherosclerosis occurs in the first few years of life (Fredrickson *et al.*, 1978; Goldstein and Brown, 1978) Other genetic defects in the LDL receptor pathway in man are also known (Fig. 2).

On the basis of the cited studies and experiments performed in other laboratories (for review, see Havel *et al.*, 1979), it has been suggested that LDL functions to transport cholesterol from absorptive and synthetic sites (intestine and liver, respectively) to extrahepatic parenchymal cells, which utilize the sterol for structural and metabolic purposes. In the absence of receptors or with a diminished number, LDL clearance from plasma is impaired and the atherogenic consequences of hypercholesterolemia become manifest.

II. The LDL Receptor Pathway in Adrenal Cortex

The elucidation of the LDL receptor pathway in fibroblasts immediately raised the possibility that a similar sequence might play a role in delivering cholesterol to steroid-secreting cells. In general, steroid-secreting cells require much more cholesterol than other cells since, in addition to the cholesterol needed for membrane synthesis, these cells require cholesterol for conversion to steroids. Accordingly, in 1975 we set out to look for the LDL receptor pathway in adrenal cells. Table I lists the four models systems that we have used to demonstrate its presence and physiological significance. In the remainder of this paper, we discuss each of these systems in detail. The data are then utilized to assemble a general working model for cholesterol homeostasis in the adrenal gland.

A. THE FIRST MODEL: MOUSE ADRENAL TUMOR CELLS IN CULTURE (Y-1 CLONE)

The first steroid-secreting cells that were demonstrated to possess an LDL receptor pathway were the Y-1 clone of functioning mouse adrenal tumor cells (Faust *et al.*, 1977). Early studies by Kowal (1970) had shown that these cells,

TABLE I

LDL Metabolism in Adrenal Cortex: Four Model Systems

1. *Mouse* adrenal tumor cells in culture (Y-1 clone)
2. *Rats* treated *in vivo* with 4-aminopyrazolopyrimidine (4-APP)
3. *Bovine* adrenal cortex
   a. Cells in culture
   b. Membranes prepared from *in vivo* tissues
4. *Human* fetal adrenal membranes

which were placed in culture by Sato and co-workers (Buonassisi *et al.*, 1962; Yasumura *et al.*, 1966), responded to ACTH by secreting 11β-hydroxydihydroprogesterone (11β-hydroxy-DHP) as the primary steroid. Their failure to produce corticosterone has been attributed to a loss of the 21-β-hydroxylase enzyme in tissue culture (Kowal, 1970). Figure 3 shows the amount of 11β-hydroxy-DHP secreted into the medium by the Y-1 cells when they were incubated in serum from which the lipoproteins had been removed (lipoprotein-deficient serum). When the cells were incubated in the absence of ACTH (Fig. 3A), little steroid was produced. The addition of human LDL caused only a slight enhancement. When the cells were incubated in the presence of ACTH, but still in the absence of lipoproteins, some increase in the output of 11β-hydroxy-DHP was observed (Fig. 3B). However, the response to ACTH was limited by the availability of lipoprotein cholesterol, as evidenced by the observation that the addition of human LDL produced a 3-fold increase in the amount of steroids secreted over 48 hours (Fig. 3B). The addition of human or mouse HDL did not stimulate steroid secretion. These data suggested that the mouse Y-1 adrenal cells might possess an LDL receptor that allows them to utilize the cholesterol of LDL for steroid synthesis (Faust *et al.*, 1977).

The presence of this receptor was demonstrated formally by incubating the Y-1 cells with ^{125}I-labeled LDL (^{125}I-LDL) at 4°C. As shown in Fig. 4, the adrenal cells bound the ^{125}I-LDL at a surface binding site that showed saturability and high affinity. When the cells were subsequently treated with heparin, most of the

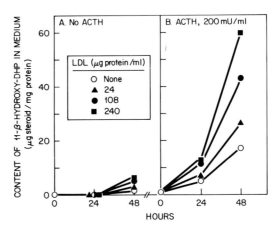

FIG. 3. Enhancement of steroid secretion by human low-density lipoprotein (LDL) in mouse Y-1 adrenal cells previously incubated in lipoprotein-deficient serum. On day 7 of cell growth, each monolayer received 2 ml of medium containing lipoprotein-deficient serum in the absence (A) or the presence (B) of 200 mU of ACTH per milliliter. On day 8 (zero time), the medium was replaced with fresh medium of the same composition but containing the indicated concentration of human LDL. After incubation at 37°C for an additional time as indicated, the medium was removed for measurement of its content of 11β-hydroxy-DHP and the cells were harvested for measurement of their total protein content. From Faust *et al.* (1977).

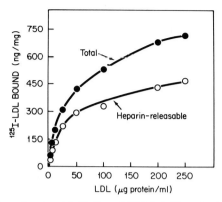

FIG. 4.   Total and heparin-releasable binding of ^{125}I-labeled low-density lipoprotein (^{125}I-LDL) to mouse Y-1 adrenal cells at 4°C. On day 7 of cell growth, each monolayer received 2 ml of medium containing lipoprotein-deficient serum and 200 mU of ACTH per milliliter. On day 8, the cells were chilled to 4°C for 30 minutes, after which the indicated concentration of human ^{125}I-LDL (152 cpm/ng) was added to the medium. After incubation at 4°C for 2 hours, each monolayer was washed extensively, and the amount of total (●) and heparin-releasable (○) ^{125}I-LDL bound to the cells was determined. From Faust *et al.* (1977).

surface-bound ^{125}I-LDL was released. These findings are similar to those in human fibroblasts in which ^{125}I-LDL can be released from the receptor by exposure to sulfated gylcosaminoglycans, such as heparin and dextran sulfate (Goldstein *et al.*, 1976).

The lipoprotein receptor on the mouse adrenal cells was shown to bind both human and mouse LDL. On the other hand, neither human or mouse HDL competed for ^{125}I-LDL binding, indicating that the mouse adrenal receptor, like the human fibroblast receptor, was specific for LDL (Faust *et al.*, 1977). When the cells were incubated with ^{125}I-LDL continuously at 37°C, the receptor-bound LDL was internalized by the cell and the protein component was hydrolyzed in lysosomes, yielding [^{125}I]monoiodotyrosine, which was excreted into the culture medium. When the adrenal cells were incubated with ^{125}I-LDL in the presence of chloroquine, a nonspecific inhibitor of lysosomal enzymes (Goldstein *et al.*, 1975a), the hydrolysis of the lipoprotein was blocked, and intact ^{125}I-LDL accumulated progressively within lysosomes. Through the use of LDL whose cholesteryl ester component had been labeled with [^{3}H]cholesteryl linoleate, we showed that the cholesteryl ester component of LDL was also hydrolyzed within lysosomes (Faust *et al.*, 1977).

Uptake of LDL by the Y-1 cells regulated the processes of cholesterol synthesis and cholesterol esterification. When the cells were grown in the absence of lipoproteins, the activity of HMG-CoA reductase, the rate-controlling enzyme in cholesterol synthesis, was high. The resulting high rate of cholesterol synthesis within the cell was able to support cell growth. However, under these conditions, the cells did not accumulate any stored cholesteryl esters, and steroid secretion in response to ACTH was minimal. When LDL was taken up through the receptor pathway, the free cholesterol released from the lysosomal hydrolysis of the lipoprotein satisfied the cholesterol requirement of the cells and suppressed HMG-CoA reductase (Faust *et al.*, 1977). The data in Fig. 5 show the degree of suppression of this enzyme that was obtained when the cells were incubated with either human or mouse LDL. On the other hand, mouse or human HDL, which did not bind to the LDL receptor, did not deliver cholesterol to cells or suppress HMG-CoA reductase activity.

The uptake of LDL-cholesterol by the Y-1 adrenal cells led to an enhancement in the rate at which the cells incorporated [^{14}C]oleate into cholesteryl [^{14}C]oleate. This enhancement was due to an increase in the activity of the microsomal cholesterol-esterifying enzyme ACAT (Faust *et al.*, 1977). As a result of this increased synthesis of cholesteryl esters, the Y-1 adrenal cells accumulated large amounts of stored cholesteryl esters in the presence of LDL (Fig. 6A). HDL caused no such effect. Similarly, LDL caused a marked stimulation in the rate of secretion of 11β-hydroxy-DHP, whereas HDL had no effect (Fig. 6B).

Figure 7 shows the time course of metabolism of LDL labeled with [^{3}H] cholesteryl linoleate after its addition to the monolayers of Y-1 adrenal cells. The left panel shows that in the absence of ACTH the content of [^{3}H]cholesteryl esters increased rapidly and reached a steady-state plateau. These esters were continually being hydrolyzed, generating free cholesterol, which also rose in the

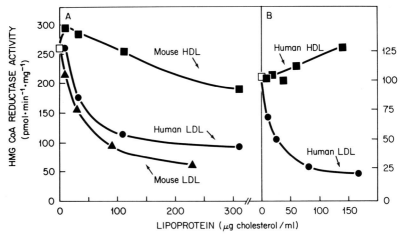

FIG. 5. Comparison of the ability of human and mouse low-density lipoprotein (LDL) and high-density lipoprotein (HDL) to suppress HMG CoA reductase activity in mouse Y-1 adrenal cells. On day 7, each monolayer received 2 ml of medium containing lipoprotein-deficient serum supplemented with the indicated concentration of one of the following lipoproteins. Experiment A: □, none; ●, human LDL; ▲, mouse LDL; or ■, mouse HDL. Experiment B: □, none; ●, human LDL; or ■, human HDL. After incubation for 24 hours at 37°C, the cells were harvested for measurement of HMG-CoA reductase activity. From Faust *et al.* (1977).

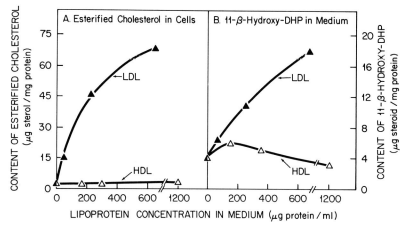

FIG. 6. Accumulation of esterified cholesterol (A) and stimulation of 11β-hydroxy-dihydroprogesterone secretion (B) in the presence of mouse low-density lipoprotein (LDL) but not high-density lipoprotein (HDL) in mouse adrenal Y-1 cells. On day 7, each monolayer received 2 ml of medium containing lipoprotein-deficient serum and 100 mU of ACTH per milliliter. On day 8, each monolayer received the same medium containing the indicated concentration of either mouse LDL or mouse HDL. After incubation for 24 hours at 37°C, the medium was removed for measurement of its content of 11β-hydroxy-DHP and the cells were harvested for measurement of their content of esterified cholesterol. From Faust *et al.* (1977).

cell until it too reached a steady state after about 24 hours (Fig. 7A). Even in the absence of exogenous ACTH, some of the free [³H]cholesterol was converted to 11β-hydroxy-DHP (Fig. 7a, triangles). In the presence of ACTH the conversion of the LDL-derived [³H]cholesterol to 11β-hydroxy-DHP was markedly accelerated (Fig. 7B, triangles). The kinetics suggest that [³H]cholesterol liberated from the hydrolysis of LDL must first equilibrate with a cellular pool of [³H] cholesterol before it is converted to steroids. We also showed that the addition of ACTH caused a 2- to 3-fold increase in the number of LDL receptors in the Y-1 cells, thus explaining the increased availability of cholesterol for steroid synthesis (see Fig. 16).

The experiments with the Y-1 cells demonstrated that, when these cells were grown in the steady state in the presence of LDL and when they were maximally stimulated with ACTH, approximately 75% of the secreted steriod was derived from the LDL-cholesterol obtained through the receptor-mediated pathway and 25% was derived from cholesterol synthesized within the cells (Faust *et al.*, 1977). At lower levels of steroid secretion, the proportion derived from LDL-cholesterol was even higher. In all its biochemical aspects, the LDL receptor of the Y-1 cells was similar to the LDL receptor in human fibroblasts. Moreover, the cholesterol derived from LDL regulated the same three events that it did in fibroblasts: suppression of HMG CoA reductase, stimulation of the ACAT, and suppression of the synthesis of LDL receptors.

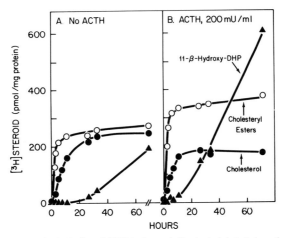

FIG. 7. Uptake and hydrolysis of [³H]cholesteryl linoleate-labeled low-density lipoprotein (LDL) and secretion of 11β-hydroxy-[³H]DHP in mouse adrenal Y-1 cells incubated in the absence (A) and in the presence (B) of ACTH. On day 7, each monolayer received 2 ml of medium containing lipoprotein-deficient serum in the absence (A) or in the presence (B) of 200 mU/ml of ACTH. On day 8 (zero time), the medium was replaced with fresh medium of the same composition but containing 1 μg of protein per milliliter of [³H]cholesteryl linoleate-LDL (50,000 cpm/nmol of cholesteryl linoleate). After incubation at 37°C for the indicated time, the medium was removed and its content of 11β-hydroxy-[³H]DHP (▲) was measured by thin-layer chromatography. The monolayers were than washed and harvested for measurement of the cellular content of [³H]cholesteryl linoleate (○) and [³H]cholesterol (●) by thin-layer chromatography. From Faust *et al.* (1977).

B. THE SECOND MODEL: RATS TREATED *in Vivo* WITH 4-AMINOPYRAZOLOPYRIMIDINE

To demonstrate that the adrenal gland *in vivo* was normally dependent upon lipoprotein-derived cholesterol for steroid hormone synthesis, we employed a rat model using the drug 4-aminopyrazolopyrimidine (4-APP) (Balasubramaniam *et al.*, 1976; Andersen and Dietschy, 1976). Henderson (1963) had demonstrated that this drug, which is an adenine analog, blocked the secretion of lipoproteins from liver in rats. Figure 8, taken from the work of Balasubramaniam *et al.* (1977b), shows that when rats were treated with 4-APP the plasma cholesterol level fell by more than 90% over the ensuing 24 hours. In association with the fall in plasma cholesterol levels, the cholesteryl ester content of the adrenal gland fell by more than 95% over 48 hours (Balasubramanian *et al.*, 1977b). In rats with normal plasma cholesterol levels, the rate of cholesterol synthesis in the adrenal is low (Dietschy and Wilson, 1970), and this was associated with a low activity of the rate controlling enzyme HMG-CoA reductase (Fig. 8B). However, when adrenal cholesteryl ester levels fell in the 4-APP-treated rat, the activity of HMG-CoA reductase rose by as much as 200-fold (Balasubramaniam *et al.*, 1977a,b), and cholesterol synthesis was increased by up to 50-fold (Andersen

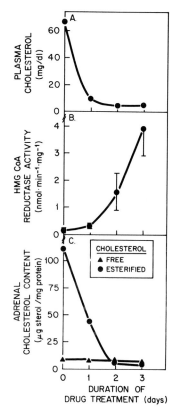

FIG. 8. Plasma cholesterol levels (A), adrenal HMG-CoA reductase activity (B), and adrenal cholesterol content (C) as a function of duration of administration of 4-aminopyrazolopyrimidine (4-APP) to rats. Daily doses of 4-APP (50 mg/kg) were administered intraperitoneally to rats for the number of days indicated. The rats were killed 24 hours after the last dose, and the indicated measurements were made. Each point represents the mean of values obtained from three rats. The brackets represent 1 SEM for the HMG-CoA reductase values. From Balasubramaniam *et al.* (1977b).

and Dietschy, 1976; Balasubramaniam *et al.*, 1977b). The fall in adrenal cholesteryl esters and the rise in HMG-CoA reductase was prevented when the animals were treated with dexamethasone, indicating that the massive stimulation of HMG-CoA reductase requires both hypocholesterolemia and high ACTH levels (Balasubramaniam *et al.*, 1977b).

Figure 9 shows that when the adrenal cholesteryl esters had been depleted by 4-APP treatment, the subsequent infusion of human LDL raised the plasma cholesterol level, replenished the adrenal cholesteryl esters, and suppressed HMG CoA reductase. As in the cultured mouse Y-1 adrenal cells, the accumulation of cholesteryl esters from LDL in the 4-APP-treated rat was associated with a marked enhancement in ACAT activity. Table II shows that in the 4-APP-

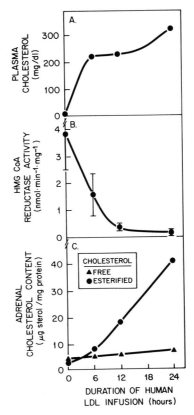

FIG. 9. Effect of human low-density lipoprotein (LDL) on the plasma cholesterol level (A), adrenal HMG-CoA teductase activity (B), and adrenal cholesterol content (C) of rats previously treated with 4-aminopyrazolopyrimidine (4-APP). Four groups of rats were treated intraperitoneally with 4-APP (50 mg/kg per day) for 3 days. The animals in three of these groups were then given an intravenous bolus injection of human LDL (20 mg of cholesterol), followed by a continuous infusion of the lipoprotein at the rate of 1.6 mg of cholesterol per hour for the indicated time. The control rats received no LDL. Each point represents the mean of values obtained from two or three rats. The brackets represent 1 SEM for the HMG-CoA reductase values. From Balasubramaniam *et al.* (1977b).

treated rat the ACAT activity of the adrenal gland decreased in parallel with the decrease in the esterified cholesterol content and the increase in HMG-CoA reductase activity. Subsequent infusion of LDL produced a 10-fold enhancement in the activity of the ACAT enzyme. The fatty acid composition of the cholesteryl esters that accumulated in the adrenal reflected this endogenous esterification activity. This follows from the observation that the cholesteryl esters of infused LDL were predominantly cholesteryl linoleate, while the esters that accumulated in the cell were predominantly cholesteryl oleate (Balasubramaniam *et al.*, 1977b). Thus, the increase in adrenal cholesteryl ester content did not

TABLE II

Reciprocal Changes in Activities of HMG-CoA Reductase and ACAT in Adrenal Gland of Rats Treated with 4-APP and Then Infused with Human LDL[a-c]

Treatment of rats	Plasma cholesterol level (mg/dl)	HMG-CoA reductase activity (nmol min^{-1} mg^{-1})	ACAT activity (pmol min^{-1} mg^{-1})	Content of esterified cholesterol (μg sterol/mg)
None	46	0.03	630	68
4-APP	3	6.40	65	5
4-APP + LDL infusion	128	0.05	678	35

[a] From Balasubramaniam et al. (1977b).

[b] Two groups of rats were treated intraperitoneally with 4-APP (50 mg/kg/day) for 3 days. The control rats received daily intraperitoneal injections of sodium phosphate buffer. Twelve hours after the third injection of 4-APP, each group of rats received an intravenous bolus injection either of 0.15 M NaCl or of human LDL (32 mg of cholesterol) as indicated. Twelve hours after the injections (on day 4) all animals were killed. Each value represents the mean ± 1 SEM of values obtained from three rats.

[c] HMG-CoA, 3-hydroxy-3-methylglutaryl coenzyme A; ACAT, acyl-CoA:cholesteryl acyl-transferase; 4-APP, 4-aminopyrazolopyrimidine; LDL, low-density lipoprotein.

result simply from the uptake of intact LDL, but rather arose from the reester-
ification of free cholesterol derived from the uptake and lysosomal hydrolysis of
the cholesteryl esters of LDL.

In a subsequent study it was shown that the regulation of cholesterol synthesis
in the adrenal of the 4-APP-treated rat resulted not only from changes in
HMG-CoA reductase activity, but also reflected changes in 3-hydroxy-3-
methylglutaryl coenzyme A synthase (HMG-CoA synthase), the enzyme immediately preceding HMG-CoA reductase in the cholesterol biosynthetic pathway (Balasubramaniam et al., 1977a). The data in Table III demonstrate the
parallel increase in HMG-CoA synthase and HMG-CoA reductase in the
4-APP-treated rat. In contrast, acetoacetyl-CoA thiolase and mevalonate
kinase, the enzymes immediately preceding and following the synthase and
reductase in the cholesterol synthetic pathway, did not change significantly. The
data in Fig. 10 also demonstrate that HMG-CoA synthase and reductase were
suppressed in parallel when the cholesterol content of the plasma was restored by
infusion of human LDL into the 4-APP-treated rats. Once again, thiolase and
kinase activities did not change.

An interesting by-product of these studies was the observation that adrenal
HMG-CoA reductase and HMG-CoA synthase normally undergo a diurnal
rhythm. As shown in Fig. 11, the high point of the cycle was seen at about 1:00
AM, the midpoint of the dark phase. The peak occurred several hours after the
peak in plasma corticosterone levels (Balasubramaniam et al., 1977a), suggesting that cholesterol synthesis was activated after the gland had secreted large
amounts of steroid.

In related studies, we showed that 3 hours after the infusion of ACTH into
otherwise untreated rats the cholesteryl ester content of the adrenal gland dropped
by about 50% and HMG-CoA reductase activity rose. However, in these intact
animals, which had normal plasma lipoprotein levels, the continuation of the
ACTH infusion led to a rise in the level of adrenal cholesteryl esters to control
levels by 6 hours and to a fall in HMG-CoA reductase activity during the same
interval (Balasubramaniam et al., 1977b).

Taken together, the above experiments demonstrate that the adrenal gland of
the rat responds to ACTH immediately by hydrolyzing its stored cholesteryl
esters and transiently activating cholesterol synthesis. However, when plasma
cholesterol is available, the uptake of plasma lipoprotein cholesterol soon takes
place, and the gland returns to a new steady state with low HMG-CoA reductase
levels and high cholesteryl ester stores. When plasma cholesterol is not available
owing to 4-APP treatment, cholesteryl ester levels in the gland continue to fall,
and cholesterol synthesis continues to rise.

The general pattern of these results was similar to the pattern of regulation that
had been demonstrated in the cultured mouse Y-1 cells. However, one important
difference was noted. Whereas in the Y-1 cells the cholesterol requirement was
satisfied by a lipoprotein receptor that specifically bound LDL and did not

TABLE III

Effect of 4-APP on Enzymes of the Cholesterol Biosynthetic Pathway in Rat Adrenal Gland[a–c]

Treatment of rats	Cytosolic acetoacetyl-CoA thiolase (nmol min^{-1} mg^{-1})	Cytosolic HMG-CoA synthase (nmol min^{-1} mg^{-1})	Microsomal HMG-CoA reductase (nmol min^{-1} mg^{-1})	Cytosolic mevalonate kinase (nmol min^{-1} mg^{-1})
(a) Control	310	0.29	0.12	3.3
(b) 4-APP	240	4.1	6.1	2.3
(b)/(a)	0.8	14	51	0.7

[a] From Balasubramaniam et al. (1977a).

[b] Rats were treated as indicated, adrenal glands from four rats were pooled, cytosolic and microsomal fractions were prepared, and enzyme activities were determined as previously described.

[c] 4-APP, 4-aminopyrazolopyrimidine; HMG-CoA, 3-hydroxy-3-methylglutaryl coenzyme A.

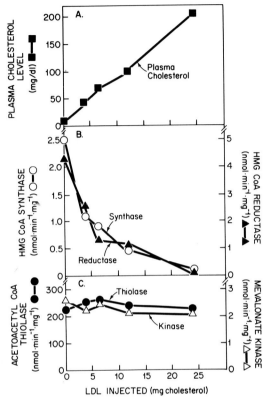

FIG. 10. Effect of various doses of human low-density lipoprotein (LDL) on the plasma cholesterol level (A), adrenal HMG CoA synthase and reductase activities (B), and adrenal acetoacetyl-CoA thiolase and mevalonate kinase activities (C) of rats previously treated with 4-aminopyrazolopyrimidine (4-APP). Five groups of rats (three rats per group) were treated with 4-APP for 3 days. Twelve hours after the last dose of 4-APP, four groups of rats received the indicated amount of human LDL intravenously as a bolus. The control group received an intravenous injection of 0.15 M NaCl. All the animals were killed 12 hours later (on day 4). From Balasubramaniam *et al.* (1977b).

recognize HDL, in the intact rat HDL was several times more effective than LDL in supplying cholesterol to the adrenal gland (Balasubramaniam *et al.*, 1977b). The data in Fig. 12 show that administration of human HDL to the 4-APP-treated rat produced an increase in the cholesteryl ester content of the adrenal gland and suppressed HMG-CoA reductase activity. Similar results were obtained using rat HDL.

Andersen and Dietschy (1976, 1977) have also observed that both HDL and LDL can deliver cholesterol to the adrenal gland of the 4-APP-treated rat. In careful quantitative comparisons, these authors showed that, whereas the maximal rate of uptake of cholesterol was similar from HDL and LDL, the concentra-

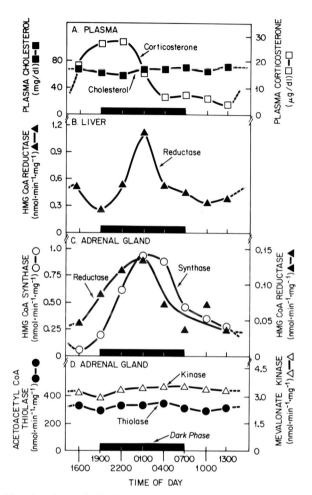

FIG. 11.   Diurnal variations in the level of plasma corticosterone (A) and in the activities of hepatic HMG-CoA reductase (B), adrenal HMG-CoA synthase and reductase (C), and adrenal acetoacetyl-CoA thiolase and mevalonate kinase (D) in the rat. Twenty-four rats were housed in cages in which lighting was supplied between the hours of 0700 and 1900 daily. After 3 weeks of such treatment, groups of three animals were killed at intervals of 3 hours as indicated. Blood was collected, and the livers and adrenal glands from the three animals were excised and pooled for homogenization. From Balasubramaniam *et al.* (1977a).

tion of HDL-cholesterol required for half-maximal uptake was 4-fold less than that required for LDL-cholesterol (Dietschy, 1978).

At least four explanations can be suggested to account for the rat data: (1) the rat adrenal gland possesses a receptor that can somehow bind both human HDL and LDL, even though these two lipoproteins share no proteins in common; (2) the rat adrenal gland possesses a receptor that is specific for a distinct lipoprotein that can be derived from both human HDL and LDL during circulation in the

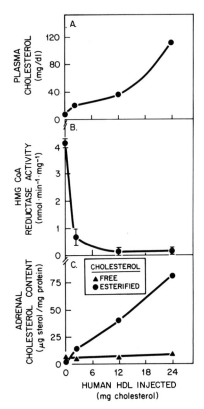

FIG. 12. Effect of human high-density lipoprotein (HDL) on the plasma cholesterol level (A), adrenal HMG-CoA reductase activity (B), and adrenal cholesterol content (C) of rats previously treated with 4-aminopyrazolopyrimidine (4-APP). Four groups of rats were treated intraperitoneally with 4-APP (50 mg/kg per day) for 3 days. Twelve hours after the last dose of 4-APP, three groups of rats received the indicated amount of human HDL intravenously as a bolus. The control group received no HDL. All the animals were killed 12 hours later (on day 4). Each point represents the average of values obtained from two or three rats. The brackets represent 1 SEM for HMG-CoA reductase values. From Balasubramaniam *et al.* (1977b).

4-APP-treated rat; (3) the rat adrenal gland possesses two distinct receptors, one for HDL and one for LDL; or (4) no specific receptors analogous to the mouse Y-1 adrenal cells are involved and the rat adrenal takes up cholesterol by a mechanism that shows no lipoprotein specificity. At present it is not possible to decide among these four possibilities. Gwynne and co-workers (1976) showed that radiolabeled free cholesterol was taken up more rapidly from HDL than from LDL in rat adrenal slices, but unidirectional flux was not measured and the uptake of labeled cholesterol may actually have represented isotope exchange.

It should be pointed out that the rat has the lowest plasma level of LDL of any mammalian species. In contrast to the human, where the plasma LDL-cholesterol level is 2- to 3-fold higher than the HDL-cholesterol level, in the rat the HDL-cholesterol level is 2- to 3-fold higher than the LDL-cholesterol level (Havel *et al.*, 1979). Because of this deficiency of LDL, it might be expected that the rat uses some mechanism in addition to the LDL receptor to supply large amounts of cholesterol to the adrenal gland. A different situation seems to exist in larger animals including the cow, swine, dog, and man. In these species the concentration of plasma LDL is much higher than in the rat, and in each of these species a specific high-affinity LDL binding site can be demonstrated on isolated adrenal membranes (discussed below).

C. THE THIRD MODEL: BOVINE ADRENAL CORTEX

1. Adrenocortical Cells in Culture

The studies of the Y-1 cells of the mouse and the adrenal gland of the 4-APP-treated rat established the principle that plasma lipoprotein cholesterol could be used as the primary source of adrenal cholesterol for conversion to steroid hormones. However, as discussed above, the data suggested that different mechanisms of lipoprotein uptake might be involved in the two systems. The cultured mouse Y-1 cells used a specific receptor that only recognized LDL, whereas the rat adrenal gland *in vivo* appeared able to use cholesterol that was infused intravenously either in the form of LDL or HDL. To determine whether this difference was related to a species difference or to a difference in the behavior of cultured cells versus cells in the body, we recently turned to a system that allows a direct comparison of *in vivo* and *in vitro* results. These studies were made possible by the recent work of Gospodarowicz *et al.* (1977) and Hornsby and Gill (1977, 1978), who have developed a method to establish primary cultures of functioning adult bovine adrenocortical cells. Cells are dissociated from the adrenal cortex by digestion with collagenase and are then plated in Petri dishes. When grown in the presence of fibroblast growth factor, the cells divide and form confluent monolayers. They can be subcultured for up to 50 generations, and they respond to ACTH, cholera toxin, or prostaglandins by secreting steroids into the culture medium (Hornsby and Gill, 1977, 1978). However, since the cells rapidly lose the 11β-hydroxylase enzyme, they produce a variety of 11-deoxysteroids instead of cortisol or corticosterone (Simonian *et al.*, 1978).

Hornsby and Gill kindly sent us a vial of primary bovine adrenocortical cells, and we were able to maintain the line in cell culture (Kovanen *et al.*, 1979b). The data in Fig. 13A demonstrate that when the cells were grown in the absence of lipoproteins and in the absence of a stimulus to steroid secretion, only small amounts of fluorogenic steroids were secreted. The addition of LDL or HDL under these conditions did not stimulate steroid secretion significantly. When the cells were grown in the presence of cholera toxin, steroid output remained low in the absence of lipoproteins (Fig. 13B). However, under identical conditions the

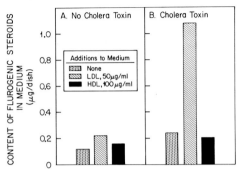

FIG. 13. Fluorogenic steroid secretion by monolayers of bovine adrenocortical cells after addition of cholera toxin and human lipoproteins to the culture medium. On day 6 of cell growth, each monolayer received 2 ml of medium containing lipoprotein-deficient serum and either no cholera toxin (A) or 0.8 μg of cholera toxin per milliliter (B). On day 7 (zero time), the medium was replaced with the identical medium supplemented with one of the following human lipoproteins: none, 50 μg of protein per milliliter of low-density lipoprotein (LDL) or 100 μg of protein per milliliter of high-density lipoprotein (HDL). Every 24 hours the medium was replaced with fresh medium containing the indicated addition. On day 10 the medium was removed for measurement of fluorogenic steroids that had accumulated during the 24-hour interval between days 9 and 10. The average content of cell protein in each dish at the end of the experiment was 300 μg. From Kovanen *et al.* (1979b).

addition of LDL produced a 5-fold stimulation of fluorogenic steroid secretion. The addition of HDL produced no such effect. Similar results were obtained with either bovine or human lipoproteins.

The data in Fig. 14 further illustrate the dependence of the bovine adrenocortical cells on the presence of LDL in order to achieve maximal steroid output. When the cells were incubated with increasing amounts of ACTH, there was little stimulation of steroid secretion unless LDL was present in the medium (Fig. 14A). Similar results were obtained with cholera toxin (Fig. 14B). These data suggested that the bovine adrenocortical cells in culture possessed a specific LDL receptor that was similar to the one previously described for human fibroblasts and cultured mouse Y-1 adrenal cells.

To demonstrate this receptor directly, we incubated the bovine adrenocortical cells with increasing amounts of ^{125}I-LDL and ^{125}I-HDL. The data in Fig. 15A show that as the concentration of ^{125}I-LDL was increased in the culture medium the cellular content of radioactivity rose with saturation kinetics. No high-affinity uptake process of ^{125}I-HDL could be demonstrated. Similarly, the cells degraded the ^{125}I-LDL by a saturable high-affinity process (Fig. 15B). No high-affinity degradation of either human or bovine ^{125}I-HDL could be demonstrated.

Additional experiments showed that human or bovine LDL, but not human or bovine HDL, suppressed HMG-CoA reductase activity, stimulated cholesteryl ester formation, and increased the cholesteryl ester content of the bovine adrenocortical cells (Kovanen *et al.*, 1979b). These results were identical to those previously obtained with the cultured mouse Y-1 Cells (Faust *et al.*, 1977).

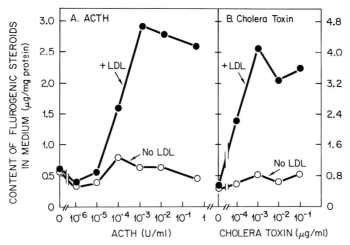

FIG. 14. Stimulation of fluorogenic steroid secretion in monolayers of bovine adrenocortical cells by varying concentrations of ACTH (A) and cholera toxin (B) in the absence (○) and in the presence (●) of human low-density lipoprotein (LDL). On day 6 of cell growth, each monolayer received 2 ml of medium containing lipoprotein-deficient serum and the indicated concentration of either ACTH or cholera toxin. On days 7 and 8 the medium was replaced with the identical medium supplemented with no LDL (○) or 50 μg of protein per milliliter of LDL (●). On day 9, the medium was removed for measurement of the amount of fluorogenic steroids that had accumulated during the 24-hour interval between days 8 and 9. From Kovanen et al. (1979b).

Conversion of LDL-cholesterol to steroids was demonstrated directly with the use of LDL in which the endogenous cholesteryl esters had been replaced with exogenous [³H]cholesteryl linoleate (Krieger et al., 1978). When this reconstituted lipoprotein was incubated with the bovine adrenocortical cells in the presence of cholera toxin, the cholesteryl esters of LDL were rapidly converted to ³H-labeled cholesterol and secreted steroids. The major ³H-labeled secreted steroid that was detected was 11-deoxycortisol (Kovanen et al., 1979b).

In both the bovine adrenocortical cells and the mouse Y-1 adrenal cells, the activity of the LDL receptor was susceptible to metabolic and hormonal regulation. The data in Fig. 16A show that when bovine adrenocortical cells were incubated in the absence of LDL the activity of the LDL receptor was relatively high and the activity could be stimulated an additional 3-fold by the addition of cholera toxin. When the cells were grown in the presence of LDL and in the absence of a stimulus to hormone secretion, LDL receptor activity was quite low. Under these conditions, the addition of cholera toxin also produced an increase in LDL receptor activity. We calculated that in the presence of LDL the amount of LDL-cholesterol supplied by this increase in LDL receptor activity could account for all of the measured increase in steroid production in the presence of cholera toxin in the bovine adrenocortical cells. Similar results were obtained with ACTH (Kovanen et al., 1979b). The data in Fig. 16B show that ACTH also

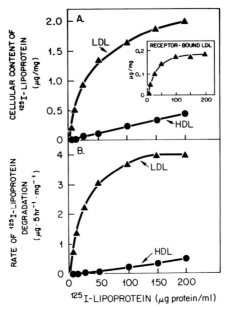

FIG. 15.   Saturation curves for total uptake (A) and degradation (B) of human ^{125}I-labeled low-density lipoprotein (^{125}I-LDL) (▲) and human ^{125}I-labeled high-density lipoprotein (^{125}I-HDL) (●) in monolayers of bovine adrenocortical cells. On day 6 of cell growth, each monolayer received 2 ml of medium containing lipoprotein-deficient serum and 0.4 μg/ml of cholera toxin. On day 8 the medium was replaced with the identical medium supplemented with the indicated concentration of either ^{125}I-LDL (87 cpm/ng) or ^{125}I-HDL (64 cpm/ng). After incubation for 5 hours at 37°C, the total cellular content of ^{125}I-labeled lipoprotein (A) and total amount of ^{125}I-labeled lipoprotein degraded (B) were determined. The inset in panel A shows the amount of ^{125}I-LDL released from the surface when the cells were subsequently incubated with dextran sulfate. From Kovanen *et al.* (1979b).

caused an increase in LDL receptor activity in the mouse Y-1 adrenal cells, whether the cells were grown in the absence or in the presence of LDL. The observed regulation of LDL receptor activity in these cultured adrenal cells was consistent with the pattern previously observed in fibroblasts. In the presence of LDL, cells develop an amount of receptor activity that is just sufficient to supply the cholesterol needed for growth and metabolic purposes. Maximal LDL receptor levels develop only when there is an enhanced demand for cholesterol or when plasma LDL is not available (Brown and Goldstein, 1975).

2. Membranes Prepared from Fresh Bovine Adrenal Cortex

The demonstration of functional LDL receptors in cultured bovine adrenocortical cells laid the foundation for the study of such receptors in membranes prepared from fresh adrenal cortex. To demonstrate high-affinity binding in such isolated membranes, we used an ultracentrifugation assay that had been shown to measure cell surface receptor activity in membranes prepared from cultured

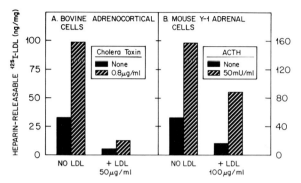

FIG. 16. Regulation of low-density lipoprotein (LDL) receptor activity in bovine adrenocortical cells (A) and in mouse Y-1 adrenal cells (B) by prior incubation with cholera toxin (A) or ACTH (B) in the presence and in the absence of LDL. The cells were incubated for either 24 hours (A) or 48 hours (B) in medium containing the indicated addition. They were then washed thoroughly and incubated for 3 hours with ¹²⁵I-labeled LDL at 37°C. The amount of ¹²⁵I-labeled LDL bound to the receptor was determined with the heparin release assay.

human fibroblasts (Basu *et al.*, 1978). In this assay, cells are homogenized with a Polytron homogenizer and the membranes sedimenting between 8000 g and 100,000 g are isolated. The membranes are incubated with ¹²⁵I-LDL, and the bound and free lipoproteins are separated by centrifugation at 100,000 g using an air-driven ultracentrifuge (Kovanen *et al.*, 1979a).

To demonstrate that this assay was applicable to adrenal membranes, we prepared membranes from monolayers of cultured bovine adrenocortical cells under conditions in which the number of receptors could be estimated from studies of LDL metabolism in the intact cells. The data in Fig. 17A show that when these membranes were incubated with increasing concentrations of ¹²⁵I-LDL *in vitro*, saturable and high-affinity binding of the ¹²⁵I-LDL to the membranes could be demonstrated. The dashed line in Fig. 17A shows this high-affinity binding, which is defined as the difference between the ¹²⁵I-LDL binding observed in the absence of excess unlabeled LDL (total binding) and the ¹²⁵I-LDL binding observed in the presence of an excess of unlabeled LDL (nonspecific binding). The amount of high-affinity binding in the isolated membrane fraction was similar to the amount detected by incubation of the intact monolayers with ¹²⁵I-LDL (Kovanen *et al.*, 1979a,b).

Figure 17B shows the results of the same assay performed on the membrane fraction isolated from fresh bovine adrenal cortex. The affinity of the binding site for ¹²⁵I-LDL was similar in the membranes from the cultured cells and in the membranes from fresh tissue. Like the LDL receptor in the cultured cells, the binding site in the membranes from fresh tissue was shown to bind bovine or human LDL, but not human or bovine HDL (Kovanen *et al.*, 1979a,b). The LDL binding site in fresh membranes also resembled the LDL receptor in the cultured

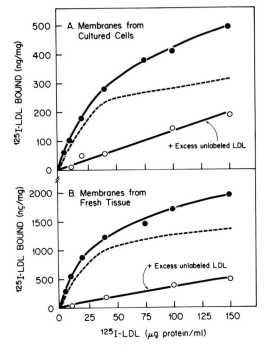

FIG. 17.   Concentration dependence of ^{125}I-labeled low-density lipoprotein (^{125}I-LDL) binding to bovine adrenocortical membranes prepared from cultured cells (A) and from fresh tissue (B). Membranes were prepared from cultured bovine adrenocortical cells grown in the absence of LDL and from fresh bovine adrenal cortex. Each reaction tube contained 145 μg of membrane protein and the indicated concentration of human ^{125}I-LDL (245 cpm/ng) in the absence (●) or in the presence (○) of 1 mg/ml of unlabeled human LDL. After incubation for 40 minutes at 0°, the amount of ^{125}I-LDL bound to the membranes was determined by ultracentrifugation assay. The dashed line shows the high-affinity binding, which was calculated by subtracting the amount of ^{125}I-LDL bound in the presence of the excess unlabeled LDL from that bound in the absence of the excess unlabeled LDL. From Kovanen *et al.* (1979a).

bovine adrenocortical cells in two other respects: it was susceptible to destruction by Pronase, and the binding required a divalent cation, either calcium or manganese (Kovanen *et al.*, 1979a).

The data in Fig. 18A show that the amount of ^{125}I-LDL bound to membranes of adrenal cortex was proportional to the amount of membrane protein added to the assay. High-affinity binding of ^{125}I-LDL was undetectable in bovine erythrocytes, which were used as a control (Fig. 18B).

We concluded from these studies that membranes from the bovine adrenal cortex expressed a specific high-affinity LDL binding site that was similar to the functional LDL receptor that had been demonstrated in the cultured bovine adrenocortical cells. The data strongly suggested that *in vivo* this LDL receptor supplied cholesterol to the adrenal cortex for steroid hormone synthesis.

To test this hypothesis in another way, we compared the LDL binding activity

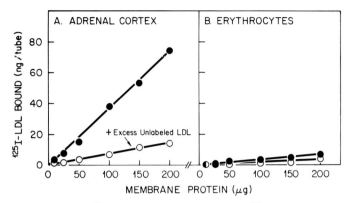

FIG. 18. Comparison of ^{125}I-labeled low-density lipoprotein (^{125}I-LDL) binding to membranes from bovine adrenal cortex (A) and from bovine erythrocytes (B). Each reaction tube contained the indicated amount of membrane protein and 12.5 μg/ml of bovine ^{125}I-LDL (988 cpm/ng in panel A and 507 cpm/ng in panel B) in the absence (●) or in the presence (○) of 500 μg of unlabeled LDL per milliliter. After incubation at 0° for 40 minutes, the amount of ^{125}I-LDL bound to the membranes was determined by ultracentrifugation assay. From Kovanen *et al.* (1979a).

in the membranes of adrenal cortex with that of membrane fractions prepared from 17 other tissues of the cow. The data in Fig. 19 show that the amount of high-affinity binding per milligram of membrane protein was 6 times higher in the adrenal cortex than in the medulla of the same glands. Similarly, the amount of high-affinity LDL binding was much greater in the corpus luteum than in the ovarian interstitium. The occurrence of large amounts of LDL binding activity in these two steroid hormone-secreting tissues lent strong support to the thesis that this activity represented an LDL receptor that was supplying cholesterol for steroid hormone synthesis.

Although the amounts of binding in the other tissues were lower than those of the adrenal cortex and corpus luteum, definite high-affinity ^{125}I-LDL binding activity could be demonstrated in membranes from adipose tissue, myocardium, skeletal muscle, thymus, kidney, lung, ileum, jejunum, and testes. In the liver, there was a large amount of nonspecific binding of ^{125}I-LDL, and this precluded an accurate assessment of the amount of high-affinity binding (Kovanen *et al.*, 1979a).

D. THE FOURTH MODEL: HUMAN ADRENAL MEMBRANES

The availability of an assay for high-affinity ^{125}I-LDL binding to tissue membranes has allowed us to begin to study the distribution of ^{125}I-LDL binding activity in human tissues. As a first step, we have studied this activity in a series of human fetuses that were obtained as a result of spontaneous abortion between weeks 16 and 20 of pregnancy. Figure 20A shows that membranes prepared from

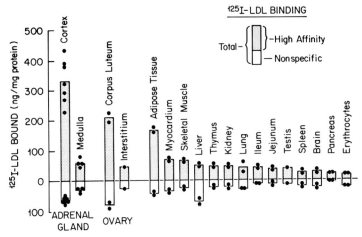

FIG. 19. Comparison of ^{125}I-labeled low-density lipoprotein (^{125}I-LDL) binding activity to membranes prepared from different bovine tissues. The indicated bovine tissues were homogenized, and the 8000 g to 100,000 g membrane pellet was isolated. Each reaction tube contained 75 μg of membrane protein and 12.5 μg of bovine ^{125}I-LDL per milliliter (500–900 cpm/ng) in the absence or in the presence of 500 μg/ml of unlabeled bovine LDL. After incubation at 0° for 40 minutes, the amount of ^{125}I-LDL bound to the membranes was determined by ultracentrifugation assay. Total binding represents the amount of ^{125}I-LDL bound to the membranes in the absence of excess unlabeled LDL. High-affinity binding and nonspecific binding are those components of the total binding that were, respectively, inhibited and not inhibited competitively by the presence of the excess unlabeled LDL. Each point represents the average of duplicate assays performed on the membranes obtained from one animal. Data from Kovanen *et al.* (1979a).

one human fetal adrenal gland bound ^{125}I-LDL with high affinity and saturability. Binding of the radioactive ligand was inhibited competitively by unlabeled LDL. High-affinity binding of ^{125}I-HDL to the same membranes was also detected, but the amount of such binding was much lower than that for LDL (Fig. 20B).

The specificity of the ^{125}I-LDL binding site in the human fetal adrenal membranes was tested by means of competition studies. The data in Fig. 21 show that unlabeled LDL competed with ^{125}I-LDL for binding to the membranes, 50% competition occurring at an LDL concentration of approximately 10 μg of protein per milliliter. In contrast, HDL did not achieve 50% competition, even at concentrations as high as 500 μg of protein per milliliter.

High-affinity ^{125}I-LDL binding could also be demonstrated in membranes prepared from the fetal testis (Fig. 22A). Distinct saturable ^{125}I-LDL binding was also detected in membranes prepared from two fetal livers (Fig. 22B). The relative amount of binding in the fetal liver membranes was 5-fold lower than that in the membranes from the fetal testis. The data in Fig. 23 show the amounts of ^{125}I-LDL binding activity per milligram of membrane protein in various tissues of the human fetus. The binding activity in the adrenal gland was 30-fold higher than that seen in any other tissue except the gonad (testis). This distribution of

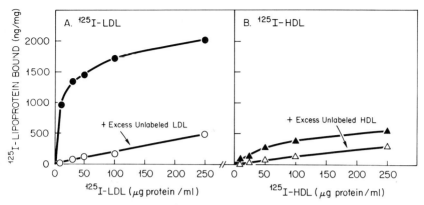

FIG. 20. Concentration dependence of ^{125}I-labeled low-density lipoprotein (^{125}I-LDL) binding (A) and of ^{125}I-labeled high-density lipoprotein (^{125}I-HDL) binding (B) to human fetal adrenal membranes. Membranes from the adrenal gland of a 16-week-old human fetus were prepared, and binding assays were performed as described by Kovanen *et al.* (1979a). Each reaction tube contained 75 μg of membrane protein and the indicated concentration of human ^{125}I-LDL (280 cpm/ng) in the absence (●) or in the presence (○) of 1 mg of unlabeled human LDL per milliliter (panel A) or ^{125}I-HDL (350 cpm/ng) in the absence of (▲) or in the presence (△) of 1 mg of unlabeled HDL per milliliter (panel B). After incubation for 40 minutes at 0°C, the amount of ^{125}I-labeled lipoprotein bound to the membranes was determined by ultracentrifugation assay.

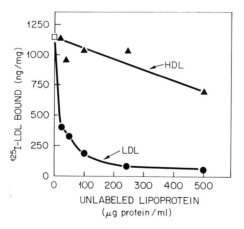

FIG. 21. Comparison of the ability of low-density lipoprotein (LDL) (●) and high-density lipoprotein (HDL) (▲) to compete with ^{125}I-labeled LDL for binding to membranes from human fetal adrenal gland. Membranes from the adrenal gland of a 16-week-old human fetus were prepared and binding assays were performed as described by Kovanen *et al.* (1979a). Each reaction tube contained 75 μg of membrane protein, 12.5 μg of ^{125}I-LDL per milliliter (237 cpm/ng), and the indicated concentration of either unlabeled LDL (●) or HDL (▲). After incubation at 0° for 40 minutes, the amount of ^{125}I-LDL bound to the membranes was determined by ultracentrifugation assay.

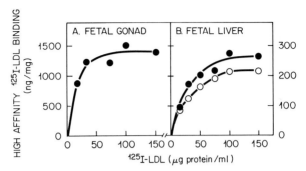

FIG. 22. Concentration dependence of ^{125}I-labeled low-density lipoprotein (^{125}I-LDL) binding to membranes from human fetal gonads (A) and liver (B). Membranes were prepared from the gonads (testes) and liver of a 16 week-old male fetus (●). Membranes were also prepared from the liver of a 20-week-old fetus (○). Binding assays were performed as described by Kovanen *et al.* (1979a). Each reaction tube contained either 17 μg (gonad) or 75 μg (liver) of membrane protein and the indicated concentration of ^{125}I-LDL (234 cpm/ng) in the absence or in the presence of 1 mg of unlabeled LDL per milliliter. After incubation for 40 minutes at 0°C, the amounts of total and nonspecific ^{125}I-LDL binding to the membranes were determined by ultracentrifugation assay. The values for high-affinity binding were calculated by subtracting the amount of ^{125}I-LDL bound in the presence of excess unlabeled LDL from that bound in the absence of the excess unlabeled LDL.

^{125}I-LDL binding activity was similar to the results previously obtained with the adult cow (Kovanen *et al.,* 1979a).

We also measured HMG-CoA reductase activity as an index of the capacity for cholesterol synthesis in the various human fetal tissues. The data in Fig. 24 show that HMG-CoA reductase activity was extremely high in the microsomes prepared from the human fetal adrenal and the gonad (testis). The finding of high HMG-CoA reductase activity in the same steroid-secreting tissues that showed high ^{125}I-LDL receptor activity suggests that these two tissues have a large requirement for cholesterol. The fetal liver also had a relatively high HMG-CoA reductase activity, whereas enzyme activity in the other human fetal tissues was low (Fig. 24).

The data in Fig. 25 compare the binding of ^{125}I-LDL to membranes prepared from the adrenal gland and liver of several different species. These assays were all performed under one set of conditions in which the tissue membranes were incubated with human ^{125}I-LDL at 12.5 μg of protein per milliliter in the absence or in the presence of an excess of unlabeled human LDL. The data show that the amount of high-affinity ^{125}I-LDL binding was highest in the adrenal of the human fetus. High levels of binding activity were also seen in the adrenal of the dog, cow, and swine. In all these species the binding was much greater in the adrenal gland than in the liver. On the other hand, no significant high-affinity binding activity was detected in the adrenal gland of the rabbit and the rat. The mouse adrenal showed a low but clearly detectable level of high-affinity ^{125}I-LDL binding activity.

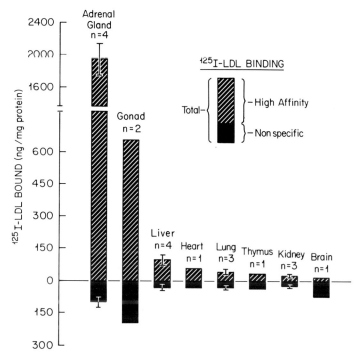

FIG. 23. Comparison of ^{125}I-labeled low-density lipoprotein (^{125}I-LDL) binding activity in human fetal membranes prepared from various organs. Membranes were prepared from 16- to 20-week-old human fetuses as described by Kovanen *et al.* (1979a) and incubated with human ^{125}I-LDL as described in the legend to Fig. 19. High-affinity and nonspecific binding were calculated as described in the legend to Fig. 19. All the gonads were testes. Each bar represents the mean ± 1 SEM of results obtained from the indicated number of human fetuses.

Considered together with the other data in this review, the data in Fig. 25 are consistent with the thesis that the adrenal gland of the human fetus, the dog, the cow, swine, and perhaps the mouse rely on LDL for a large part of their steroid hormone production. In contrast, the evidence for high-affinity binding of human ^{125}I-LDL in adrenal tissues from the rabbit and the rat is not convincing. These species differences would appear to explain the difference between cholesterol metabolism in the cultured mouse Y-1 adrenal cells and bovine adrenocortical cells on the one hand and the rat treated with 4-APP on the other. Cells from the mouse and the cow appear to express LDL receptor activity in culture that is equivalent to that occurring *in vivo*. On the other hand, we have yet to find evidence for a specific LDL receptor in membranes from the rat adrenal gland. The mechanism for cholesterol uptake from lipoproteins in this species may well differ from that of the other species studied and account for the fact that HDL as well as LDL appear to supply cholesterol to the adrenal of the 4-APP-treated rat in contrast to the preferential utilization of LDL in other species.

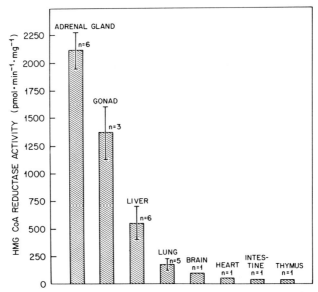

FIG. 24. Comparison of microsomal HMG-CoA reductase activity in various human fetal tissues. Fresh fetal tissues were homogenized in a Dounce homogenizer, microsomal fractions were prepared, and HMG-CoA reductase was assayed as previously described by Kovanen *et al.* (1978). Each bar represents the mean ± 1 SEM of results obtained from the indicated number of human fetuses. The ages of the fetuses ranged from 16 to 22 weeks. All fetuses were male.

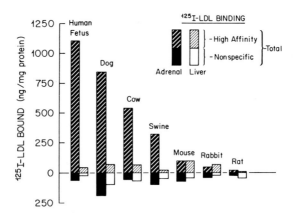

FIG. 25. Comparison of ^{125}I-labeled low-density protein (^{125}I-LDL) binding activity in adrenal and liver membranes from various species. Membranes were prepared according to the method of Kovanen *et al.* (1979a). The membranes were prepared either from whole adrenal gland (human fetus, mouse, rabbit, and rat) or from adrenal cortex (dog, cow, and swine). The membranes were incubated with 12.5 μg of human ^{125}I-LDL per milliliter in the presence or in the absence of 500 μg of unlabeled human LDL per milliliter as described in the legend to Fig. 19. High-affinity binding and nonspecific binding were calculated as described in the legend to Fig. 19.

III. Summary: A Working Model for Cholesterol Metabolism in the Adrenal Cortex

The studies in the four model systems discussed above allow the formulation of a hypothetical working model to explain some aspects of cholesterol metabolism in the adrenal cortex. In this model, which is shown schematically in Fig. 26, the adrenal is considered to have a small pool of metabolically active free cholesterol that is rapidly turning over. In the steady state, the input and output of cholesterol from this metabolically active cholesterol pool must be balanced. The net input into this pool comes from three sources: (1) uptake of cholesterol from lipoproteins; (2) endogenous synthesis of cholesterol within the gland; and (3) hydrolysis of stored cholesteryl esters. Net output of cholesterol from this pool occurs when cholesterol is converted to steroid hormones that are secreted from the gland and when cholesterol is esterified to form cholesteryl ester droplets (Fig. 26A).

The adrenal gland contains at least two pools of cholesterol in addition to the

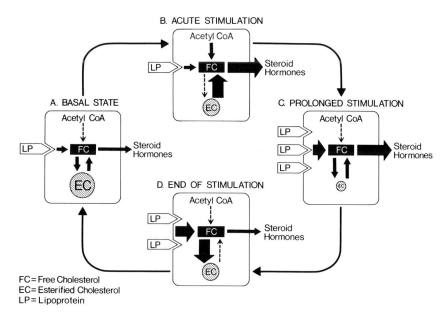

FIG. 26. Model for cholesterol homeostasis in the adrenal gland, showing sequential changes in cholesterol input and output during acute and prolonged stimulation of steroid secretion. This model is based on a compilation of the data obtained in the cultured mouse Y-1 cells, the cultured bovine adrenocortical cells, and the rat treated with 4-aminopyrazolopyrimidine (4-APP). In the two-cell culture systems that have been studied, low-density lipoprotein is the lipoprotein that specifically delivers cholesterol to the adrenal gland. The lipoprotein specificity for the cholesterol delivery process in the rat adrenal has not yet been elucidated. See text for details. LP, lipoprotein; FC, free cholesterol; EC, esterified cholesterol.

metabolically active pool. One of these is a fixed pool of free cholesterol in cell membranes. Studies in tissue culture indicate that this pool of membrane cholesterol is not available (in a net sense) to provide cholesterol for steroid synthesis. The second pool of cholesterol is contained in storage droplets, where the cholesterol is esterified with fatty acids. As discussed below, these cholesteryl esters exert a buffer function that tends to stabilize the free cholesterol content of the adrenal gland during transient fluctuations in steroid demand.

When the adrenal gland is stimulated acutely with ACTH, the initial response is a rapid output of steroids (Fig. 26B). The substrate for this initial burst of synthesis comes from cholesterol that is drained from the small pool of metabolically active free cholesterol in the gland. This sterol is immediately replenished by the hydrolysis of stored cholesteryl esters. In addition, cholesterol synthesis is activated through an enhancement in the activity of HMG-CoA reductase (and HMG-CoA synthase in the rat). If the stimulus to steroid secretion is prolonged, net cholesteryl ester hydrolysis eventually ceases, cholesterol synthesis declines, and the enhanced cholesterol output becomes balanced primarily by an accelerated uptake of cholesterol from plasma lipoproteins (Fig. 26C). Data from the two adrenal cell culture systems (mouse and bovine) as well as from the 4-APP-treated rat indicate that as long as plasma cholesterol is available the bulk of the cholesterol used to support steroid synthesis over the long term comes from plasma lipoproteins, and only a minor portion comes from endogenous cholesterol synthesis. In the cultured mouse and bovine cells, the enhanced uptake of lipoprotein-cholesterol occurs as the result of an increase in the number of cellular LDL receptors.

When the number of LDL receptors is adequate and when the plasma concentration of LDL is normal, sufficient cholesterol enters the adrenal cell during prolonged stimulation to support a high rate of steroid synthesis (Fig. 26C). The cellular content of cholesteryl esters is variable, depending on whether lipoprotein uptake is greater than or less than the steroid secretion rate. When the stimulus to steroid secretion ceases, a transient situation exists in which lipoprotein uptake exceeds steroid output. During this interval, the cholesteryl esters of the adrenal are restored (Fig. 26D), after which the LDL receptors become suppressed and the gland returns to a basal state (Fig. 26A).

In the model systems so far studied, endogenous synthesis of cholesterol in the adrenal is important in several situations: (1) when insufficient plasma lipoproteins are available, a situation that is probably never encountered in normal physiology; (2) transiently, when there is a sudden stimulus to steroid secretion and sufficient time has not elapsed for full induction of lipoprotein receptor activity; and (3) when the rate of steroid synthesis is so great that maximal lipoprotein receptor activity cannot supply sufficient cholesterol and supplementary cholesterol synthesis within the gland is required.

The strongest evidence for the role of LDL receptors in the adrenal lipoprotein uptake process comes from the studies of cultured adrenal cells. In the mouse and bovine adrenal cells, LDL receptors have been demonstrated directly to supply the bulk of the cholesterol for steroid synthesis. Numerous types of independent evidence have documented the existence of functional LDL receptors in these two cultured cell systems. The evidence that similar LDL receptors also function in the adrenal cortex *in vivo* is indirect and rests on two observations: (1) that LDL binding sites similar to those in the cultured mouse and bovine cells can be demonstrated in isolated membranes from the adrenal cortex of these two species, and (2) that the amount of LDL binding activity in steroid-secreting organs of the cow and the human fetus is much higher than that in other organs. The results in the 4-APP-treated rat support the notion that the adrenal gland relies on plasma cholesterol, although the mechanism for lipoprotein uptake in this species has not yet been clarified. It is possible that under some circumstances *in vivo* adrenal cells of the rat and perhaps other species may express a mechanism in addition to the LDL receptor that allows them to derive cholesterol from HDL.

In addition to the need for *in vivo* demonstration of the function of LDL and possibly HDL receptors in intact adrenals, several key questions remain unresolved: (1) What is the mechanism by which the adrenal gland senses the content of metabolically active cholesterol and thereby coordinately regulates lipoprotein receptor activity, cholesterol synthesis, and cholesteryl ester formation? (2) What is the mechanism by which cholesterol is transported from one cellular compartment (i.e., the lysosome) to another compartment (i.e., the mitochondrion)? Are cytoplasmic transport proteins involved? (3) If LDL receptors are important in normal human adrenal physiology, why is adrenal insufficiency not ordinarily seen in patients who have no circulating LDL (abetalipoproteinemia) or in patients who have a genetic deficiency of LDL receptors (familial hypercholesterolemia)? Can HDL somehow supply adrenal cholesterol in these patients, or do they derive all of their adrenal steroids from cholesterol synthesized within the gland? The answers to these and other questions should provide deeper insights into the important role of lipoprotein receptors in adrenal physiology.

ACKNOWLEDGMENTS

We are indebted to many colleagues who have contributed to various aspects of this work, including Jerry R. Faust, S. Balasubramaniam, Sandip K. Basu, Gloria Y. Brunschede, and Lynda Letzig. This research has been supported by Grant P01-HL-20948 from the National Institutes of Health.

REFERENCES

Albers, J. J., and Bierman, E. L. (1976). *Biochim. Biophys. Acta* **424,** 422.
Andersen, J. M., and Dietschy, J. M. (1976). *Biochem. Biophys. Res. Commun.* **72,** 880.
Andersen, J. M., and Dietschy, J. M. (1977). *J. Biol. Chem.* **252,** 3652.

Anderson, R. G. W., Goldstein, J. L., and Brown, M. S. (1976). *Proc. Natl. Acad. Sci. U.S.A.* **73,** 2434.

Anderson, R. G. W., Brown, M. S., and Goldstein, J. L. (1977). *Cell* **10,** 351.

Balasubramaniam, S., Goldstein, J. L., Faust, J. R., and Brown, M. S. (1976). *Proc. Natl. Acad. Sci. U.S.A.* **73,** 2564.

Balasubramaniam, S., Goldstein, J. L., Faust, J. R., Brunschede, G. Y., and Brown, M. S. (1977b). *J. Biol. Chem.* **252,** 1771.

Balasubramaniam, S., Goldstein, J. L., and Brown, M. S. (1977a). *Proc. Natl. Acad. Sci. U.S.A.* **74,** 1421.

Basu, S. K., Goldstein, J. L., and Brown, M. S. (1978). *J. Biol. Chem.* **253,** 3852.

Bersot, T. P., Mahley, R. W., Brown, M. S., and Goldstein, J. L. (1976). *J. Biol. Chem.* **251,** 2395.

Bilheimer, D. W., Ho, Y. K., Brown, M. S., Anderson, R. G. W., and Goldstein, J. L. (1978). *J. Clin. Invest.* **61,** 678.

Bloch, K. (1945). *J. Biol. Chem.* **157,** 661.

Borkowski, A. J., Levin, S., Delcroix, C., and Klastersky, J. (1970). *J. Appl. Physiol.* **28,** 42.

Borkowski, A., Delcroix, C., and Levin, S. (1972a). *J. Clin. Invest.* **51,** 1664.

Borkowski, A., Delcroix, C., and Levin, S. (1972b). *J. Clin. Invest.* **51,** 1679.

Bradley, W. A., Rohde, M. F., Gotto, A. M., and Jackson, R. L. (1978). *Biochem. Biophys. Res. Commun.* **81,** 928.

Brown, M. S., and Goldstein, J. L. (1974). *Proc. Natl. Acad. Sci. U.S.A.* **71,** 788.

Brown, M. S., and Goldstein, J. L. (1975). *Cell* **6,** 307.

Brown, M. S., and Goldstein, J. L. (1976). *Science* **191,** 150.

Brown, M. S., and Goldstein, J. L. (1979). *Harvey Lect.* **73,** 163.

Brown, M. S., Dana, S. E., and Goldstein, J. L. (1973). *Proc. Natl. Acad. Sci. U.S.A.* **70,** 2162.

Brown, M. S., Dana, S. E., and Goldstein, J. L. (1974). *J. Biol. Chem.* **249,** 789.

Brown, M. S., Dana, S. E., and Goldstein, J. L. (1975a). *Proc. Natl. Acad. Sci. U.S.A.* **72,** 2925.

Brown, M. S., Dana, S. E., and Goldstein, J. L. (1975b). *J. Biol. Chem.* **250,** 4025.

Brown, M. S., Faust, J. R., and Goldstein, J. L. (1975c). *J. Clin. Invest.* **55,** 783.

Brown, M. S., Anderson, R. G. W., and Goldstein, J. L. (1977). *J. Supra. Struct.* **6,** 85.

Buonassisi, V., Sato, G., and Cohen, A. I. (1962). *Proc. Natl. Acad. Sci. U.S.A.* **48,** 1184.

Deutsch, D. G., Heinrikson, R. L., Foreman, J., and Scanu, A. M. (1978). *Biochim. Biophys. Acta* **529,** 342.

Dexter, R. N., Fishman, L. M., and Ney, R. L. (1970). *Endocrinolology* **87,** 836.

Dietschy, J. M. (1978). Personal communication.

Dietschy, J. M., and Wilson, J. D. (1970). *N. Engl. J. Med.* **282,** 1128, 1179, 1241.

Faust, J. R., Goldstein, J. L., and Brown, M. S. (1977). *J. Biol. Chem.* **252,** 4861.

Fredrickson, D. S., Goldstein, J. L., and Brown, M. S. (1978). *In* "The Metabolic Basis of Inherited Disease" (J. B. Stanbury, J. B. Wyngaarden, and D. S. Fredrickson, eds.), p. 604. McGraw-Hill, New York.

Goldstein, J. L., and Brown, M. S. (1974). *J. Biol. Chem.* **249,** 5153.

Goldstein, J. L., and Brown, M. S. (1976). *Curr. Topics Cell. Reg.* **11,** 147.

Goldstein, J. L., and Brown, M. S. (1977). *Annu. Rev. Biochem.* **46,** 897.

Goldstein, J. L., and Brown, M. S. (1978). *Johns Hopkins Med. J.* **143,** 8.

Goldstein, J. L., Dana, S. E., and Brown, M. S. (1974). *Proc. Natl. Acad. Sci. U.S.A.* **71,** 4288.

Goldstein, J. L., Brunschede, G. Y., and Brown, M. S. (1975a). *J. Biol. Chem.* **250,** 7854.

Goldstein, J. L., Dana, S. E., Faust, J. R., Beaudet, A. L., and Brown, M. S. (1975b). *J. Biol. Chem.* **250,** 8487.

Goldstein, J. L., Basu, S. K., Brunschede, G. Y., and Brown, M. S. (1976). *Cell* **7,** 85.

Gospodarowicz, D., Ill, C. R., Hornsby, P. J., and Gill, G. N. (1977). *Endocrinology* **100,** 1080.

Gwynne, J. T., Mahaffee, D., Brewer, H. B., and Ney, R. L. (1976). *Proc. Natl. Acad. Sci. U.S.A.* **73,** 4329.

Havel, R. J., Goldstein, J. L., and Brown, M. S. (1979). *In* "Diseases of Metabolism" (P. K. Bondy and L. E. Rosenberg, eds.). Saunders, Philadelphia, Pennsylvania. In press.

Hechter, O., Zaffaroni, A., Jacobson, R. P., Levy, H., Jeanloz, R. W., Schenker, V., and Pincus, G. (1951). *Recent Prog. Horm. Res.* **6**, 215.

Henderson, J. F. (1963). *J. Lipid Res.* **4**, 68.

Ho, Y. K., Brown, M. S., Bilheimer, D. W., and Goldstein, J. L. (1976a). *J. Clin. Invest.* **58**, 1465.

Ho, Y. K., Brown, M. S., Kayden, H. J., and Goldstein, J. L. (1976b). *J. Exp. Med.* **144**, 444.

Ho, Y. K., Faust, J. R., Bilheimer, D. W., Brown, M. S., and Goldstein, J. L. (1977). *J. Exp. Med.* **145**, 1531.

Hornsby, P. J., and Gill, G. N. (1977). *J. Clin. Invest.* **60**, 342.

Hornsby, P. J., and Gill, G. N. (1978). *Endocrinology* **102**, 926.

Jackson, R. L., Morrisett, J. D., and Gotto, A. M. (1976). *Physiol. Rev.* **56**, 259.

Kane, J. P. (1977). *In* "Lipid Metabolism in Mammals" (F. Synder, ed.), Vol. I, p. 209. Plenum, New York.

Kovanen, P. T., Goldstein, J. L., and Brown, M. S. (1978). *J. Biol. Chem.* **253**, 5126.

Kovanen, P. T., Basu, S. K., Goldstein, J. L., and Brown, M. S. (1979a). *Endocrinology* **104**, 610.

Kovanen, P. T., Faust, J. R., Brown, M. S., and Goldstein, J. L. (1979b). *Endocrinology* **104**, 599.

Kowal, J. (1970). *Recent Prog. Horm. Res.* **26**, 623.

Krieger, M., Brown, M. S., Faust, J. R., and Goldstein, J. L. (1978). *J. Biol. Chem.* **253**, 4093.

Kuehl, K. S., Ramm, L. E., and Langdon, R. G. (1977). *Fed. Proc. Fed. Am. Soc. Exp. Biol.* **36**, 828 (abstract).

Mahley, R. W. (1978). *In* "Disturbances in Lipid and Lipoprotein Metabolism" (J. M. Dietschy, A. M. Gotto, and J. A. Ontko, eds.), p. 181. Am. Physiol. Soc., Bethesda, Maryland.

Mahley, R. W., Innerarity, T. L., Pitas, R. E., Weisgraber, K. H., Brown, J. H., and Gross, E. (1977). *J. Biol. Chem.* **252**, 7279.

Morris, M. D., and Chaikoff, I. L. (1959). *J. Biol. Chem.* **234**, 1095.

Shireman, R., Kilgore, L. L., and Fisher, W. R. (1977). *Proc. Natl. Acad. Sci. U.S.A.* **74**, 5150.

Simonian, M., Hornsby, P. J., and Gill, G. N. (1978). Personal communication.

Steinberg, D., Nestel, P. J., Weinstein, D. B., Remaut-Desmeth, M., and Chang, C. M. (1978). *Biochim. Biophys. Acta* **528**, 199.

Yasumura, H., Buonassisi, V., and Sato, G. (1966). *Cancer Res.* **26**, 529.

DISCUSSION

J. H. Clark: The first thing I think about in cholesterol synthesis and ACTH action is the depletion of cholesterol from adrenal pools. Yet you are telling me that ACTH is causing cholesterol to be taken up.

M. S. Brown: I think that one must distinguish between an acute response and a steady-state response. There is no question that acutely ACTH activates a cholesterol ester hydrolase in the adrenal gland and there is a rapid hydrolysis of cholesterol esters. Some of this free cholesterol may leak out of the gland, and some is used for steroid hormone synthesis. The initial result is a depletion of cholesterol esters. However, if you continue to follow the animal, the cholesterol esters climb back up again. If you take an intact rat and give it ACTH, and measure the cholesterol ester content of the adrenal, the cholesterol content falls and reaches a low point after about 3 hours. If you continue ACTH administration, even though steroid hormone secretion continues at maximal rates, the cholesterol esters do not fall further, and they even increase somewhat. As long as plasma cholesterol is available, we have not been able to produce a complete depletion of cholesterol esters by ACTH in the rat adrenal.

M. Sherman: Are the concentrations of heparin required to release LDL from adrenal receptors comparable to those in a patient with coronary artery disease treated with heparin? In other words, could increased cholesterol biosynthesis be an undesirable side effect of heparin treatment?

M. S. Brown: The amount of heparin required to release LDL is really enormous, and it would be much higher than you would see *in vivo* with heparin administration.

G. L. Flickinger: Dr. Brown, I would like to congratulate you for this excellent presentation. Extension of your concepts about lipoprotein receptors and their role in cholesterol metabolism to steroid-secreting cells provides us with a new framework for studying yet another mechanism whereby steroidogenesis may be regulated. Recently we have begun to examine the role of circulating cholesterol as a precursor for steroid synthesis in ovarian tissue. Our initial studies were carried out in superovulated immature rats treated with 4-APP. The findings with this model were reported at the 60th Annual Meeting of the Endocrine Society, Miami, 1978 (G. Flickinger, M. Christie, and J. Strauss, Abstract #374) and they were similar to the changes that you have described today in the adrenal of APP-treated rats.

Further studies were then undertaken to determine relationships between ovarian function and sterol metabolism throughout the lifespan of luteal tissue in superovulated rats (Fig. A). Secretion of progesterone, as assessed by plasma concentrations of this hormone, rises continuously to reach maximum levels on days 6–8 (day of hCG treatment = day 0), and thereafter it declines (Fig. A,

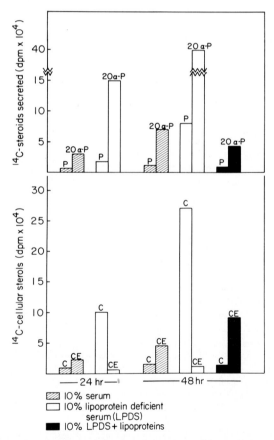

FIG. A.   Relationship between ovarian function and steroid metabolism in luteal tissue of superovulated rats. P,=progesterone; 20α-P,=20α-hydroxypreg-4-3n-3-one; C,=cholesterol; CE, cholesteryl esters.

lower panel). Although the magnitude of the changes is less, the pattern of free cholesterol content of the ovary is similar to that of plasma progesterone. The low ovarian concentrations of cholesteryl ester (days 1–4) suddenly rise 6-fold between days 4 and 6. A few days later the sterol ester levels decline in conjunction with the fall in plasma progesterone. These cyclic changes were then related to the ovarian activities of HMG-CoA reductase and acyl-CoA: cholesterol acyltransferase (ACAT) (Fig. A, top panel). HMG-CoA reductase activity increased 5-fold between days 1 and 2, and thereafter it rapidly declined so that the lowest activity coincided with the period of greatest progesterone secretion and sterol accumulation. In contrast the ovarian levels of ACAT activity paralleled the changes in ovarian sterol ester concentrations. These findings, as well as those from the APP-treated rats, suggested to us that blood lipoproteins, rather than endogenous biosynthesis, served as the major source of cholesterol for progestin formation in luteal tissue of the rat. Furthermore, it would appear that blood cholesterol upon entering the luteal cells suppressed HMG-CoA reductase activity and stimulated ACAT activity as you have described today in the mouse and rat adrenal.

To examine more specifically the role of lipoproteins, we have turned to studies of rat granulosa cells in tissue culture. These cells from large preovulatory follicles of PMS-LH stimulated immature rats are cultured for 2 days in media containing 10% human male serum and ovine prolactin. During this period the cells become luteinized and they begin to secrete progestins. On day 3 the medium is changed so that it contains either 10% human serum (controls) or 10% lipoprotein-deficient serum (LPDS). At the same time ^{14}C-acetate is added to the dishes and the cells are incubated for either 24 or 48 hours prior to the measurement of radiolabeled sterols and steroids (Fig. B). In addition, certain cultures incubated in the presence of LPDS for 24 hours are then fed human serum lipoproteins (600 μg of cholesterol), and the incubations are continued for another 24 hours.

As shown in Fig. B, during the first 24 hours in culture the incorporation of [^{14}C]acetate into cellular free cholesterol and secreted progestins is enhanced when the cells are exposed to LPDS. The formation of [^{14}C]acetate for sterol and steroid synthesis between luteal cells exposed to and deprived of lipoproteins are more accentuated after 48 hours of culture. However, if cells grown in the presence of LPDS are fed lipoproteins, the incorporation of [^{14}C]acetate into free cholesterol and progestins is suppressed, while the formation of [^{14}C]cholesteryl ester is increased during the subsequent 24 hours of incubation. These findings with cultured granulosa cells are similar to your studies with the mouse Y-1 adrenal cell, and hence they support your concepts about the role of lipoproteins in the regulations of intracellular cholesterol and steroid metabolism. Whether these effects of lipoproteins on ovarian cells are mediated via receptors for lipoproteins remains to be determined.

Although you have not here presented any studies about the ovary, a recent publication from your laboratory [P. T. Kovanen, J. L. Goldstein, M. S. Brown, *J. Biol. Chem.* **253,** 5126 (1978)] described high levels of HMG-CoA reductase activity in the corpus luteum of rabbit throughout pregnancy. I would like to hear your comments on why the rabbit CL seems to differ from our findings with the luteal cell of the rat?

M. S. Brown: The data that you have shown appear quite clean and convincing. With regard to the last question: there are going to be species differences in many of these processes. I think that our finding in the rabbit corpus luteum that there was massive HMG-CoA reductase activity that was maintained throughout pregnancy may be a peculiarity of the rabbit. It would be interesting to follow this phenomenon in the pregnant rat. I imagine that what you saw with your HCG administration will take place. That is, the reductase will go up initially and eventually fall. This is really what we expected to see in the rabbit, but you know the rabbit is peculiar in that the plasma cholesterol drops to very low levels during pregnancy and it may be that for that reason the rabbit retains the ability to synthesize more cholesterol within the ovary.

The thing that would interest me with regard to your work in the rat would be whether you have compared various lipoproteins in terms of restoring the cholesterol ester content or suppressing the reductase.

G. L. Flickinger: The results that I showed with the cultures of rat granulosa cells were obtained when a lipoprotein preparation containing both LDL and HDL was added to the media. In more

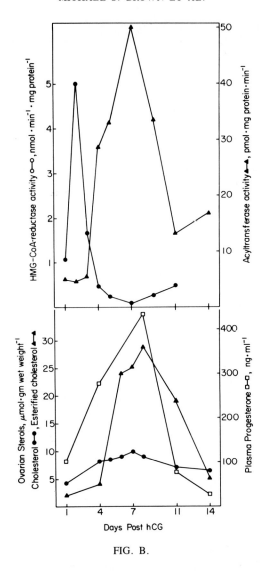

FIG. B.

recent studies we have carried out the same experiments with purified HDL and LDL. Both lipoproteins were effective in altering the utilization of [^{14}C]acetate.

M. S. Brown: That is the observation that we have made *in vivo* in the rat adrenal as well. It would be interesting to work out the specificity of that lipoprotein uptake process, and you have a system that should allow you to study the specificity of that receptor quite well.

M. D. Siperstein: I was particularly intrigued by the observation of the coordinate stimulation of HMG-CoA synthase, which probably occurs in other tissues as well. Specifically, I wanted to ask whether, if you treat with 4-APP for longer periods of time, you see the stimulation of the postmevalonate steps that is also seen in the other tissues but tends to be delayed. And second, the

ACTH stimulation of binding, or receptor, sites is rather striking and, I think, very important. If one does the same study using fibroblasts in culture, does one see any ACTH stimulation? That is obviously another way of showing the specificity of your binding or perhaps receptor sites.

M. S. Brown: To take the last one first, ACTH in fibroblasts has no effect either on the receptors or on any other aspect of cholesterol metabolism yet tested. The interesting thing is that dibutyryl cAMP does not have any effect on any of these parameters in fibroblasts where dibutyryl cAMP reproduces the ACTH effects in the adrenal cells. So it is not only the receptor, but the actual response to cAMP, that differs in fibroblasts and adrenal cells.

M. D. Siperstein: This finding I think speaks even more strongly for the specificity of the ACTH effect than does the red cell experiment.

M. S. Brown: Yes, that is true. Now with regard to the postmevalonate steps, we did not study them in these experiments. I believe that John Dietschy has not seen any change in mevalonic acid incorporation into cholesterol at a time when the reductase activity and acetate incorporation were changing rapidly. The problem with 4-APP is that one cannot extend the experiments very long because the animals become very sick, and so I do not know whether we would see changes at later time points. The capacity for incorporating mevalonate into cholesterol is relatively high. The results are reminiscent of your studies in the liver. We are struck with the fact that tissues may retain the capacity to incorporate mevalonate into cholesterol, and we do not know whether they ever use this capacity. These enzymes must be synthesized all the time, and yet it looks as though most of the time the adrenal is being supplied with cholesterol from the plasma. Therefore, HMG-CoA reductase is suppressed and these enzymes are never really utilized. Yet they are retained, perhaps for some massive response should it ever be needed. In a pinch it may be easier to induce one or two enzymes than to induce the whole pathway.

M. D. Siperstein: It just shows how important the adrenal function is.

A. White: Sayers, Fry, and Long showed a number of years ago that rat adrenal responded to ACTH *in vivo* with a dramatic, acute lowering of total cholesterol content. In view of your data showing a low response of the rat adrenal, have you tested rat adrenal cells *in vitro* to which you added low-density lipoprotein plus ACTH? Can these cells in the right environment show the higher responses you have obtained with other rat cells as well as adrenal cells from other species?

M. S. Brown: There seems to be a time lag for induction of the lipoprotein uptake mechanism in the rat adrenal. If one stimulates a rat with ACTH and follows the cholesterol ester level in the adrenal gland at hourly intervals, the cholesterol ester level is found to drop by about two-thirds and to reach a nadir at 3 hours after the start of ACTH administration. But then we find that if one continues the ACTH administration, the cholesterol esters become replenished. We believe that the initial hydrolysis of cholesterol ester seems to be necessary to cover a time period until one can induce a high rate of uptake of plasma cholesterol. Once a high rate of lipoprotein uptake is established, the lipoproteins now supply most of the cholesterol that the adrenal needs and cholesteryl esters are replenished.

A. White: In the data that you showed in your diurnal variation studies, the increase in corticoid production and alterations in the cholesterol content of the adrenal were not accompanied by alterations in the plasma levels of cholesterol. Since we generally believe that as the cholesterol level of the blood declines the liver adds more cholesterol, what is the nature of that signal in the liver? Second, since HMG-CoA reductase has been highly purified, do we know anything about the interaction of cholesterol and the enzyme?

M. S. Brown: In the rat, plasma cholesterol level is constant throughout the day. It does not show a diurnal rhythm. However, cholesterol synthesis in liver shows a peak at the midpoint of the dark cycle. Now remember that cholesterol synthesis in the liver is supplying cholesterol not only for the plasma, but also for bile acids. The relation between the peak of cholesterol synthesis and the peak of bile acid synthesis has not been well worked out. The observation is simply that one has a diurnal rhythm of hepatic cholesterol synthesis. Where the extra cholesterol goes is not clear. In regard to your second question; HMG-CoA reductase has recently been purified, and there are many exciting observations regarding this enzyme. Circumstantial evidence suggests that the enzyme may be regulated by a phosphorylation and dephosphorylation cycle in addition to regulation of enzyme synthesis. In other words, there may be a short-term control involving a phosphorylation with resultant inactivation and a long-term control involving suppression of synthesis of the enzyme in liver. Cytosolic factors have been identified which in the presence of ATP and ADP will inactivate the HMG-CoA reductase by what appears to be a kinase reaction. The role of this inactivation in metabolism has not been well worked out yet at all.

F. Naftolin: The control of this particular intake mechanism is very interesting. Regarding the kinetics, in your Y-1 cultures it appeared that more entered, but that the rate of entry could not be seen to be very different under the influence of ACTH. How does ACTH do this? Can you in some way change the ACTH response, i.e., by regulation or autoregulation of cell membrane receptors? Also, is ACTH the only thing that does it? Have you looked at endorphins and gonadotropins in this regard?

M. S. Brown: To take first things first, I believe you are referring to the experiment in which we incubated the Y-I cells with tritiated lipoprotein (Fig. 7). If you sum the individual points at every time point, you see that the total uptake rate is about 2-fold higher in the presence of ACTH. You have to add all three forms—the esters, the free cholesterol, and the secreted steroid.

F. Naftolin: But the rate appeared to be the same?

M. S. Brown: If you look more carefully at the data you will see that the rate is 2-fold higher with ACTH. Remember, also, that we are measuring only one of several steroids produced by these cells. If we plotted the entire steroid output in the presence of ACTH, the difference would be even greater. We have not examined the question of whether other hormones regulate the receptor. It seems to us that the regulation of the receptor and the regulation of the reductase are both secondary consequences of changes in some critical cholesterol pool and are not due to a direct effect of the ACTH. For example, if we stimulate with ACTH in the presence of aminoglutethimide and block the conversion of cholesterol to steroids, we have no effect on receptors or reductase. In other words, what is required is an initial drainage of cholesterol into the mitochondria and then that is the signal for increasing cholesterol synthesis and increasing LDL receptor activity.

F. Naftolin: What happens if you pulse the ACTH three times? Do you have the same rate of LDL entry the third time as the first time?

M. S. Brown: We have not done that study.

O. Dominguez: I think that the situation with esterified cholesterol, free cholesterol, and steroid hormone production has certain important relations and several points had not been clearly seen. Actually, esterified cholesterol that drops very dramatically by ACTH is one point; the free cholesterol that is released in these circumstances perhaps does not necessarily go into steroid biosynthesis all the way through; part of it goes into the structures of the cell. A portion of esterified cholesterol that goes into a free form and remains free in the medium, without being incorporated into the membrane structures, may be exposed to a very high level of 3β-hydroxydehydrogenase isomerase and may form cholesterone, which will lose its side chain and may end excreted as coprostanol, following a metabolic pathway not turned into steroid biosynthesis. The steroid biosynthesis perhaps involves various mechanisms. Besides *de novo* synthesis from acetyl-CoA or some of the free cholesterol freshly released from esterified cholesterol, I still consider the possibility of cholesteryl sulfate as a potential precursor of steroid hormones. How many of these various alternative possibilities end in steroid hormones is something that still remains unknown.

I was wondering whether, among the esters that you are considering, other types of esters besides fatty acids, such as sulfates, are included. Cholesterol and Δ^5-3β-hydroxysteroid sulfates are also formed in the liver. It has been shown that in placenta, for example, pregnenolone sulfate from blood is the major source of progesterone biosynthesis. A similar situation could occur in the adrenal, the testis, or the ovary. Δ^5-3β-ol-steroid sulfates still may play an important role, determining and limiting, via Δ^5-3β-ol steroid sulfatase, the amount of free pregnenolone involved in hormone steroid biosynthesis. Steroid sulfatase, for example, is stimulated by ACTH through a mechanism not involving cAMP. Apparently, ATP and ADP seem to be cofactors required by the desulfation, and they enhance the sulfatase activity. Is the cholesterol sulfate included among the esters that you are discussing, or is it not included in the picture? Otherwise, one has to find other explanations for the possible uptake of precursor sulfates that could be involved in hormone steroid biosynthesis.

M. S. Brown: We do not add any cholesterol sulfate to the culture medium. In other words, the adrenal cells in culture seem to be able to secrete steroid hormones without cholesterol sulfate. There is no cholesterol sulfate in the LDL. We have not studied the addition of cholesterol sulfate as a separate entity.

J. Kowal: In the studies performed by us to which you referred, using less sophisticated approaches, we came up with the idea that cholesterol could be synthesized in two ways in adrenal cultures. Because of our ignorance about the LDL pathway, we emphasized the importance of the endogenous synthesis route. I would like to ask a couple of questions related to this. We had also found that inhibition of steroid synthesis presented the increase in cholesterol synthesis. As a result we recognized that cholesterol was really regulating its own synthesis rather than any direct effect of ACTH. I might say that we were initially looking for some regulatable enzymes before cholesterol to pregnenolone conversion. If one holds the LDL levels constant so that it is not rate limiting, can you still see an increase in endogenous synthesis with ACTH?

M. S. Brown: Yes. If one has serum in the medium and adds ACTH, one gets stimulation of HMG-CoA reductase.

J. Kowal: Therefore, one does not have to have a deficiency of exogenous cholesterol in order to see an increase in endogenous synthesis?

M. S. Brown: That is correct. Our data measuring the reductase are similar to yours in which cholesterol synthesis was measured. When you add ACTH to the Y-1 cells you get an increase in cholesterol synthesis, even if you have maximum amounts of lipoproteins present. They use both endogenously synthesized and lipoprotein-derived cholesterol. If one quantitates the data one finds that at least 75% of the sterol is coming from the lipoproteins. The remainder is coming from synthesis.

J. Kowal: There are old data suggesting that if you expose cells, e.g., fibroblasts or adrenals, with serum containing high levels of lipoprotein the cells absorb the proteins until they explode. When we had done this we found no increase in steroid production. But a question arises from this. Is the available pool of cholesterol an absolute requirement that exogenous cholesterol enters through the receptor system, or can you blast cells with cholesterol and have that cholesterol utilized?

M. S. Brown: One can get effects by adding cholesterol in solvents such as ethanol, in which case the free cholesterol crosses the plasma membrane passively and without a requirement for the receptor. Our observation is that both in fibroblasts and in the Y-1 cells it takes massive amounts of cholesterol to reproduce the effects of small amounts of lipoproteins. You have to give enough cholesterol to practically stuff the cells with cholesterol before you turn off synthesis, whereas lipoproteins achieve this suppression at much lower levels. Clearly, the route of cholesterol delivery is important, and the lipoproteins appear to use the most efficient physiological route.

J. Kowal: And of course all this points to one thing—that the site of action of ACTH still has something to do with the conversion of cholesterol to pregnenolone. Do you have any information suggesting how the cholesterol gets into the mitochondria?

M. S. Brown: That is one of the questions that we posed at the end of the talk. We now have a new organelle with which to contend. Previously, we had the problem of hydrolyzing cholesterol esters and getting that cholesterol into the mitochondria. We now have to get the cholesterol out of the lysosome and then into the mitochondria, and how that is done is a critical question.

J. Weisz: These studies have obviously numerous important implications. They certainly identify, I think, the lysosome as an important member of the intracellular organelles that are regulating steroidogenesis by controlling the accessibility of a precursor to the steroidogenic enzymes. I was forced into looking at the lysosome in this role by one of my postdoctoral fellows, Dr. Larry Zoller. During his Ph.D. studies, Dr. Zoller noticed that when he stimulated dispersed adrenal cells with ACTH, looked at corticosone production on the one hand and changes in subcellular organelles by morphormetric measurements at the electron microscopic level on the other, the lysosome was among the very first organelles that showed any changes. These changes occurred by 30 minutes after introduction of the ACTH [S. Malamad, L. C. Zoller, and G. J. Macdonald, *Endocrine Soc. Meet. 1976* (Abstract #388)].

During the last 2 years, working in my laboratory, Dr. Zoller has looked at this question using quantitative cytochemical techniques for measuring lysosomal membrane permeability developed by Dr. Chayen and Dr. Bitensky as used in their bioassay of TSH and presented here 3 years ago. We applied this approach to examine the changes in lysosome membrane permeability in different portions of the membrana granulosa of the preovulatory type of follicles during the last 4 days of their development, i.e., during the 4 days of the estrous cycle. Now, in the membrana granulosa of the preovulatory follicles it is the granulosa cells situated peripherally that appear to be steroidogenic. They contain lipids, Δ^5-3β-ol steroid dehydrogenase, and, as we have shown recently, cytochrome P-450. We have found a very gratifying correlation between the changes in lysosome membrane permeability in granulosa cells in the periphery during the estrous cycle and known changes in ovarian steroid secretion attributable to the follicles. Thus, lysosome membrane permeability increased during diestrus II and reached maximum in proestrus at a time when these cells may be implicated first in estrogen production and then in the progesterone surge that occurs in response to LH on the afternoon of proestrus.

I would also like to make one suggestion. One organ that might be interesting to look at in terms of the regulation of the availability of lipid precursors for steroidogenesis is the testis of the rat. Unlike other steroidogenic organs, it does not contain any lipid droplets. Of course, it does manage to put out quite a lot of testosterone, albeit in fluctuating amounts, but accumulates lipids only in the hypophectomized animals. Lipids are also present in the rat fetal testes.

B. F. Rice: A number of years ago we carried out a study with human fetal testes in tissue culture [*Steroids* **7**, 79 (1966); *Clin. Res.* **18**[2], 463 (1970)]. The tissues were grown with [1-^{14}C]acetate added to the medium. The major purpose of the study was to evaluate steroid hormone biosynthesis. A by-product of the study was an evaluation of cholesterol biosynthesis (^{14}C labeled from [1-^{14}C]-acetate, dpm) and mass of cholesterol (μg) and phytosterols (μg) in tissues and medium. We were very surprised to find that radioactive cholesterol (dpm) and nonradioactive cholesterol (μg) were being secreted into the medium. In reviewing the literature, we found that Kritchevsky at the Wistar Institute had reported biosynthesis and secretion of radioactive cholesterol by fibroblasts in tissue culture. I wonder if your final scheme should include output of cholesterol from cells as well as input of cholesterol, or do you think these data I have mentioned are artifacts of tissue culture?

M. S. Brown: It is very difficult to distinguish between net secretion and exchange of free cholesterol. If you have lipoproteins present in the culture medium, and if you incubate a cell with [^{14}C]acetate, it gets incorporated into cholesterol, and then there is a 1-to-1 exchange of labeled cholesterol molecules in the cell with cholesterol present in lipoproteins. It is really hard to sort out exchange from net secretion of cholesterol in the tissue culture system. I think in the adrenal there is evidence that net secretion of cholesterol does occur *in vivo* under some circumstances, and perhaps we should have that in our model.

H. L. Bradlow: In one of your figures on the rat studies you showed that there was a cyclic change in HMG-reductase and synthesis that peaks after the corticosterone peak and is apparently quantitatively small, like a vestigial catch-up process for cholesterol. Can you suppress this if you load up the rat with cholesterol by giving LDL as an infusion or some other process? Also, on the contrary, if you give aminoglutethimide and block the demand for cholesterol, will these cyclic responses go on? Are they autonomous responses that happen willy-nilly, or are they responses to the need for cholesterol in the gland?

M. S. Brown: Those are two excellent questions, and unfortunately we have not done either of those experiments.

A. Crastes De Paulet: Could it be possible that, in a way independent of the delivery of cholesterol to the cell, the LDL-modified adenyl cyclase activity of adrenal cells plasma membrane, as suggested by an analog with the effect of the LDL on adipocyte plasma membrane recently shown by Chapman [*Nature* **269,** 697 (1977)], this hypothesis being enhanced by the high level of LDL binding sites in adipocyte. So my question is: Could there be some modification of the activity of adenyl cyclase in adrenal cells by LDL?

M. S. Brown: We have not studied directly any effect of LDL on adenyl cyclase. In fibroblasts we cannot find any relation between agents that affect cAMP metabolism and LDL receptor activity.

A. H. Payne: Do you believe that the difference in receptor activity in bovine testes compared to fetal testes is a species difference or difference between adult versus fetal tissue?

M. S. Brown: We really have no idea yet. I would suspect it is a fetal versus adult difference. The fetal testis, as you know, is a fairly large organ and it puts out a lot of testosterone. As I understand it, in the fetal testes, there is a much higher percentage of Leydig cells as compared with the adult. Unless you have isolated Leydig cells, it is hard to compare the measurements of activity.

A. H. Payne: Have you differentiated between receptor activity in fetal ovaries and fetal testes?

M. S. Brown: Those gonads all happened to be testes. It turns out that all the fetuses we studied were male—we have not yet studied the ovary.

K. Sterling: I believe you stated that an ethanol solution of free cholesterol would permit cholesterol to get into adrenal cells without the usual pathway of LDL receptors; my question, then, is: If we drink a little bit too much and get too high a serum ethanol concentration, is there a risk that this awful stuff (cholesterol) will be getting into our fibroblasts, our coronaries, and our myocardium by other than the usual pathway?

M. S. Brown: There is no evidence that ethanol enhances cholesterol deposition in tissues. Whatever epidemiologic evidence exists says that moderate ethanol intake somehow protects against atherosclerosis.

Estrogen and Antiestrogen Action in Reproductive Tissues and Tumors

BENITA S. KATZENELLENBOGEN, HEMLATA S. BHAKOO,
EVAN R. FERGUSON, NANCY C. LAN, TOCHIRO TATEE, TEN-LIN S. TSAI,
AND JOHN A. KATZENELLENBOGEN

Departments of Physiology and Biophysics and Chemistry, University of Illinois, and School of Basic Medical Sciences, University of Illinois College of Medicine, Urbana, Illinois

I. Introduction

It has long been known that several reproductive tissues undergo marked stimulation of growth and differentiation in response to sex steroid hormones. A major aim of research in this laboratory has been to try to elucidate the mechanisms by which estrogens and antiestrogens regulate the growth of reproductive tissues and of tumors that develop in reproductive tissues.

This chapter will describe selected aspects of the regulation of tissue responsiveness to estrogen, with particular focus on the status and function of the estrogen receptor as a determinant of tissue responsive capacity. The first part of the chapter will describe studies in the uterus aimed at determining the factors influencing the estrogenic potency of compounds, and the latter part of the chapter will describe studies in hormone-dependent mammary tumors, as well as in uterus, aimed at defining the mechanisms by which antiestrogens are able to dramatically alter tissue sensitivity to estrogen.

II. Time Course of Estrogen-Stimulated Biosynthetic Events in the Uterus and Correlations with Hormone-Receptor Binding

In response to the administration of estradiol, the uterus of the immature or ovariectomized adult rat undergoes a rigidly programmed sequence of biochemical and physiological events that culminate in tissue growth. During the normal development of the rat, uterine growth takes place over a period of several weeks, but one can induce this growth in a dramatic fashion simply by injecting a dose of estrogen into an immature rat. This hormone-induced uterine growth, which now occurs over a period of a few days, involves increases in all metabolic activities and increased water uptake, vascularization, and cell division. The temporal sequence of events initiated in this tissue after administration of estradiol can be seen in Fig. 1.

259

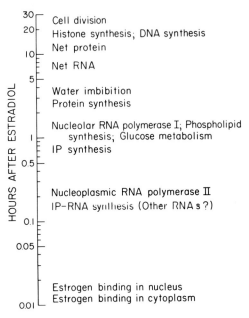

FIG. 1.   Temporal sequence of events initiated in the immature or ovariectomized rat uterus after *in vivo* injection of estradiol-17β at zero time. Note that time (hours) is on a logarithmic scale (0.01 hour = 0.6 minute). From Katzenellenbogen and Gorski (1975).

The very earliest event that can be detected after exposure to hormone (Fig. 1) is the binding of hormone in the cytoplasm of the uterine cell; this is followed by a very rapid appearance of hormone in the nucleus (Williams and Gorski, 1972). By 10 minutes after hormone injection, one can detect by indirect means (Katzenellenbogen and Gorski, 1975) the synthesis of a particular RNA for a specific estrogen-induced protein, which will be abbreviated throughout as IP for induced protein (Notides and Gorski, 1966; DeAngelo and Gorski, 1970; Katzenellenbogen and Gorski, 1972). By 15–30 minutes, there is an increase in the activity of RNA polymerase II (DNA-like RNA synthesis; Glasser *et al.*, 1972). The actual synthesis of the estrogen-induced protein, IP, is detected (Barnea and Gorski, 1970) by 40–60 minutes. One hour after estrogen treatment, several metabolic parameters have increased—glucose metabolism (Smith and Gorski, 1968), phospholipid synthesis (Aizawa and Mueller, 1961; Spooner and Gorski, 1972), RNA polymerase I activity (ribosomal RNA synthesis; Gorski, 1964; Glasser *et al.*, 1972; Courvelin *et al.*, 1976; Weil *et al.*, 1977), and template capacity (for RNA synthesis) of uterine chromatin (Barker and Warren, 1966; Teng and Hamilton, 1968; Glasser *et al.*, 1972). Although RNA polymerase activity is significantly elevated by 1 hour, an increase in uterine RNA content is not achieved until 8–12 hours (Mueller *et al.*, 1958; Billing *et al.*, 1969). Between 2 and 4 hours, there is an increase in the rate of protein synthesis

(Mueller et al., 1961; Noteboom and Gorski, 1963; Hamilton, 1963; Teng and Hamilton, 1967, 1970; Eilon and Gorski, 1972). An increase in net RNA content of the uterus begins about 8 hours after hormone, and increases in net protein content are seen by 12–18 hours (Mueller et al., 1958; Billing et al., 1969). Increases in the rate of DNA (Kaye et al., 1972) and histone synthesis (Anderson and Gorski, 1971) begin near 18 hours after estrogen treatment; both are a prelude to the cell division that begins in the uterus at approximately 24 hours (Mueller et al., 1958; Kaye et al., 1972; Stormshak et al., 1976).

Studies in several laboratories (Anderson et al., 1972, 1973; Gorski and Raker, 1973; reviewed in Clark et al., 1978b, and Katzenellenbogen and Gorski, 1979) including our own have tried to determine the temporal and quantitative relationships between estrogen binding and the "turning on" of different responses and stimulation of tissue growth.

Some of our early studies focused on the estrogen-induced protein, IP, because the synthesis of this protein and its presumptive mRNA are two of the earliest events that occur after estrogen binding, and we found that synthesis of this protein could be elicited in vitro with relatively low concentrations of estrogen (Katzenellenbogen and Gorski, 1972). This in vitro system, therefore, enabled us to analyze some aspects of estrogen action and to make quantitative correlations with receptor events under conditions of minimal metabolism of the compounds under study. [Although the physical properties of IP have been studied carefully, the function of this protein is still unknown. For detailed reviews on the induced protein, see Katzenellenbogen and Gorski (1975, 1979).]

Figure 2, which shows the polyacrylamide gel electrophoretic pattern of newly labeled proteins obtained from uteri exposed to estradiol in vitro, documents the selective induction of IP. As can be seen from the pattern of radioactivity of the newly labeled proteins, but even more clearly from the ^{3}H:^{14}C or estradiol-treated:control ratio, there is a correspondence of ^{3}H and ^{14}C incorporation in all regions of the gel, except in one where there is an increased incorporation in the estrogen-stimulated uteri corresponding to the induced protein.

Of particular interest is the relationship between the magnitude of IP induction (quantitated from double-labeled gel profiles; Katzenellenbogen and Gorski, 1972; Bhakoo and Katzenellenbogen, 1977a) and the amount of nuclear-bound [^{3}H]estradiol at different estradiol concentrations. Using the in vitro induction system, one can study this relationship quantitatively (Fig. 3). Maximal IP induction and maximal binding of [^{3}H]estradiol to nuclear receptor are obtained with 2 to 3 $\times$ 10^{-8} M estradiol, and 2 to 3 $\times$ 10^{-9} M estradiol yields a 50% response with both. Thus, the in vitro induction of IP clearly occurs in the physiological range and appears to parallel the dose-response of estrogen binding in the uterus.

Using this estrogen-responsive in vitro uterine system, we investigated the effectiveness of IP induction by different estrogens (Ruh et al., 1973). We were especially interested in comparing the effects of estrone and estriol on the

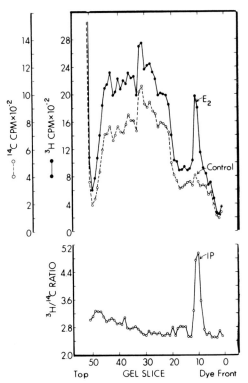

FIG. 2. Electrophoretic distribution on polyacrylamide gels of uterine soluble proteins synthe-sized *in vitro* following a 1-hour *in vitro* incubation with 3.7×10^{-8} M estradiol-17β. Uteri (3 per group) excised from untreated animals were first incubated with either 3.7×10^{-8} M estradiol or ethanol only (1%) in 2.0 ml of Eagle's HeLa medium for 60 minutes at 37°C and then allowed to incorporate labeled leucine (^{3}H for estradiol-treated and ^{14}C for control uteri) into protein for 2 hours at 37°C in the presence of 28 μg of actinomycin D per milliliter. Control and estradiol-treated uteri were homogenized together, and the supernatant fraction of centrifuged homogenates was separated by polyacrylamide gel electrophoresis. The radioactivity and ^{3}H:^{14}C ratio in each gel slice were determined. IP, estrogen-induced protein; E$_2$, estradiol. From Katzenellenbogen and Gorski (1972).

induction of IP synthesis and on nuclear binding, because they are established estrogens but their binding (Geynet *et al.*, 1972) and biological potency (Szego and Roberts, 1953; Hisaw, 1959; Miller, 1969) are known to be different. Estrone and estriol, as well as estradiol-17β, were able to induce the synthesis of IP *in vitro*. Quantitatively, the induction for all three steroids was found to closely parallel the specific uptake of the steroid into the nuclear fraction. This in turn was found to closely correlate with the relative affinity of these steroids for the cytoplasmic estrogen-binding protein (estradiol-17β > estriol > estrone). Half-maximal induction of IP synthesis or half-saturation of nuclear or cytosol binding sites required approximately three times as much estrone and two times

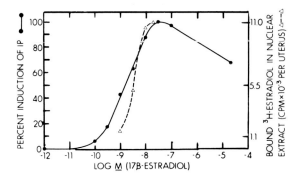

FIG. 3. Effect of *in vitro* estradiol-17β concentration on the rate of estrogen-induced protein (IP) synthesis. Uteri (5 per group) excised from untreated rats were incubated in 2.0 ml of Eagle's HeLa medium containing various concentrations of estradiol-17β (or ethanol for controls) for 60 minutes at 37°C. At this time, [³H]leucine plus actinomycin D were added to experimental flasks and [¹⁴C]-leucine plus actinomycin D were added to control flasks, and amino acid incorporation was allowed to proceed for 2 hours at 37°C. Uterine soluble proteins were subjected to electrophoresis on polyacrylamide gels, and IP synthesis was quantitated. Results are expressed relative to IP induction with 3×10^{-8} M estradiol being 100%. Values for bound [³H]estradiol in immature rat uterine nuclear extracts after a 60-minute incubation with various concentrations of [³H]estradiol in Eagle's HeLa medium at 37°C are from Giannopoulos and Gorski (1971). From Katzenellenbogen and Gorski (1972).

as much estriol as estradiol (estradiol $= 2 \times 10^{-9}$ M) (Fig. 4). In this *in vitro* system, there was minimal metabolism of estrone to estradiol and no metabolism of estriol, implying that these compounds are in their own right biologically active estrogens in terms of this early uterine response. A similar proportionality exists between IP synthesis and estrogen dose injected *in vivo;* half-maximal stimulation of IP synthesis and half-maximal localization of nuclear receptor occurs with ca. 0.2 μg of injected estradiol (Fig. 5).

The correlation between nuclear receptor levels and IP response elucidated in these studies (Figs. 4 and 5) addresses a significant problem concerning the

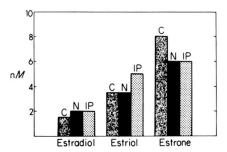

FIG. 4. Concentrations of estradiol, estriol, and estrone required for 50% saturation of cytosol (C) and nuclear (N) binding sites and 50% of maximal induction of estrogen-induced protein (IP) synthesis. From Ruh *et al.* (1973).

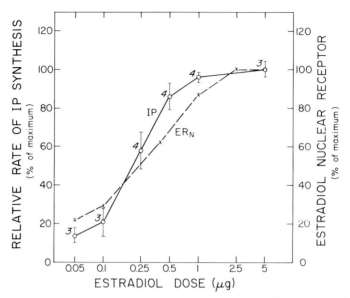

FIG. 5.   Dose-response relationship between the amount of estradiol-17β injected *in vivo* and the relative rate of IP synthesis or quantity of nuclear estradiol receptor (ER_N). Immature female rats (3 per group) received different doses of estradiol (0.05–5 μg sc) in saline (experimentals) or saline alone (controls). At 1 hour after the injection, rats were sacrificed and uteri were excised and labeled with radioactive amino acid (^{3}H-labeled leucine for estradiol-treated and ^{14}C-labeled leucine for control uteri) in Eagle's HeLa medium for 2 hours at 37°C for determination of IP synthesis. The data are expressed as percent of maximal response, that obtained with 5 μg of estradiol. Each point represents the mean $\pm$ SEM with the number of determinations per point indicated in italics. Estradiol nuclear receptor was determined by a nuclear exchange assay in the three-times washed nuclear pellet of uteri exposed to estradiol or saline alone for 1 hour *in vivo*. The amount of nuclear receptor is expressed as percent of maximum, that obtained with 5 μg of estradiol. From Bhakoo and Katzenellenbogen (1977a).

action of the estrogen–receptor complex in the nucleus. Although differing concentrations of the different estrogens are required to achieve equivalent levels of binding and response, the quantity of filled nuclear receptor appears to determine the magnitude of the IP response (Fig. 6). Further, the fact that the relationship between nuclear receptor binding and response is the same for the three estrogens, and is linear, implies that a receptor in the nucleus is equally effective in inducing IP synthesis regardless of which estrogen is bound to it (Fig. 6).

The linear relationship between response and binding illustrated in Fig. 6 raises several questions concerning current models of estrogen action. The linearity of this relationship throughout the range of binding sites, particularly at the higher levels of binding sites, suggests that the only limiting factor in response is the amount of receptor available. If, for example, there was another limiting factor, one would expect the response to plateau at higher levels of

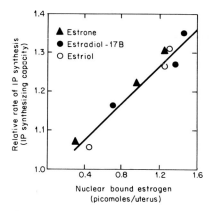

FIG. 6. Relative rate of estrogen-induced protein (IP) synthesis as a function of nuclear bound estrogen (estradiol, estriol, or estrone). Uteri incubated for 1 hour *in vitro* with $2 \times 10^{-9} M$, 1×10^{-8} M, or $5 \times 10^{-8} M$ estrogen were assayed for IP induction or were used for determination of the amount of specifically bound hormone in nuclear fractions of such uteri. From Katzenellenbogen and Gorski (1975).

estrogen–receptor complex in the nucleus. A second limiting factor is part of many models of steroid hormone action in which a specific nuclear "acceptor" is proposed to interact with the steroid–receptor complex. Therefore, if nuclear acceptor sites do exist, they do not appear to be a limiting factor, at least in terms of this response.

The studies described above (Figs. 4 and 6) indicate that estriol is a good inducer of early events such as IP synthesis; yet it is well known that estriol is a poor stimulator of uterine growth (Szego and Roberts, 1953; Hisaw, 1959; Miller, 1969). Therefore, in the next series of studies, our aim was to determine the basis of the weak uterotrophic activity of estriol and to determine how chemical modification of the estriol molecule would affect its estrogenic potency and temporal pattern of interaction with estrogen receptors in the uterus. It was hypothesized that structural modifications that would make the estriol a prohormone (etherification of the phenolic hydroxyl group) or might retard subsequent metabolic inactivation (introduction of a 17α-ethynyl group) might make estriol a much more potent estrogen, because continual metabolism to an active form and/or retarded metabolic inactivation would increase the biological persistence of the compound by providing effective circulating levels of active hormone for a more extended period of time than are observed with the parent compound. Therefore, we investigated the estrogenic potencies of several estriol derivatives prepared by the Eli Lilly Company, namely, 17α-ethynylestriol (EE$_3$), estriol-3-cyclopentyl ether (E$_3$CPE), and 17α-ethynylestriol-3-cyclopentyl ether (EE$_3$CPE), and found that the modifications that result in prolonged uterine growth also result in a prolonged maintenance of hormone–receptor complex in the uterine nucleus.

Dose-response curves indicating the effectiveness of E_3, EE_3, E_3CPE, and EE_3CPE in increasing uterine weight (uterotrophic activities) are plotted in Fig. 7. The animals were injected with each compound once daily for 3 days, and uterine wet weight was determined at 24 hours after the last, third, injection (72-hour response). It is clear that E_3 is the least effective of the compounds tested. A daily dose of at least 2 μg is required before any uterine weight increase is seen. Addition of a cyclopentyl ether group at the 3-position of estriol (E_3CPE) shifts the dose-response curve slightly to the left, but E_3CPE appears to be a significantly better estrogen than estriol only when given at a high dose (10 μg/rat). If an ethynyl group is introduced at the 17α-position of estriol (EE_3), the estrogenic activity is increased dramatically. A nearly 2-fold elevation of uterine weight is elicited by the lowest dose of EE_3 tested (0.03 μg), and further increasing the dose of EE_3 results in only a slight, further weight increase. The dose-response for EE_3 is slightly better than that of estradiol (E_2) at low doses (below 0.3 μg/day), but responses elicited by the two compounds appear quantitatively similar at the 0.3 μg or higher dose levels. The very high estrogenic potency of EE_3CPE is apparent at dose levels above 0.3 μg/day.

After a single injection of 5-μg doses of E_3, EE_3, EE_3CPE, or E_2, the prolonged and marked estrogenic effect of EE_3CPE on uterine wet weight can be clearly seen (Fig. 8). All compounds elicit an early (3–6 hour) increase in uterine weight. While the onset of the increase is delayed in the case of EE_3CPE (no increase at 1 hour), presumably owing to the requirement for metabolic

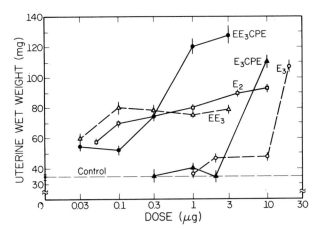

FIG. 7.   Dose-response curves showing the uterotrophic activities of estriol, estradiol, and estriol derivatives. Rats (21 days old) were injected subcutaneously with the indicated daily dose of E_3, E_3CPE, EE_3, EE_3CPE, or E_2 in 0.5 ml of saline once daily at 24-hour intervals on 3 successive days, and uterine wet weights were determined at 24 hours after the last injection. Control animals received saline alone. Each value is the mean of determinations from at least 5 individual animals ± SEM. E_2, estradiol; E_3, estriol; EE_3, 17α-ethynylestriol; E_3CPE, estriol-3-cyclopentyl ether; EE_3CPE, 17α-ethynylestriol-3-cyclopentyl ether. From Lan and Katzenellenbogen (1976).

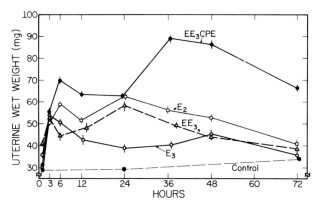

FIG. 8. Uterine wet weight as a function of time after a single injection of estriol, estradiol, or estriol derivatives. Rats (21 days old) were injected with 5 μg of E_3, E_2, EE_3, EE_3CPE, or saline (controls) at the time indicated prior to killing and excision of uteri. Each uterine wet weight value is the mean of determinations from five individual animals ± SEM. From Lan and Katzenellenbogen (1976).

activation in the animal, most striking is the very prolonged and marked elevation of uterine wet weight (and dry weight, not shown) seen after EE_3CPE. Following the initial ca. 6-hour peak in uterine weight, there is a very prolonged and even more pronounced elevation of uterine weight at 36–48 hours, with weight still remaining over 2-fold above the control at 72 hours after a single injection. EE_3 and E_2, which are considerably more potent than E_3 in the 3-day uterotrophic assay, give a more prolonged uterine weight elevation than does E_3; yet neither of these compounds results in a uterine weight that is much above the control at 72 hours. Hence, of the four compounds, EE_3CPE clearly evokes the most pronounced true uterine growth.

Figure 9 compares the time course of nuclear receptor levels and uterine wet weight after a single subcutaneous injection of 5 μg of estriol, estradiol, or estriol derivatives. EE_3, E_3, and E_2 all elicit a rapid (maximal by 0.5 to 1 hour) uptake of receptor into the nucleus and show an equivalent wet weight response at 3 hours. However, there is a rapid decline in nuclear receptor levels after E_3 injection (at control by 24 hours), and this is paralleled by a corresponding inability of estriol to maintain uterine wet weight; nuclear receptor levels decline less rapidly after EE_3 or E_2 and uterine weight also remains elevated for a longer time. Of the four compounds, EE_3CPE shows the most dramatic and prolonged maintenance of high nuclear receptor levels and elevated uterine weight.

Thus, chemical modifications of the estriol molecule which result in a prolonged stimulation of uterine growth also result in a prolonged maintenance of hormone–receptor complex in the nucleus. These studies indicate that estriol is a weak estrogen because of its brief duration of interaction with receptor and give strong support to the concept (Anderson *et al.*, 1972, 1973, 1975; Gorski and

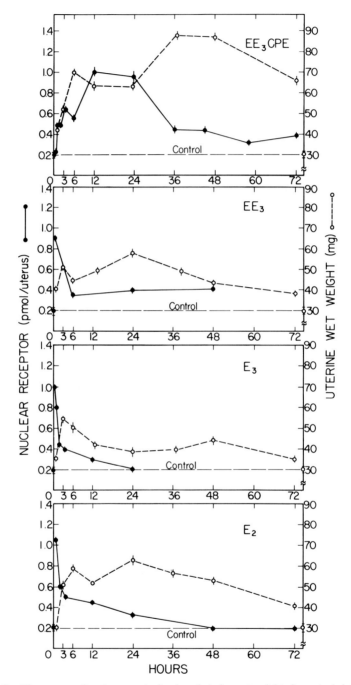

FIG. 9.   Time course of nuclear receptor levels and uterine wet weight after a single injection of 5 μg (sc in saline) of EE$_3$CPE, EE$_3$, E$_3$, or E$_2$. From Lan and Katzenellenbogen (1976).

Raker, 1974) that true uterine growth requires the direct and prolonged influence of the estrogen–receptor complex in the nucleus.

III. Mode of Action of Antiestrogens

A. INTERACTIONS OF ANTIESTROGENS WITH THE UTERUS

Antiestrogens are typically nonsteroidal compounds that prevent estrogens from expressing their full effects on estrogen target tissues, and, as such, they antagonize a variety of estrogen-dependent processes, including uterine growth and the growth of estrogen-dependent mammary tumors. They also act to stimulate pituitary gonadotropin output and subsequent ovulation in certain women by antagonism of estrogen feedback at the level of the hypothalamus and pituitary. It should be noted, however, that these compounds are not pure antagonists in some tissues, such as the uterus, and show some estrogenicity themselves. The structures of some of these compounds are shown in Fig. 10. The compounds that we have used in the studies reported here, CI-628 and U-11,100A, have a characteristic triphenylethylene structure. Their structural relationship to the better known antiestrogen Clomiphene and the estrogen diethylstilbestrol (DES) is apparent.

Our main interest in working with these compounds has been to try to elucidate some of the molecular aspects of their mode of action. Conceivably, the an-

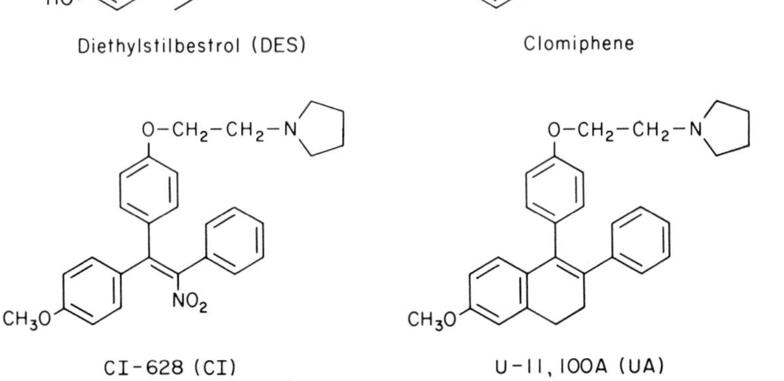

FIG. 10.   Structures of the antiestrogens CI-628, U-11,100A, and Clomiphene. Note their structural similarity to diethylstilbestrol (DES).

tagonistic action of an antiestrogen could take place at any of the stages of estrogen interaction with the receptor mechanism of target cells or at hypothetical control points postreceptor (Fig. 11). An antiestrogen might: (1) interfere with the cellular uptake of estradiol (E_2); (2) compete for cytoplasmic complex formation; (3) interfere with the transformation of the estrogen receptor to an active form; (4) interfere with transfer of the receptor complex to the nucleus or with its proper association with nuclear sites; (5) interfere with nuclear turnover or release of receptor and regeneration of cytoplasmic receptor; and/or (6) exert a postreceptor block (such as at the level of transcription).

There is evidence from the studies to be reported here and from the studies of other laboratories [reviewed in part in McGuire *et al.* (1978) and Katzenellenbogen (1978); and see below] suggesting that antiestrogens act at points 2, 4, and 5. That is, they compete for cytoplasmic complex formation; they appear to alter the association of the receptor complex and the nuclear binding sites; and they interfere with the regeneration of the cytoplasmic receptor.

Figure 12 shows typical uterotrophic assays utilized to demonstrate the agonist and antagonist character of antiestrogens. Although antiestrogens alone do increase uterine weight, the stimulation seen after 3 days is less than that elicited by a low (0.125 μg) dose of estradiol. Concomitant administration of antiestrogen with estradiol significantly diminishes the uterine response to estradiol, and, on the basis of such assays, these compounds are considered to be estrogen antagonists.

In some early studies, we examined the effects of antiestrogens on the subcellular distribution of estrogen receptors in the immature (day 20–23) rat uterus (Fig. 13). Like estradiol, the antiestrogens move cytoplasmic receptor sites into

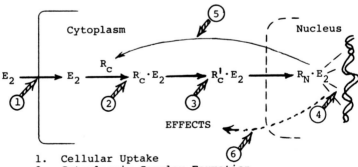

1. Cellular Uptake
2. Cytoplasmic Complex Formation
3. Transformation of Complex
4. Transfer to Nucleus and Association
     with Nuclear Sites
5. Regeneration of R_C
6. Postreceptor Block

FIG. 11.   Possible mechanisms of action of antiestrogens, indicating points at which antiestrogens might interact in target cells.

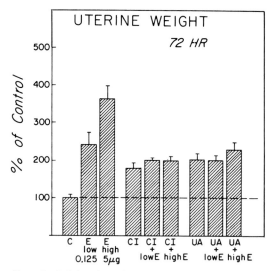

FIG. 12. The effect of administration of estradiol or antiestrogen alone, or estradiol plus antiestrogen, on uterine weight. Estradiol (E) (low dose, 0.125 μg or high dose, 5 μg) or antiestrogen (50 μg) or a combination thereof was injected once daily at 24-hour intervals on 3 successive days, and uterine wet weight was determined at 24 hours after the last, third, injection. Each determination employed five or six immature rat uteri. C = control; CI = CI-628; UA = U-11,100A. Values represent the mean ± SEM. From Katzenellenbogen and Ferguson (1975).

the nucleus. However, whereas the estradiol–receptor complex is lost from the nucleus rather rapidly and cytoplasmic receptor levels are replenished soon thereafter, the antiestrogens retain some receptor in the nucleus for a prolonged period of time and cytoplasmic receptor levels remain depleted for a long period. These findings confirmed the earlier reports of Clark *et al.* (1973) and Rochefort and Capony (1973) demonstrating prolonged nuclear retention and cytoplasmic depletion of receptor following administration of nafoxidine (U-11,100A).

We wanted to explore the state of the uterus in terms of its responsiveness to estrogen, during this period when antiestrogen had depleted the cytoplasmic receptor. Further studies showed that during the period in which antiestrogen has depleted the cytoplasmic receptor, the uterus is incapable of responding to estradiol as monitored by the synthesis of the estrogen-induced protein (Fig. 14) or by uterine weight gain (Katzenellenbogen and Ferguson, 1975). However, after estradiol, the more rapid return of uterine responsiveness to estrogen parallels the return of cytoplasmic receptor.

In studies described earlier with estriol derivatives, we found that some long-acting estrogens (such as EE$_3$CPE) evoked a retention of nuclear receptor similar to that seen with some antiestrogens, and this caused us to wonder whether some of the effects ascribed to antiestrogens might be due to the fact that they are long-acting compounds and that pharmacokinetic differences between

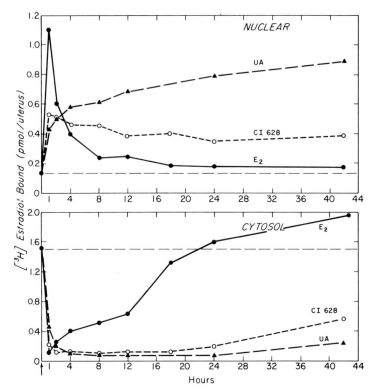

FIG. 13.   Content of specific estrogen binding sites present in nuclear (upper panel) and cytosol (lower panel) fractions of the immature rat uterus as a function of time after a single injection of estradiol-17β (5 μg sc per rat) or antiestrogen (50 μg sc per rat) as determined by the nuclear and cytosol exchange assays. Each point represents the mean of two closely corresponding determinations in duplicate per point (3 uteri/group) and is corrected for nonspecific binding. Cytosol exchange data is after 24 hours of exchange and hence represent "total cytosol sites." In the upper and lower panels, values on the ordinate connected to lightly dashed lines are those obtained for the control (saline-injected) uteri. From Katzenellenbogen and Ferguson (1975).

the most commonly studied antiestrogens and estradiol might be obscuring the basic differences between these two classes of compounds. Therefore, we decided to compare in detail differences in the actions of long-acting estrogens and antiestrogens on the uterus.

As seen in Fig. 15, we compared the action of a long-acting estrogen, EE₃CPE, and a long-acting antiestrogen, U-11,100A, and have analyzed single and multiple injection regimens in studying the effects of these compounds on uterine growth and on estrogen receptor distribution between nuclear and cytoplasmic compartments. After a single injection (solid line), both compounds show relatively similar effects on receptor distribution and uterine weight gain. They both show a gradual movement of receptor to the nucleus (Fig. 15, middle

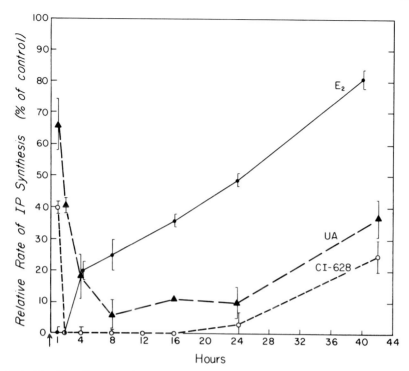

FIG. 14. The effect of a prior injection of antiestrogen or estradiol on the subsequent ability of estradiol to induce estrogen-induced protein (IP) synthesis. Note that this figure represents the relative rate of IP synthesis that results from the second injection (5 μg of estradiol, E_2) given at the indicated time after an initial injection of estradiol or antiestrogen at zero time. Immature rats (6 per group) were injected with estradiol (5 μg sc) or antiestrogen (50 μg sc) at zero time; at the indicated time thereafter (beginning at 1 hour), rats received an injection of either estradiol (5 μg sc) or saline alone. At 1 hour after the second injection, uteri were excised and allowed to incorporate labeled leucine (^{3}H for experimentals and ^{14}C for controls) into protein for 2 hours at 37°C. Control and estradiol-treated uteri in each set were homogenized together. After centrifugation, the supernatant fraction was separated by polyacrylamide gel electrophoresis and the relative rate of IP synthesis (experimental/control) was determined by gel analysis; 100% is set as the relative rate of IP synthesis seen in the immature rat uterus at 1 hour after a subcutaneous injection of 5 μg of estradiol. Each point represents the mean ± SEM of two to three determinations employing three experimental and three control rat uteri per determination. Arrow indicates the time of the first injection (estradiol or antiestrogen). From Katzenellenbogen and Ferguson (1975).

panels) and maintenance of elevated levels of nuclear receptor for 24–48 hours. Both compounds also show a gradual depletion of cytoplasmic receptor sites, and receptor levels remain low for 24 hours, after which time they increase. Both compounds also evoke similar uterine weight increases after a single injection.

Differences between the two compounds, however, become evident after multiple injections. After multiple injections of antiestrogen (dashed line; 50 μg every 24 hours), there is prolonged maintenance of elevated levels of nuclear

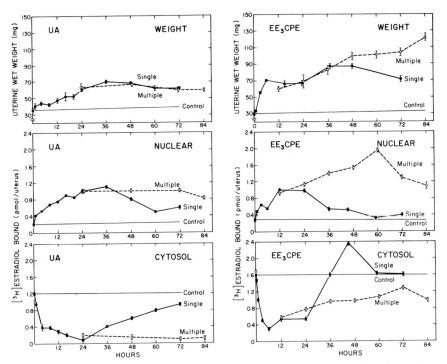

FIG. 15.   Temporal effects of single or multiple injections of U-11,100A (UA) (left panels) or 17α-ethynylestriol-3-cyclopentyl ether (EE₃CPE) (right panels) on uterine weight and uterine content of specific estrogen binding sites in the nuclear and cytosol fractions. Immature rats received either (a) a single injection of UA (50 μg) or EE₃CPE (5 μg) at zero time or (b) multiple injections of UA (50 μg every 24 hours) or EE₃CPE (5 μg every 12 hours) and were sacrificed at the indicated times. Uteri were weighed, and the content of specific estrogen binding sites present in the nuclear (middle panel) and cytosol (lower panel) fractions of uteri was determined by the nuclear and cytosol exchange assays. Multiple injections of UA (50 μg) every 12 hours showed receptor and weight patterns similar to that seen after 24-hour injections. Uterine weight values (upper panels) are the mean ± SEM with six uteri per point. For nuclear and cytosol receptor content, each value is the mean ± SEM of three determinations per point (3 uteri per group) and is corrected for nonspecific binding. From Katzenellenbogen et al. (1977).

receptor and a depletion of cytoplasmic receptor, but there is no further increase in uterine wet weight above that elicited by a single injection. In contrast, with multiple injections of EE₃CPE, nuclear receptor levels continue to increase beyond the levels seen at 12 hours and cytosol receptor levels are never fully depleted. Multiple injections of EE₃CPE, likewise, result in a continued rise in uterine weight to levels considerably above those evoked by a single injection. It should be noted that, at the doses studied, the distribution of receptor that develops after multiple injections of the two compounds is different: after antiestrogen (UA), almost all, over 90%, of receptor is in the nucleus, whereas in the case of the estrogen (EE$_3$CPE), 35–50% of the total receptor remains in the cytoplasm.

However, regardless of whether the uterus continues to grow (as with EE$_3$CPE) or stops growing after 24–48 hours (as with UA), the receptor content on a cell basis is similar in both cases (Katzenellenbogen *et al.*, 1977). Hence, uterine responsiveness to estrogen and continued uterine growth appear not to be related to the total receptor content of the cell but rather appear to be dependent on a proper distribution of receptor within the cell. These studies suggest that some of the antagonistic actions of antiestrogens may derive from their ability to effect a marked perturbation in the subcellular distribution of receptor whereby very little, ca. 10%, of receptor is cytoplasmic and further estrogen receptor accumulation is blocked. Other studies (Koseki *et al.*, 1977; Jordan *et al.*, 1978) have indicated, however, that full depletion of cytoplasmic receptors may not be required for the antagonistic effects of antiestrogens on uterine growth, suggesting that other mechanisms, as well, may be involved in antiestrogen action.

B. ANTIESTROGEN INTERACTION WITH EXPERIMENTAL MAMMARY TUMORS

Since antiestrogens are able to antagonize the actions of estrogens, these compounds hold the potential of being noninvasive, nonsurgical agents capable of controlling the growth of estrogen-dependent tumors. Hence, we (Tsai and Katzenellenbogen, 1977) have analyzed the effectiveness of the antiestrogen U-23,469 (U-23), previously shown to be potent in antagonizing estrogen-induced uterine growth (Ferguson and Katzenellenbogen, 1977), in preventing the development of 7,12-dimethylbenz[a]anthracene (DMBA)-induced rat mammary tumors, and in eliciting the regression of established tumors, and we have attempted to elucidate the mechanisms of its tumor antagonism. Inasmuch as one of the problems frequently associated with antiestrogen therapy has been the development of photosensitivity in patients (Bloom and Boesen, 1974, Heuson *et al.*, 1975), we were particularly interested in using in this study the antiestrogen U-23,469, which is structurally related to the antiestrogen nafoxidine (UA) (see Fig. 16), but which is nonphototoxic and hence may prove to be more suitable for human use.

Virgin female Sprague–Dawley rats that receive DMBA at 47–50 days of age and then receive U-23 (250 μg sc in 0.15 M NaCl daily) have a greatly reduced number of mammary tumors and a markedly decreased tumor area. Treatment with U-23 for increasing time periods (3, 6, or 12 weeks) beginning 2 weeks after DMBA results in a progressive decrease in tumor size and number and a progressive delay in onset of tumor appearance; U-23 treatment beginning 1 week after DMBA or given prior to DMBA is even more effective (Fig. 17).

The time course of tumor regression (3 months after DMBA) by U-23 or ovariectomy (OVX) is similar with 50% regression in ca. 2 weeks, and both elicit

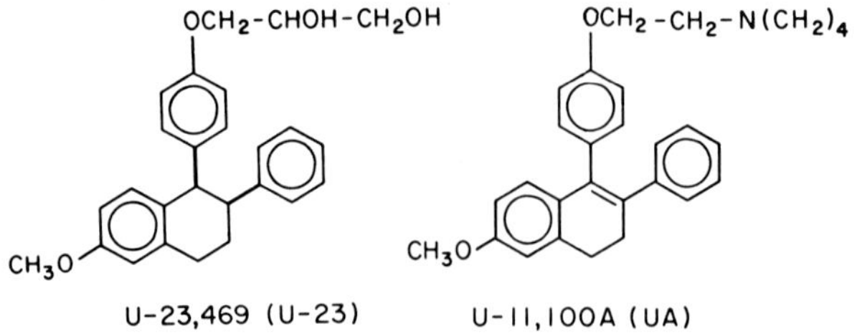

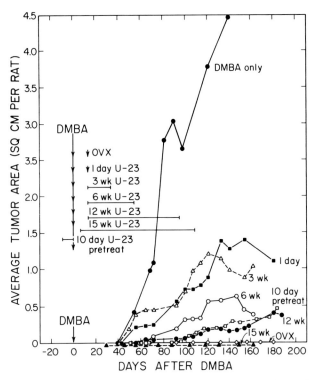

FIG. 16. Structure of the nonsteroidal antiestrogen U-23,469 and the structure of a related antiestrogen, U-11,100A (nafoxidine).

FIG. 17. The influence of treatments on the development and growth of 7,12-dimethylbenz[*a*] anthracene (DMBA)-induced rat mammary tumors. Female Sprague–Dawley rats received DMBA at 47–50 days of age, and then, after a 2-week period, groups of rats were ovariectomized (OVX) or they received U-23,469 (U-23) injections of 250 μg/day either for 1 day or for 3, 6, or 12 weeks. Another group was pretreated with U-23,469 for 10 days before DMBA administration and another group received 15 weeks of U-23,469 exposure starting at only 1 week after DMBA. There were 8–13 rats per treatment group and 58 rats in the control group. Values represent the average tumor area per rat of animals in these different groups. From Tsai and Katzenellenbogen (1977).

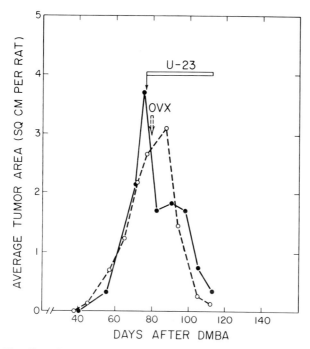

FIG. 18.   The effect of U-23,469 (U-23) treatment or ovariectomy (OVX) on the regression of established tumors. At the time indicated (arrow) after DMBA treatment, animals (15 per group) received U-23,469 injections (250 μg sc in 0.5 ml of 0.15 M NaCl/day, 6 days/week) for 36 days or were ovariectomized and followed for 34 days. Values represent the average tumor area per rat for each group of 15 rats. From Tsai and Katzenellenbogen (1977).

regression of almost all tumors (>90%) (Fig. 18). As seen in Fig. 19, estradiol (5 μg/rat per day) is able to reactivate these regressed tumors; tumors caused to regress by ovariectomy or antiestrogen treatment begin regrowth soon after the administration of estradiol.

In an attempt to understand the mechanism by which this antiestrogen might be eliciting tumor regression, we examined its effects on tumor estrogen and progesterone receptors. Table I summarizes the effects of these different treatments on receptor levels in mammary tumors. We have determined here the levels of nuclear-estrogen receptor, cytosol-estrogen receptor, and cytosol-progesterone receptor and the ratio of nuclear to total estrogen receptor. In tumors induced by DMBA, we find approximately 0.2 pmol of cytoplasmic estrogen receptor per 100 mg of tissue [59 ± 9 ($n = 30$) fmol per milligram of cytosol protein] and approximately one-half of the receptor is in the nucleus. Likewise, high levels of progesterone cytosol receptor are found. This appears to be the case whether tumors are assayed from cycling animals at random stages during the estrous cycle (Table I, Group 1a) or whether tumors are assayed from animals at 19 hours after ovariectomy (Table I, Group 1b). Hence, these data

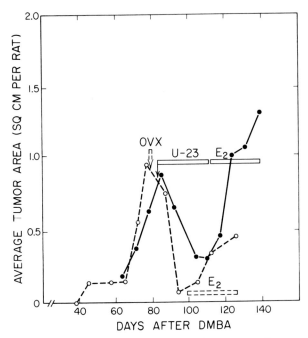

FIG. 19. The ability of estradiol (E_2) to elicit regrowth of tumors caused to regress by U-23,469
(U-23) treatment or ovariectomy (OVX). Animals received DMBA at 47 days of age, and at the times
indicated (arrows) rats (6 per group) were ovariectomized or received U-23,469 injections (250 μg sc
in 0.15 M NaCl per day) for 28 days prior to administration of estradiol (5 μg sc in 0.15 M NaCl per
day) for 27 days. Values represent the average tumor area per rat for the six rats in each group. From
Tsai and Katzenellenbogen (1977).

have been pooled (Group 1c) and are used for statistical comparison with the
other experimental treatment groups (Table I, Groups 2–5).

The statistically significant changes induced by the treatments are as follows.
After U-23 treatment (Table I, Group 4), as tumors regress, approximately 90%
of the receptor is found in the nucleus. After ovariectomy (Table I, Group 2),
little (30%) of the total receptor is in the nucleus, and cytoplasmic receptor levels
are high; as expected in the absence of ovarian estrogen, the progesterone cytosol
receptor level is very low. In tumors regressing under U-23 treatment (Table I,
Group 4), the progesterone receptor level is considerably higher than is that seen
in mammary tumors regressing due to ovariectomy. Receptor levels were also
studied during tumor reactivation by estradiol. In both cases (Table I, Groups 3
and 5), receptor assays were done 24 hours after the last injection of estradiol,
and it is seen that estradiol treatment shifts the estrogen receptor distribution to
that more resembling the DMBA-only control group (Table I, Group 1c).

In uteri of such animals, a generally similar picture is seen (Tsai and Katzenellenbogen, 1977). After ovariectomy, cytosol progesterone receptor levels are

TABLE I

Mammary Tumor Estrogen and Progesterone Receptor Levels[a,b]

Treatment	$\dfrac{E \cdot R_N}{E \cdot R_N + E \cdot R_C}$ (%)	Picomoles per 100 mg of tissue		
		$E \cdot R_N$	$E \cdot R_C$	$P \cdot R_C$
1a. DMBA only (no 19 hr OVX)	60	0.28 ± 0.09[c] (20)[d]	0.19 ± 0.03 (19)	1.33 ± 0.18 (10)
1b. DMBA only[e] (19 hr OVX)	43	0.19 ± 0.03 (22)	0.25 ± 0.06 (11)	1.48 ± 0.15 (20)
1c. DMBA only (pooled)	52	0.23 ± 0.04 (42)	0.21 ± 0.03 (30)	1.43 ± 0.12 (30)
2. OVX-regressing[f]	30	0.33 ± 0.07 (8)	0.79 ± 0.31[g] (6)	0.14 ± 0.07[g] (6)
3. OVX $\rightarrow E_2$[h]	62	0.26 ± 0.06 (5)	0.16 ± 0.04 (5)	0.42 ± 0.16[g] (5)
4. U-23,469-regressing[i]	90	0.54 ± 0.06[g] (18)	0.06 ± 0.02[j] (18)	1.14 ± 0.23 (17)
5. U-23,469 $\rightarrow E_2$[k]	58	0.21 ± 0.03 (10)	0.15 ± 0.05 (7)	1.05 ± 0.06 (11)

[a] From Tsai and Katzenellenbogen (1977).

[b] $E \cdot R_N$, nuclear-estrogen receptor; $E \cdot R_C$, cytosol-estrogen receptor; $P \cdot R_C$, cytosol-progesterone receptor; OVX, ovariectomy; E_2, 17β-estradiol.

[c] Mean ± SE.

[d] Numbers in parentheses = number of tumors assayed.

[e] Tumors were assayed 19 hours after bilateral ovariectomy.

[f] Regressing tumors were assayed 3–5 weeks after ovariectomy.

[g] $p < 0.01$ versus DMBA-only pooled value.

[h] At 3 weeks after ovariectomy, each rat received subcutaneous injections of 5 μg of E_2 in 0.5 ml of 0.15 M NaCl daily 6 days/week for 3 weeks. The tumors were assayed 24 hours after the last E_2 injection.

[i] Each rat received subcutaneous injections of 250 μg of U-23,469 in 0.5 ml of 0.15 M NaCl daily 6 days/week for approximately 4 weeks. The tumors were assayed 24 hours after the last U-23,469 injection and 19 hours after bilateral ovariectomy.

[j] $p < 0.05$ versus DMBA-only pooled value.

[k] After 4 weeks of U-23,469 injections, each rat received E_2 injections for 4 weeks. Tumors were assayed 24 hours after the last E_2 injection.

greatly diminished in uteri, as in tumors, while cytosol estrogen receptor levels are high, and in both tissues, little (ca. one-third) estrogen receptor is in the nucleus. During U-23 treatment, cytosol estrogen receptor content is very low in uterus, as in regressing tumor, and over 90% of the receptor is in the nucleus.

These receptor studies suggest that the effectiveness of this antiestrogen in antagonizing mammary tumor development and growth may reside in its ability to markedly perturb the distribution of estrogen receptor, maintaining over 90% of receptor in the nucleus with concomitant low levels of cytoplasmic estrogen receptor, a situation that should render the mammary tissue incapable of responding to the animal's own endogenous estrogens and hence unable to grow. These findings, however, do not preclude that antiestrogens may also influence mammary tumor growth by additional mechanisms. We do know that antiestrogens do reduce the level of prolactin binding in tumors (Kelley *et al.*, 1977; Katzenellenbogen *et al.*, 1979), and this may be another means by which mammary tumor regression is elicited in this tumor system.

C. STUDIES WITH RADIOLABELED ANTIESTROGENS

All the antiestrogen studies that have been discussed to this point have employed unlabeled compounds. With the hope of looking directly at the interaction of antiestrogens with receptor, we have prepared two of the antiestrogens (CI-628 and U-23,469) in tritium-labeled form. In studies presented below, we have found that the interaction of radiolabeled antiestrogen with the estrogen receptor parallels that of estradiol in many respects.

Figure 20 shows high-affinity estrogen-specific binding of tritiated CI-628 in uterine cytosol. Panel A shows CI-628 (CI) binding in the presence and in the absence of unlabeled estradiol; the difference between these curves, which is presumed to represent estrogen-specific binding sites, is plotted directly in panel B and as a Scatchard plot in panel C. An equilibrium dissociation constant of $1.7 \times 10^{-9} M$ is found for the interaction of CI with the estrogen receptor. In the same sample, the K_d for estradiol was determined to be $1.0 \times 10^{-10} M$. Thus, the binding affinity of CI relative to that of estradiol is 6%. This estimate of binding affinity of CI, determined here directly using radiolabeled compound, corresponds closely to that estimated earlier by competitive protein binding methods, 4–8% (Korenman, 1970; Katzenellenbogen and Katzenellenbogen, 1973; Ferguson and Katzenellenbogen, 1977). The number of binding sites is also equivalent to those seen with saturating levels of tritiated estradiol (dashed horizontal line, panel B).

Figure 21 shows sucrose density gradient analyses of tritiated CI–cytoplasmic-receptor complexes and tritiated E_2–receptor complexes on low-salt gradients. When run under normal assay conditions, over 90% of the estradiol–receptor complexes sediment at 8 S, whereas 70% of the tritiated CI activity (which appeared to be estrogen-competible sites) sedimented at 4.5 S, only 30% sedimenting at 8 S. These observations raised the question of whether these

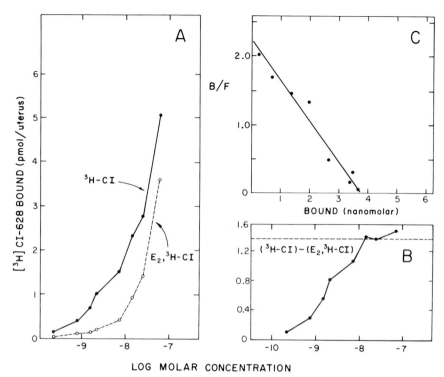

FIG. 20. Interaction of ³H-labeled CI-628 with immature rat uterine cytosol estrogen receptor *in vitro*. Cytosol, after exposure to $10^{-6} M$ unlabeled E_2 or vehicle for 1 hour at 0°, was then incubated with varying concentrations of ³H-labeled CI for 17 hours at 0°C. Cytosol concentration in the final incubations was 3.0 uterine equivalents per milliliter. The amount of ³H-labeled CI bound was then determined by charcoal–dextran adsorption (15% v/v, 15 minutes at 0°C). In all panels, the concentrations of free CI have been corrected for the low-affinity binding. (A) Binding curves for [³H]CI-628 with and without estradiol pretreatment. (B) Plot of the difference between the curves for [³H]CI alone and [³H]CI binding after E_2 pretreatment ("estrogen-specific" binding sites). Horizontal dashed line represents the concentration of estrogen-specific binding sites determined in parallel incubations employing [³H]estradiol. (C) Replot of data of panel (B) according to the equation of Scatchard. From Katzenellenbogen *et al.* (1978).

differences in sedimentation behavior might be a manifestation of differences in estrogen and antiestrogen interaction with receptor. This seemed particularly pertinent because analogous findings of differences in sedimentation velocities of receptor complexes had been reported earlier with two other antihormones, the antiglucocorticoid cortexolone (Turnell *et al.*, 1974) and the antimineralocorticoid spironolactone (Marver *et al.*, 1974).

Therefore, we asked whether we were seeing two interconverted receptor species or whether the antiestrogenic ligand was dissociating from receptor and being picked up by nonreceptor proteins in the 4 S region. Several studies indicate that ligand dissociation accounts for these results.

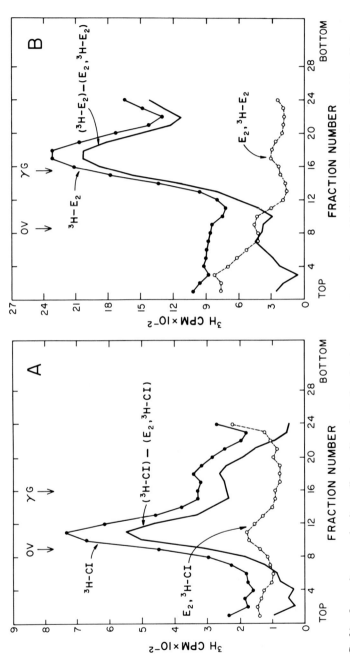

FIG. 21. Low-salt sucrose density gradient profiles of cytoplasmic estrogen–receptor complexes with [³H]CI or [³H]E₂. Cytosol (2.14 uteri/ml) was incubated with $3 \times 10^{-9} M$ [³H]CI (panel A) or $3 \times 10^{-8} M$ [³H]E₂ (panel B) in the presence or in the absence of $10^{-6} M$ unlabeled E₂. After 8 hours at 0°C, samples were treated with charcoal–dextran (15% v/v, 15 minutes at 0°C), and 300-μl aliquots were mixed with the ¹⁴C-labeled marker proteins and layered onto gradients. Centrifugation was for 13 hours at 4°C at 246,000 g. OV, ovalbumin; γG, γ-globulin. From Katzenellenbogen et al. (1978).

Figure 22 indicates that antiestrogen–receptor complexes can be found in the 8 S form under appropriate conditions. In this case, cytosol receptor filled with unlabeled CI-628 has been run on a sucrose gradient containing a high concentration of unlabeled CI-628 throughout the gradient to ensure the saturation of receptor with CI during the gradient run. After the run, the gradient was fractionated and [³H]estradiol was exchanged into the receptor sites to assay the receptor content of the individual fractions. Under these conditions, the CI–receptor complex is all found in the 8 S form. Jordan and Prestwich (1977) and Capony and Rochefort (1978) have also reported the finding of [³H]tamoxifen–receptor complexes in the usual 8 S form when gradient spins were done for a short period of time to minimize ligand dissociation. Hence, the cytoplasmic antiestrogen–receptor complexes and estrogen–receptor complexes are not discernible as physically different by the criteria we have used thus far.

After administration of tritiated antiestrogen *in vivo*, radioactivity can be found associated with specific estrogen receptor sites in uterine nuclei. Salt-extracted

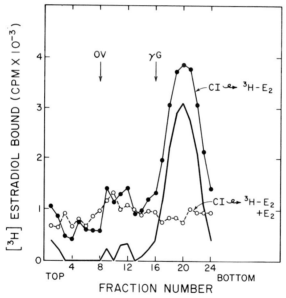

FIG. 22. Low-salt sucrose density gradient analysis of cytoplasmic estrogen–receptor complexes with CI-628. Immature rat uterine cytosol (4.5 uteri/ml) was incubated with $3 \times 10^{-7} M$ unlabeled CI-628 for 8 hours at 0°C. Samples were then layered onto low-salt 5 to 20% sucrose gradients containing $3 \times 10^{-7} M$ unlabeled CI-628 throughout the gradient. Samples were centrifuged for 13 hours at 4°C at 246,000 g and then fractionated as usual. Fractions were individually treated with charcoal–dextran (15% v/v, 15 minutes at 0°C), and each fraction was then made $5 \times 10^{-9} M$ in [³H]estradiol or $5 \times 10^{-9} M$ in [³H]estradiol plus $5 \times 10^{-7} M$ in unlabeled estradiol. Fractions were then incubated with the [³H]estradiol for 17 hours at 2°C, and bound estradiol was assayed after charcoal–dextran treatment (5% v/v, 10 minutes at 0°C) of fractions. ¹⁴C-labeled marker proteins were run in parallel gradients.

nuclear receptor–[³H]CI complexes sediment at 5.4 S on high-salt-containing sucrose gradients, as do [³H]E₂–nuclear receptor complexes (Fig. 23).

Studies we had done earlier with a series of structurally modified antiestrogens suggested that some antiestrogens, such as CI-628, possessing a methyl ether group might undergo metabolism to form a compound with a higher affinity for receptor and a faster onset of action (Ferguson and Katzenellenbogen, 1977). Therefore, we investigated the chemical nature of the antiestrogen associated with the nuclear receptor. Thin-layer chromatographic analysis of ethyl acetate extracts of the nuclear receptor peak fractions from sucrose gradients (Fig. 24) shows that a more polar metabolite of CI-628 is selectively bound to the 5.4 S receptor.

Pharmacokinetic studies (Fig. 25) reveal that high levels of CI persist in serum and uterus for long periods of time (half-cleared in 18–24 hours), whereas estradiol is much more rapidly cleared (half-cleared in 30 minutes). Hence, it is likely that the prolonged *in vivo* activity of this antiestrogen derives, at least in part, from its slow rate of clearance and that the agent active *in vivo* may be a metabolite of CI-628.

Studies with another long-acting antiestrogen U-23,469 (U-23, which was used in the mammary tumor studies) indicate that it is also rapidly converted to a more polar metabolite that selectively accumulates in the target cell nucleus. As seen in the thin-layer chromatograms of Fig. 26, by 1 hour after the *in vivo* administration of [³H]U-23 there is already some metabolite present in the nucleus, and by 13 hours it accounts for almost all the nuclear radioactivity. U-23 itself has a low affinity for the cytoplasmic estrogen receptor [approximately 0.1% that of estradiol (Ferguson and Katzenellenbogen 1977)]. Preliminary characterization indicates that the metabolite is the demethylated material, which has an affinity for receptor more than 100 times that of the parent compound.

In addition, specific nuclear antiestrogen–receptor complexes can be detected after administration of [³H]U-23 *in vivo*. Salt-extractable nuclear receptor complexes sediment at 5.4 S on high-salt sucrose gradients (Fig. 27) as do estradiol–receptor complexes, and chromatographic analysis reveals that it is only the metabolite that accumulates in the nuclear receptor fraction.

D. AN EVOLVING MODEL OF ANTIESTROGEN ACTION

How can we draw this information together into a working model of antiestrogen action (Fig. 28)? After exposure to estrogen, the steroid binds to the cytoplasmic receptor present in the target cell. The cytoplasmic receptor becomes localized in the nucleus, and the nuclear receptor interacts with chromatin in a manner such that a whole series of biochemical and physiological responses are elicited, as long as the level of hormone is adequate. Hence, the tissue responds and part of this response entails replenishment of cytoplasmic receptor which

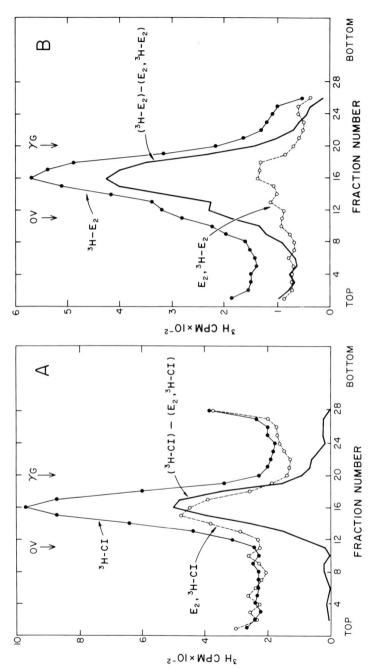

FIG. 23. High-salt sucrose density gradient centrifugation profiles of salt-extracted nuclear receptor complexes after exposure to [³H]CI-628 (panel A) or [³H]estradiol (panel B) *in vivo*. Groups of rats were pretreated for 1 hour *in vivo* with 5 μg of unlabeled E₂ or with vehicle saline alone and then received a subcutaneous injection of 50 μg of [³H]CI or 3 μg of [³H]E₂ (containing 0.9 μg of [³H]E₂ plus 2.1 μg of E₂). At 1 hour after injection, uteri were excised and the three-times washed 800 g nuclear pellet was extracted with buffer containing 0.4 M KCl for 1 hour at 0°C. Extracts were treated with 10% charcoal–dextran prior to addition of ¹⁴C-labeled marker proteins, and 300-μl aliquots (containing 1.6 uterine equivalents, panel A; 1.0 uterine equivalents, panel B) were layered onto gradients. Centrifugation was for 17 hours at 4°C at 270,000 g. From Katzenellenbogen *et al.* (1978).

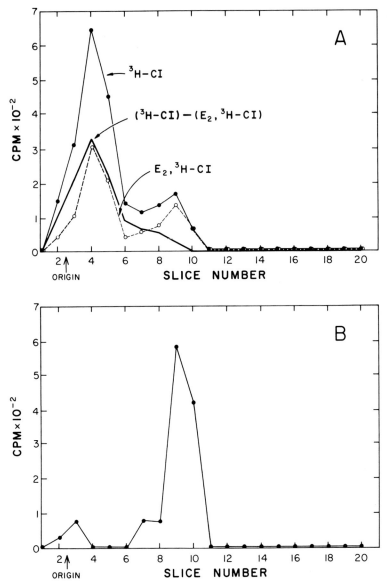

FIG. 24. Thin-layer chromatographic analysis of [³H]CI-628 from salt-extracted uterine nuclear-estrogen receptor purified on sucrose density gradients. Nuclear receptor was labeled *in vivo* with [³H]CI (50 μg) with or without prior injection of estradiol and was then extracted with buffer containing 0.4 M KCl and subjected to high-salt sucrose density gradient centrifugation. The peak region of the gradient (fractions 12–20) was extracted with ethyl acetate and analyzed by thin-layer chromatography. (A) The chromatograms of material from animals treated with [³H]CI alone (——) or [³H]CI after unlabeled E_2 pretreatment (---). The boldface curve indicates the difference between these two profiles, which represents radioactivity associated with estrogen-specific nuclear binding sites. (B) The chromatographic profile of [³H]CI-628. From Katzenellenbogen *et al.* (1978).

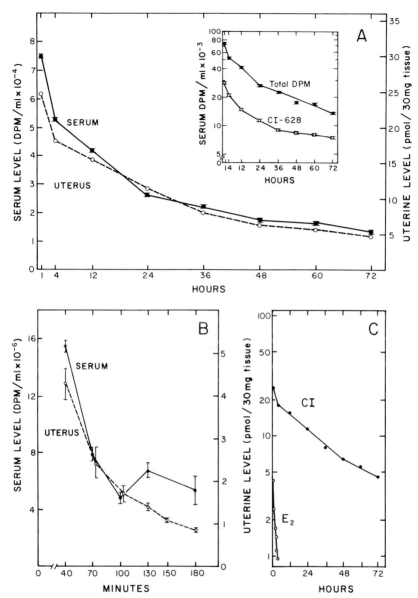

FIG. 25. Rates of clearance of [³H]CI-628 and [³H]estradiol from uterus and serum. (A) Immature rats (2 or 3 per group) were injected at zero time with 48.6 μg of CI-628 per rat containing 0.7 μg (25 μCi) of [³H]CI, and serum and uterine radioactivity were determined at 1–72 hours after injection. For serum radioactivity, each point is the mean ± SEM of three determinations from the pooled serum samples (3 rats per group). For uterine content, each point is the mean of two determinations. The inset is a semilogarithmic plot of total serum disintegrations per minute (dpm) and dpm which comigrated with CI-628 on thin-layer chromatography. (B) Immature rats (2 per group) were injected at zero time with 3 μg of estradiol (E₂) containing 0.5 μg of [³H]E₂ (88 μCi), and serum and uterine radioactivity were determined. Error bars indicate the range of the determinations. (C) Semilogarithmic plot comparing rates of clearance of CI-628 and estradiol from uterus. Data are taken from panels A and B (dashed lines). From Katzenellenbogen *et al.* (1978).

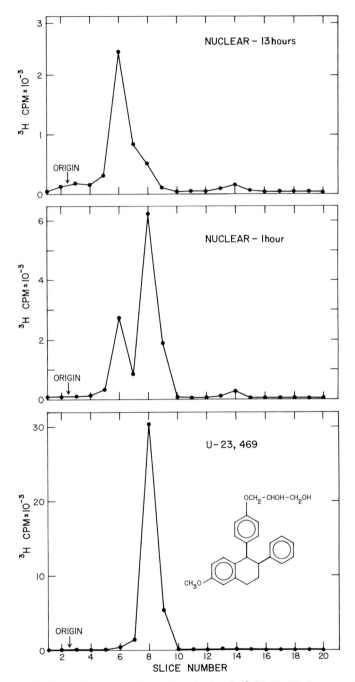

FIG. 26. Thin-layer chromatographic profiles of authentic [³H]U-23,469 (lower panel) and of uterine nuclear radioactivity after *in vivo* injection of [³H]U-23,469. Immature rats were injected with [³H]U-23,469 (25 μg sc per rat), and at 1 hour and 13 hours after injection, uteri were excised and homogenized; the three-times washed nuclear pellet was then ethanol extracted. Ethanol extracts were analyzed on thin-layer silica gel plates developed in anesthetic ether:ethanol (98:2 v/v).

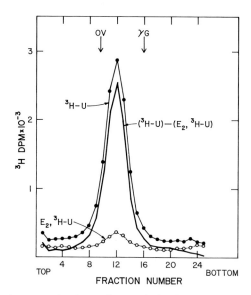

FIG. 27. High-salt sucrose density gradient analysis of salt-extracted nuclear receptor complexes after exposure to [³H]U-23,469 (³H-U) *in vivo*. Groups of rats were pretreated for 1 hour *in vivo* with 5 µg of unlabeled estradiol (E₂) or with vehicle saline alone, and each then received a subcutaneous injection of 25 µg of [³H]U. At 2 hours after injection, uteri were excised and the three-times washed 800 g nuclear pellet was extracted with buffer containing 0.4 M KCl for 1 hour at 0°C. Extracts were treated with charcoal–dextran prior to addition of ¹⁴C-labeled marker proteins, and 350-µl aliquots (containing 1.2 uterine equivalents) were layered onto gradients. Centrifugation was for 17 hours at 4°C at 270,000 g.

renews the capacity of the tissue to respond further to hormone. This replenishment of cytoplasmic receptor is believed to occur both by resynthesis of receptor and by recycling of some receptor from the nucleus back to the cytoplasmic compartment (Sarff and Gorski, 1971; Mester and Baulieu, 1975; Bhakoo and Katzenellenbogen, 1977b).

Therefore, with a long-acting estrogen or with the continuous administration of an estrogen, there is the continuous influx of new cytoplasmic receptor and a continuation of tissue response.

When an antiestrogen or a more active metabolite of the antiestrogen enters the target cell, it also binds to the cytoplasmic receptor. By the criteria we have used thus far, the interaction of antiestrogen with cytoplasmic receptor does not appear to be different from the interaction of estrogen with this receptor, but we have indicated R_C as R_C' here to indicate that the receptor complex with antiestrogen may be different, as suggested by some binding studies of Rochefort and Capony (1977). The antiestrogen–receptor complex does move into the nucleus and binds to chromatin, but its nuclear interaction must be different because it initiates only some responses, and in some tissues, like the chick oviduct, it does

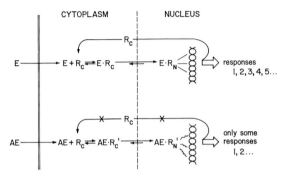

FIG. 28. Model for antiestrogen action, indicating our present state of knowledge about how estrogens (E) and antiestrogens (AE) interact with the estrogen-receptor system in target cells. R_C, cytoplasmic receptor; R_N, nuclear receptor.

not appear to evoke any estrogenlike responses (Sutherland *et al.*, 1977), although receptor does localize in the nucleus. Differences in the salt extractability of nuclear receptor–estrogen complexes versus nuclear receptor–antiestrogen complexes (Baudendistel and Ruh, 1976; Ruh and Baudendistel, 1977; Katzenellenbogen *et al.*, 1978) may be a manifestation of genuine differences in the chromatin interaction of these compounds.

After antiestrogen, cell division eventually becomes arrested and likewise there is no net increase in receptor content in the tissue. While this is most likely due to a block in further synthesis of new cytoplasmic receptor, the absence of new cytoplasmic sites could also be explained by an increase in receptor degradation that parallels receptor synthesis. The tissue, now with reduced levels of cytoplasmic receptor, is rendered incapable of responding to estrogen.

It is clear that there is still much that is not yet understood about the basis of antiestrogen action. We hope that additional studies will serve to elucidate in greater detail the differential effects of these compounds on different cell populations (Clark *et al.*, 1978a) and the nature of the receptor interactions that may serve to characterize the agonist/antagonist activities of these compounds in a variety of estrogen-sensitive target tissues.

ACKNOWLEDGMENTS

Research from our laboratories discussed in this chapter was supported in part by research grants CA 18119 and HD 06726 (to B. S. Katzenellenbogen) and AM 15556 (to J. A. Katzenellenbogen) from the United States Public Health Service, American Cancer Society grant BC-223, and a Camille and Henry Dreyfus Foundation award (to J. A. Katzenellenbogen) and Ford Foundation grant 700-0333.

REFERENCES

Aizawa, H., and Mueller, G. C. (1961). *J. Biol. Chem.* **236,** 381.

Anderson, J. N., Clark, J. H., and Peck, E. J., Jr. (1972). *Biochem. Biophys. Res. Commun.* **48,** 1460.

Anderson, J. N., Peck, E. J., Jr., and Clark, J. H. (1973). *Endocrinology* **92,** 1488.

Anderson, J. N., Peck, E. J., Jr., and Clark, J. H. (1975). *Endocrinology* **96,** 160.

Anderson, N. O., and Gorski, J. (1971). *Fed. Proc., Fed. Am. Soc. Exp. Biol.* **30,** 361 (Abstr. No. 952).

Barker, K. L., and Warren, J. C. (1966). *Proc. Natl. Acad. Sci. U.S.A.* **56,** 1298.

Barnea, A., and Gorski, J. (1970). *Biochemistry* **9,** 1899.

Baudendistel, L. J., and Ruh, T. S. (1976). *Steroids* **28,** 223.

Bhakoo, H. S., and Katzenellenbogen, B. S. (1977a). *Mol. Cell. Endocrinol.* **8,** 105.

Bhakoo, H. S., and Katzenellenbogen, B. S. (1977b). *Mol. Cell. Endocrinol.* **8,** 121.

Billing, R. J., Barbiroli, B., and Smellie, R. M. S. (1969). *Biochim. Biophys. Acta* **190,** 60.

Bloom, H. J. G., and Boesen, E. (1974). *Br. Med. J.* **2,** 7.

Capony, F., and Rochefort, H. (1978). *Mol. Cell. Endocrinol.* **11,** 181.

Clark, J. H., Anderson, J. N., and Peck, E. J., Jr. (1973). *Steroids* **22,** 707.

Clark, J. H., Hardin, J. W., Padykula, H. A., and Cardasis, C. A. (1978a). *Proc. Natl. Acad. Sci. U.S.A.* **75,** 2781.

Clark, J. H., Peck, E. J., Jr., Hardin, J. W., and Eriksson, H. (1978b). *In* "Receptors and Hormone Action" (B. W. O'Malley and L. Birnbaumer, eds.), Vol. 2, pp. 1–31. Academic Press, New York.

Courvelin, J. C., Bouton, M. M., Baulieu, E. E., Nuret, P., and Chambon, P. (1976). *J. Biol. Chem.* **251,** 4843.

DeAngelo, A. B., and Gorski, J. (1970). *Proc. Natl. Acad. Sci. U.S.A.* **66,** 693.

Eilon, G., and Gorski, J. (1972). *Fed. Proc., Fed. Am. Soc. Exp. Biol.* **31,** 245 (Abstr. No. 189).

Ferguson, E. R., and Katzenellenbogen, B. S. (1977). *Endocrinology* **100,** 1242.

Geynet, C., Millet, C., Truong, H., and Baulieu, E. E. (1972). *Gynecol. Invest.* **3,** 2.

Giannopoulos, G., and Gorski, J. (1971). *J. Biol. Chem.* **246,** 2524.

Glasser, S. R., Chytil, F., and Spelsberg, T. C. (1972). *Biochem. J.* **130,** 947.

Gorski, J. (1964). *J. Biol. Chem.* **239,** 889.

Gorski, J., and Raker, B. (1974). *Gynecol. Oncol.* **2,** 249.

Hamilton, T. H. (1963). *Proc. Natl. Acad. Sci. U.S.A.* **49,** 373.

Heuson, J. C., Engelman, E., Blonk-Vander Wijst, J., Maass, H., Drochmans, A., Michel, J., Nowakowski, H., and Gorins, A. (1975). *Br. Med. J.* **2,** 711.

Hisaw, F. L., Jr. (1959). *Endocrinology* **64,** 276.

Jordan, V. C., and Prestwich, G. (1977). *Mol. Cell. Endocrinol.* **8,** 179.

Jordan, V. C., Rowsby, L., Dix, C. J., and Prestwich, G. (1978). *J. Endocrinol.* **78,** 71.

Katzenellenbogen, B. S. (1978). *In* "Hormones, Receptors, and Breast Cancer" (W. McGuire, ed.), pp. 135–157. Raven, New York.

Katzenellenbogen, B. S., and Ferguson, E. R. (1975). *Endocrinology* **97,** 1.

Katzenellenbogen, B. S., and Gorski, J. (1972). *J. Biol. Chem.* **247,** 1299.

Katzenellenbogen, B. S., and Gorski, J. (1975). *In* "The Biochemical Actions of Hormones" (G. Litwack, ed.), Vol. 3, pp. 187–243, Academic Press, New York.

Katzenellenbogen, B. S., and Gorski, J. (1979). *In* "Neurobiology of Reproduction" (R. Goy and D. Pfaff, eds.), Vol. 8 of "Handbook of Behavioral Neurobiology." Plenum, New York, in press.

Katzenellenbogen, B. S., and Katzenellenbogen, J. A. (1973). *Biochem. Biophys. Res. Commun.* **50,** 1152.

Katzenellenbogen, B. S., Ferguson, E. R., and Lan, N. C. (1977). *Endocrinology* **100,** 1252.

Katzenellenbogen, B. S., Katzenellenbogen, J. A., Ferguson, E. R., and Krauthammer, N. (1978). *J. Biol. Chem.* **253**, 697.

Katzenellenbogen, B. S., Tsai, T. L. S., Rorke, E., and Rutledge, S. (1979). *Proc. Ann. Endocrine Soc. Mtg.* **61**, 146 (Abst. No. 296).

Kaye, A. M., Sheratzky, D., and Lindner, H. R. (1972). *Biochim. Biophys. Acta* **261**, 475.

Kelley, P. A., Asselin, J., Caron, M. G., Labrie, F., and Raynaud, J. P. (1977). *J. Natl. Cancer Inst.* **58**, 623.

Korenman, S. G. (1970). *Endocrinology* **87**, 1119.

Koseki, Y., Zava, D. T., Chamness, G. C., and McGuire, W. L. (1977). *Endocrinology* **101**, 1104.

Lan, N. C., and Katzenellengoben, B. S. (1976). *Endocrinology* **98**, 220.

McGuire, W. L., Horwitz, K. B., Zava, D. T., Garola, R. E., and Chamness, G. C. (1978). *Metabolism* **27**, 487.

Marver, D., Stewart, J., Funder, J. W., Feldman, D., and Edelman, I. S. (1974). *Proc. Natl. Acad. Sci. U.S.A.* **71**, 1431.

Mester, J., and Baulieu, E. E. (1975). *Biochem. J.* **146**, 617.

Miller, B. G. (1969). *J. Endocrinol.* **43**, 563.

Mueller, G. C., Herranen, A. M., and Jervell, K. F. (1958). *Recent Prog. Horm. Res.* **14**, 95.

Mueller, G. C., Gorski, J., and Aizawa, Y. (1961). *Proc. Natl. Acad. Sci. U.S.A.* **47**, 164.

Noteboom, W. D., and Gorski, J. (1963). *Proc. Natl. Acad. Sci. U.S.A.* **50**, 250.

Notides, A. and Gorski, J. (1966). *Proc. Natl. Acad. Sci. U.S.A.* **56**, 230.

Rochefort, H., and Capony, F. (1973). *C. R. Acad. Sci. Ser. D* **276**, 2321.

Rochefort, H., and Capony, F. (1977). *Biochem. Biophys. Res. Commun.* **75**, 277.

Ruh, T. S., and Baudendistel, L. J. (1977). *Endocrinology* **100**, 420.

Ruh, T. S., Katzenellenbogen, B. S., Katzenellenbogen, J. A., and Gorski, J. (1973). *Endocrinology* **92**, 125.

Sarff, M., and Gorski, J. (1971). *Biochemistry* **10**, 2557.

Smith, D. E., and Gorski, J. (1968). *J. Biol. Chem.* **243**, 4169.

Spooner, P., and Gorski, J. (1972). *Endocrinology* **91**, 1273.

Stormshak, F., Leake, R., Wertz, N., and Gorski, J. (1976). *Endocrinology* **99**, 1501.

Sutherland, R., Mester, J., and Baulieu, E. E. (1977). *Nature (London)* **267**, 434.

Szego, C. M., and Roberts, S. (1953). *Recent Prog. Horm. Res.* **8**, 419.

Teng, C. S., and Hamilton, T. H. (1967). *Biochem. J.* **105**, 1091.

Teng, C. S., and Hamilton, T. H. (1968). *Proc. Natl. Acad. Sci. U.S.A.* **60**, 1410.

Teng, C. S., and Hamilton, T. H. (1970). *Biochem. Biophys. Res. Commun.* **40**, 1231.

Tsai, T. L., and Katzenellenbogen, B. S. (1977). *Cancer Res.* **37**, 1537.

Turnell, R. W., Kaiser, N., Millholland, R. J., and Rosen, F. (1974). *J. Biol. Chem.* **249**, 1133.

Weil, A. P., Sidikaro, J., Stancel, G. M., and Blatti, S. P. (1977). *J. Biol. Chem.* **252**, 1092.

Williams, D., and Gorski, J. (1972). *Proc. Natl. Acad. Sci. U.S.A.* **69**, 3464.

DISCUSSION

J. H. Clark: We have studied the extent to which Nafoxidine stimulates the hypertrophy of the epithelium of the uterus. Clearly a single injection of Nafoxidine causes the cell height of the epithelium to exceed that which is produced by implants of estradiol. However, Nafoxidine fails to stimulate growth of the stroma or myometrium. Therefore Nafoxidine and compounds like it, such as Clomid and CI-628, are extremely potent estrogens (agonists) in the epithelium whereas they act as antagonists or partial agonists in the stroma and myometrium.

The studies of differential cell stimulation have also demonstrated that fetal or neonatal exposure to either Nafoxidine or Clomid causes extensive hyperestrogenization of epithelial cells, and results in the appearance of abnormalities of the reproductive tract. This occurs both in the offspring of rats treated during pregnancy and in the mother rats. Thus Nafoxidine and Clomid appear to hyperestrogenize some estrogen-sensitive tissues and mimic the effects of chronic estrogen exposure.

In summary, I believe that these drugs should be labeled as agonists or antagonists depending on the specific tissue or cell type in question and should not be referred to simply as antiestrogens. This is a general and often misleading term. Even though triphenylethylene derivatives do clearly have antiestrogenic capacity in some systems, it is dangerous to assume that this effect is seen in all systems. There are many examples in the literature of estrogenlike responses to the so-called antiestrogens. The interpretation of these effects has often been colored by the assumption that these drugs were "totally" antiestrogenic, when, in fact, the estrogenlike responses to triphenylethylene derivatives are easily explainable by the estrogenic properties of these drugs.

B. Katzenellenbogen: I agree completely. I am aware of these interesting studies, and I think it is important as well in tissues outside of the uterus, for example, in breast tumors, that we know really where these compounds are acting. Likewise, I think it interesting that there appear to be differences in the estrogenic or agonist activity of these compounds—if you compare studies in the rat or in other mammals with studies in the chick.

J. H. Clark: The recent paper by Sutherland *et al.* demonstrating that nafoxidine is an antagonist in the chick oviduct needs a slight qualification. Once again, Nafoxidine may be stimulating the oviduct epithelium, as in the uterus, while acting as a pure antagonist in the gland cells of the oviduct. Since the DES-treated oviduct is largely made up of gland cells, a stimulation of epithelial cells would go unnoticed in these studies.

L. E. Faber: We have collected considerable data on the sedimentation behavior of the mammalian progestin receptor. Our findings may be described by the following interactions:

$$4.5 \text{ S} \rightleftharpoons 5.5 \text{ S} \rightleftharpoons 7 \text{ S} \rightleftharpoons \text{Higher molecular weight forms}$$

The 4.5 S subunit combines either with itself or another macromolecule to form the 5.5 S complex, which in turn may be converted to the 7 S species. The 7 S receptor may then aggregate with other proteins to form the higher molecular weight species. Most of our data concern the 5.5 S to 7 S conversion. We have multiple lines of evidence indicating that one function of the ligand is to drive the equilibria to the right, and favor formation of the 7 S complex. Biological potency of a progestin may be correlated to the state of aggregation of the receptor, implying biological relevance to the 7 S and high molecular weight complexes.

At the time of cytosol preparation, the progestin receptor is at a concentration of approximately 10^{-7} M, and in close proximity to other proteins. Effects of cell disruption include reducing the concentration of the receptor and changing the ionic milieu. Further dilution of the cytosol results in progressive decreases in the sedimentation coefficient of the receptor, indicating a dissociation of subunits, and/or ions and cofactors. The points that I want to make are that the larger forms of the receptor (> 7 S) are important and that one function of the ligand is to increase the interactions of the receptor with other proteins. These observations may be of importance to our understanding of *in vitro* activation and nuclear translocation.

B. S. Katzenellenbogen: These are very interesting points to raise. The only thing that I would add at this point is that with some of the antiestrogens, at least under *in vivo* conditions, it appears that the ligand probably interacting with the cytoplasmic receptor *in vivo* is not in fact the administered compound. For example, we have done heat-activation or receptor-transformation studies with CI-628; it is a very weak receptor transformer, yet we know it to be very effective in moving sites into the nucleus *in vivo,* and what we presently have to do obviously is look with the correct or probably more biologically active antiestrogenic ligand.

L. E. Faber: The first reduction product of progesterone metabolism, 5α-pregnanedione, is an ineffective progestin that interacts with all forms of the progestin receptor. The 5α-pregnanedione–receptor complex also binds to nuclear preparations under *in vitro* conditions. The only real differences we can see in the binding of 5α-pregnanedione and progesterone reside in the larger forms of the receptor, where progesterone is more effective in maintaining the integrity of the 7 S receptor.

F. Naftolin: In dealing with the A-ring dihydroxylated estrogens, the so-called catechol estrogens, which bind to receptors with relatively lower but definite affinity, we have been wondering whether the demonstrable effects of these estrogen metabolites are due to their agonist–antagonist activities or to interference with other biological processes. For example, catechol estrogens inhibit catechol *o*-methyltransferase and are methylated, which may interfere with biogenic amine metabolism. Perhaps it would help to consider the estrogen molecule as having a "binding" and an "activity-modulating" end. For example, Dr. Muller and his colleagues recently published work showing that phenolic alkyds which are chemically like steroid A rings can cause competitive dissociation of estradiol from cytosol receptor. I wonder whether you could help us out of our dilemma. Could it be that the A ring is the part of the estrogen molecule that is important in binding and the other rings are the ones that are important in other (qualitative) actions that give the estrogenic activity under the circumstances?

B. S. Katzenellenbogen: I can perhaps answer that partially. We do know that the affinity for receptor is very much greater if one of the rings (I don't know whether you want to call this the A ring) containing the methyl ether function is cleaved to the hydroxyl. In other words, antiestrogens possessing a methyl ether group and, likewise, methyl ether derivatives of estradiol have very negligible affinity for receptor, and receptor affinity is considerably increased by demethylation. With John Katzenellenbogen's laboratory, we have done some work on structure–activity relationships with the antiestrogens, and the presence of the nitrogen-containing substituent in many of them is apparently very important for their antiestrogen activity. We hope perhaps to look at a graded series of structurally modified compounds to try to distinguish what functions will promote agonist versus antagonist action. At the moment, it is not clear whether they will parallel each other or dissociate at some point.

O. H. Pearson: There is no question that the introduction of antiestrogens constitutes a major advance in the treatment of women with breast cancer. In our hands, using an antiestrogen called Tamoxifen we obtain remissions that are comparable in incidence and duration to those of surgical hypophysectomy. In addition, there are some patients after total hypophysectomy who can get further improvement from antiestrogen. It was also found that, after removal of ovaries and adrenals, antiestrogens can produce further improvement. In those patients who have undergone ablative procedures, it is possible to measure estradiol, estrone, and estriol in the serum indicating that these estrogens are still circulating although in very low quantities. Thus, we think that Tamoxifen is an antiestrogen and that it can work better than actual removal of endocrine organs. It is also effective in premenopausal women whose ovaries are functioning and producing large amounts of estrogen; however, it does stimulate increased estrogen production by the ovary and yet at the same time tumors can regress, while the patient may continue to menstruate. This leads to the question whether there are differences of the action of antiestrogens in the uterus versus mammary cancer or the pituitary gland.

A second question deals with the DMBA tumor. This was referred to as an estrogen-dependent tumor. We believe that in the human estrogen is probably the most important hormone stimulating tumor growth. In the rat, however, we are not convinced, and we think that all these effects of antiestrogen could be indirect on prolactin secretion because estrogen is a major stimulus for prolactin secretion. You mentioned that prolactin receptors were decreased, but I think it would be very interesting to know whether estrogen is really doing anything in this DMBA tumor, despite its receptors and the transport mechanism as far as stimulation of the tumor. I think the only way to answer that is perhaps to do it in hypophysectomized rats, where we have never been able to get estrogen to do anything in stimulating tumor growth.

B. S. Katzenellenbogen: Clearly, the DMBA rat system is probably not the perfect model for human breast cancer. It represents a model system that is worthwhile and may represent some fraction of human breast cancer, but breast cancer is probably a whole spectrum in terms of hormonal dependence. In any event, in our own studies, and as other laboratories have reported also, we find that in the DMBA system prolactin receptor levels in tumors are decreased by antiestrogen administration, as it is by ovariectomy and/or administration of high levels of estrogen. In our own hands, we find that the reduction in prolactin receptor level is not as great in antiestrogen-treated tumors as it is following ovariectomy or high levels of estrogen. We do not know, for example, how many prolactin receptors are needed for tumor stimulation, so that when we see a 40% decrease in receptor population, we do not know how this really correlates with growth. So I think that clearly there are data in the literature to suggest that prolactin may play a very important if not predominant role, as your work has shown. These tumors clearly grow very well in response to estrogens, and it seems to me that, if these tumors are either denied estrogen receptors or prolactin receptors, either one of these may be adequate to elicit significant tumor regression. But we have not done studies in the hypophysectomized system, and probably that would be worthwhile. You mentioned also about the effects of estrogens versus antiestrogens in different tissues, and I think that this is an area that obviously requires further work.

J. R. Pasqualini: In relation to estradiol effect on specific proteins, I would like to present recent data concerning progesterone and estradiol receptors during fetal life. In Table A are indicated the presence of these receptors in the fetal uterus of guinea pig. As is indicated, estradiol receptors appear very early in fetal development (37–38 days of gestation). On the other hand, progesterone receptors are present only at the end of gestation. These data suggest the possibility that estradiol could stimulate the progesterone receptors in fetal uterus. To demonstrate this, first we observed that tritiated estradiol injected to the mother can cross the placenta and reaches the fetus [1–1.5% of the injected radioactivity was found in the fetuses 30 minutes after subcutaneous injection of 40 μCi of [^{3}H]estradiol (specific activity 47 μCi/mmol) to the mother]. After this we injected 1 mg/kg of estradiol daily to pregnant guinea pigs (end of gestation) for 4 days, and we observed that in the fetal uterus of the stimulated animals the number of progesterone receptors was 4–7 times greater than in control animals (Table B). This indicates that this response effect of estradiol is present during fetal life.

T. G. Muldoon: I have recently resumed some studies on the mechanism of action of 4-mercuri-17β-estradiol that we had started some years ago. This is a persistent, rather potent estrogen that binds covalently to the cytosol receptor in an affinity-labeling type mechanism. I have now shown that the complex will transform to a 5 S form analogous to what we find with estradiol, and it does very slowly translocate into the nucleus; however, once it gets into the nucleus it does not bind to anything specifically—one can completely wash it out with buffer alone without the necessity for

TABLE A

Progesterone and Estradiol Receptors in the Fetal Cytosol of Guinea Pig Uterus during Fetal Evolution[a]

Days of gestation	PROGESTERONE (femtomoles)		ESTRADIOL (femtomoles)	
	Per milligram of protein	Per gram of tissue	Per milligram of protein	Per gram of tissue
37–38	ND	ND	85	2,300
44–45	ND	ND	390	12,500
48–49	26	700	—	—
50–52	29	750	410	14,500
62–66	64	2070	720	28,000

[a] The cytosol fraction of the fetal uterus was obtained after homogenization in Krebs-Henseleit buffer and ultracentrifugation at 150,000 g. Incubation was carried out in $4 \times 10^{-9} M$ [^{3}H]estradiol or [^{3}H]progesterone without or with a 100-fold excess of the unlabeled steroids, at 4°C for 4 hours. The specific binding was calculated from the difference in binding between these two incubations using the dextran–charcoal method. The values represent the average of 3 determinations.

TABLE B

Effect of Estradiol on the Number of Cytosol-Progesterone Receptors in the Guinea Pig Fetal Uterus[a]

	Specific progesterone binding sites (fmol/mg protein)	
Days of gestation	Control animals	Treated animals
56–57	27	97
63–64	62	407

[a] Pregnant guinea pigs were injected subcutaneously 1 mg/kg daily with estradiol in saline solution (treated animals) or only with the saline solution (control animals) for 4 days. The mothers were anesthetized with ether, the fetuses were sacrificed by decapitation and exsanguinated, and the uterus was removed. The preparation of cytosol and the determination of specific binding were carried out as indicated in the footnote to Table A. The values represent the average of 2 determinations.

high-salt solubilization. This leads me to ask about your ethynylestriol cyclopentyl ether, which is also taken up very slowly and is a persistent estrogen. Have you looked at the nature of the nuclear binding?

B. S. Katzenellenbogen: We have not directly, because we have not used radiolabeled material. We could do it by indirect exchange assays, and as far as we can tell, the nuclear receptor complexes seem fully exchangeable with tritiated estradiol. Our assumption is that it is ethynylestriol that is in fact binding to the receptor, and we know that this actually has a high affinity for receptor, so I would expect that its nuclear receptor interaction would be with quite a high affinity, perhaps different from the mercuri-estradiol. We have no evidence for an affinity-labeling type of mechanism here.

H. W. Dickerman: I would like to draw attention to the nonspecific DNA binding of the estradiol receptors. This was certainly first seen by Kleinsmith and ultimately well discussed by Yamamoto and Alberts. I would like to take the opportunity to change that word from nonspecific, perhaps to relatively specific and relatively nonspecific; in other words, there is some degree of selectivity in the binding of an estradiol receptor to DNA, and it may have some relevance to the retention of the antiestrogens. First of all, we elected to use oligo(dt) cellulose in binding assay, following the lead of Thrower and Lin in England. This was the work of Dr. Ken Thanki in my laboratory. Essentially, we found a very profound effect of ionic strength upon the association of estradiol receptors from the cytosol of uterus as well as mouse kidney to oligo(dT) cellulose.

Isotonic concentration was the optimum for the binding of tritiated estradiol receptors from, in this case, mouse uterus to oligo(dT) cellulose (Fig. A). The nature of the salt is not very important within certain limits—sodium chloride would do as well. Divalent cations stimulate a much lower amplitude of binding and also would be operating at a much lower concentration, but ammonium chloride, e.g., could also substitute. Tris-chloride, by the way, is a very effective salt to use in the demonstration of oligo(dT) cellulose binding. Now, not only is the binding salt stimulated, but we do not need temperature activation for the receptor to bind to oligo(dT), as opposed to the reports of Wittliff on DNA cellulose and the uterine receptor of rat as well as the mammary gland receptor. The selectivity is also apparent in the fact that α-fetoprotein from mouse amniotic fluid, which is a high-affinity estradiol binding protein, does not bind in this assay at all.

In Fig. B, on the left-hand side (panel A), we are looking again at binding, binding this time too at the optimum salt concentration, 0.15 M KCl, to cellulose, oligo(dT) cellulose, and oligo(dA) cellulose. This makes a point that was first alluded to by Chamness and McGuire, and also to a certain extent by André and Rochefort. This is a cytosol, and there is an apparent saturation as one increases the input of receptor from the cytosol. In this case the cytosol was from the mouse kidney. However,

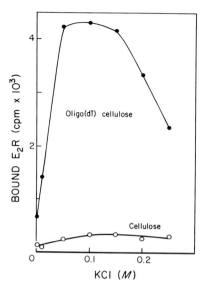

FIG. A.   Effect of ionic strength on association of estradiol receptors (E_2R) from mouse uterus to oligo(dT) cellulose and cellulose.

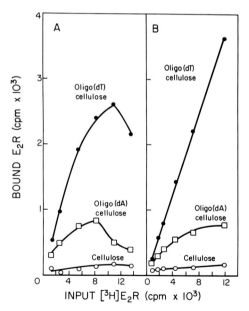

FIG. B.   (A) Effect of input receptor from mouse kidney cytosol on binding at optimum salt concentration (0.15 M KCl) to cellulose, oligo(dT) cellulose, and oligo(dA) cellulose. (B) Uptake after trivial purification and ammonium sulfate precipitation.

just trivial purification with ammonium sulfate precipitation converts the kinetics of the situation, or, I should say, the uptake, as seen in the right-hand side (panel B), so that there is linear uptake without any sign of saturation with oligo(dT) cellulose, but not with oligo(dA) cellulose. Oligo(dC) cellulose behaves exactly like (dT). In summary, we see a distinct preference for oligodeoxypyrimidines as opposed to oligo(dA). We have not yet extended our work to oligo(dG).

This falls in line with some of the observations that have been made recently showing preferential binding of the rabbit uterine receptor to poly(dA-T), work done by Kallos and Hollander and reported in *Nature*. What I was getting at is that it is not nonspecific binding that the estradiol receptor is confronting in DNA, but a relatively selective binding, searching our double-stranded regions, searching out (dA-T) stretches, searching out perhaps (dT)-rich surfaces of the helix. Where this may have relevance to the retention of antiestrogen is somewhat like the observation that Yamamoto made with the glucocortocoid-resistant mutant lymphocytes—that class of mutants in which the glucocorticoid receptor bound too avidly to DNA cellulose; in other words, that it got stuck on to nonspecific sequences and was not able to move over to an activator region. It may be that there is a conformational change in the estradiol receptor upon binding antiestrogens, such that the complex cannot depart from nonspecific or relatively nonspecific DNA sites to a more important site, and I would be interested to know whether you have any differential studies using Albert's DNA cellulose columns of receptors complexed to estradiol as opposed to antiestrogens?

B. S. Katzenellenbogen: I should, since I did my sabbatical work in their laboratories, but I am afraid that I have nothing to tell you at the moment. Your comments are certainly relevant to the whole topic of antiestrogen and estrogen action. I have comments that relate indirectly to what you are bringing up here. Henri Rochefort has shown that the antiestrogen receptor cytoplasmic complex does bind to DNA, as does the estrogen receptor complex, yet, as you point out, it is certainly not clear where these complexes are interacting or to what possible specific bases. The other comment I have is that it is still quite unclear where even the estrogen receptor complex is interacting in the nucleus, and, as a result, it makes analysis of what antiestrogen receptor complexes are doing in the nucleus even more complicated or difficult to analyze, although I think it is certainly at an approachable stage.

J. H. Clark: Your findings are very interesting, but you can obtain similar findings with glass tubes; i.e., KCl concentrations between $0.1\ M$ and $0.2\ M$ augment the ability of receptor hormone complexes to "stick" to many charged surfaces. Therefore one has to be very careful in the determination of specific and nonspecific binding. Also, I think that it is an absolute necessity to do competitive binding inhibition of that binding by adding cold complexes and by showing that they compete for these sites.

H. W. Dickerman: We have used α-fetoprotein, we have used albumin—they do not bind, and they do not show selective binding. We find that a heat-inactivated receptor will not show any preferential binding, so it does seem to have a certain constraint, which suggests that we are looking selectively at receptor interaction.

H. L. Bradlow: For the labeled U-23 compound studies, at 1 hour you had a mixture of the parent compound and the metabolite present in the nucleus, and at 13 hours only the metabolite was present. Are you implying that the conversion occurs in the nuclear area, or are you getting an exchange in which the metabolite is going in and displacing the parent compound?

B. S. Katzenellenbogen: We think that probably the metabolism occurs in the liver, probably by the microsomal mixed function oxidases, and that it just takes time to generate enough metabolite to interact with the uterus. I should point out that the chromatograms that I showed (Fig. 26) were of total nuclear radioactivity, not of receptor-associated radioactivity. We know in fact that there is very little translocation of receptor to the nucleus with this compound by 1 hour. When we have analyzed for receptor-associated radioactivity, the only thing that we detected is in fact the metabolite.

H. L. Bradlow: So that at 1 hour the only thing that was actually bound to chromatin or to nuclear receptor was the metabolite, and the parent compound was present only as free radioactivity.

B. S. Katzenellenbogen: Yes, that is correct.

C. Lazier: I am glad you mentioned chickens. In chick livers there are some interesting features of antiestrogen actions, and one feature is that neither Nafoxidine nor CI-628 is estrogenic at all in terms of vitellogenin production. Both compounds give a small increase in the nuclear receptor, but it is never any more than 10% of the equivalent dose of estradiol. Also, we require relatively small doses of the antiestrogen in order to inhibit the estrogenic response, and this is in marked contrast to the situation in the uterus. We get half-maximal inhibition of serum vitellogenin with a molar ratio of antiestrogen to estrogen of only 0.6. There is probably some metabolism of the antiestrogen in the chick liver, but we do not know anything about that yet.

A. Crastes de Paulet: In your last figure, where you compare the stage of the action of estrogen and antiestrogens, you give the same dimensions to the arrows of the equilibrium of the formation and dissociation of the complex RC-estrogen and RC-antiestrogen; does this mean that you think the association and dissociation rates are the same for estrogens and antiestrogens?

B. S. Katzenellenbogen: The answer would really depend on what antiestrogen you discuss. The affinity for cytoplasmic receptor can vary tremendously depending on the actual antiestrogen. The demethylated form of the two compounds (CI-628 and U-23,469) that I described have quite significant affinities for estrogen receptor. In fact, a demethylated form of CI-680 (which is very similar to CI-628) has an affinity for estrogen receptor twice as great as that of estradiol for the receptor. With CI-628 itself, which has a fairly low affinity, approximately 4% that of estradiol, we know that the decrease in affinity is due to an enhanced rate of dissociation. In other words, its association rate, as we published, for receptor is similar to that of estradiol.

A. Crastes de Paulet: Did you have the association and dissociation rates measured for these different antiestrogens?

B. S. Katzenellenbogen: Yes, we have published data on association and dissociation rates with CI-628 and with the other antiestrogens, we likewise are generating that sort of information.

B. Robaire: On the question of the use of the word antiestrogens, we would like to suggest that perhaps the terminology developed by pharmacologists of agonist, partial agonist, partial antagonist, and antagonist of estradiol might be more useful and less confusing than the use of the word antiestrogen. I agree with Dr. Clark.

S. L. Cohen: I would like to point out that while estriol might not be an antiestrogen uterotrophically, it may still be an antiestrogen for some other activities in the body; for example, nobody has countered Lemon's work on preventing the appearance of the mammary tumors caused by dibenzanthracene by the simultaneous administration of estriol, and we also have some work on the myometrial effect of the estrogen estriol, in which we believe it is acting as an antiestrogen. We found, by assaying the estradiol and the estriol content of the nuclear receptors of human myometrium during pregnancy and during labor, that during pregnancy the estriol:estradiol ratio is about 2:1 and during labor the reverse is true. The estradiol:estriol ratio was about 2:1. This is due not to a decrease in the estriol, but to the increase in the estradiol content of the myometrium. This led us to suppose that perhaps the estriol is playing a role in pregnancy by combining with myometrial receptors the estradiol content of nuclear receptors below stimulatory levels. Another thing: we have also done some assays on mammary tissue of estradiol and estriol. Nobody has done estriol assays in receptors before this radioimmunoassay showed a lot of estriol, much more than estradiol. Examination of urine from patients with mammary tumors have indicated only one estrogen that can be high, and that is the catechol estradiol; this makes us wonder whether the antibody used for estriol might not cross react with catechol estradiol because they both have 3-hydroxyl groups, 2 on 1 end ring and 1 on the other end ring, but which end has the 2 groups and which end the 1 group is reversed to estriol and for catechol estradiol.

B. S. Katzenellenbogen: I would just comment that in uterine studies estriol itself is a poor stimulator of uterine growth. Yet studies that we have done with more prolonged derivatives of estriol—and I think Jim Clark has done some of the nicest work [J. N. Anderson, E. J. Peck, Jr., and J. H. Clark, *Endocrinology* **96:** 160 (1975)] here—and likewise some earlier studies by B. G. Miller [*J. Endocrniol.* **43,** 563 (1969)], showed that, if one kept sufficient levels of estriol around either by multiple injection or by administering it in a prohormonal form so it was able to constantly interact with receptor, the receptor complex was just as effective. So I think that part of the lack of efficacy of estriol under conditions of single injection is due to the brevity of its interaction with receptor.

J. H. Clark: Yes, I would agree, and add that Lemon's work has been contradicted by Rudali's work in which he showed that the incidence of mammary cancer in mice was facilitated to the same degree by estriol as it is by estradiol.

H. Schwartz: In your talk and, generally, in the work of those who deal with the steroid receptors, attention is paid to the role of the cytosol receptor, its translocation to the nucleus, and return to the cytosol. What evidence is there for a role of nuclear acceptor site number in control of steroid hormone action?

B. S. Katzenellenbogen: I would not want to leave the impression that I think the cytoplasmic receptor is any more important than the nuclear receptor or what the receptor complex is doing in the nucleus. It is clear that antiestrogen studies point out that, while lack of continuing sensitivity to estrogen appears to be due to the depleted cytoplasmic receptor, these compounds do interact in the nucleus and turn on certain things but not other things, so it is clear that where they are interacting in the nucleus—to specific acceptor sites or DNA binding sites or whatever—is probably very important in understanding whether they are agonists or antagonists.

H. Schwartz: Are there instances in which you find a decrease or increase in acceptor number?

B. S. Katzenellenbogen: Perhaps Jim Clark should address that question, since he has done some of those studies.

J. H. Clark: It is a difficult question because we do not have a complete system of assay for acceptor sites. We can determine a limited number of nuclear sites that are correlated with retention of the receptor–hormone complex, and show in turn that those are required to maximize uterine growth. However, what we really need is a cell-free system with which to demonstrate a limited number of nuclear binding sites that are competitively inhibited by nonlabeled receptor–hormone complexes. Coupled to this system should be a well-defined response elicited by the formation of receptor hormone–acceptor site complexes.

Effects of FSH on Gonadal Functions

JENNIFER H. DORRINGTON AND D. T. ARMSTRONG

Banting and Best Department of Medical Research, University of Toronto,
Toronto, Ontario, Canada, and
Departments of Physiology and Obstetrics and Gynaecology,
University of Western Ontario, London, Ontario, Canada

I. Introduction

FSH regulates directly the metabolic activity of two cell types in the gonads of mammals, these being the granulosa cells of the ovary and the Sertoli cells of the testis. These cell types are present in the fetal gonad and clearly play an important role in the early stages of gonadal differentiation. At the onset of testicular development, the cortex involutes and the medulla proliferates. Sertoli cell progenitors originate from the epithelium of the gonad, penetrate into the medulla region, and associate with germ cells to give rise to sex cords (Zuckerman and Baker, 1977). The incorporation of germ cells into the spermatic cords of the medulla is one of the earliest indications that the gonad is destined to become a testis. The cords differentiate into seminiferous tubules lined with immature Sertoli cells in close contact with the primitive germ cells.

The ovarian cortex is formed by the proliferation of the surface epithelium, and the germ cells tend to remain in this region near the periphery of the gonad. The germ cells proliferate mitotically and then enter meiotic prophase. Shortly after birth in most mammals all the oocytes have entered the "resting phase" (dictyate) of meiosis and are enveloped in a layer of epithelial cells, which are the immature granulosa cells (Zuckerman and Baker, 1977).

Sertoli cells and granulosa cells therefore appear to originate from the same embryonic cells, i.e., the epithelial cells on the surface of the gonad. It has also been suggested that the rete ovarii may contribute to the granulosa cell population (Byskov *et al.*, 1977), but it is not clear whether these cells differ functionally from the cells derived from the germinal epithelium. Throughout their development in the gonads the germ cells remain in intimate association with either Sertoli cells or granulosa cells.

II. Sites of Action of Gonadotropins

In the mature animal, the gonads perform two functions: the production of gametes and the synthesis and secretion of steroid hormones, and both these

301

processes require the presence of gonadotropins. A first step in attempting to determine the mechanisms involved in the control of these functions was to establish which cell types in the gonads responded directly to gonadotropins.

A. THE TESTIS

Increased 3′,5′-AMP production was used as an index of hormonal responsiveness in the testis. These early studies showed that LH increased 3′,5′-AMP levels in the interstitial cell component of the testis but not in the seminiferous tubule fraction (Dorrington and Fritz, 1974a). FSH on the other hand did not influence 3′,5′-AMP levels in the interstitial cells but did stimulate its production in isolated seminiferous tubules (Kuehl *et al.*, 1970), the response to FSH progressively decreasing with increasing age of animal (Fig. 1) (Dorrington and Fritz, 1974b). Suspensions of spermatocytes and spermatids obtained from immature seminiferous tubules failed to respond to FSH, whereas experimental

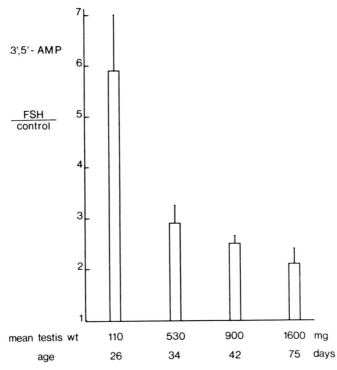

FIG. 1.   Ratios of the cAMP levels after the addition of FSH (10 μg/ml) *in vitro* to that obtained in the absence of exogenous FSH, in tubules isolated at various stages during the development of the rat testis. Tubules (30 mg wet weight) were incubated in 1 ml of Krebs–Ringer bicarbonate buffer, pH 7.4, containing 1 mg of glucose per milliliter and 10 m*M* theophylline at 32°C for 20 minutes. From Dorrington and Fritz (1974b).

manipulations that increased the percentage of Sertoli cells within the tubule (e.g., hypophysectomy, cryptorchidism) enhanced the FSH effect (Dorrington and Fritz, 1974a,b). The conclusion reached from these studies was that interstitial cells and Sertoli cells probably constituted the principal cell types within the testis which responded to LH and FSH, respectively, and this provided the incentive for the development of methods for the isolation of enriched cell preparations. The method devised to obtain Sertoli cell-enriched aggregates from immature testes involved sequential enzyme digestion with trypsin and DNase, and collagenase (Dorrington et al., 1975). The aggregates obtained were contaminated with germ cells, but many of these were lost when the aggregates were cultured in a chemically defined medium. Sertoli cells adhered to the surface of the culture flask and spread out, releasing germ cells into the culture medium. Other germ cells degenerated and were phagocytosed by Sertoli cells; consequently, the proportion of Sertoli cells increased with increasing time in culture (Table I). The germ-cell population present in Sertoli cell monolayers can be depleted further by using the testes of rats irradiated in utero as the starting material for the preparation. Pregnant females were exposed to 125 rad of irradiation at day 19 of gestation, which destroyed the spermatogonia in the gonads of the male embryo. The testes of the resulting male offspring were consequently depleted of germ cells, providing a valuable source of Sertoli cell-enriched material (Means et al., 1976).

Sertoli cell-enriched aggregates responded to FSH with an increase in $3',5'$-AMP levels immediately after preparation, and the response to FSH increased as the cells became established in culture and contaminating germ cells were lost (Fig. 2). These studies showed unequivocally that Sertoli cells were target cells for FSH action in the testis. This was important since it led to the concept that, even though FSH was required for initiation of the first wave of spermatogenesis and for the restoration of spermatogenesis after hypophysectomy, these effects

TABLE I
Differential Cell Counts in Sertoli Cell-Enriched Preparations[a]

	Percentage distribution[b] of cells			
Cell type	Initial aggregates	Cultured for 2–3 days	Cultured for 4–6 days	Trypsin removed cultures
Sertoli cells	70.3 ± 2.6	85.0 ± 2.9	88.0 ± 0.7	93.0 ± 1.3
Germinal cells	23.1 ± 4.2	8.7 ± 1.4	10.5 ± 1.1	3.7 ± 1.4
Unidentified or degenerating cells	6.7 ± 1.8	6.3 ± 0.8	1.0 ± 0.7	3.3 ± 0.3

[a] From Fritz et al. (1975).

[b] Percentage distribution was obtained by identifying 470–1150 cells from each of three different preparations for each class listed, utilizing electron microscopy for structural identification.

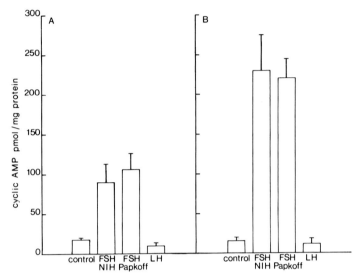

FIG. 2.   The effect of FSH (10 µg of NIH-FSH-S10 per milliliter and 0.5 µg of Papkoff's highly purified FSH per milliliter) and LH (10 µg of NIH-LH-S18 per milliliter) on the levels of cAMP in Sertoli cell preparations (from 18–20-day-old rats) when incubated (A) immediately after preparation and (B) after 48 hours in culture. Cell incubations were carried out for 20 minutes at 32°C in 1 ml of Krebs–Ringer bicarbonate buffer containing 1 mg of glucose per milliliter and 0.5 mM 3-isobutyl-1-methylxanthine. Each bar represents the mean + SEM of 3 or 4 experiments. From Dorrington *et al.* (1975).

were not due to a direct action of FSH on the germ cell population but rather on the supporting Sertoli cells (Fritz, 1978).

LH, testosterone, or DHT alone will maintain production of spermatozoa, albeit at a somewhat reduced yield, if administered immediately after hypophysectomy of adult rats (Steinberger, 1971; Ahmad *et al.*, 1973). Studies on the specific binding of labeled LH (or hCG) to testicular preparations and the ability of LH to modulate Leydig cell metabolism—for example, by increasing 3',5'-AMP production, protein kinase activation, and androgen synthesis—have indicated that LH acts exclusively on Leydig cells (Catt *et al.*, 1974). Androgens synthesized by Leydig cells in response to LH diffuse into the lymph, which bathes the basal compartment of the tubule. The inability of the seminiferous tubule to synthesize significant amounts of steroids from cholesterol indicates that the tubule relies upon this extratubular source of the androgen required for spermatogenesis (Cooke *et al.*, 1972; van der Vusse *et al.*, 1973). To determine the sites of action of testosterone in the tubule several approaches have been used, including the localization of androgen receptors, the induction of morphological and biochemical responses to androgens, and genetic approaches. The evidence that has accumulated from these varied approaches has been reviewed recently by Fritz (1978) and will not be reiterated here. Suffice it is to note that these data indicate that myoid and Sertoli cells are target cells for androgens in the tubule.

Taken together, the developments outlined above constitute a landmark in our understanding of spermatogenesis, since they suggest that gonadotropins and androgens do not interact *directly* with germ cells, but act upon the somatic cells of the testis (Fig. 3). FSH and testosterone are required to establish spermatozoa production, and this is effected by actions upon Sertoli cells. This suggests that a hormonally responsive Sertoli cell is a prerequisite for germ-cell differentiation; if this is so, then it is clearly important to define the normal functions of the Sertoli cell and to determine how they are influenced by FSH and androgens.

B. THE OVARY

The growing follicle also provides a fascinating example of a differentiating system that requires the interaction of polypeptide and steroid hormones. The trigger that initiates the growth of a small follicle is not known, but once this signal is received many follicles develop to the preantral stage without becoming atretic (Peters, 1969; Pederson, 1970). Granulosa cells in these small follicles contain FSH binding sites, and treatment of neonatal rats with FSH will stimulate follicular growth (Eshkol and Lunenfeld, 1972). The majority of follicles that reach the preantral stage are destined to undergo atresia, and only a small proportion complete the final stages of differentiation and ovulate. The acquisition of binding sites for gonadotropins, the capacity to synthesize steroids, and the ability to respond to steroids are critical factors in dictating the ultimate fate of the follicle, that is, ovulation or atresia.

LH binds specifically to interstitial (or stromal) cells, thecal cells and the

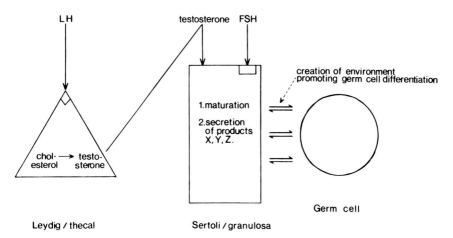

FIG. 3. Summary of the primary sites of action of gonadotropins and testosterone on the cell types in the gonads.

granulosa cells of large follicles (Zeleznik *et al.*, 1974). The end response to this interaction in interstitial cells (Savard *et al.*, 1965) and thecal cells (Fortune and Armstrong, 1977; Makris and Ryan, 1975; Erickson and Ryan, 1976) is increased androgen production. The androgen produced passes into the blood and diffuses into the granulosa cell layers, where it serves as a substrate for the synthesis of estrogens and 5α-reduced androgens (see below) and also binds to cytosol receptors (Schreiber and Ross, 1976). In the ovary, FSH binds exclusively to granulosa cells (Zeleznik *et al.*, 1974). Estrogen synthesized by granulosa cells in the presence of testosterone and FSH binds to receptors that are also localized in granulosa cells, to induce increased DNA synthesis and mitosis (Goldenberg *et al.*, 1972). A similar control system to that prevailing in the testis appears to occur in the ovary, in that the gonadotropins, and steroids synthesized in response to gonadotropin actions, influence the metabolism of the somatic cells. There is no evidence in the mammalian ovary to suggest that the oocytes respond directly to hormones, and hormonal influences appear to be mediated via somatic cell interactions (Fig. 3).

The support cells under hormonal control sustain an environment conducive to germ cell development. Factors required for the completion of the developmental program of germ cells may fall into two classes: (1) unique secretion products and (2) specific recognition sites on the cell surfaces of Sertoli and germ cells. Cell-membrane antigens have been found on spermatocytes and Sertoli cells (Millette and Bellve, 1977; Tung and Fritz, 1978), but much more work is required before any role in cell recognition and interaction can be presumed. The culture system has provided us with an ideal means of studying secreted products under a variety of different hormonal stimuli and over a range of ages throughout development. The products known to be secreted by Sertoli cells and granulosa cells are summarized in Table II.

III. Steroidogenesis in the Testis

It has been established that the interstitial cells of the testis synthesize androgens from endogenous cholesterol and that this process is regulated by LH. The ability of interstitial cells to secrete estrogens has been questioned; however, the controversy now appears to have been resolved, since two presentations (Canick *et al.*, 1978; Valladares *et al.*, 1978) at a recent Endocrine Society meeting showed that these cells contain aromatase activity and have the capacity to synthesize estrogens. The extent to which the interstitial cells contribute to the total estrogen output at various ages is still not clear.

Sertoli cells contain inclusions, such as lipid droplets, abundant smooth endoplasmic reticulum, and numerous mitochondria, that are typical of steroid-producing cells, and on the basis of these observations it was suggested that the Sertoli cell may be a source of the steroid hormones required for germ cell differentiation (Lacy and Pettitt, 1970). During the last 5 years we have at-

TABLE II

Products Secreted by Cultured Sertoli Cells and Granulosa Cells under Various Hormonal Stimuli

Product	Immature Sertoli cell[a]	Granulosa cell[a]
Steroids		
Progesterone	−	+ (FSH + Tt)
Androgens	−	−
Estrogens	+ (FSH)	+ (FSH)
Proteins		
Androgen binding protein	+ (FSH, Tt)	−
Plasminogen activator	+ (FSH)	+ (FSH, LH)
Inhibin	+	+
Proteoglycans	+	+ (FSH)
Müllerian duct		
inhibiting factor	+	−
Carbohydrate		
Inositol	+	−

[a] −, Nondetectable; +, detectable. Hormonal requirements are given in parentheses. Tt, testosterone.

tempted to define the steroidogenic potential of Sertoli cells and ascertain the hormonal requirements for enhanced synthesis.

A. SYNTHESIS OF ANDROGENS

The ability of seminiferous tubules from 35-day-old rats and Sertoli cell-enriched aggregates, prepared from isolated tubules, to convert [^{14}C]-pregnenolone to androgens was compared to whole-testis preparations from animals of the same age. The whole-testis preparations converted pregnenolone to testosterone and also to 5α-androstanediols and androsterone. Isolated tubules also converted pregnenolone to testosterone; however, the amounts converted were trivial compared to the capacity of the whole testis. Sertoli cell-enriched aggregates prepared from isolated tubules by the standard procedure (Dorrington *et al.*, 1975) and incubated immediately were unable to convert significant amounts of pregnenolone to androgens (Table III). Since we had shown that granulosa cells from immature rats converted pregnenolone to progesterone only in the presence of FSH (discussed below), Sertoli cells were cultured under the same conditions; however, no progesterone synthesis occurred. The data were consistent with the generally accepted view that most, if not all, of the androgen required for spermatogenesis is supplied by interstitial cells.

Since Sertoli cells cannot synthesize testosterone but rely upon interstitial cells for this steroid, the next logical question to ask was: Does the Sertoli cell utilize testosterone as a substrate to provide other steroids found in tubular fluid? We

TABLE III

*Metabolism of [¹⁴C]Pregnenolone by Whole-Testis Preparations
and Sertoli Cell-Enriched Preparations from 35-Day-Old Rats[a]*

	Percentage of total radioactivity recovered	
	Whole testis	Sertoli cells
Pregnenolone[b]	63.0 ± 4.0	97.1 ± 1.0
Progesterone	7.9 ± 2.4	0.4 ± 0.2
17α-Hydroxyprogesterone	3.1 ± 0.6	0.2 ± 0.1
Androstenedione	3.2 ± 0.5	ND
Testosterone	1.3 ± 0.2	ND
Androstanediol	5.5 ± 1.6	ND
Androsterone	12.0 ± 2.2	ND

[a] Total testis tissue from 35-day-old rats (40 mg wet weight) and freshly prepared Sertoli cell-enriched aggregates (approximately 2 mg of protein) obtained from isolated tubules by the enzyme digestion procedure (Dorrington *et al.*, 1975) were incubated in 1 ml of Krebs–Ringer bicarbonate buffer containing 1 mg of glucose and 500 ng of [¹⁴C]pregnenolone for 2 hours at 32°C in an atmosphere of 95% O_2 and 5% CO_2. The results were expressed as the mean ± SEM of the percentage of the total radioactivity recovered after incubation of 2 mg of protein. Three separate experiments were performed for each set of observations reported. ND, not detected.

[b] Unmetabolized substrate.

approached this problem by incubating cultured Sertoli cell preparations with [¹⁴C]testosterone and searching for labeled products. As shown in Fig. 4, labeled DHT, 5α-androstanediols, androsterone, and androstenedione were identified, and the proportions were similar to those obtained when tubules from immature rats were incubated under the same conditions. Treatment of Sertoli cells (from 20-day-old rats) in culture with FSH and testosterone did not influence the products formed (Dorrington and Fritz, 1975); however, Welsh and Wiebe (1978) have shown that FSH stimulates the activity of both 5α-reductase and 3α-hydroxysteroid dehydrogenase in Sertoli cells of younger animals (10 days of age).

B. SYNTHESIS OF ESTROGENS

Sertoli cells have been implicated as sites of testicular estrogen biosynthesis since the observations of Zuckerman and McKeown in 1938, on the feminization of dogs with Sertoli cell tumors (reviewed by Armstrong and Dorrington, 1977). To test this notion directly, Sertoli cell-enriched aggregates were cultured for 24 hours in the absence of hormones, after which time test substances were added. Medium was collected at frequent intervals and extracted with diethyl ether. Estradiol content of the ether extracts as well as the ethanolic extracts of the cells before and after incubation, were determined by radioimmunoassay (Dorrington and Armstrong, 1975). Cells incubated in the presence of testosterone alone

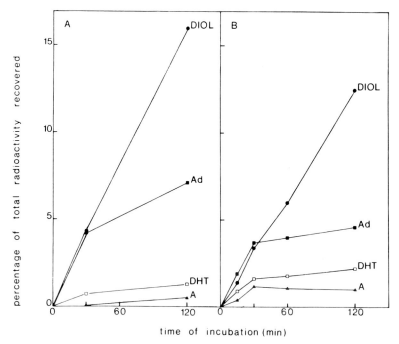

FIG. 4. Time course of the conversion of [¹⁴C]testosterone to metabolites by (A) Sertoli cell-enriched preparations from 20-day-old rats and (B) tubules from immature rats (26–28 days of age). Tubules (80 mg wet weight) or cell preparations (2 mg of protein) were incubated with 1 μg of [¹⁴C]testosterone. All results are expressed as the mean ± SEM of the percentage of the total radioactivity recovered after incubation of 5.0 mg of protein. The metabolites formed were 5α-androstanediol (DIOL), DHT, androstenedione (Ad), and androsterone (A). All but 0.5% of the radioactivity not accounted for by these metabolites was unchanged [³H]testosterone.

synthesized low levels of estradiol-17β. No effect of NIH-FSH-S10 (5 μg/ml) on the conversion of testosterone to estradiol-17β was found for approximately 4 hours. After this initial lag phase estradiol-17β synthesis was stimulated by FSH and persisted for at least 20 hours (Fig. 5). Having described this phenomenon, our concerns fell into three categories: (1) Were the Sertoli cells in our preparations synthesizing estradiol or were the other cell types contributing to the synthesis of this steroid? (2) Was the effect specific for FSH? (3) Was the material measured by the radioimmunoassay (RIA) estradiol-17β?

To answer the first question, Sertoli cell preparations were isolated from testes deficient in germ cells, as a result of irradiation *in utero,* and the effect of FSH was compared with that obtained from Sertoli cell preparations isolated from normal rats. As shown in Fig. 6, the responses to FSH were similar, suggesting that germ cells were not required for estrogen biosynthesis. Peritubular myoid cells did not synthesize estradiol-17β when cultured in medium containing testosterone and gonadotropins. Further evidence that Sertoli cells were the sites

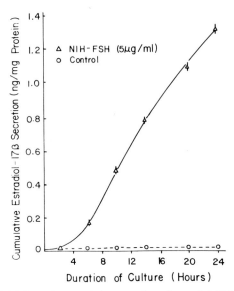

FIG. 5.   Effect of FSH on the cumulative secretion of estradiol-17β throughout a 24-hour incubation period in medium containing testosterone. Medium containing either testosterone (0.5 μM) alone (○) or testosterone and 5 μg of NIH-FSH-S10 per milliliter (△) was added at zero time and replaced after 2, 6, 10, 14, and 20 hours. From Dorrington *et al.* (1978a).

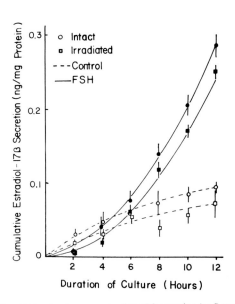

FIG. 6.   Effect of irradiation *in utero* on estradiol-17β secretion by Sertoli cells during 12-hour culture with 0.5 μM testosterone. From Dorrington *et al.* (1976a).

of estrogen biosynthesis stemmed from studies in which FSH and testosterone were added at various times after plating the cells. As shown in Table I, the percentage of other contaminating cells decreased with increasing time in culture. Also any contaminating interstitial cells lose hormonal responsiveness after a short time in culture. Nevertheless, the response to FSH was greater when added after 5 days in culture than when added after 1 day. Taken together, the evidence is overwhelmingly in support of Sertoli cell involvement in estrogen biosynthesis by our cultured cell preparations.

That the stimulatory effect on Sertoli cells was due to FSH, not to any contaminating material, was confirmed using a preparation of highly purified FSH, having a potency 100 times that of NIH-FSH-S10 (as judged by the hCG augmentation assay) and no detectable LH activity (gift from Dr. M. R. Sairam). The maximum response was the same for both NIH-FSH and Sairam-FSH, and the difference in the ED_{50} (0.15 μg/ml for NIH-FSH and 0.002 μg/ml for Sairam-FSH) was consistent with the relative potencies of those preparations (Fig. 7). Some stimulation of Sertoli cells was observed in the presence of high concentrations of NIH-LH (5 μg of NIH-LH-S18/ml), but this was probably due to the low level of FSH contaminating the LH preparation.

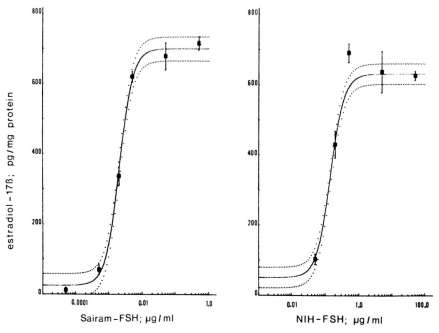

FIG. 7. Logarithmic dose-response curves for the effects of Sairam-FSH (activity approximately 100 NIH-FSH-S10 units per milligram) and NIH-FSH-S11 on estradiol synthesis by Sertoli cells from 18–20-day-old rats cultured for 24 hours in the presence of testosterone (0.5 μM). The ED_{50}s are 0.002 and 0.15 μg/ml, respectively. Each value is a mean of 3 or 4 replicates. From Dorrington *et al*. (1978b).

A good deal of circumstantial evidence supported the reliability of the RIA for the measurement of estradiol-17β. Two different antisera, one raised against estradiol-6-bovine serum albumin (obtained from G. Niswender), and the other raised against estradiol-17-hydrogen succinate bovine serum albumin (obtained from V. C. Estergreen) (Nett *et al.*, 1973) gave similar values. Other workers using a different batch of antiserum have confirmed our results (Rommerts *et al.*, 1979). Further purification of the medium on Sephadex LH$_{20}$ did not influence the values obtained (Dorrington *et al.*, 1976a). Significant amounts of assayable material were found only in the presence of an aromatizable substrate, i.e., testosterone, androstenedione, 19-hydroxytestosterone, and 19-hydroxyandrostenedione, but not in the presence of DHT, which is not aromatized (Dorrington *et al.*, 1976b). The production of estrone (measured by RIA) paralleled that of estradiol under all conditions tested and comprised approximately 10% of the total estrogen synthesized. In spite of the above evidence we sought a more definitive confirmation of the data obtained in the RIA. This was achieved by incubating Sertoli cells from 10-day-old rats with [^{14}C]testosterone for 24 hours in the presence and in the absence of FSH, and looking for conversion to estradiol-17β. [^{3}H]Estradiol-17β was added before extraction with ether and was used to correct for losses during the purification procedure. The extracts were spotted on thin-layer plates and developed in two different solvent systems: (1) ether:hexane, 3:1; (2) benzyene:ethyl acetate, 1:1. The areas corresponding to the authentic estradiol-17β were eluted, a portion was counted, and the rest was acetylated in pyridine and acetic anhydride. The acetates were purified by thin-layer chromatography in benzene:ethyl acetate, 5:2. As shown in Table IV, the amount of ^{14}C radioactivity that comigrated with the [^{3}H]estradiol did not change significantly after chromatography in the second solvent system and after formation of the acetate derivative. Further support for the identity of the estradiol-17β has been obtained by J. Zamecnik and D. T.

TABLE IV

Synthesis of [^{14}C]Estrogen from [^{14}C]Testosterone by Sertoli Cells from 10-Day-Old Rats

	[^{14}C]Estradiol (dpm)		[^{14}C]Estrone (dpm)	
	C	FSH	C	FSH
TLC in 2 systems[a]	245	2802	208	482
Acetylation	216	2598		
	Estradiol (pg/mg protein)		Estrone (pg/mg protein)	
Amount synthesized[b]	160	1968	82	289

[a] Thin-layer chromatography in (1) ether:hexane, 3:1; (2) benzene:ethyl acetate, 1:1.

[b] Calculated from specific activity of the [^{14}C]testosterone.

Armstrong using gas chromatographic–mass spectrometric analysis [presented in the discussion]. Verhoeven *et al.* (1979) have also confirmed that the metabolite produced from [³H]testosterone by Sertoli cell-enriched cultures is in fact estradiol-17β by recrystallization to constant specific activity in the presence of cold estradiol-17β.

It was fortuitous that in our first experiments Sertoli cells were prepared from 20-day-old rats, since Sertoli cells from 30-day-old (and 40-day-old) rats synthesized only low levels of estradiol-17β in the presence of testosterone and neither FSH nor dibutyryl cAMP stimulated the process, even in cells cultured in the presence of 0.5 mM methylisobutylxanthine (MIX). The effects of FSH on estradiol-17β synthesis by Sertoli cells prepared from rats 5 and 10 days of age, however, were more dramatic than at 20 days of age (Fig. 8). It is important in any consideration of estrogen biosynthesis in the testis to emphasize that the contribution made by Sertoli cells is maximum before the first wave of spermatogenesis is initiated, and, if important physiologically, then the effects are presumably exerted during prepubertal development.

The concept of the Sertoli cell as a site of steroid hormone biosynthesis has

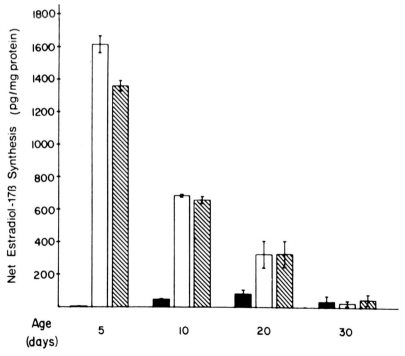

FIG. 8.   Estradiol-17β synthesis by Sertoli cells from rats of different ages, cultured for 24 hours in the presence of 0.5 μM testosterone. Each bar represents the mean ± SEM of three replicates. From Armstrong and Dorrington (1977).

been perpetuated over several years. From the work described above, we can now clearly define the ability of the Sertoli cell to modulate the steroidal environment within the tubule. It is clear that the Sertoli cell cannot synthesize testosterone from endogenous sources; however, when incubated in the presence of exogenous testosterone, immature Sertoli cells can synthesize 5α-reduced androgens (DHT, 5α-androstane-3α,17β-diol, and androsterone), androstenedione, estradiol-17β, and estrone. The synthesis of estrogens from testosterone is markedly stimulated by FSH, dibutyryl cAMP, or choleratoxin. Even though the capacity to synthesize estrogens in response to FSH (under our culture conditions) is lost in cells isolated from rats 30 days of age or older, the ability to synthesize 5α-reduced androgens persists, even in unstimulated cells. The steroidogenic capacities of immature Sertoli cells are summarized in Fig. 9.

We have also looked at the ability of other cell types in the tubule to metabolize testosterone. Cell suspensions consisting of 85–90% spermatocytes prepared from immature rats formed [^{14}C]DHT as a major metabolite of [^{14}C]-testosterone. A small amount of [^{14}C]5α-androstane-3α,17β-diol was also formed, but this was probably due to the low level of contamination with Sertoli cells (Dorrington and Fritz, 1975). Spermatids, on the other hand, have little if any 5α-reductase or 3α-hydroxysteroid dehydrogenase activity. Peritubular myoid cells did not synthesize detectable amounts of estrogen when incubated in the presence of testosterone (unpublished observations).

IV. Mechanism of Action of FSH on Estrogen Biosynthesis

Whatever the physiological role of estradiol-17β produced by Sertoli cells is in immature rats, this steroid has provided us with an end product of Sertoli cell function, which can be readily and accurately measured, for the investigation of FSH action. As shown in Figs. 5 and 6, the effect of FSH on estradiol synthesis was not manifested for approximately 4 hours. We have been particularly

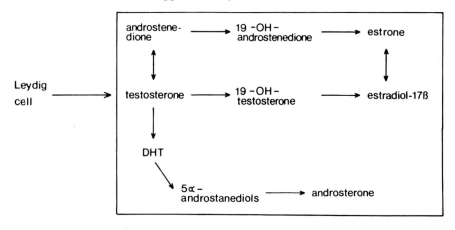

FIG. 9.   Summary of the steroidogenic capacities of immature Sertoli cells.

interested in the series of biochemical events that are triggered in Sertoli cells by FSH and proceed during this initial lag period. The rapid effect of FSH on cAMP production by Sertoli cells and the ability of dibutyryl cAMP and choleratoxin to duplicate the effects of FSH on Sertoli cell functions (Fritz *et al.*, 1977) are consistent with the view that cAMP is a mediator of FSH action.

Treatment of immature or mature hypophysectomized rats with FSH increases testicular protein synthesis (Means, 1975). We showed that the rate of incorporation of [³H]leucine into trichloroacetic acid (TCA)-precipitable material was also increased in Sertoli cells cultured for 2 days in the presence of FSH (Dorrington *et al.*, 1975). In order to determine whether ongoing protein synthesis was required for the expression of the FSH effect on estrogen biosynthesis, we studied the effects of puromycin on this process. Exposure of Sertoli cells to 5 × $10^{-6} M$ and 5 × $10^{-5} M$ puromycin for 30 minutes inhibited the incorporation of [³H]leucine into TCA-precipitable material and the inhibition persisted for up to 24 hours (Fig. 10). In the same experiment, cells were preincubated for 30 minutes with puromycin (5 × $10^{-6} M$ and 5 × $10^{-5} M$), after which testosterone and FSH were added and the amounts of estrogen synthesized during the

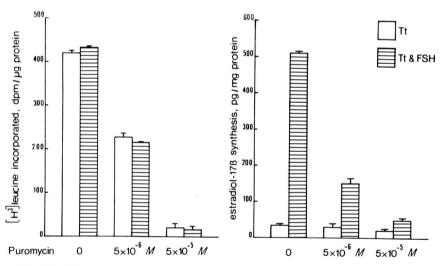

FIG. 10. Effect of puromycin on the incorporation of [³H]leucine into TCA-insoluble material and on estradiol synthesis by Sertoli cells isolated from 16-day-old rats. Leucine incorporation: Sertoli cell preparations were maintained in culture for 24 hours, preincubated with puromycin for 30 minutes, after which testosterone (Tt) alone (0.5 μM) or testosterone (0.5 μM) and FSH (5 μg/ml) were added. After 24 hours the medium was removed and 2 ml of Krebs–Ringer bicarbonate buffer containing 1 mg of glucose per milliliter and 1/10 the amino acids in standard MEM and 1 μCi of [³H]leucine per milliliter (final concentration of leucine 0.04 mM) were added. Incubations were terminated after 2 hours by the addition of TCA (Dorrington *et al.*, 1975). Estradiol synthesis: After 24 hours in standard medium, cells were preincubated with puromycin for 30 minutes. Testosterone (0.5 μM) alone or testosterone and FSH (5 μg/ml) were then added and incubation was continued for 24 hours. Values are the mean ± SEM of three replicate cultures. From Dorrington *et al.* (1978a).

subsequent 24-hour period were measured. Both concentrations of puromycin inhibited the effect of FSH on estrogen biosynthesis (Fig. 10).

In a subsequent series of experiments, testosterone alone or testosterone and FSH were added at zero time and puromycin ($5 \times 10^{-5} M$) was added at 0, 1, 2, 3, 4, and 6 hours. All incubations were continued for 24 hours, and estradiol levels present in the medium and cells were assayed. Puromycin, added at 0, 1, or 2 hours after the addition of testosterone and FSH, abolished the FSH effect during the subsequent incubation period. When puromycin was added 3 hours after the addition of hormones, some stimulation of estrogen biosynthesis by FSH was apparent. When the addition of puromycin was delayed until 4 or 6 hours after treatment with FSH, no inhibition of hormone action was found (Fig. 11). The inability of puromycin to influence FSH-stimulated estrogen synthesis when added 4 hours after the addition of FSH showed that the cells were viable after exposure to this concentration of inhibitor. It is clear from these experiments that treatment of cells with FSH for 4 hours prior to the addition of puromycin is essential in order to attain a maximum response.

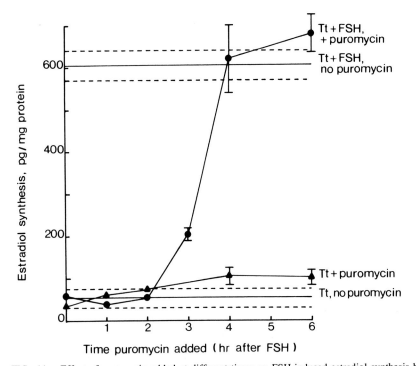

FIG. 11.   Effect of puromycin added at different times on FSH-induced estradiol synthesis by Sertoli cells from 16-day-old rats. After 24 hours in culture, testosterone (Tt, 0.5 μM) or testosterone and FSH (5 μg/ml) were added. At different times after the addition of hormones (i.e., 0, 1, 2, 3, 4, 5, or 6 hours) puromycin ($5 \times 10^{-5} M$) was added, and all incubations were allowed to proceed for 24 hours. Values are the means $\pm$ SEM of three replicate flasks. From Dorrington et al. (1978a).

To determine whether the proteins required for elevated estrogen biosynthesis were synthesized on preexisting mRNA or from newly synthesized mRNA, the effect of an inhibitor of RNA synthesis, actinomycin D, was studied. Pretreatment of Sertoli cells with 0.15 and 0.25 μg of actinomycin D per milliliter of culture medium for 30 minutes inhibited the incorporation of [³H]uridine into RNA (Fig. 12). Preincubation of Sertoli cells with the same concentrations of actinomycin D for 30 minutes was effective in inhibiting the stimulatory effect of FSH on estrogen synthesis from exogenous testosterone during the subsequent 24-hour incubation.

Using an experimental design similar to that employed above for puromycin, actinomycin D (0.25 μg/ml) was added at 0, 1, 2, or 4 hours after the addition of testosterone and FSH, and the estrogen content of the medium was measured at 8, 16, and 24 hours (Fig. 13). Actinomycin D added at the same time as, or 1 hour after, the addition of FSH and testosterone was effective in reducing the amount of

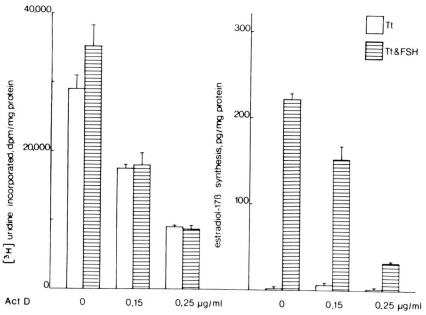

FIG. 12. Effect of actinomycin D (Act D) on the incorporation of [³H]uridine into TCA-insoluble material, and on estradiol synthesis by Sertoli cells isolated from 16-day-old rats. Uridine incorporation: Sertoli cell preparations were maintained in culture for 24 hours, preincubated with actinomycin D for 30 minutes, after which testosterone (Tt) alone (0.5 μM) or testosterone and 5 μg FSH/ml were added. [³H]Thymidine (1 μCi/ml) was added, and incubations were terminated after 2 hours by the addition of TCA. Similar results were obtained when the incubations with [³H]thymidine were performed 24 hours after the addition of testosterone. Estradiol synthesis: After 24 hours in culture in standard medium, cells were preincubated with actinomycin D for 30 minutes. Testosterone (0.5 μM) alone or testosterone and FSH (5 μg/ml) were then added, and incubations were continued for 24 hours. Values are means ± SEM of three replicate cultures.

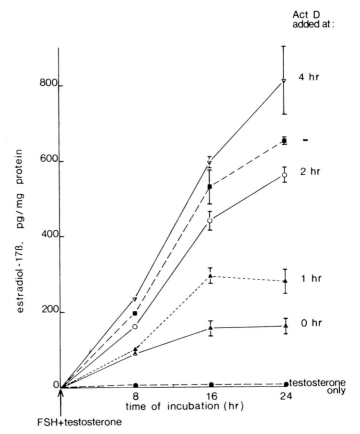

FIG. 13.   Effects of actinomycin D (Act D) (0.25 μg/ml) on FSH-induced estradiol-17β synthesis by Sertoli cells from 16-day-old rats. After 24 hours in culture in standard medium, testosterone
(0.5 μM) or testosterone and FSH (5 μg/ml) were added. At different times after the addition of
hormone (i.e., 0, 1, 2, or 4 hours), actinomycin D was added and medium was removed at 8, 16, and
24 hours and assayed for estradiol-17β.

estrogen synthesized. When puromycin was added 2 or 4 hours after treatment
with FSH, little effect on estrogen biosynthesis over the 24-hour period was
observed (Fig. 13). Thus treatment of cells with FSH for 2 hours prior to the
addition of actinomycin D is required for maximum response.

It can be concluded from the above experiments that ongoing RNA synthesis is
required for 2 hours and protein synthesis for 4 hours immediately following the
addition of FSH in order to achieve the maximum estrogen response. This does
not necessarily indicate that FSH stimulates the RNA and proteins required for
promoting estrogen synthesis, but does show that the RNA and proteins synthesized during this initial 4-hour period (initial lag phase, see Fig. 5) are prerequi-
sites for the expression of the FSH effect.

V. Control of Follicular Steroidogenesis

The studies on Sertoli cells illustrated the ways in which FSH may influence the levels of steroids present in the seminiferous tubule. Since Sertoli cells and granulosa cells are derived from the same embryonic cell line and continue to share a number of structural and biochemical properties in the differentiated gonad, we were intrigued by the possibility that similar mechanisms of action of FSH on steroid biosynthesis might be operative in the follicle. Unlike the situation in the testis, estrogen has a clearly defined physiological role in the female. Estrogen administered to hypophysectomized female rats caused proliferation of granulosa cells, a decrease in the number of atretic follicles, and consequently an increase in ovarian weight (Goldenberg et al., 1972). Estrogen is therefore important as a granulosa cell mitogen during the rapid phase of growth prior to ovulation. The successive stages of granulosa cell differentiation can be characterized by their response to estradiol and FSH; in the early stages, estradiol facilitates the ability of FSH to increase the numbers of FSH receptors, and at a later stage promotes the effect of FSH on LH receptors (Richards et al., 1976).

A. ESTROGEN BIOSYNTHESIS

The experiments of Greep et al. (1942) provided the first indications that FSH and LH may be acting upon separate cell types to stimulate estrogen biosynthesis. When FSH alone was administered to hypophysectomized immature rats follicular growth and antrum formation were noted, whereas interstitial cells were not stimulated. The uteri and vaginas were atrophic, indicative of estrogen deprivation. In the presence of LH alone there was little follicular growth and the uteri remained atrophic but the thecal and interstitial cells were stimulated, as judged by histological criteria (i.e., increased cytoplasm and decreased nuclear chromophilia). When FSH and LH were administered together, follicular and interstitial cells were stimulated, accompanied by uterine growth and vaginal cornification, which are indices of estrogen secretion. Direct measurements of estrogen secretion by isolated mouse follicles in culture supported the notion that LH and FSH acted synergistically to stimulate estrogen biosynthesis (Ryle et al., 1974). These studies indicated that LH and FSH were required to control estrogen biosynthesis in the follicle, but did not identify the cell types involved and gave no information about the biochemical sites and mechanisms of action of gonadotropins. In order to gain some insight into this process, investigations were initiated on isolated follicular components.

Sprague-Dawley rats, hypophysectomized at 21 days of age, were injected subcutaneously once daily (from day 24 to day 28) with 1 mg of estradiol-17β in sesame oil in order to stimulate granulosa cell proliferation. The animals were killed at 29 days of age. In some experiments normal 28–29-day-old Wistar rats were used without prior treatment or after treatment for 3–5 days with estradiol-17β. At autopsy the ovaries were removed under aseptic conditions and granulosa cells were collected by puncturing the follicles on the surface of the ovary with a fine needle with the aid of a dissecting microscope. Slight pressure was applied to the ovary, and the granulosa cells released into the medium were recovered by centrifugation. Aliquots were distributed among Falcon plastic culture dishes and cultured at 37°C for various lengths of time in a water-saturated atmosphere of 95% air and 5% CO_2.

Granulosa cells isolated from normal immature rats (28 days of age) synthesized low or insignificant amounts of estradiol-17β when cultured for 3 days in the absence of an aromatizable substrate. Under these conditions, the addition of gonadotropins failed to increase appreciably the amount of estradiol-17β synthesized. Incubated in the presence of testosterone, FSH dramatically stimulated the synthesis of estradiol-17β. Luteinizing hormone, on the other hand, had no effect on estrogen production by cells cultured with testosterone and also did not influence the response to FSH (Fig. 14). Pretreatment of 28-day-old rats with estradiol-17β for 4 days increased the yield of the granulosa cells. Qualitatively,

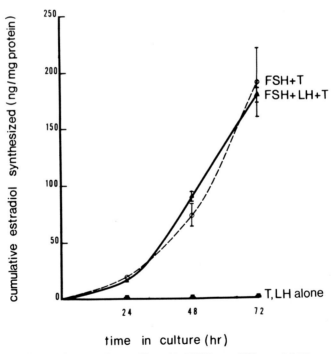

FIG. 14.   Effects of 0.25 μg of Papkoff's purified FSH per milliliter and 0.25 μg of Papkoff's purified LH per milliliter on the synthesis of estradiol-17β by granulosa cells isolated from ovaries of normal immature rats (28 days of age) when cultured in medium containing 0.5 μM testosterone (T) for 72 hours.

the responses to FSH and testosterone were the same in granulosa cells from normal and estrogen-treated rats (Table V, Fig. 14), but quantitatively the response was greater and more consistent in cells from estrogen-treated intact rats (Fig. 15). As shown in Table V, the addition of testosterone alone to granulosa cells from estrogen-treated intact rats caused a significant increase in the production of estradiol-17β, and this occurred during the first day of culture.

Estrone was also synthesized from testosterone in the presence of FSH and comprised approximately 15% of the total estrogen produced. The amount of both estrogens depended upon the concentration of FSH (Fig. 16). A similar stimulatory action of FSH on estradiol-17β and estrone synthesis from exogenous testosterone could be demonstrated using granulosa cells isolated from estrogen-treated hypophysectomized rats (Fig. 17).

In the placenta, testosterone and androstenedione are converted to estradiol-17β and estrone, respectively, by a series of reactions involving two successive oxidations of C-19, yielding the 19-hydroxy and the 19-oxo derivatives, the cleavage of the C-10—C-19 bond followed by the oxidation of ring A by the removal of hydrogen from C-1 and C-2 (Engel, 1973). A similar sequence of reactions appears to occur in the ovary. In order to determine the step in the biosynthetic pathway that may be influenced by FSH in granulosa cells, the rates of conversion of testosterone, androstenedione, and their 19-hydroxylated derivatives to estradiol-17β and estrone in the presence and in the absence of FSH were compared. In the absence of FSH all four substrates were converted to estrogens at very slow rates. In the presence of FSH, however, the conversion of all four substrates to both estradiol-17β and estrone was stimulated (Fig. 17). Whether the conversion of 19-hydroxytestosterone and 19-hydroxyandrostenedione to estrogens is the only site in the biosynthetic pathway from androgens to estrogens that is influenced by FSH cannot be determined from these data. Since aromatase is an enzyme complex catalyzing a series of closely

TABLE V

Effect of Papkoff's Purified FSH (0.25 µg/ml) and Papkoff's purified LH (0.25 µg/ml) on the Synthesis of Estradiol-17β by Granulosa Cells[a] Cultured in the Presence or the Absence of Testosterone (0.5 µM) for 72 Hours

Test substance	Estradiol-17β synthesized (ng/mg protein)
—	0.4 ± 0.2
FSH	0.5 ± 0.2
LH	0.2 ± 0.1
Testosterone	4.3 ± 1.6
Testosterone + FSH	822.8 ± 82.5
Testosterone + LH	14.5 ± 0.1

[a] Granulosa cells were isolated from the ovaries of immature rats (28 days of age) which had been pretreated with estradiol-17β (1 mg/day) for 5 days.

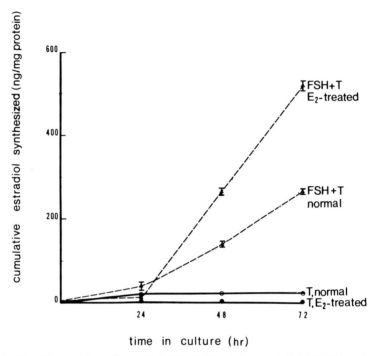

FIG. 15. Effects of Papkoff's purified FSH (0.25 μg/ml) on estradiol-17β (E$_2$) synthesis by granulosa cells from untreated immature rats (28 days of age), and rats of the same age pretreated with estradiol-17β (1 mg/day) for 5 days, when cultured for 72 hours in medium containing 0.5 μM testosterone (T).

integrated reactions, it is possible that each step may be accelerated by influencing the complex as a whole.

In all the above experiments using granulosa cells from immature rats, LH was essentially without effect on estrogen production under all conditions tested, consistent with other reports that these granulosa cells do not contain LH receptors. Since granulosa cells from preovulatory follicles are known to contain both FSH and LH receptors, the formation of preovulatory follicles was induced in immature females by treating them with 12 IU of pregnant mare serum gonadotropin (PMSG). Two days after treatment (i.e., at 26 days of age) granulosa cells were isolated from normal untreated animals and cultured under identical conditions. Granulosa cells that had been exposed to PMSG *in vivo* produced much larger amounts of estradiol-17β from exogenous testosterone during the first day of culture than those from untreated rats, and the addition of gonadotropins *in vitro* did not cause any significant stimulation. During the second day in culture, estradiol-17β production declined markedly in the absence of gonadotropins. Both FSH and LH were effective in sustaining high levels of

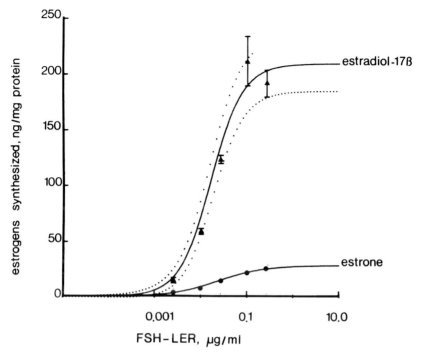

FIG. 16.   Logarithmic dose-response curves for the effects of purified FSH (obtained from L. E. Reichert) on the synthesis of estradiol-17β and estrone from exogenous testosterone (0.5 μM) by granulosa cells isolated from immature rats (25 days of age) pretreated with estradiol-17β (1 mg/day) for 3 days. Each value is the mean ± SEM of 6 replicates.

estradiol-17β production by cells from PMSG-treated rats, whereas only FSH stimulated cells from the untreated immature rats (Armstrong *et al.*, 1979). It is not clear whether FSH and LH act upon the same cells or on different populations of granulosa cells in the preovulatory follicles.

During the estrous cycle of the rat, estrogen required extragonadally for uterine development and intragonadally for follicular growth and maturation appears to be synthesized predominantly by granulosa cells. It seems likely that FSH is the important factor in initiating and controlling estrogen biosynthesis in the developing follicle. Primed with estrogen, the follicle proceeds through a rapid phase of growth and FSH induces the appearance of LH receptors on granulosa cells. It is possible that at this more advanced stage of differentiation LH, as well as FSH, may play a role in controlling the conversion of androgens to estrogens.

Granulosa cells failed to produce detectable amounts of immunoreactive androgens (testosterone and DHT) from endogenous sources in the presence or the absence of FSH or LH, consistent with previous reports that granulosa cells are

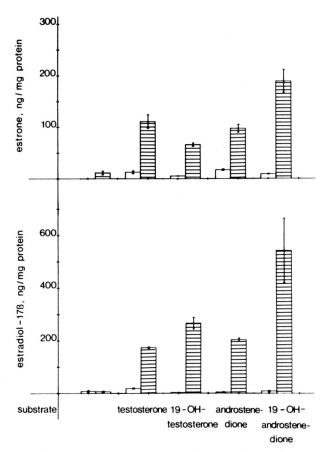

FIG. 17.   Synthesis of estradiol and estrone by granulosa cells from 28-day-old rats, which had been hypophysectomized at 21 days of age and treated with estradiol-17β (1 mg/day) from days 24 to 27. Cells were cultured in the presence of various substrates (0.5 μM). Open bars: amounts of estrogen synthesized by cells incubated in the presence of substrate alone; hatched bars: amounts synthesized in the presence of substrate and 0.25 μg of FSH per milliliter (obtained from L. E. Reichert).

deficient in the enzymes required to form androgens from C_{21} precursors. It seems clear that granulosa cells can convert androstenedione and testosterone to estrogens but cannot synthesize the substrate necessary for this reaction. In contrast, thecal cells contain LH receptors and respond to LH with increased androgen production (Fortune and Armstrong, 1977). Determination of the extent to which thecal cells can synthesize estrogens will depend upon the development of procedures for the isolation of homogeneous cell populations. It is clearly difficult to remove all contaminating granulosa cells from thecal preparations obtained from small experimental animals. A comparison of "clean" and "crude" preparations of thecal tissue from proestrous rat follicles showed that the removal of most of the granulosa cells reduced the amount of estradiol secreted to barely detectable levels (Fortune and Armstrong, 1978).

From the available evidence it is reasonable to conclude that follicular estrogen biosynthesis in the rat requires the cooperation of two cell types: The theca interna cells, under the influence of LH, produce androgens that are transported to granulosa cells, where, in the presence of FSH, they are converted to estrogens. This hypothesis received support from experiments conducted *in vivo*. The administration of LH alone or together with FSH for 3 days to hypophysectomized immature rats increased ovarian androgen content, whereas FSH was ineffective. Neither gonadotropin alone increased the ovarian content of estradiol-17β, but when administered together, the levels of this steroid were markedly increased (Armstrong and Papkoff, 1976). Furthermore, the ovarian contents of estradiol-17β were markedly increased by FSH when administered together with testosterone or androstenedione, but not when administered with DHT.

The results of both *in vitro* and *in vivo* studies on the rat support the conclusion that FSH and LH regulate ovarian estrogen secretion by actions at biochemically distinct sites. It is possible that the theca interna tissue in larger species (monkey, human) may provide an additional source of estrogen (Channing and Coudert, 1976), the amount depending upon the species and the physiological status. In a recent study of estrogen biosynthesis by human ovaries there was a good correlation between the amount of estrogen present and the number of granulosa cells (McNatty and Baird, 1978). It was calculated that the granulosa cells could contribute 80% of the total estrogen synthesized by the follicle.

To determine whether the syntheses of other metabolites of testosterone were also influenced by FSH, the levels of two 5α-reduced androgens, 5α-androstane-3α,17β-diol and androsterone, were measured in the culture medium in addition to estradiol-17β. As shown in Fig. 18, both these metabolites were synthesized from exogenous testosterone, more being produced during the first day of culture than the subsequent 2 days. The synthesis of both 5α-reduced androgens was independent of the presence of FSH, in contrast to the synthesis of estradiol-17β, which was markedly stimulated by FSH in the same cell preparations.

B. PROGESTERONE BIOSYNTHESIS BY GRANULOSA CELLS

In addition to synthesizing androgens and estrogens, the follicle also produces progesterone. Plasma progesterone levels are elevated at two stages during the estrous cycle of the rat (Barraclough *et al.*, 1971; Smith *et al.*, 1975). There is a preovulatory increase coincident with the surge of LH and FSH on the afternoon

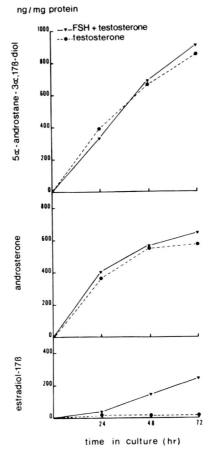

ng / mg protein

FIG. 18. Synthesis of 5α-androstane-3α,17β-diol, androsterone, and estradiol-17β by granulosa cells from untreated immature rats (28 days of age) cultured for 72 hours in medium containing testosterone (0.5 μM) alone, or testosterone (0.5 μM) and 0.25 μg of purified FSH per milliliter.

of proestrus. On the morning of estrus the levels return to basal values and remain low for at least a day before rising again as luteinization proceeds and the corpus luteum is formed (Smith *et al.*, 1975).

Within 1 hour of adding LH or FSH to follicles removed from rats on the morning of proestrus and maintained in culture, there was a significant increase in progesterone levels (Lindner *et al.*, 1974). This response seemed to be too rapid to be a reflection of luteinization, but rather may be comparable to the preovulatory progesterone increase. Since granulosa cells had previously been shown to synthesize progesterone, a study of the factors required to initiate progesterone synthesis in immature rat granulosa cells was undertaken.

The amounts of progesterone secreted by granulosa cells from estrogen-treated hypophysectomized and normal immature rats cultured for 3 days are shown in Figs. 19 and 20. Cells cultured in medium alone, or in medium containing testosterone (0.5 μM) alone, secreted negligible amounts of progesterone. FSH (0.25 μg/ml) stimulated progesterone secretion by granulosa cells from estrogen-treated immature rats to a small extent during the first day in culture, after which time no further increases were observed. In the presence of testosterone (0.5 μM) and FSH (0.25 μg/ml), the progesterone level in the medium after 1 day in culture was 15-fold greater than that produced by FSH alone. Secretion of progesterone continued under these conditions for the next 2 days, but the rate was lower than that observed during the first day of culture (Fig. 20). Granulosa cells obtained from estrogen-treated immature rats did not respond to LH (0.25 μg/ml) alone or to testosterone (0.5 μM) and LH added together. When the cells were incubated in the presence of testosterone (0.5 μM) the amount of progesterone released from the cells depended upon the concentration of FSH, detectable increases being produced by 10 ng of FSH per milliliter and maximal levels by 250 ng of FSH per milliliter.

As discussed above, FSH stimulates the conversion of testosterone to estradiol-17β by similarly prepared granulosa cells. However, it seemed unlikely that the ability of testosterone to augment the effect of FSH on progesterone levels was due to its conversion to estrogens, since exogenous estradiol-17β was not as effective as testosterone in enhancing the FSH effect (Fig. 20). This conclusion received further support from the observation that DHT, a potent androgen that cannot be converted to estrogens, was even more effective than testosterone in stimulating progesterone synthesis in the presence of FSH. Even

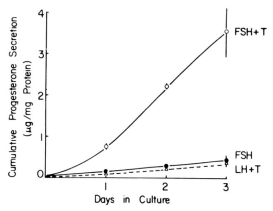

FIG. 19. Progesterone secretion by cultured granulosa cells from 28-day-old rats which had been hypophysectomized at 21 days of age and treated with estradiol-17β (1 mg/day) from day 23 to day 27. FSH: purified Papkoff FSH, 0.25 μg/ml; LH: purified LH 0.25 μg/ml; T: 0.5 μM testosterone. Progesterone secretion by cells cultured in medium alone, or in medium containing testosterone or LH, was undetectable. From Armstrong and Dorrington (1976).

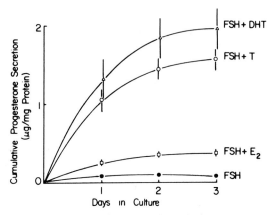

FIG. 20.   Progesterone secretion by cultured granulosa cells from 25-day-old rats pretreated with estradiol-17β (1 mg/day) for 3 days. FSH: purified Reichert FSH, 0.25 μg/ml; DHT: 0.5 μM 17β-hydroxy-5α-androstan-3-one; T: 0.5 μM testosterone; E$_2$: 0.5 μM estradiol-17β. Secretion by cells cultured in medium alone or containing LH, DHT, T, or E$_2$ was undetectable. From Armstrong and Dorrington (1976).

though high levels of progesterone are synthesized in the presence of DHT and FSH, estradiol synthesis is insignificant, providing further evidence that rat granulosa cells cannot convert progesterone to testosterone. This synergistic action of FSH and androgens was demonstrated independently by Nimrod and Lindner (1976).

Granulosa cells are target cells for androgens as shown by the presence of androgen receptors in granulosa cell cytosol (Schreiber and Ross, 1976) and by the present demonstration that androgens influence granulosa cell metabolism. Elevated ovarian androgen levels occur in prepubertal rats within minutes after the injection of LH (Armstrong *et al.*, 1976), and it is tempting to speculate that this androgen, of thecal (Fortune and Armstrong, 1976) or interstitial cell (Louvet *et al.*, 1975) origin, together with increased levels of gonadotropins, may produce the marked preovulatory increase in progesterone levels in rats on the afternoon of proestrus. The steroidogenic capacities of rat granulosa cells are summarized in Fig. 21.

VI. Mechanism of Action of FSH and Testosterone on Progesterone Biosynthesis

The way in which FSH and testosterone stimulate Sertoli and granulosa cells to synthesize the components required for germ cell differentiation is one of the most fundamental problems in reproductive biology. It was particularly interesting therefore to find that both these hormones were required for the initiation of progesterone biosynthesis, and provided us with a means of studying the mechanisms of interaction of the hormones. Nimrod (1977a,b) has investigated several

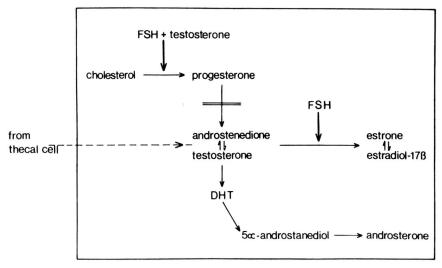

FIG. 21. Summary of the steroidogenic capacities of granulosa cells isolated from immature rats.

possible ways by which androgens may facilitate the effect of FSH on progesterone biosynthesis. He found that androgens did not influence the amount of [^{125}I]FSH bound to granulosa cells, adenylate cyclase activity, or phosphodiesterase activity. Androgens potentiated the effect of dibutyryl cAMP (Nimrod, 1977a) and choleratoxin (Dorrington et al., 1978), indicating that androgens exert their effect at a step subsequent to cAMP formation. It was possible that androgens influenced progesterone levels by inhibiting catabolism to 5α-pregnane compounds, but when this was investigated no effect was apparent (Nimrod, 1977b).

The conversion of cholesterol to progesterone involves two enzyme systems; the first cleaves the side-chain of cholesterol to give pregnenolone and the second converts pregnenolone to progesterone. The latter system involves two enzymes, Δ^5-3β-hydroxysteroid dehydrogenase, which oxidizes the Δ^5-3-hydroxy function to a Δ^5-3-keto group, and Δ^5-3-ketosteroid isomerase, which catalyzes the shift in the C5—C6 double bond to the C4—C5 position. To determine whether FSH and androgens influenced the conversion of pregnenolone to progesterone, granulosa cells were cultured for 2 days in the presence and in the absence of hormones; after this, the cells were washed, and 1 ml of Dulbecco's buffer containing [^{14}C]pregnenolone (2 μg) was added. The reaction was stopped after 30 minutes by the addition of 0.4 ml of 0.1 N NaOH, and the steroids, pregnenolone, progesterone, 17α-hydroxyprogesterone, and 20α-hydroxy-Δ^4-pregnen-3-one were extracted, purified, and identified as described previously (Dorrington and Fritz, 1975). Cells incubated in the absence of hormones for 2 days were unable to convert significant amounts of [^{14}C]pregnenolone to [^{14}C] progestins. Some conversion to [^{14}C]progesterone was detected in cells that had been treated with testosterone (0.5 μM) or DHT (0.5 μM), but this was low compared to the effect of FSH alone (Table VI). Testosterone did not act synergistically with FSH to increase the conversion of [^{14}C]pregnenolone to [^{14}C]progesterone.

It was possible that FSH might regulate the synthesis of progesterone by influencing the substrate or cofactor availability or the amount of the enzyme. To differentiate among those possibilities the enzyme activity was assayed under optimal conditions in a cell-free system. After culture of granulosa cells in the presence and the absence of FSH for 2 days, the cells were scraped from the culture dishes with a rubber policeman and homogenized in 0.1 M phosphate buffer pH 7.4, containing per milliliter 0.25 mg NAD and 12.5 μmol of MgSO$_4$. The homogenate (0.2 ml) containing approximately 75 μg of protein was added to tubes containing [^{14}C]pregnenolone (2 μg). The reaction was terminated, after incubation for various periods of time, by the addition of NaOH, and the steroids were extracted and purified. As shown in Fig. 21 the activity of the Δ^5-3β-hydroxysteroid dehydrogenase/Δ^5-3-ketosteroid isomerase system assayed under optimal conditions dramatically increased in those cells that had been treated with purified FSH alone (Fig. 22).

The effect of FSH on the Δ^5-3β-hydroxysteroid dehydrogenase/Δ^5-3-ketosteroid isomerase system is independent of the presence of testosterone. Testosterone (alone or together with FSH) therefore must stimulate directly or indirectly the conversion of cholesterol to pregnenolone. We are currently attempting to determine the mechanisms involved.

TABLE VI

Metabolism of [^{14}C]Pregnenolone by Granulosa Cells Isolated from Estrogen-Treated Normal Rats[a]

	Percentage of total radioactivity recovered			
Metabolite	Control	FSH	Testosterone	FSH and testosterone
Progesterone	0.4	21.8	1.2	20.5
20α-Hydroxy-Δ^4-pregnen-3-one	0.1	4.3	0.2	2.2
17α-Hydroxyprogesterone	0.1	0.1	0.1	—

[a] Granulosa cells were isolated from 25-day-old rats that had been pretreated for 3 days with estradiol-17β (1 mg/day). Cells were cultured for 2 days in the presence or the absence of FSH and testosterone (0.5 μm). Cells were washed, 1 ml of Dulbecco's medium was added contaning 2 μg of [^{14}C]pregnenolone. Incubations were for 30 minutes. Approximately 100 μg of protein were present in each culture flask. Values are the means of three replicate cultures.

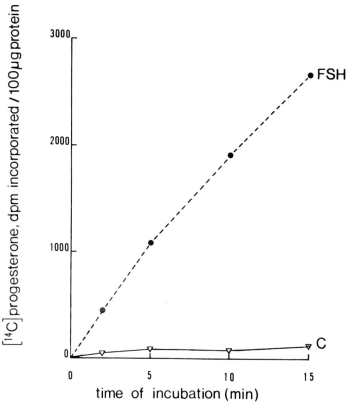

FIG. 22. Conversion of [^{14}C]pregnenolone to [^{14}C]progesterone by homogenates of granulosa cells that had been cultured in the presence and in the absence of FSH for 2 days. Cells were isolated from the ovaries of 25-day-old rats pretreated with estradiol-17β for 3 days.

VII. Summary

LH and FSH interact with the somatic cells of the gonads to stimulate the synthesis and secretion of metabolites (steroids, proteins, etc.) into the circulation and into the fluid that bathes the germ cells. Steroids are ubiquitous in mammalian systems and are involved in many aspects of differentiation. The mechanisms by which steroid synthesis is controlled in the gonads therefore has bearing on many problems related to growth and development. In addition to influencing extragonadal tissues, steroids (androgens and estrogens) are essential for the maintenance of gonadal functions. Because of their importance in controlling gametogenesis, we have endeavored during the last few years to determine the cell types involved in the synthesis of steroids and to understand the control mechanisms involved.

The Sertoli cells of the testis and the granulosa cells of the ovary are unique in that they are the only cells that respond to FSH. Studies on these cultured cells have shown that FSH is intimately involved in determining the profile of steroids produced. In the immature Sertoli cells, FSH stimulates the conversion of testosterone to estrogens and 5α-reduced androgens. FSH also stimulates the synthesis of ABP, thereby influencing the amount of testosterone and DHT that is specifically bound. In granulosa cells, FSH stimulates the conversion of testosterone to estrogens. In addition to acting as a substrate for estrogen synthesis, testosterone augments the effect of FSH on progesterone synthesis. A better understanding of the hormonal control of the metabolism and secretion of Sertoli and granulosa cells may give insight into the defects that underlie infertility and, furthermore, may lead to the development of new methods for the control of gametogenesis.

REFERENCES

Ahmad, N., Haltmeyer, G. C., and Eik-Nes, K. B. (1973). *Biol. Reprod.* **8,** 411.

Armstrong, D. T., and Dorrington, J. H. (1976). *Endocrinology* **99,** 1411.

Armstrong, D. T., and Dorrington, J. H. (1977). *In* "Regulatory Mechanisms Affecting Gonadal Hormone Action" (J. A. Thomas and R. L. Singhal, eds.), p. 217. Univ. Park Press, Baltimore, Maryland.

Armstrong, D. T., and Papkoff, H. (1976). *Endocrinology* **99,** 1144.

Armstrong, D. T., Dorrington, J. H., and Robinson, J. (1976). *Can. J. Biochem.* **54,** 796.

Armstrong, D. T., Goff, A., and Dorrington, J. H. (1979). *In* "Ovarian Follicular Development and Function" (R. Midgley and W. A. Sadler, eds.). NIH Workshop, Santa Cruz, p. 169.

Barraclough, C. A., Collu, R., Massa, R., and Martini, L. (1971). *Endocrinology* **88,** 1437.

Byskov, A. G., Skakkebaer, N. E., and Stafanger, G. (1977). *J. Anat.* **123,** 77.

Canick, J. A., Makris, A., Gunsalus, G. L., and Ryan, K. J. (1978). *Endocrine Soc. 60th Annu. Meet. Abstr.* **128,** p. 138.

Catt, K. J., Tsuruhara, T., Mendelson, C., Ketelslegers, J. M., and Dufau, M. L. (1974). *In* "Hormone Binding and Target Cell Activation in the Testis" (M. L. Dufau and A. R. Means, eds.), p. 1. Plenum, New York.

Channing, C. P., and Coudert, S. P. (1976). *Endocrinology* **98,** 590.

Cooke, B. A., van Beurden, W. M. O., Rommerts, F. F. G., and van der Molen, H. J. (1972). *FEBS Lett.* **25,** 83.

Dorrington, J. H., and Armstrong, D. T. (1975). *Proc. Natl. Acad. Sci. U.S.A.* **72,** 2677.

Dorrington, J. H., and Fritz, I. B. (1974a). *Endocrinology* **94,** 395.

Dorrington, J. H. and Fritz, I. B. (1974b). *In* "Gonadotropins and Gonadal Function" (N. R. Moudgal, ed.), p. 500. Academic Press, New York.

Dorrington, J. H., and Fritz, I. B. (1975). *In* "Hormonal Regulation of Spermatogenesis" (F. French, V. Hansson, E. M. Ritzen, and S. N. Nayfeh, eds.), p. 37. Plenum, New York.

Dorrington, J. H., Roller, N., and Fritz, I. B. (1975). *Mol. Cell. Endocrinol.* **3,** 57.

Dorrington, J. H., Fritz, I. B., and Armstrong, D. T. (1976a). *In* "Regulatory Mechanisms of Male Reproductive Physiology" (D. H. Spilman, T. J. Lobl, and K. T. Kirton, eds.), p. 63 (Sixth Brook Lodge Workshop on Problems on Reproductive Biology. Kalamazoo, Michigan, October, 1975). Am. Elsevier, New York.

Dorrington, J. H., Fritz, I. B., and Armstrong, D. T. (1976b). *Mol. Cell. Endocrinol.* **6,** 117.

Dorrington, J. H., Fritz, I. B., and Armstrong, D. T. (1978a). *Biol. Reprod.* **18,** 55.

Dorrington, J. H., Fritz, I. B., and Armstrong, D. T. (1978b). *Int. J. Andrology,* Suppl. 2, 53.

Engel, L. (1973). *In* "Handbook of Physiology" (R. O. Greep and E. B. Astwood, eds.), Section 7, Endocrinology, Vol II, Part 1, p. 467. Am. Physiol. Soc., Washington, D.C.

Erickson, G. F., and Ryan, K. J. (1976). *Endocrinology* **99**, 452.

Eshkol, A., and Lunenfeld, B. (1972). *In* "Gonadotropins" (B. B. Saxena, G. G. Beling, and H. M. Gandy), p. 335. Wiley, New York.

Fortune, J. E., and Armstrong, D. T. (1977). *Endocrinology* **100**, 1341.

Fortune, J. E., and Armstrong, D. T. (1978). *Endocrinology* **102**, 227.

Fritz, I. B. (1978). *In* "Biochemical Actions of Hormones" (G. Litwack, ed.), Vol. 5, p. 249. Academic Press, New York.

Fritz, I. B., Griswold, M., Louis, G., and Dorrington, J. H. (1976). *Mol. Cell Endocrinol.* **5**, 289.

Goldenberg, R. L., Vaitukaitis, J. L., and Ross, G. T. (1972). *Endocrinology* **90**, 1492.

Greep, R. O., van Dyke, H. B., and Chow, B. F. (1942). *Endocrinology* **30**, 635.

Kuehl, F. A., Patanelli, D. J., Tarnoff, J., and Humes, J. L. (1970). *Biol. Reprod.* **2**, 154.

Lacy, D., and Pettitt, A. J. (1970). *Br. Med. Bull.* **26**, 87.

Lindner, H. R., Tsafriri, A., Lieberman, M. E., Zor, U., Koch, Y., Bauminger, S., and Barnea, A. (1974). *Recent Prog. Hormone Res.* **30**, 79.

Louvet, J. P., Harman, S. M., Schreiber, J. R., and Ross, T. T. (1975). *Endocrinology* **97**, 366.

McNatty, K. P., and Baird, D. T. (1978). *J. Endocrinol.* **76**, 527.

Makris, A., and Ryan, K. J. (1975). *Endocrinology* **96**, 694.

Means, A. R. (1975). *In* "Handbook of Physiology" (Am. Physiol. Soc., J. Field, ed.), Vol. 5. p. 203. Williams & Wilkins, Baltimore, Maryland.

Means, A. R., Fakunding, J. L., Huckins, C., Tindall, D. J., and Vitale, R. (1976). *Recent Progr. Hormone Res.* **32**, 477.

Millette, C. F., and Bellve, A. R. (1977). *J. Cell Biol.* **74**, 86.

Nett, T. M., Holtan, D. W., and Estergreen, V. L. (1973). *J. Anim. Sci.* **37**, 962.

Nimrod, A. (1977a). *Mol. Cell. Endocrinol.* **8**, 189.

Nimrod, A. (1977b). *Mol. Cell. Endocrinol.* **8**, 201.

Nimrod, A., and Lindner, H. R. (1976). *Mol. Cell. Endocrinol.* **5**, 315.

Pederson, T. (1970). *Acta Endocrinol. (Copenhagen)* **64**, 304.

Peters, H. (1969). *Acta Endocrinol. (Copenhagen)* **62**, 98.

Richards, J. S., and Midgley, A. R. (1976). *Biol. Reprod.* **14**, 82.

Rommerts, F. F. G., Kruger-Sewnarain, B. C., Grootegoed, J. A., de Jong, F. H., and van der Molen, H. J. (1979). *Acta Endocrinol.* in press.

Ryle, M., Court, J., and Morris, R. J. (1974). *J. Endocrinol.* **61**, xxiii.

Savard, K., Marsh, J. M., and Rice, B. F. (1965). *Recent Prog. Horm. Res.* **21**, 285.

Schreiber, J. R., and Ross, G. T. (1976). *Endocrinology* **99**, 590.

Smith, M. S., Freeman, M. F., and Neill, J. D. (1975). *Endocrinology* **96**, 219.

Steinberger, E. (1971). *Physiol. Rev.* **51**, 1.

Tung, P. S., and Fritz, I. B. (1978). *Dev. Biol.* **64**, 297.

Valladares, L. E., Sarkar, D., and Payne, A. H. (1978). *Endocrine Soc. 60th Annu. Meet.*, Abstr. 129, p. 139.

van der Vusse, G. J., Kalkman, M. L., and van der Molen, H. J. (1973). *Biochim. Biophys. Acta* **297**, 179.

Verhoeven, G., Dierickx, P., and deMoor, P. (1979). *Mol. Cell. Endocrinol.* **13**, 241.

Welsh, M. J., and Wiebe, J. P. (1978). *Endocrinology* **103**, 838.

Zeleznik, A. J., Midgley, A. R., and Reichert, L. E. (1974). *Endocrinology* **95**, 818.

Zuckerman, S., and Baker, T. G. (1977). *In* "The Ovary" (S. Zuckerman and B. J. Weir, (eds.), 2nd ed., Vol. 1, p. 41. Academic Press, New York.

Zuckerman, S., and McKeown, T. (1938). *J. Pathol. Bacteriol.* **46**, 7.

DISCUSSION

N. A. Samaan: Dr. Dorrington, may I ask what is the effect of prolactin on the granulosa cells regarding the production of estrogens?

J. H. Dorrington: Prolactin alone or in the presence of FSH or testosterone did not influence estradiol production by the granulosa cell cultures. Prolactin, however, did suppress the stimulatory effect of FSH and testosterone on estrogen biosynthesis, but this was not significant until the third day of treatment. Progesterone synthesis was examined in the same cultures, and in this case prolactin enhanced the effect of FSH and testosterone.

N. A. Samaan: I asked this question because we found that in the prolactin pituitary tumors, the LH and FSH may be normal or even higher after stimulation with LHRH, but the important thing is that the estrogens are low and, when the prolactinoma is removed successfully with return of normal menses, the LH and FSH may not change. Actually some of them may go down during stimulation with LHRH, but the estrogen will go up, so it seems that the prolactin may have a direct effect on the ovary with inhibition of estrogen formation.

J. H. Dorrington: The inhibitory effect of prolactin on estrogen production by cultures of rat granulosa cells supports your conclusions. I should add that the inhibitory effect of prolactin can be demonstrated more readily when the cells are incubated for 24 hours with FSH and testosterone and subsequently with either testosterone alone or prolactin and testosterone. The decline in estrogen biosynthesis was more rapid in those cells treated with prolactin.

A. H. Payne: Figures A and B present data from studies done by Luis Valladares in my laboratory. These studies show that in the adult rat testis LH induces aromatase activity. Animals were treated for 6 days either with saline or LH at doses indicated in Fig. A. Aromatase activity was assayed on day 7. Aromatase activity was determined by measuring the conversion of [^{3}H]-testosterone to [^{3}H]estradiol during a 3-hour period of incubation, using a cell-free homogenate of whole testes plus an NADPH generating system. The final estradiol was recrystallized with authentic estradiol. As you can see in Fig. A, we could not observe any aromatase activity in animals that were not treated with LH. However, when rats were treated twice daily with LH, aromatase activity was demonstrated. Figure A illustrates the effect of increasing concentrations of LH on aromatase activity as represented by the filled circles on the line. Administration of increasing doses of LH resulted in increasing aromatase activity, with maximum induction observed at 4 μg of LH per day. That the effect of LH was an effect on aromatase activity, not an effect on LH, on increasing the substrate, testosterone, is illustrated by the superimposed open bars, which represent endogenous testicular testosterone concentration. Testosterone concentration did not vary with the amount of LH given per day.

Figure B shows that the effect on aromatase activity was specific for LH and that FSH treatment did not induce aromatase activity. The dose of FSH or LH administered is expressed as equivalents of NIH-FSH-S1 or NIH-LH-S1, respectively. As I have mentioned, no aromatase activity could be

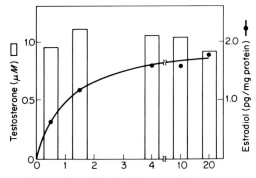

FIG. A. Effect of different doses of ovine LH on testicular aromatase activity and testicular testosterone concentration. The indicated dose of oLH was administered subcutaneously for 6 days to adult rats, and aromatase activity was determined on day 7.

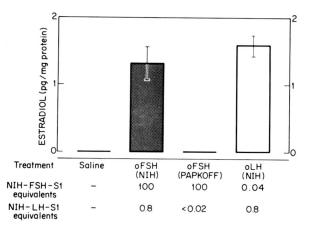

Treatment	Saline	oFSH (NIH)	oFSH (PAPKOFF)	oLH (NIH)
NIH-FSH-S1 equivalents	–	100	100	0.04
NIH-LH-S1 equivalents	–	0.8	<0.02	0.8

FIG. B.   Effect of ovine FSH and LH treatment on testicular aromatase activity. Hormones were administered subcutaneously daily for 6 days to adult rats, and aromatase activity was measured on day 7.

detected in saline-treated animals. Treatment with NIH-FSH equal to 100 μg of NIH-FSH-S1 resulted in induction of aromatization as illustrated by the stippled bar. Animals receiving daily administration of NIH-LH equivalent to the LH contamination found in the NIH-FSH preparation exhibited the same degree of induction aromatization as illustrated by the open bar. In sharp contrast, purified ovine FSH, kindly supplied by Harold Papkoff, did not induce testicular aromatase activity. From this we conclude that in the adult animal induction of aromatase is under the control of LH rather than FSH. I would like to mention also that we separated interstitial tissue from seminiferous tubules in testes from LH-treated rats and detected aromatase activity only in the interstitial tissue, not in the seminiferous tubules.

J. H. Dorrington: Dr. Ken Ryan and his colleagues also presented, at the Endocrine Society Meeting this year in Miami Beach, data that showed effects of LH on the aromatase activity of isolated Leydig cells from immature rats. Your studies together with those of Dr. Ryan show convincingly that the Leydig cells contain aromatase, which can be stimulated by LH. The Leydig cells may contribute to the levels of estrogen found in the immature rat and may also be a source of estrogen in the adult animal under certain conditions. As I discussed earlier, we were unable to demonstrate any effect of FSH on estradiol production by cultured Sertoli cells isolated from rats 30 days of age or older. This is consistent with the inability of FSH to stimulate aromatase activity when administered to the adult animal.

K. J. Ryan: It would be helpful to have some developmental picture as to when the Sertoli cells and Leydig cells actually gain this capacity for aromatization. Have you studied this?

J. H. Dorrington: We have not looked at the synthesis of estrogens by Leydig cells. The youngest animals that we used for the preparation of Sertoli cells were 5 days of age. The response of these cells to FSH was considerably greater than that obtained from Sertoli cells of 10-day-old rats.

B. M. Sanborn: I would like to congratulate Dr. Dorrington on opening up for us much food for thought in terms of the interaction on a molecular level between different hormones in both the male and female gonads. I would like to relay some recent unpublished observations made by a colleague, Dr. Robert Tcholakian, in the Department of Reproductive Medicine and Biology, University of Texas Medical School at Houston, that are pertinent to the subject. Dr. Tcholakian has found that Sertoli cells from the testes of 36-day rats metabolize [¹⁴C]testosterone in the presence of FSH to a variety of androgens and to a substance that migrates in chromatographic systems like 17β-estradiol but does not crystallize as 17β-estradiol. In contrast, FSH moderately stimulates these cultures to form estradiol-like radioimmunoassayable material from unlabeled testosterone. In looking at an earlier age, Dr. Tcholakian employed both [³H]testosterone and [¹⁴C]testosterone in metabolic studies on Sertoli cell cultures from the testes of 18-day animals. Here again FSH increased the accumulation of estradiol-like material as measured by radioimmunoassay. In the presence of FSH, [¹⁴C]-testosterone is metabolized to a component that migrates like estradiol in chromatography but, as seen in the top half of Table A (see columns 5 and 7 giving the percent deviation from the mean for both the ¹⁴C and ³H data), it does not crystallize as authentic estradiol as seen by deviations of 95–21% whereas the [³H]estradiol that was added as tracer for recovery purposes does crystallize to constant specific activity within acceptable variation limits. The bottom half of Table A shows the same phenomenon using [³H]testosterone as substrate and [¹⁴C]estradiol as the tracer. Here again note that the tritiated material, which is migrating chromatographically like estradiol, does not crystallize to constant specific activity, but that crystallization to constant specific activity of the authentic estradiol tracer is obtained. These metabolic data suggest that estradiol itself does not accumulate in measurable amounts when Sertoli cells are exposed to testosterone under our conditions, even though estradiol-like activity is detected by radioimmunoassay. Dr. Tcholakian is at present attempting to identify this material by a variety of physical means.

J. H. Dorrington: One point that concerns me about the data is that there is no effect of FSH on the synthesis of the metabolite that migrates with estradiol on chromatography. There is an effect of FSH, however, on the synthesis of estradiol-like material as measured by radioimmunoassay. This differential effect of FSH indicates that the substances measured by the two independent assays are not the same.

B. M. Sanborn: Yes, the effect of FSH under our conditions in terms of the radioimmunoassay-

TABLE A

Recrystallization of 17 β-Estradiol (E₂)-like Material Isolated after
Incubation of Sertoli Cells from 18-Day Rats
with Labeled Testosterone (T)

Substrate	Recovery tracer	Sequential crystallization	^{14}C (dpm/mg)	% Dev.[a] ($\bar{x}$, ^{14}C)	^{3}H (dpm/mg)	% Dev.[a] ($\bar{x}$, ^{3}H)
[¹⁴C]T	[³H]E₂	I	815	95	170	0.4
		II	330	21	171	0.2
		III	110	74	171	0.2
		I	363	85	313	0.4
		II	133	30	319	1.5
		III	87	55	311	1.1
		I	360	92	177	2.5
		II	122	35	176	1.9
		III	82	56	165	4.4
[³H]T	[¹⁴C]E₂	I	640	1.0	1553	100
		II	639	0.8	934	21
		III	620	2.2	383	49
		IV	636	0.4	217	72
		I	499	1.0	863	132
		II	490	0.8	148	60
		III	493	0.2	104	72
		I	667	3.6	1304	23
		II	621	3.6	1041	2
		III	644	0.0	838	21

[a] Percent deviation.

able material is considerably less than what you see in the first place, and in this case total metabolism was somewhat depressed by FSH. Certainly the 5α-reductase activity was depressed by FSH. However, it is true that we did not see a parallel stimulation of the unidentified metabolite by FSH, but I should stress that Dr. Tcholakian is not at the present time equating this material with what reacts in immunoassay. However, it is clear to us that something formed in this system behaves chromatographically like estradiol but does not crystallize as estradiol. I think that it is a very interesting substance to find out about.

J. H. Dorrington: Could you give us any idea of the nature of the substance?

B. M. Sanborn: Not at the moment.

D. T. Armstrong: With regard to the identity of the substance produced by Sertoli cells when cultured according to Dr. Dorrington's procedures in medium containing FSH and an aromatizable substrate, I believe we can be quite confident that it is estradiol-17β. My colleague, Dr. J. Zamecnik, has analyzed extracts of medium in which Sertoli cells from 15-day-old rats were cultured, by the technique of gas chromatography–mass fragmentography [J. Zamecnik, D. T. Armstrong, and K. Green, *Clin. Chem.* **24,** 627 (1978)].

Quantitative data for estradiol produced by both Sertoli and granulosa cells are presented in Table B. The stimulatory effect of FSH on both cell types is evident, and there is reasonably good agreement between results obtained by the GC-MS technique and those obtained by radioimmunoassay. Whether or not this resolves any differences between our findings and those of Dr. Sanborn, I think it does indicate fairly conclusively that what we are measuring is, indeed, estradiol.

B. M. Sanborn: I want to stress again that these are Dr. Tcholakian's findings (not in any negative sense, certainly). I would tend to agree with you, and I think we are coming down to the point where it is probably not the methodology, but possibly the cultures themselves. We may have to resolve this by exchanging samples. Nonetheless, it is a very interesting question.

R. Jewelewicz: Several years ago we had the opportunity to treat two hypogonadotropic patients with a pure preparation of FSH having very little LH content, which was obtained from NIH. After 10–12 days of treatment with 300–400 IU per day, there was significant enlargement of the ovaries but no steroidogenesis. Only after the addition of small amounts of LH, estrogen production started; within 4–5 days these patients' estrogens reached about 100 μg/24 hour urine, and the patients ovulated following HCG. Is the human follicle different from that of the rat?

J. H. Dorrington: On the contrary, it seems that the control of estrogen production by the human follicle may be very similar to that in the rat follicle. The information that you have given fits in beautifully with the two-cell type–two-gonadotropin model proposed for the synthesis of estrogens in the rat follicle. FSH stimulates the activity of the aromatase enzyme in granulosa cells, but cannot stimulate testosterone production by thecal cells. In the absence of an aromatizable substrate,

TABLE B

Estradiol-17β Production by Cultured Sertoli and Granulosa Cells

Culture conditions	Estradiol-17β (pg/ml culture medium) as measured by	
	RIA[a]	GC-MS[b]
Sertoli cells + testosterone	—	105
Sertoli cells + testosterone + FSH	—	416
Granulosa cells + testosterone	142	< 100
Granulosa cells + testosterone + FSH	5345	6416

[a] Radioimmunoassay.

[b] Gas chromatographic–mass spectrometric analysis.

therefore, no estrogen is produced. A low level of LH is required to stimulate testosterone production by thecal cells. Thus, in the presence of LH and FSH, testosterone is synthesized by the theca, FSH activates the aromatase enzyme system in granulosa cells, and estrogen is produced.

A. L. Goodman: How representative are these findings of what occurs in follicles that are actually destined to ovulate? On a purely random basis, a sampling of follicles from the ovary would presumably yield mostly follicles ultimately destined for atresia. A dying leaf, before it falls off the tree, will turn color because a new enzyme is active to produce new pigments. How much of your data is representative of the milieu of a follicle that will yield a viable oocyte, and how much is characteristic of a dying leaf, i.e., an atretic follicle?

J. H. Dorrington: I think that we shall have to develop better techniques for the isolation of follicles before we can really address ourselves to this particular problem.

A. L. Goodman: Have you no way in your system of coculturing the oocyte, that is, keeping the gamete viable along with the granulosa cells that you are culturing?

J. H. Dorrington: No, we have not done any experiments as yet along those lines.

J. Weisz: Before expanding on Dr. Goodman's question, first let me congratulate you. I think this was very lucid presentation of the series of beautiful studies providing evidence how, in another area, steroids and trophic hormones interact in a very fascinating way. Another site where such an interaction can be observed is, of course, the anterior pituitary gland. But to go back to this question of how we can relate some of these findings to what goes on during the normal estrous cycle in the rat. It is here that I had a little difficulty because the same conditions, i.e., FSH and androgens, that stimulate estrogen production appear to be the ones that also stimulate progesterone production. Yet in the normal cycle these two events, i.e., secretion of estrogen and progesterone, occur sequentially during the preovulatory period. I suspect that my prejudices are the same as yours; I think it is the preovulatory follicles, seven per ovary in the rat, that are the source first of the estradiol between diestrus II and proestrus and then of the progesterone secreted during the LH surge.

Δ^5-3β-ol steroid dehydrogenase is actually present in the membrane granulosa of the preovulatory follicle by diestrus II, and we have now measured the changes in the activity of the enzyme in the enzyme in the preovulatory follicle throughout the estrous cycle quantitatively by microdensitometry. The enzyme appears to be steroidogenic by a number of other criteria, such as the presence of lipid droplets and glucose-6-phosphate dehydrogenase activity. The activity of Δ^5-3β-ol-steroid dehydrogenase and glucose-6-phosphate dehydrogenase increases significantly during diestrus II to reach a peak by proestrus. Thus, though the presence of FSH may be essential for the appearance of some or all of these components of the steroidogenic machinery in the membrane granulosa of the preovulatory follicle, there must be a number of other regulatory factors that hold in abeyance the steroid dehydrogenase required, since it appears that, until the LH surge, it is only aromatization that can be accomplished in the membrane granulosa. With the LH surge aromatization is suppressed and progesterone synthesis and secretion can take place. I wonder whether some of our problems in translating your observations to the regulation of steroidogenesis during the normal estrous cycle in the rat might not be due to the fact that you are using immature animals in which follicles were induced artificially? It may be of interest to compare the morphology and cytochemistry of these follicles during their development with that of the preovulatory type of follicles in the normal adult rat during the infertile cycle.

J. H. Dorrington: I would like to thank you for your interesting comments. I speculate that the temporal sequence of events is as follows: During the rapid phase of growth prior to ovulation FSH induces the appearance of a number of enzymes in granulosa cells, including the aromatase system and Δ^5-3β-ol-steroid dehydrogenase. In the presence of low levels of testosterone from the theca, estrogen is synthesized by the granulosa cells and acts as a mitogen for granulosa cell proliferation. Even though Δ^5-3β-ol-steroid dehydrogenase is induced by FSH at an early stage, no progesterone is synthesized, and this may be because pregnenolone is not available as a substrate. Our work has indicated that testosterone alone or together with FSH is required for the synthesis of pregnenolone, and it is possible that the manifestations of androgen action are not apparent until the time of the LH surge. High levels of testosterone are present in the serum for a short period of time coincident with the gonadotropin surge. This high level of androgen may be an important trigger, together with the high levels of gonadotropins, in stimulating preovulatory progesterone production by granulosa cells.

J. Weisz: An additional observation of ours may be relevant here. A typical preovulatory progesterone surge can be elicited with follicular cystic ovaries with LH alone [Cortes *et al.*, *Endocrinology* **89**, 878 (1971)]. I do not know to what extent there is an increase in testosterone secretion; at the same time, however, there is clearly no requirement for any additional FSH for progesterone synthesis to occur. This could be used as a model to test your hypothesis.

B. F. Rice: I too would like to add my congratulations for this very provocative talk. I think we are very fortunate to have in the audience people who have made major contributions in several of the areas you have discussed. It might be well if we could see where they are compatible and where they are incompatible—specifically on number 1. It has been shown by some members of this group that androgens are the precursors for estrogens and this occurs not only in the ovary and testes, but in extra gonadal tissues. This brings me to my first question: What do you think all the estradiol is doing in the Sertoli cells, and is this really very important if you can demonstrate the same conversion in extra gonadal tissues.

As to my second question. I wish you had shown a slide of the Dorrington concept of the action of gonadotropins and the Greep concept of the action of gonadotropins, so that we could have gone over them one by one and compared them in terms of where they stand today. Since you did not have a slide, I wonder if you could do it for us now, and ask Dr. Greep what he thinks of it.

J. H. Dorrington: With respect to the first question, estradiol-17β receptors are present in Leydig cells from 4 days of age, whereas they have not been detected in Sertoli or germ cells. If the estradiol-17β produced by Sertoli cells is important during the prepubertal stage, then presumably this is due to effects on Leydig cell metabolism. Several years ago L. Samuels [*Endocrinology* **85**, 96 (1969)] showed that estrogen treatments of mice with cryptorchid testes depressed the testicular production of testosterone by reducing the activities of a number of enzymes involved in the conversion of progesterone to testosterone. Estradiol may hold testosterone production by Leydig cells in abeyance during the prepubertal stages of development to avoid precocious puberty. With respect to the second point, the summary of the sites of action of gonadotropins was presented earlier.

K. Ahren: May I come back to the time sequence of this interesting FSH effect on the follicle. You have used mostly the estrogen-treated immature rat to get your granulosa cells and, in some experiments, PMSH-treated immature animals. Can these experiments give you any idea of when in the estrous cycle this FSH effect on the aromatase starts? The aromatase activity is apparently high in the granulosa cells isolated early in proestrus before the LH-FSH surge: addition of testosterone to such cells increases markedly estradiol-17β formation whereas simultaneous addition of FSH gives no further stimulation [L. Hamberger, T. Hillensjö, and K. Ahren, *Endocrinology* **103**, 771 (1978)].

J. H. Dorrington: Estrogen treatment of hypophysectomized or intact immature rats (25 days of age) causes proliferation of the granulosa cells, but the follicles do not have antra. The granulosa cells obtained from these follicles cannot synthesize estrogen when cultured in the presence of testosterone. The ability to convert testosterone to estrogen is acquired after exposure of the cells to FSH for 24 hours. We have induced the formation of preovulatory follicles by treatment with PMS, and granulosa cells from these follicles contain aromatase and synthesize estrogen from exogenous testosterone when cultured in the absence of FSH. Aromatase activity is presumably induced after the preantral stage, but our data do not tell us when this occurs *in vivo*.

N. B. Schwartz: There was a correlation I noted on your ontogenic slides with some data that Dr. Janice Lorenzen has obtained in my laboratory. I refer to your data on the early susceptibility of the Sertoli cell to FSH with waning susceptibility beyond 20 days or so. This correlates very well with our observations that the serum FSH of the immature male rat is suppressible by follicular fluid from porcine ovaries. We can suppress FSH in the 6-, 12-, and 34-day-old male. As the males get older the FSH is no longer reliably suppressible by this "folliculostatin" material, which is very similar to inhibin from the testes. Would you like to speculate on whether this is just a coincidental correlation or whether it has something to do with the changing regulation of FSH or perhaps of sensitivity to inhibin feedback?

J. H. Dorrington: To try to correlate these two pieces of data is very difficult because the cells are not treated *in vivo,* but the FSH is administered to the cultures.

N. B. Schwartz: Yes, I understand that. Let me put my question in another way. I know that you obtain from Sertoli cell culture medium material that suppresses FSH secretion by the pituitary in the experiments you did with Labrie. Do you find that you get more or less of this in Sertoli cell cultures from the older animals, which are no longer as susceptible to FSH suppression by ovarian folliculostatin?

J. H. Dorrington: We have looked at "inhibin-like" material in culture medium from Sertoli cells isolated from 35-day-old rats only. We have not studied the developmental aspects of the synthesis of this material or the hormonal control of its synthesis by Sertoli cells. We require more information in both these areas before your question can be answered adequately.

W. Odell: I was struck by the change in the aromatase activity as the male aged and was struck with the correlation of the fall in FSH that occurs *in vivo* as rats age. If I summarize the data, one could postulate that this is an *in vivo* cause and effect. For example, you find that aromatase subsides progressively for 5, 10, 15, 20, up to about 30 days. We have presented data to indicate that LH has a very small effect on testosterone effect *in vivo* at 10 days and that this effect progressively increases; i.e., a given dose of LH produces a progressively greater increment in blood testosterone as the animal ages between 5 and 40 days [W. D. Odell and R. S. Swerdloff, *Recent Prog. Horm. Res.* **32,** 245 (1976)]. Simultaneously, during this period you have shown that FSH stimulates the Sertoli aromatase activity. One thus might construct the concept that *in vivo* aromatase activity is stimulated by the high *in vivo* FSH. As this FSH falls, the activity falls. The same FSH that is high at the beginning also induces LH receptor formation, permitting the whole process of puberty to occur. The intratesticular estrogen production that must exist from your data may not relate at all to plasma estrogen levels, but could have a local effect on either inhibiting spermatogenesis or inhibiting Leydig cell response to LH.

J. H. Dorrington: Actually, there appears to be a correlation between the ability of Sertoli cells to respond to FSH in culture and plasma levels of estrogen in immature rats. B. B. Saksena (5th Annual Workshop on the Testis, Oslo, 1978) reported high levels of estradiol in circulating blood at days 1, 5, and 8 and a large increase at day 12. Estradiol concentration fell to low levels by 22 days of age. With respect to the possible physiological roles of estrogen in the immature testis, Dufau and her colleagues have demonstrated a direct effect of estrogen on the inhibition of synthesis of androgens by Leydig cells.

H. Papkoff: Around 1964, shortly after we had obtained some of first highly purified preparations of ovine FSH, we tested them in the then prevailing LH bioassay, the Greep ventral prostate test employing young hypophysectomized male rats. We were surprised to find a high degree of activity that would equate to a 10–20% contamination of LH in terms of the NIH-LH-S1. A series of experiments led us to conclude, however, that this was not a contamination problem but an intrinsic property of the FSH [*Acta Endocrinol.* **48,** 439 (1964)]. In view of what you now know about the actions of FSH, can you offer a modern interpretation of our results?

J. H. Dorrington: Several investigators have looked for effects of FSH on testosterone production *in vivo* and on various preparations of testicular tissue, including isolated Leydig cells. These studies have consistently failed to demonstrate any effect of FSH on testosterone production.

H. Papkoff: We, too, have tested highly purified ovine FSH *in vitro* with isolated rat interstitial cells and find only a very small stimulation of testosterone at very high dose levels.

J. H. Dorrington: I should add that the Leydig cells are the only cells in the testis that contain cholesterol side-chain cleavage and are capable of synthesizing testosterone.

K. M. Henderson: The results of studies carried out by Drs. Moon, Tsang, Simpson, and Armstrong in our laboratory show estradiol production by human granulosa and theca cells cultured for 24 hours, the tissue being obtained from two individual patients. The control and FSH-treated cultures of granulosa cells produce very low amounts of estradiol, and the corresponding cultures of thecal tissue produce no detectable amounts of estradiol at all. Granulosa cells when cultured in the presence of testosterone produce large amounts of estradiol, and this estradiol production is further stimulated when the granulosa cells are cultured with both FSH and testosterone. Thecal tissue, however, still fails to produce any detectable amounts of estradiol when cultured in the presence of either testosterone or FSH plus testosterone. In contrast to the effects of FSH on granulosa cells, hCG does not further stimulate estradiol production by granulosa cells cultured in the presence of testosterone. HCG also does not stimulate estradiol production by thecal tissue in either the presence or the absence of testosterone. These results indicate that human granulosa cells have the capacity to produce large amounts of estradiol when cultured with testosterone and that this aromatizing capacity can be stimulated by FSH. Thecal tissue in contrast would appear to lack aromatase activity.

Although thecal tissue fails to produce any estradiol, it does have the capacity to produce cAMP and androgens and both cAMP and androgen production can be stimulated by hCG, but not by FSH. These results, taken together, support the two-cell model of estrogen biosynthesis in that thecal tissue, under the stimulatory action of LH produces, androgens that are then aromatized to estradiol by the granulosa cells under the influence of FSH.

J. H. Dorrington: I would like to thank you for presenting these very interesting data. For extra information, I would like to quote recent work of K. P. McNatty and D. T. Baird [*J. Endocrinol.* **76,** 527 (1978)], in which they examined follicles from 53 women. They showed a good correlation between the FSH levels, the number of granulosa cells present in the follicles, and the levels of estrogen. From these data they calculated that the granulosa cells could contribute as much as 80% of the total estrogen in the ovary.

M. New: My comment is prompted by the statement you made about sexual precosity being prevented by the Sertoli production of estrogen, which I presume then, would suppress Leydig cell production of testosterone. If I may make any correlations from the rats to the human, I would like to report that the young human testicle has a surge of testosterone in which the testosterone levels in the infant at about 6 weeks of age reach that of adult man. Then it wanes and stays down until puberty. During the period of the very high levels of testosterone, there is perfectly normal peripheral conversion of testosterone to estrogens. It is therefore very puzzling to think of what the Sertoli cell is doing, making all this estrogen from testosterone in the young testicle. Do you have a comment about that?

J. H. Dorrington: The changes in the levels of testosterone can be explained on the basis of changing populations of Leydig cells. Shortly after birth there are many Leydig cells in the testis, which would synthesize the large amounts of testosterone you mentioned. Later the number of Leydig cells per testis decreases quite dramatically and stays low until puberty, when the Leydig cells repopulate the intertubular space. H. J. van der Molen and his colleagues [*J. Endocrinol.* **57,** 277 (1973)] calculated that the adult rat testis contributes about 21% of the total circulating estradiol, but we have no comparable data for the immature rat.

K. J. Ryan: The last question implied that the Sertoli cell was making a lot of estrogen. This has not been demonstrated *in vivo* yet, but only in tissue culture. How much estrogen do you think is made in the Sertoli cell, and is it acting locally or is it being exported? Isn't that the question implied by Dr. New?

J. H. Dorrington: The 20-day-old rat testis contains approximately 1.5 mg of Sertoli cell protein, so if the levels of estradiol produced *in vivo* are comparable to those produced in culture, then the amounts would be in the range of 300–500 pg per testis in 24 hours at this particular stage of development.

K. J. Ryan: Do you think the estrogen is acting locally?

J. H. Dorrington: It is possible that estrogen produced by Sertoli cells influences the metabolism of Leydig cells, since those cells are the only cells in the testis in which estradiol-17β receptors have been detected. However, data from your group [J. A. Canick, A. Makris, G. L. Gunsalas, and K. J. Ryan, *Endocrine Soc.* Abst. 128, p. 138 (1978)] have indicated that the aromatase activity of Leydig cells is much higher than that in the tubules at this particular stage of development; if this is the case *in vivo,* then it is difficult to assess the physiological significance of the estrogen synthesized by Sertoli cells.

J. Kowal: In response to Dr. Rice's question, I would think that the fact that FSH stimulates aromatase in Sertoli cells would set them apart from tissues, since I am not aware that it stimulates aromatase activity in the skin, liver, etc. The adrenals produce a lot of androgens. Do any of these circulating androgens play a role as substrate in reaction in granulosa cells, or could they?

J. H. Dorrington: Presumably the testosterone in the circulation could diffuse through the thecal cell layer to the granulosa cells, but this would not occur when the thecal cells were producing testosterone and the intrafollicular concentration of testosterone was high. The thecal cells in close proximity to the granulosa cells are presumably the major sites of synthesis and contribute the major part of the testosterone that is utilized.

W. F. Crowley: As a preliminary to our studies using a long-acting LRF agonist (D-Trp[6]-Pro[9]-NEt-LRF), to treat hypogonadotropic human males, we have done a dose-response curve in normal male volunteers; during the administration of this analog, we have noticed that the testosterone levels double while LH levels increase to 15 or 20 times baseline values. An interesting observation that might be relevant to what Dr. Payne has said is that the estradiol levels in these men triple to levels of 110 pg/ml from their normal baseline of about 35 pg/ml. This estradiol rise precedes that of testosterone, beginning at 8 hours and peaking from 24 to 48 hours whereas the testosterone peaks at about 48 hours. It also does not occur in men who are hypogonadotropic and have a blunted or absent testosterone response to acute testing with the LRF analog despite small gonadotropin responses. Such estradiol responses, presumably testicular in origin, also occur after HCG administration in normal males, although not quite to the level that we have seen after the LRF analog. Since we were aware of your data indicating a decline in the Sertoli cell response with advancing age, we were looking around for other likely candidates for it, and perhaps Dr. Payne's Leydig cell responses to HCG may provide an explanation.

R. O. Greep: I retired from the ring quite some time ago, and the thought of getting into the ring again frightens me. I doubt that there is any point in rehashing these old ideas. I think what Dr. Rice had in mind was a 1941 paper in which I had assumed that the theca under the stimulation of LH was producing estrogen. I gave up on that in the early 1960s when Ryan and Smith took the theca and granulosa apart for the first time, incubated them in culture, and showed that the granulosa was entirely capable of steroidogenic synthesis. It seemed to me that the only gap in your presentation tonight, Dr. Dorrington, was a discussion of what the gonadotropins do to the theca cells. Would you like to comment on that? I think I understand your concept of their action, but I would like for you to speak on the role of the theca.

J. H. Dorrington: Fortune and Armstrong have isolated thecal tissue from rat follicles and have shown that it will respond to LH with increased production of androgens. In summary, thecal cells contain LH receptors (but not FSH receptors) and respond to LH to give androgens, which can then be utilized for estrogen biosynthesis in granulosa cells.

K. J. Ryan: I think that what Rice was referring to was the Greep concept that both FSH and LH are necessary for follicular development and steroidogenesis. The work of Dorrington and Armstrong has reinforced this, with FSH being first to stimulate aromatization and estrogen production by the granulosa and LH being responsible for the testosterone production by the theca cells, the substrate for estrogen formation. The two gonadotropins are necessary for estrogen production, and the estrogen stimulates the response of the follicle to the gonadotropins; I think Dr. Richards will be speaking more about this when she talks about the development of FSH and LH receptors (see next chapter), because this idea of the FSH effect on the granulosa and the LH effect on the theca, at least in the early developmental stage of the follicle, brings together the early Greep concept that both gonadotropins are necessary, and it points out where each works in the cycle.

Hormonal Control of Ovarian Follicular Development: A 1978 Perspective

JoAnne S. Richards

Reproductive Endocrinology Program, Department of Pathology,
The University of Michigan, Ann Arbor, Michigan

I. Introduction

Just prior to ovulation the mammalian follicle contains an oocyte suspended by cumulus cells in a cavity, the antrum (Fig. 1). The cumulus cells are contiguous with the membrana granulosa and comprise an avascular microenvironment about the oocyte. Any substances entering this area from the vascular theca cell layer must first traverse a basement membrane. In the human, a preovulatory follicle would have a similar structure and would contain one of the 2 million oocytes estimated to be present in the ovary at birth (Baker, 1963). Since a maximum of 400 follicles ovulate during the entire active reproductive years of a woman, this follicle actually would represent 1 of 400 that ever reach maturity. The remaining 99% of the oocytes and follicles degenerate by a process called atresia. Thus, I was surprised recently when it was pointed out to me by a misinformed male that "the whole part of sex is getting the sperm to the egg, not the hormone to the cell." But I will challenge by saying that it is the hormone getting to the cell that allows the egg to "flirt with" the sperm.

Quite specifically, the hormones known to be involved in follicular development are the pituitary hormones luteinizing hormone (LH), follicle-stimulating hormone (FSH), and prolactin and the ovarian steroid hormones progesterone, testosterone, and estradiol. The ovarian follicular target cells for these hormones are the membrana granulosa and the theca. The objective of this presentation is to provide evidence to indicate that it is *first* the ability of follicles to synthesize estradiol and *second* the combined actions of estradiol and the pituitary gonadotropins on granulosa cell function that dictate which few follicles make it, leaving the rest along the way.

Whatever I say would not be possible without members of the Reproductive Endocrinology Program who have contributed extensively to these studies. Jan Uilenbroek, Riaz Farookhi, and James Ireland have examined gonadotropin receptors in follicular cells during the estrous cycle (Uilenbroek, 1978), during atresia (Farookhi and Richards, 1978; Farookhi, 1978), and in hypophysectomized immature female rats (Ireland and Richards, 1978a,b). Meena Rao and

343

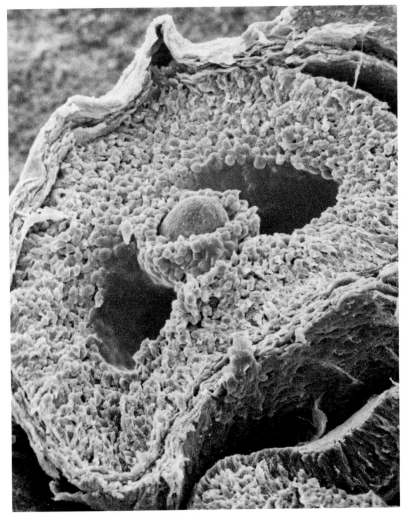

FIG. 1.   Scanning electron micrograph of a rat preovulatory follicle. Provided by P. Bagavandoss; reproduced from Bagavandoss *et al.* (1977).

Julie Jonassen have done all the work on LH-induced desensitization of granulosa cells involving both the loss of LH receptor (Rao *et al.*, 1977) and LH-responsive adenylate cyclase (Jonassen and Richards, 1978). Anne Hirshfield examined the kinetics of rat follicular growth (Hirshfield and Midgley, 1978). P. Bagavandoss has been examining follicular cell morphology and kindly provided the scanning electron micrograph (Fig. 1: Bagavandoss *et al.*, 1977). Tony Zeleznik and Rees Midgley were the first in our laboratory to study granulosa cell function and to demonstrate FSH induction of LH receptor (Zeleznik *et al.*, 1974).

At that time I was "bound" to estradiol receptors in the rat corpus luteum. Thus, I actually began work in the ovarian follicle by entering through the back door. I needed an ovarian target tissue that was known to respond to estradiol and in which I could demonstrate "real" estradiol receptors. I was trying desperately to prove that the estradiol binding I was observing in the rat corpus luteum during pregnancy was not a contaminant, something emanating from the brown paper towels on which I was dissecting the corpora lutea. Now, because receptors have gained more acceptability and respectability, the issue of brown paper towels seems to have been forgotten.

What I observed when I examined estradiol receptors in granulosa cells of ovaries of immature female rats is shown in Fig. 2. Working on the assumption that cytosol receptors were translocated to the nucleus only in the presence of estradiol, I reasoned that nuclear receptor content in granulosa cells would be increased when follicular estradiol production was also increased. Thus, pregnant mare's serum gonadotropin (PMSG) or ovine FSH (oFSH) was administered to immature intact rats. Much to my surprise, nuclear content of estradiol receptor, measured by the nuclear exchange assay and expressed as molecules per granulosa cell, decreased when ovarian estradiol had increased. These results prompted a long quest in the hypophysectomized immature rat to determine whether the decrease in estradiol receptor content occurred in response to the FSH-like or LH-like activity of these two hormone preparations. It turned out that LH rather than FSH caused this decrease and that it was most pronounced in association with LH-induced luteinization or atresia (Richards, 1975). Thus, these efforts drew me away from estradiol action in the rat corpus luteum to estradiol action in the follicle, and particularly to estradiol interactions with the pituitary gonadotropins in granulosa cell function.

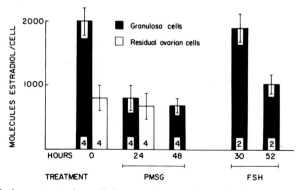

FIG. 2.   Nuclear content of estradiol receptor in granulosa cells of immature rats treated with pregnant mare's serum gonadotropin (PMSG) (25 IU) or ovine follicle-stimulating hormone (oFSH) (250 μg). From Richards (1975).

II. Follicular Growth and Cell Function during the Rat Estrous Cycle and Pregnancy

The growth of a follicle appears to begin with the growth of the primary oocyte, its enclosure within a single layer of granulosa cells, formation of a basement membrane, and attachment of surrounding theca cells. The hormonal and/or local factors regulating these early events remain unknown. In the presence of gonadotropins, however, follicular growth continues until large preantral and antral follicles are developed. Although atresia may occur at many stages, it is observed primarily in the rat and mouse in the small antral follicles (Pedersen and Peters, 1968; Hirshfield and Midgley, 1978). At this time follicles may become acutely dependent on the pituitary gonadotropins.

The kinetics of follicular growth are illustrated in Fig. 3 and have been derived primarily from studies in the mouse (Pedersen, 1970; Pedersen and Peters, 1968) and rat (Hirshfield and Midgley, 1978). The upper panel illustrates the pattern of serum concentrations of gonadotropins, FSH and LH, in 7 consecutive 4- and 5-day estrous cycles (Gay *et al.*, 1970; Butcher *et al.*, 1974; Smith *et al.*, 1975). A surge of both FSH and LH occur late in the afternoon of proestrus, and the FSH surge extends into the morning of estrus. The lower portion of the figure depicts relative changes in follicle size, from small preantral to large antral follicles, on the *y* axis. Time in days is plotted on the *x* axis. Follicles ovulating in response to the gonadotropin surge of one cycle, as indicated, actually began to grow some 19

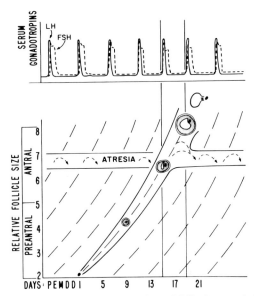

FIG. 3.   Schematic diagram of serum gonadotropins and follicular growth during the rat estrous cycle. See text for explanation.

days earlier as part of a larger pool of growing follicles. Thus, once committed to grow, a follicle is exposed to at least three consecutive surges of gonadotropins. It has been proposed that the surge preceding ovulation selects from a growing pool follicles that will ovulate and luteinize at the next proestrus (Welschen, 1973; Schwartz, 1974; Richards and Midgley, 1976). Those not selected or not capable of responding to the gonadotropin signal become atretic and fail to mature fully.

What changes occur in the large antral follicles during the 4–5-day estrous cycle? As illustrated, serum gonadotropin concentrations are low and relatively constant from metestrus through early proestrus. If exogenous gonadotropins are administered during this period, ovulation can be stimulated on diestrus, but not on estrus (Welschen, 1973). Therefore, follicular growth appears to be associated with increased responsiveness to the gonadotropins, possibly related to a change in receptor content for FSH, LH, or both. To examine changes in gonadotropin receptors, large follicles were isolated on each day of the estrous cycle by microdissection. Granulosa cells were expressed and incubated with radiolabeled hFSH or hCG. Figure 4 demonstrates that receptor content for FSH, expressed as counts per minute of $[^{125}I]hFSH$ bound per microgram of DNA, remained constant throughout the estrous cycle. However, receptor content for LH, expressed as counts per minute of $[^{125}I]hCG$ bound per microgram of DNA, markedly increased on proestrus, *prior* to the LH/FSH surge (Uilenbroek, 1978; Richards *et al.*, 1979a; Uilenbroek and Richards, in press). *In vivo* au-

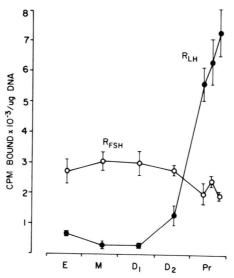

FIG. 4.   Receptors for FSH (R_{FSH}) and LH (R_{LH}) in granulosa cells of antral follicles isolated on each day of the rat estrous cycle. Receptors for FSH and LH were measured as described previously (Zeleznik *et al.*, 1974; Richards *et al.*, 1976). Days of the estrous cycle are estrus (E), metestrus (M), diestrus 1 (D1), diestrus 2 (D2), and proestrus (Pr).

toradiography of ovaries obtained 2 hours after an intravenous injection of [^{125}I]hCG also indicated that theca and granulosa cells of large antral follicles on proestrus bound more radioiodinated hCG than did the theca and granulosa cells of an adjacent small antral follicle (Uilenbroek, 1978; Amsterdam *et al.*, 1975).

Since the estrous cycle of the rat is short compared to the cycles of other mammals, we examined what changes occur in follicular growth in the rat during pregnancy when the luteal phase is extended for 22 days, a period more closely resembling that of other species, including the human. Figure 5 depicts schematically the changes in serum gonadotropins (Linkie and Niswender, 1972; Cheng, 1976) and the kinetics of follicular growth (Greenwald, 1966; Pedersen and Peters, 1971). In pregnancy, the ovulated ovum is fertilized and implants. The ovulated follicle becomes a functional corpus luteum secreting progesterone. As shown in the upper panel, serum progesterone increases and remains elevated until days 19–20, when it begins to decline and reflects the regression of the corpus luteum (Richards and Midgley, 1976; Lacy *et al.*, 1976). During this period serum concentrations of gonadotropins remain low. Parturition usually occurs on day 23 and is associated with a postpartum LH/FSH surge and ovulation (Rebar *et al.*, 1969). Note that development of these preovulatory follicles occurred in the *absence* of any preceding consecutive gonadotropin surges. Because of the marked differences in serum gonadotropin patterns in the

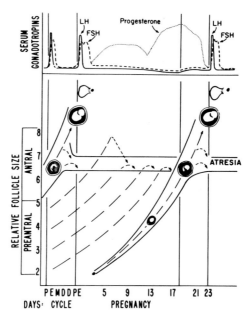

FIG. 5. Schematic diagram of serum gonadotropins and progesterone and follicular growth during pregnancy in the rat. See text for explanation.

cycle and pregnancy and because the *surge* of FSH of one cycle has been presumed to dictate the growth of preovulatory follicles in the subsequent cycle, we sought to relate changes in the functional activity of developing follicles at the end of pregnancy with those occurring during the estrous cycle.

Figure 6 illustrates the changes in receptor content for FSH and LH in granulosa cells and theca cells of follicles isolated during pregnancy as well as estradiol accumulation by individual follicles incubated *in vitro*. Receptor content for FSH and LH in granulosa cells during the estrous cycle has been repeated from Fig. 4 for purposes of direct comparison. FSH receptor in granulosa cells during pregnancy, as in the cycle, was remarkably constant between days 8 and 19, but remained at values somewhat lower than those in the cycle. An abrupt increase in FSH receptor was observed on day 20 and was maintained through day 23. In contrast, granulosa cell receptor for LH increased progressively between days 3 and 6 of pregnancy in a pattern similar to that of the cycle, day 5 of pregnancy being equivalent in time to proestrus. Ovulation does not occur spontaneously in early pregnancy, presumably because increasing concentrations of serum progesterone block an LH surge. The follicles present on days 4–6,

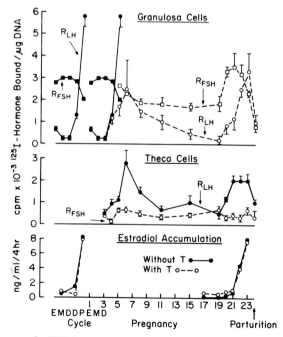

FIG. 6.   Receptors for FSH (R_{FSH}) and LH (R_{LH}) in follicular cells of antral follicles isolated on selected days during pregnancy. Estradiol accumulation was measured in individual follicles incubated in 500 μl of Medium 199 with or without 50 ng of testosterone (T) per milliliter. Estradiol was measured by double antibody radioimmunoassay (England *et al.*, 1974).

however, are capable of ovulating. Exogenous administration of 5 IU of hCG on days 4, 5, or 6 was followed by the appearance of 6–10 ova in the oviducts.

Granulosa cells of follicles developing from days 8 to 19 of pregnancy possessed decreasing amounts of LH receptor and are not capable of ovulating in response to exogenous hormone (Greenwald, 1966; Richards, unpublished observations). From days 20 to 23 of pregnancy, developing follicles exhibit a marked increase in granulosa cell LH receptor and are the ones to ovulate in response to the postpartum LH/FSH surge. After ovulation the luteinizing granulosa cells rapidly lose *both* FSH and LH receptor, as shown by the decreased binding observed 1 day postpartum, or approximately 12–18 hours after the endogenous gonadotropin surge.

Theca cells isolated from the same follicles during pregnancy exhibit little or no FSH receptor. However, theca LH receptor was increased on day 6 and on days 21–23, coincident with the growth of preovulatory follicles. These changes in LH receptor suggest that theca as well as granulosa cells of developing preovulatory follicles differentiate and gain an enhanced ability to respond to the low circulating concentrations of LH. Further, the marked similarity in the changes of LH receptors in follicles at the end of pregnancy and between diestrus and proestrus of the cycle suggest that surge concentrations of FSH and LH 4–5 days preceding ovulation are not required for stimulation of preovulatory follicular growth. Small but demonstrable increases in serum FSH and LH have been observed between days 17 and 20 of pregnancy (Linkie and Niswender, 1972; Cheng, 1976). These increases may be sufficient to sustain continued preovulatory follicular growth. This idea is supported further by the marked similarities in the abilities of follicles on proestrus and at the end of pregnancy to produce estradiol. As shown in the lower panel of Fig. 6, individual follicles were incubated with or without 50 ng of testosterone per milliliter. Estradiol accumulation (ng/ml in 4 hours) increased markedly on proestrus and between days 20 and 23 of pregnancy from values less than 50 pg/ml to concentrations greater than 5 ng/ml. The differences in estradiol accumulation with and without exogenous substrate are revealed more clearly on a logarithmic scale, as shown in Fig. 7.

In the absence of exogenous substrate, follicular production of estradiol was low (0.02 ± 0.005 ng/ml in 4 hours) on day 17 and then increased steadily from 0.04 ± 0.008 ng/ml in 4 hours on day 19 to 7 ± 1 ng/ml in 4 hours on day 23. When testosterone was included in the incubation medium as a substrate for the follicular aromatase, follicles exhibited a pronounced ability to convert testosterone to estradiol, even on day 17 of pregnancy (Fig. 7). Thus the limiting factor in follicular estradiol accumulation *in vitro* between days 17 and 21 appeared to be endogenous follicular production of androgen substrate. By day 22 of pregnancy, sufficient endogenous androgen was being produced so that additional testosterone did not increase estradiol accumulation. Furthermore, on days 22–23 total follicular aromatase activity continued to increase.

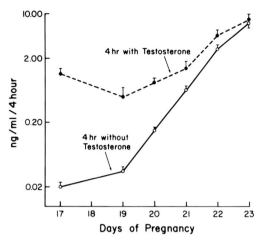

FIG. 7. Estradiol accumulation by individual follicles isolated on days 17 to 23 of pregnancy. See legend of Fig. 6.

III. LH in Follicular Cell Function

Because LH receptors in both theca and granulosa cells were increasing between days 20 and 23 of pregnancy and because LH is known to be required for estradiol synthesis, we sought to determine to what extent LH was required for these processes. To examine the effects of LH on follicular LH receptors, an antiserum against LH (LHAS) was administered (Fig. 8). This antiserum, gener-

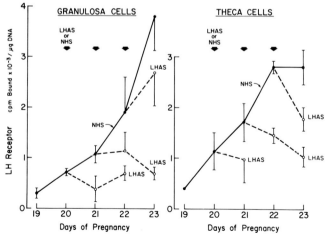

FIG. 8. Effects of antiserum against luteinizing hormone (LHAS) or normal horse serum (NHS) on LH receptors in follicular cells of developing preovulatory follicles isolated at the end of pregnancy in the rat. See text for explanation.

ated in the horse "Kae" was kindly provided by Dr. Hansel, Cornell University, and has been well characterized by the studies of Morishige and Rothchild (1974) and Gibori *et al.* (1978). Thus, this LH antiserum or normal horse serum (NHS) was administered subcutaneously on day 20, 21, or 22 of pregnancy (Fig. 8). Follicles were isolated, and receptors for LH were measured in granulosa and theca cells. When normal horse serum was administered, LH receptors increased progressively in granulosa cells from day 20 to 23 and in theca cells from day 20 to 22, giving patterns similar to those observed in Fig. 6. However, when LH antiserum was given on day 20 or day 21, the progressive increase in LH receptor was prevented in both granulosa cells and theca cells. The LH antiserum seemed less effective if administered on day 22. These results suggested that LH was responsible, at least in part, for the increase in LH receptor in both follicular cell types.

To determine how these effects of LH on LH receptors were related to the ability of follicles to produce estradiol, a similar experiment was designed and individual follicles were incubated *in vitro* to measure estradiol accumulation (Fig. 9). As with LH receptor, normal horse serum given *in vivo* did not alter the changes normally occurring in follicular estradiol production between days 20 and 23 of pregnancy (Fig. 7). Total follicular aromatase activity (measured as follicular estradiol accumulation in the presence of testosterone) increased progressively from day 21 to day 23 (Fig. 9). This increase was prevented by the

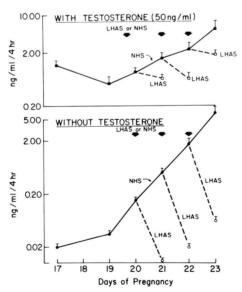

FIG. 9. Effects of antiserum against luteinizing hormone (LHAS) or normal horse serum (NHS) on estradiol accumulation by individual follicles isolated at the end of pregnancy in the rat and incubated *in vitro*.

administration of LH antiserum on day 20, 21, or 22 (Fig. 9). Even more dramatic, however, was the ability of LH antiserum to abolish estradiol production in follicles incubated without testosterone. Thus, follicles obtained from rats treated with normal horse serum and then incubated *in vitro* exhibited a marked increase in estradiol accumulation from days 20 to 23, reaching 6–8 ng/ml. However, follicles obtained from rats exposed to LH antiserum on days 20, 21, or 22 produced little or no estradiol 24 hours later. These results indicate that removal of endogenous LH by the LH antiserum had a greater effect on the ability of the follicles to produce endogenous androgen substrate than it did on follicular aromatase activity.

Figure 10 schematically summarizes these results. Between metestrus and proestrus of the estrous cycle and days 20–23 of pregnancy, small antral follicles that are unable to ovulate become large preovulatory follicles. This maturation occurs in the presence of basal concentrations of FSH and LH. However, the development is associated with marked changes in theca and granulosa cell function and an enhanced sensitivity of follicular cells to gonadotropins. Small antral follicles have a limited capacity to produce estradiol *in vitro*. We have shown that they possess some aromatase activity, localized in the granulosa cell as reported by the elegant studies of Moon and Dorrington and Armstrong (Moon *et al.*, 1975). This activity is likely maintained by FSH since abundant receptor for FSH (but not for LH) is present in these granulosa cells and because aromatase activity can be induced *in vitro* by FSH (Moon *et al.*, 1975; Erickson and Hsueh, 1978). Therefore, the *inability* of these small antral follicles to

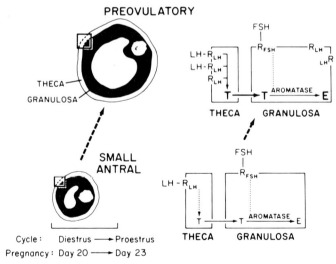

FIG. 10. Summary of changes in follicular cell function during the development of preovulatory follicles at the end of pregnancy and from metestrus to proestrus of the estrous cycle. See text for explanation.

produce substantial amounts of estradiol appears to be a consequence of their *inability* to produce aromatizable androgens, such as testosterone. Based on the studies of Fortune and Armstrong (1977), androgen synthesis has been localized in the theca. Because the number of LH receptors present in the theca cells of these small antral follicles is low, it is possible that their inability to produce androgen results from an inability of the theca cells to respond to low serum concentrations of LH.

During maturation of preovulatory follicles, receptor for LH in theca cells is increased 2- to 3-fold and is accompanied by increased synthesis of androgens. Because some aromatase activity is present in the small antral follicles, the increase in androgen leads automatically to an increase in some estradiol production. Thus, a change in theca cell function and responsiveness to LH appears to precede increased follicular estradiol synthesis. Estradiol, in turn, appears to be required for the appearance of granulosa cell LH receptor. The following discussion will focus on the roles of estradiol and FSH in granulosa cell function and examine how each hormone is involved in the appearance of granulosa cell LH receptor.

IV. Estradiol and FSH in Follicular Cell Function

In the 1930s and 1940s it was well established that estradiol, but not testosterone, would increase ovarian responsiveness to gonadotropins (Pencharz, 1940; Williams, 1945; Simpson *et al.*, 1941). In the 1960s a direct action of estradiol and the localization of estradiol binding in the ovary was demonstrated (Bradbury, 1961; Ullberg and Bengtsson, 1963). By the early 1970s the specific intraovarian localization of FSH binding to granulosa cells was demonstrated by autoradiography (Midgley, 1973). At this time, Goldenberg, Vaitukaitis, and Ross reexamined the role of estrogens and demonstrated (Goldenberg *et al.*, 1972) that prolonged treatment of hypophysectomized rats with diethylstilbestrol would increase ovarian uptake of [³H]thymidine and ³H-labeled FSH *in vivo*. These observations provoked new interest and new interpretations on the role of estrogen. I became aware of these studies when I was exploring the effect of estradiol, FSH and LH on estradiol receptors in granulosa cells (Richards, 1975). I had two questions: (1) Was increased ovarian uptake of ³H-labeled FSH *in vivo* related to an increased number of granulosa cells per ovary or to an increased concentration of FSH receptors per granulosa cell? (2) Was increased ovarian responsiveness to gonadotropins related to FSH receptors?

To examine the interactions of estradiol and FSH on granulosa cell function, the hypophysectomized immature rat has been used. After hypophysectomy on day 24 of age, rats were treated sequentially with estradiol (1.5 mg/day for 4 days) followed by highly purified hFSH (LER-1577, 2 µg/day for 2 days), kindly provided by Dr. Leo Reichert, Jr., Emory University. These treatments stimulated the sequential development of lage preantral and then antral follicles.

When the effects of these hormones on granulosa cell proliferation were examined, estradiol was found to increase the proliferation of granulosa cells (Fig. 11). This was observed when proliferation was measured either as DNA content of isolated granulosa cells or as percent of labeled cells observed following *in vivo* administration of [³H]thymidine and subsequent autoradiographic analysis (Rao *et al.*, 1978). However, even in the continued presence of estradiol, granulosa cell proliferation was not sustained, as indicated by the decrease in the labeling index and by the plateau in granulosa cell DNA content. If, however, FSH was given to the estradiol-treated rats, a new burst of proliferative activity followed (Fig. 11). This proliferative phase was not sustained either. Thus, each hormone exhibited a specific but limited capacity to evoke a proliferative response in granulosa cells.

The effects of estradiol and FSH on receptors for FSH and LH are shown in Fig. 12. Estradiol alone had no effect on the number of FSH receptors, expressed as counts per minute of ¹²⁵I-labeled hFSH bound per microgram of DNA of isolated granulosa cells. However, estradiol was required for FSH to induce the appearance of LH receptor in granulosa cells and to enhance the rate of increase of its own receptor. Thus, the increased ovarian uptake of [³H]FSH *in vivo* was

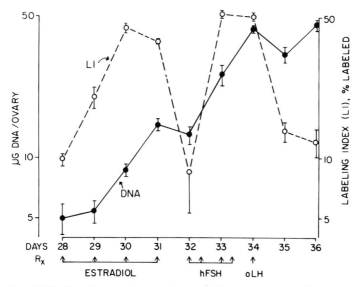

FIG. 11.   Proliferation of rat ovarian granulosa cells in response to estradiol, human follicle-stimulating hormone (hFSH), and ovine luteinizing hormone (oLH). The labeling index (LI) was obtained by counting the number of labeled cells (seven grains per nucleus) in random populations of follicles and granulosa cells following an intravenous injection of 15 μCi of [³H]thymidine. DNA was measured in granulosa cells isolated from ovaries by applying gentle pressure. DNA of isolated granulosa cells was then expressed in terms of the total DNA per ovary. From Rao *et al.* (1978) and Richards *et al.* (1978).

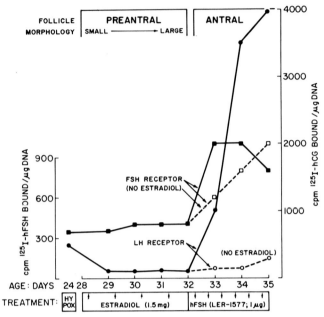

FIG. 12.   Effects of estradiol and human follicle-stimulating hormone (hFSH) on receptors for FSH and luteinizing hormone (LH) in granulosa cells of developing preantral and antral follicles. From Richards *et al.* (1976) and Ireland and Richards (1978a).

shown to reflect the increased number of granulosa cells per ovary, not the number of FSH receptors per granulosa cell (Louvet and Vaitukaitis, 1976; Richards *et al.*, 1976). Therefore, estradiol-induced responsiveness of granulosa cells to FSH was *not* related to changes in the number of FSH binding sites per cell. However, the question of how estradiol enhanced FSH stimulation of granulosa cell differentiation remained. To examine this, I have moved progressively inside the granulosa cell to examine other components of the FSH response system; namely, FSH stimulation of cAMP production, and regulation of intracellular concentrations of cAMP binding sites.

Figure 13 illustrates the effects of estradiol and FSH on cAMP accumulation in granulosa cells *in vitro*. Granulosa cells of hypophysectomized rats treated with saline, estradiol, or estradiol and FSH were isolated and incubated *in vitro* with increasing concentrations of hFSH. As shown, granulosa cells of hypophysectomized rats did produce cAMP in a dose-response manner to FSH. However, granulosa cells obtained from estradiol-primed hypophysectomized rats produced a 2-fold greater increase in cAMP. Similar results have been observed following *in vivo* administration of hFSH (Richards *et al.*, 1979a; Richards *et al.*, 1979b). Further, the amount of hFSH (0.5–2 μg of LER-1577) required to stimulate a demonstrable dose-response increase in cAMP concentrations in

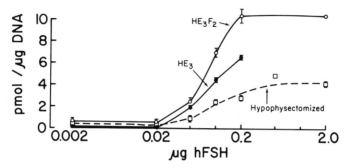

FIG. 13. Accumulation of cAMP in granulosa cells *in vitro:* response to human follicle-stimulating hormone (hFSH). Isolated, monodisperse granulosa cells were incubated in 300 μl of Medium 199 for 10 minutes at 37°C in the presence of increasing concentrations of hFSH (LER-1577; 880 IU FSH/mg, <4 IU LH/mg). cAMP was measured by radioimmunoassay, and all values were corrected for the percent of viable cells used in each assay. HE_3 designates granulosa cells collected from hypophysectomized rats treated with estradiol (E) (1.5 mg/day) for 3 days. HE_3F_2 designates granulosa cells from estradiol-primed hypophysectomized rats treated with hFSH (LER-1577; 2 μg/day) for 2 days. From Richards *et al.* (1979a,b).

granulosa cells *in vivo* is similar to the doses of hFSH required to induce a dose-response induction of LH receptor in granulosa cells *in vivo* (Fig. 14; Richards *et al.*, in press; submitted). Thus, estradiol enhances the ability of FSH to stimulate granulosa cell cAMP accumulation. Further, this enhancement occurred *without a change* in the number of FSH receptors per granulosa cell.

Next, cAMP binding sites were measured in granulosa cell cytosol (30,000 g supernatant) of saline, estradiol, or estradiol-FSH primed hypophysectomized rats (Fig. 15). The results revealed that estradiol alone had no effect on the number of cAMP binding sites, but did enhance the ability of FSH to stimulate an increase in the number of cAMP binding sites (Richards *et al.*, 1978, 1979a). This effect is reminiscent of the estradiol-mediated enhancement of FSH induction of LH receptor shown previously (Figs. 12 and 14). To characterize the cAMP binding sites, cytosols were incubated with [^{3}H]cAMP and then analyzed by polyacrylamide gel electrophoresis. A specific peak of bound radioactivity was observed in the cytosol of granulosa cells from estradiol-FSH-primed hypophysectomized rats, but not in cytosol of estradiol-treated rats (Richards *et al.*, 1979a). Clearly, an estradiol-induced "rat ovarian ovalbumin" has not been found.

V. Role of LH in Regulating Granulosa Cell Function

Because LH has also been shown to play an important role in stimulating preovulatory follicular growth in hypophysectomized rats (Lostroh and Johnson, 1966; Bates and Schooley, 1942) and because the LH antiserum decreased LH receptor in follicular cells in pregnant rats (Fig. 8), we sought to determine what

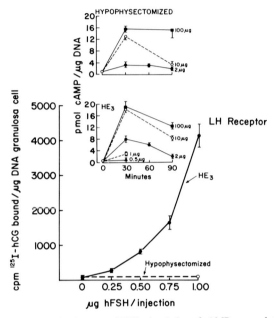

FIG. 14.   Follicle-stimulating hormone (FSH) stimulation of cAMP accumulation and luteinizing hormone (LH) receptor induction in granulosa cells *in vivo*. Hypophysectomized or estradiol-primed hypophysectomized rats (HE₃) were injected intravenously (tail vein) with various doses (0.5–100 μg) of hFSH (LER-1577). At 30, 60, and 90 minutes rats were killed, ovaries were removed, and granulosa cells were expressed and rapidly placed in boiling water for 10 minutes. A 30,000 *g* supernatant was prepared, and cAMP was measured by radioimmunoassay. To measure the FSH dose-response induction of LH receptor in granulosa cells, estradiol-primed hypophysectomized rats were given subcutaneous injections of 0.25–1.00 μg of hFSH at 12-hour intervals for 2 days. LH receptor was then measured in isolated granulosa cells. From Richards *et al.* (1979a,b).

effects LH might have *in addition* to its known enhancement of estradiol synthesis (Fig. 9). Specifically, we sought to determine whether LH might play a direct role in the induction of granulosa cell LH receptor. Thus, studies using hypophysectomized rats treated with exogenous estradiol were performed to determine those effects of LH that might occur in addition to any effect on estradiol synthesis. hCG, hFSH, or hCG and hFSH were administered to estradiol-treated hypophysectomized rats (Ireland and Richards, 1978b). As shown in Fig. 16, hCG given alone had little or no effect on granulosa cell LH receptor. A single submaximal dose of hFSH (2 μg) stimulated a small, transient rise in LH receptor, but by 48 hours all follicles were atretic. However, when hCG was given in combination with the hFSH, LH receptor increased markedly by 48 hours and large antral follicles developed. Thus, hCG acted to *increase* LH receptor and follicular growth, in a manner similar to the effects of daily administration of FSH (Fig. 12). We have postulated that the small increase in

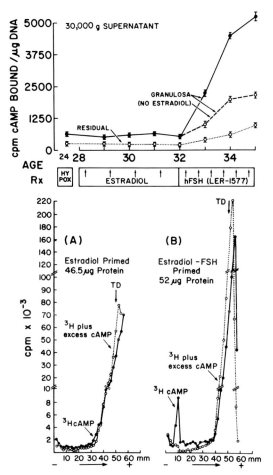

FIG. 15.   Effects of estradiol and human follicle-stimulating hormone (hFSH) on cAMP binding sites in granulosa cells cytosol. cAMP binding was measured by incubating cytosol (30,000 g supernatant) for 16 hours at 4°C with [^{3}H]cAMP ($10^{-8} M$) in the presence or the absence of unlabeled cAMP ($10^{-6} M$). Bound was separated from free by Millipore filtration using 0.45-μm filters. In the lower panel, granulosa cell cytosols of estradiol-primed or estradiol-FSH-primed rats were incubated as described above, and then bound was separated from free by polyacrylamide gel electrophoresis. From Richards *et al.* (1978).

LH receptor occurring within 24 hours after the FSH (or 36 hours after the hCG) allowed hCG to act directly on granulosa cells and to evoke responses previously associated only with FSH (Ireland and Richards, 1978b).

If hCG was acting directly on granulosa cells and if LH receptors were functionally coupled to adenylate cyclase, it should be possible to demonstrate LH stimulation of cAMP. Thus, granulosa cells of hypophysectomized rats treated with saline, estradiol, or estradiol and FSH were isolated and incubated

LH RECEPTOR

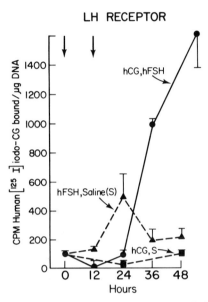

FIG. 16. Effect of human chorionic gonadotropin (hCG) on induction of LH receptor in estradiol-treated hypophysectomized immature rats. Hypophysectomized rats were treated with 1.5 mg of estradiol for 4 days. At 12-hour intervals (indicated by arrow) the rats received subcutaneous injections of human follicle-stimulating hormone (hFSH) (2 μg) followed by saline (S), hCG (5 IU) followed by saline (S) or hCG followed by hFSH. From Ireland and Richards (1978b).

with increasing concentrations of hCG. As shown in Fig. 17, hCG stimulated cAMP accumulation only in granulosa cells from rats treated with estradiol and FSH, indicating that hCG stimulation of cAMP was associated with the appearance of LH receptor (Richards *et al.*, 1979a,b). Thus, during the estrous cycle or pregnancy, the appearance of some LH receptor in granulosa cells may then allow LH as well as FSH to act directly on granulosa cells and to promote growth of the preovulatory follicles.

The interactions of estradiol, FSH, and LH are summarized schematically in Fig. 18. During the estrous cycle and at the end of pregnancy, the final stages of preovulatory follicular growth are dependent *first* on increased estradiol synthesis. This appears to be dependent on increased responsiveness of theca cells to LH and increased production of theca-derived androgens. Thus, the theca cell may hold the clue to what initiates preovulatory follicular growth. Follicles in which the theca cells do not develop responsiveness to LH may become atretic.

The *second* phase of preovulatory follicular growth is dependent on the interactions of estradiol, FSH, and LH. As discussed earlier, the FSH–cAMP response system in small antral follicles on diestrus appears to be adequate to maintain some aromatase activity. However, with increased production of androgen leading to increased concentrations of follicular estradiol, estradiol now

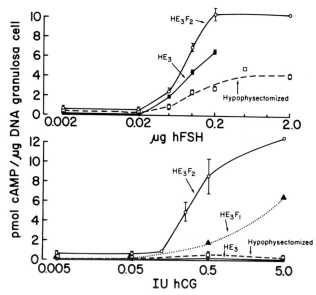

FIG. 17. Accumulation of cAMP in granulosa cells *in vitro:* response to human chorionic gonadotropin (hCG). Granulosa cells from hypophysectomized rats treated with saline, estradiol (HE₃), or estradiol followed by 1 day (HE₃F₁) or 2 days (HE₃F₂), or human follicle-stimulating hormone (hFSH) were incubated *in vitro* with increasing concentrations of hFSH (upper panel repeated from Fig. 13) or hCG (lower panel). See legend of Fig. 13.

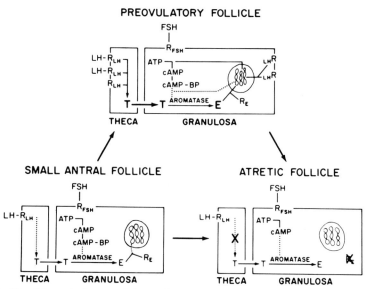

FIG. 18. Schematic diagram of changes in follicular cell function during the estrous cycle and pregnancy. See text for explanation.

appears to assume the director's role. Acting via its receptor and translocation to nuclear chromatin sites, estradiol somehow modifies granulosa cell function. One effect of estradiol is to enhance the ability of FSH to stimulate cAMP. This, in turn, appears to lead to increased cAMP binding sites, increased aromatase activity and ultimately to increased numbers of LH receptors and increased responsiveness to LH as well as FSH. These as well as other events prepare the follicles for ovulation and luteinization.

Atresia may occur if any one of these main components is blocked or lost. Studies by Riaz Farookhi indicate that FSH receptor content and FSH stimulation of cAMP in granulosa cells are quite stable even in the presence of agents such as androgen which have been shown to increase atresia (Harman *et al.*, 1975; Payne and Runser, 1958) and which he has shown can block FSH induction of LH receptor (Farookhi, 1978; Farookhi and Richards, 1978). His data strongly suggest that maintaining estradiol receptor content in granulosa cells is critical for follicular maturation.

VI. Desensitization and Follicular Cell Function

So far we have been considering the effects of hormones that induce receptors and increase ovarian cell responsiveness to themselves or to other hormones. Yet the literature is replete with demonstrations of "down regulation" and "desensitization," a word coined to describe hormone-induced loss of target cell responses to that hormone. This phenomenon also occurs in the ovary. In the ovary it is associated most dramatically with LH induction of luteinization, characterized, in part, by a loss of granulosa cell LH receptor (Richards *et al.*, 1976; Rao *et al.*, 1977). The decrease in granulosa cell LH receptor in follicles ovulated 1 day postpartum has already been mentioned (Fig. 6). However, a similar effect has been observed in granulosa cells of estradiol-FSH primed hypophysectomized rats given an ovulatory dose of oLH (60 μg) or hCG (5 IU) (Fig. 19) (Richards *et al.*, 1976; Rao *et al.*, 1977). Further, Rao *et al.* (1977) have shown that the decrease in numbers of receptors for LH occurs by mechanisms in addition to occupancy (Rao *et al.*, 1977). Unlike other systems that appear to be self-regulating, receptor for LH does not "spontaneously" reappear as serum concentrations of LH decline. Rather, another hormone, prolactin, is required to increase and maintain LH receptors in rat corpora lutea of pseudopregnancy (Holt *et al.*, 1975; Richards and Williams, 1976) and pregnancy (Gibori and Richards, 1978). This may reflect the marked differentiation involved in the transformation of a granulosa cell to a luteal cell.

Nevertheless, the decreases in LH receptor (FSH receptor and estradiol receptor) that occur during luteinization appear to be later events in the process of desensitization (Richards *et al.*, 1976; Richards, 1975). Other mechanisms are operating earlier to decrease the hormone response systems in granulosa cells. One of these is a decrease in hormone stimulation of cAMP production.

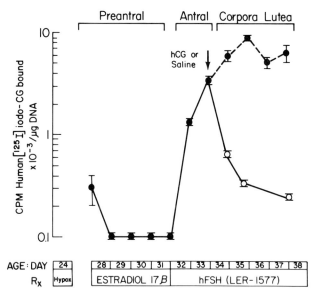

FIG. 19.   Effects of estradiol, follicle-stimulating hormone (FSH), and human chorionic gonadotropin (hCG) on follicular growth and luteinizing hormone (LH) receptor in the hypophysectomized
rat. When 5 IU of hCG were administered to estradiol-FSH-primed hypophysectomized rats, antral
follicles luteinized to form corpora lutea. This process was associated with a decrease in LH receptor
content in granulosa cells. This effect could be mimicked by administration of 10–100 μg of hFSH.
However, if lower doses of hFSH (1 μg at 12-hour intervals) are given, that is, if the regime used
during the induction of LH receptor is continued for more than 2 days, LH receptor content remains
high and follicles do not luteinize. From Richards *et al.* (1976) and Rao *et al.* (1978).

When ^{125}I-labeled hCG is administered intravenously to estradiol–FSH-
primed rats, ovarian uptake of hormone is rapid for 2 hours and continues for 8
hours (Fig. 20). cAMP accumulation in granulosa cells and residual ovarian
tissue is also rapid, but the peak is reached within 30 minutes and declines to near
basal values by 2 hours. Similar patterns are observed when FSH is given
(Richards *et al.*, 1979a). Thus, the ability of ovarian cells to produce cAMP *in
vivo* declines even though the cells continue to concentrate the hormone. Any
decrease in LH receptor occurs some 12–24 hours later, as does reduction of
adenylate cyclase activity (Hunzicker-Dunn and Birnbaumer, 1976).

Further, LH not only acts in preovulatory follicles to decrease the responsiveness of the LH response system, but LH also rapidly reduces the responsiveness
of follicles to FSH, a process of heterodesensitization (Jonassen and Richards,
1978). Thus, if FSH is administered intravenously to estradiol–FSH-treated
hypophysectomized rats which had received an intravenous challenge of hCG 2
hours previously, FSH cannot then stimulate a secondary rise in cAMP (Fig. 21).
FSH itself, however, can stimulate a marked response (Fig. 21).

The reverse experiment has given similar results. Granulosa cells of

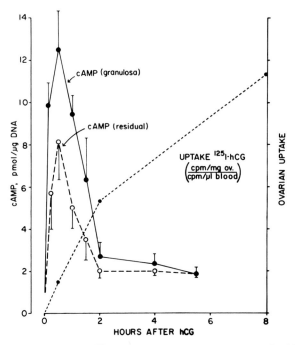

FIG. 20. Ovarian uptake of ^{125}I-labeled human chorionic gonadotropin (hCG) and cAMP accumulation by ovarian cells *in vivo*. Estradiol–FSH-treated hypophysectomized rats received 5 IU of hCG or an equivalent of 5 IU of ^{125}I-labeled hCG intravenously at $t = 0$. Ovarian uptake (cpm/mg of ovary), has been expressed relative to the amount of label in serum (cpm/μl of blood) to give an estimate of specific ovarian retention of the hormone. cAMP was measured by radioimmunoassay in expressed granulosa cells plus fluid or extracts of residual tissue (that ovarian tissue remaining after granulosa cells have been expressed). From Richards *et al.* (1978, 1979b).

estradiol–FSH-primed hypophysectomized rats stimulated first by an intravenous injection of FSH, cannot then respond to hCG or FSH at 2 hours to produce cAMP (Fig. 21). This "desensitization" of the granulosa cells to gonadotropins *in vivo* at 2 hours occurs in the absence of any demonstrable changes in available FSH or LH receptors. These results indicate that FSH and LH receptors are present on the same cells, within preovulatory follicles of estradiol–FSH-primed rats, that they may share an adenylate cyclase–cAMP response system, and that inactivation of one hormone response system is transmitted to the other hormone response system (Fig. 22). This may explain why, in estradiol- and FSH-primed rats, FSH and LH can each stimulate progesterone production, ovulation, luteinization, and the loss of both FSH and LH receptors (Rao *et al.*, 1977; Richards *et al.*, 1979a). In contrast, granulosa cells of hypophysectomized rats primed only with estradiol have FSH receptor and an FSH-responsive adenylate cyclase, but little or no LH receptor or LH-responsive adenylate cyclase (Figs. 17 and 22). In these rats heterodesensitization was *not* observed (Fig. 20). This provides further

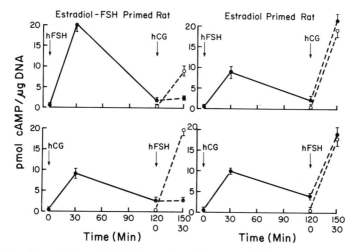

FIG. 21.   Accumulation of cAMP by ovarian cells *in vivo*. Either 5 μg of human follicle-stimulating hormone (hFSH) or 50 IU of human chorionic gonadotropin (hCG) was administered alone or sequentially to estradiol–FSH-treated hypophysectomized rats (left panels) or estradiol-treated rats (right panels). At 0, 30, 120, or 150 minutes, granulosa cells plus fluid were expressed from the ovaries; cAMP was measured by radioimmunoassay. From Jonassen and Richards (1978) and Richards *et al.* (1979a).

evidence to indicate that receptors for both FSH and LH must be present on the same cell in order for heterodesensitization to occur. Although the mechanisms are not yet understood, the rapid decrease in cAMP following hormone stimulation may provide cells with a rapid way to prevent prolonged stimulation. This may help explain why follicles on estrus, following the LH and prolonged FSH surge, seem more refractory to FSH and LH than those on any other day of the estrous cycle.

VII.   Summary

Most stages of follicular growth appear to proceed in the presence of basal concentrations of gonadotropins. Thus, during pregnancy antral follicles are

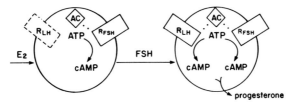

FIG. 22.   Schematic representation of receptor-response systems in granulosa cells. See text for explanation.

continuously present as new groups of follicles acquire antra and others undergo atresia (Fig. 5). The hormonal requirements for the continued growth of follicles to the preovulatory stage appear to involve small but significant increases in gonadotropins, leading to increased synthesis of follicular androgens *and* estradiol. Frederick Hisaw (1961) once wrote, "When estradiol attained the status of a hormone it was admitted into the endocrine hierarchy as queen of the realm of sexual reproduction." Perhaps he was right. For it appears to be estradiol which enhances the responsiveness of follicular granulosa cells to basal concentrations of gonadotropins, and thus enhances the appearance of granulosa cell LH receptor. Further it is the continued elevated production of estradiol from growing preovulatory follicles which ultimately signals the brain for the LH surge (Legan *et al.*, 1975). Thus, estradiol synchronizes the development of the preovulatory follicle with the LH surge.

But the follicle continues to maintain its mystique. We have begun to understand the complex cellular interactions that exist within the specialized microenvironment of each follicle. We have begun to gain insight into how steroid and pituitary protein hormones interact to cause ovarian cell differentiation. And we have begun to understand what events may be involved in atresia. Although the evolutionary significance of atresia may seem obvious enough, many of the processes involved in selecting 400 of nearly 2 million oocytes remain in an aura of mystery.

ACKNOWLEDGMENTS

Great appreciation is extended to the many people who contributed to these studies. Dr. J. L. Vaitukaitis and Dr. A. L. Steiner generously provided the antisera used in the cAMP radioimmunoassays. Dr. Leo E. Reichert, Jr. kindly provided the hormone preparations. Mark Byrne prepared the radioiodinated hormones and cAMP. Katherine Kersey performed all the cAMP, progesterone, and estradiol radioimmunoassays. Alice Rolfes validated the cAMP radioimmunoassay and characterized cAMP binding sites. Pat McKinnon and Ruth Lum helped prepare the manuscript. The research was supported in part by NIH-HD-09110, a Research Career Development Award, and a Program Project, NIH-HD-08333.

REFERENCES

Amsterdam, A., Koch, Y., Lieberman, M. E., and Lindner, H. R. (1975). *J. Cell Biol.* **67**, 894.
Bagavandoss, P., Richards, J. S., and Midgley, A. R., Jr. (1977). *Annu. Proc. Electron Microsc. Soc. Am., 35th*, p. 484.
Baker, T. G. (1963). *Proc. R. Soc. London Ser. B* **158**, 417.
Bates, R. W., and Schooley, J. P. (1942). *Endocrinology* **31**, 309.
Bradbury, J. T. (1961). *Endocrinology* **68**, 115.
Butcher, R. L., Collins, W. E., and Fugo, N. W. (1974). *Endocrinology* **94**, 1704.
Cheng, K. W. (1976). *J. Reprod. Fertil.* **48**, 129.
England, B. G., Niswender, G. D., and Midgley, A. R., Jr. (1974). *J. Clin. Endocrinol. Metab.* **38**, 42.

Erickson, G. F., and Hsueh, A. J. W. (1978). *Endocrinology* **102,** 1275.

Farookhi, R. (1978). *Annu. Meet. Soc. Study Reprod., 11th,* Abstr. 127, p. 61A.

Farookhi, R., and Richards, J. S. (1978). *Annu. Meet. Endocrine Soc., 60th,* Abstr. 343, p. 246.

Fortune, J. E., and Armstrong, D. T. (1977). *Endocrinology* **100,** 1341.

Gay, V. L., Midgley, A. R., Jr., and Niswender, G. D. (1970). *Fed. Proc., Fed. Am. Soc. Exp. Biol.* **29,** 1880.

Gibori, G., Keyes, P. L., and Richards, J. S. (1978). *Endocrinology* **103,** 162.

Goldenberg, R. L., Vaitukaitis, J. L., and Ross, G. T. (1972). *Endocrinology* **90,** 1492.

Greenwald, G. S. (1966). *Endocrinology* **79,** 572.

Harman, S. M., Louvet, J.-P., and Ross, G. T. (1975). *Endocrinology* **96,** 1145.

Hirshfield, A. N., and Midgley, A. R., Jr. (1978). *Biol. Reprod.* **19,** 597.

Hisaw, F. L. (1961). *Physiol. Reprod., Proc. 22nd Annu. Biol. Colloq.,* pp. 1–16.

Holt, J. A., Richards, J. S., Midgley, A. R., Jr., and Reichert, L. E., Jr. (1976). *Endocrinology* **98,** 1005.

Hunzicker-Dunn, M., and Birnbaumer, L. (1976). *Endocrinology* **99,** 198.

Ireland, J. J., and Richards, J. S. (1978a). *Endocrinology* **102,** 876.

Ireland, J. J., and Richards, J. S. (1978b). *Endocrinology* **102,** 1458.

Jonassen, J. A., and Richards, J. S. (1978). *Annu. Meet. Soc. Study Reprod., 11th,* Abstr. 129, p. 62A.

Lacy, L. R., Knudson, M. M., Williams, J. J., Richards, J. S., and Midgley, A. R., Jr. (1976). *Endocrinology* **99,** 929.

Legan, S. J., Coon, G. A., and Karsch, F. J. (1975). *Endocrinology* **96,** 1975.

Linkie, D. M., and Niswender, G. D. (1972). *Endocrinology* **90,** 632.

Lostroh, A. J., and Johnson, R. E. (1966). *Endocrinology* **79,** 991.

Louvet, J.-P., and Vaitukaitis, J. L. (1976). *Endocrinology* **99,** 758.

Makris, A., and Ryan, K. J. (1977). *Steroids* **29,** 65.

Midgley, A. R., Jr. (1973). *Adv. Exp. Med. Biol.* **36,** 365.

Moon, Y. S., Dorrington, J. H., and Armstrong, D. T. (1975). *Endocrinology* **97,** 244.

Morishige, W. K., and Rothchild, I. (1974). *Endocrinology* **95,** 260.

Payne, R. W., and Runser, R. H. (1958). *Endocrinology* **62,** 313.

Pedersen, T. (1970). *Acta Endocrinol.* **64,** 304.

Pedersen, T., and Peters, H. (1968). *J. Reprod. Fertil.* **17,** 555.

Pedersen, P., and Peters, H. (1971). *Fertil. Steril.* **22,** 42.

Pencharz, R. I. (1940). *Science* **91,** 554.

Rao, M. C., Richards, J. S., Midgley, A. R., Jr., and Reichert, L. E., Jr. (1977). *Endocrinology* **101,** 512.

Rao, M. C., Midgley, A. R., Jr., and Richards, J. S. (1978). *Cell* **14,** 71.

Rebar, R. W., Nakane, P. K., and Midgley, A. R., Jr. (1969). *Endocrinology* **84,** 1352.

Richards, J. S. (1975). *Endocrinology* **97,** 1174.

Richards, J. S., and Midgley, A. R., Jr. (1976). *Biol. Reprod.* **14,** 82.

Richards, J. S., and Williams, J. J. (1976). *Endocrinology* **99,** 1571.

Richards, J. S., Ireland, J. J., Rao, M. C., Bernath, G. A., Midgley, A. R., Jr., and Reichert, L. E., Jr. (1976). *Endocrinology* **99,** 1562.

Richards, J. S., Rao, M. C., and Ireland, J. J. (1978). *In* "Control of Ovulation" (D. B. Crighton, ed.), p. 197. Butterworth, London.

Richards, J. S., Uilenbroek, J. T. J., and Jonassen, J. A. (1979a). "Ovarian Follicular and Corpus Luteum Function" (C. P. Channing, J. Marsh, and W. D. Sadler, eds.), p. 11. Plenum, New York.

Richards, J. S., Jonassen, J. A., Rolfes, A. I., Kersey, K., and Reichert, L. E., Jr. (1979b). *Endocrinology* **104,** 765.

Schwartz, N. B. (1974). *Biol. Reprod.* **10,** 236.

Simpson, M. E., Evans, H. M., Fraenkel-Conrat, H. L., and Li, C. H. (1941). *Endocrinology* **28,** 37.

Smith, M. E., Freeman, M. E., and Neill, J. D. (1975). *Endocrinology* **96,** 219.

Uilenbroek, J. T. J. (1978). *Annu. Meet. Soc. Study Reprod., 11th,* Abstr. 167, p. 76A.

Uilenbroek, J. T. J., and Richards, J. S. (1979). *Biol. Reprod.* (in press).

Ullberg, S., and Bengtsson, G. (1963). *Acta Endocrinol. (Copenhagen)* **43,** 75.

Welschen, R. (1973). *Acta Endocrinol. (Copenhagen)* **72,** 137.

Welschen, R., and Dullaart, J. (1976). *J. Endocrinol.* **70,** 301.

Williams, P. C. (1945). *Nature (London)* **145,** 388.

Zeleznik, A. J., Midgley, A. R., Jr., and Reichert, L. E., Jr. (1974). *Endocrinology* **95,** 818.

DISCUSSION

F. Naftolin: Regarding the relevance of rat models to humans, one should consider which rat model is best. Since humans are largely monotocous and obligate functional corpus luteum formers, the pseudopregnant rat may be a closer model. A question to ask in this regard is whether the number of ovulations following pseudopregnancy is less than the number expected for that female rat during noncoital cycles.

J. Richards: The rate of atresia is not different during pregnancy or during cycles in the mouse and presumably the rat. The rate of atresia seems to be a fairly constant phenomenon. I think the relation to the human and whether one or more ova is ovulated is a genetic difference and involves both steroid-gonadotropin feedback mechanisms as well as the number of follicles that are actually growing at any given time. The first follicle that begins to produce some estradiol may suppress gonadotropin concentrations to amounts too low to stimulate growth of others. I mean, most follicles do not become preovulatory follicles because the gonadotropin levels are too low to signal the initiation of whatever event starts the process. The follicle or follicles that produce more estradiol become more sensitive and are able to tolerate the low levels of gonadotropin. Thus these follicles can proceed to the final stage whereas other follicles become atretic.

F. Naftolin: In addition to the descriptive material you have just given us, it seems that a correlation of your work with data on effects of follicle size and fluid content, such as developed by Channing, McNeilly, McNatty, and others, would be helpful. These may be in the exposure to hormones during the time interval of pseudopregnancy, something that controls follicle progression vs. atresia.

J. Richards: I think in the human the selection process may be due to the fact that it takes a longer period of time for any given follicle to reach the preovulatory stage. When you remove a corpus luteum or remove a follicle, it seems fairly consistent that there is a 12-day interval before another preovulatory follicle appears. Therefore, in the human follicular development is either much slower or else the time at which follicle growth is arrested in the presence of the low concentrations of gonadotropins occurs much earlier.

M. Saffran: In your eloquent paper you demonstrated a very important principle that hormones can exert their effects, even though their concentration is level, by a change in the number of receptors. I would like to add another example of that principle with the work of Mel Soloff, in our department, who has been looking at the number of uterine receptors for oxytocin in pregnancy. He has noted that, in the face of a constant level of oxytocin in the blood, there is a sharp increase in the number of receptors at the time of parturition, which may be the trigger for parturition. This work of his also adds a jewel to the crown of the queen of the hormones, estradiol, because of the number of receptors for oxytocin seems to be under the control of estradiol, giving another role to the increase in estradiol you showed during pregnancy.

B. Katzenellenbogen: I wonder whether you have done any studies in whole cells with your cAMP binding protein affinity label, and if so, what effect covalently labeling these binding proteins would have on the parameters you have been looking at.

J. Richards: No, I have not. These are very preliminary data, so I have not done such studies.

C. Robyn: Does prolactin affect follicular development in rats; especially does it affect LH receptor formation?

J. Richards: Does prolactin affect it in the granulosa cells?

C. Robyn: Yes.

J. Richards: No, there seems to be a switch in the regulation of granulosa cell LH receptor in a very interesting way. Granulosa cell induction of LH receptor requires estradiol and FSH. In rat corpora lutea LH receptor is under the control of prolactin. Therefore one has an interesting situation. The same gene may control LH receptor in the granulosa and luteal cell, or there may be two different genes. We know that FSH acts via cAMP. There is no evidence that prolactin acts via cAMP. One has to postulate either two different genes controlling an LH receptor or, perhaps, a common mechanism of FSH and prolactin action at some step beyond cAMP.

H. Friesen: Have you any rigorous evidence that gonadotropin receptors are rate limiting or regulatory in any of the systems that you have studied, and if so would you tell us which ones?

J. Richards: If there are no LH receptors in granulosa cells, the follicles do not ovulate. That is one thing to suggest that they are rate-limiting. The other evidence I have is that, as soon as an LH receptor appears, the ability of LH to stimulate cAMP in these cells is demonstrated. Further, we have data to suggest that as soon as there is some LH receptor present on granulosa cells, LH as well as FSH can act to induce the LH receptor. In that sense LH receptor also appears to be limiting for follicular growth.

K. Ahren: I think it was very wise of you to bring the interesting phenomenon of desensitization into your lecture. I have two questions related to this phenomenon. First, you related the loss of effect of the second gonadotropin injection to the loss of receptors in your system. There is, however, also an early phase in the desensitization phenomenon where there is a decreased sensitivity of the adenylate cyclase system itself, so that the adenylate cyclase cannot be fully simulated by fluoride. This has been seen in desensitization experiments with the corpus luteum. Have you seen the same phenomenon in your system with the estrogen-treated immature rat? Second, what is the significance of this desensitization? Do you have any suggestions as to where in your scheme of follicular development the desensitization phenomenon might have a physiological significance?

J. S. Richards: As to the physiological significance of desensitization, we do not know yet what a decrease in cAMP means to a cell—why or why not it might be important. However, in a number of systems that respond to cAMP by undergoing differentiation, a decrease in cAMP occurs. *Dictyostelium* (the slime mold) releases and responds to pulses of cAMP. Perhaps there is an evolutionary pattern that has been conserved. Now I do not know what that means to the cell. I do not know whether prolonged increases of cAMP would be detrimental or not; I do not think that that has been examined. So I think that the loss of LH receptor and the loss of FSH receptor are indications of differentiation, and that in order for events to continue a new hormone has to be introduced. Why that has happened remains to be learned.

K. Ahren: Have you studied the adenylyl cyclase activity in your system looking for the fluoride activation of the desensitization?

J. S. Richards: No, I have not.

S. L. Cohen: I am interested in your shift in the number of receptors. Have you given any thought to what happens to these receptors? Do you think there are proteolytic enzymes involved or that perhaps they are just covered up, possibly by the addition of amino acids or the splitting of a bond that would inactivate them?

J. S. Richards: "Loss" is kind of a funny word and misleading. Rather than thinking of a granulosa cell possessing X number of receptors on the membrane and visualizing that they are lost one after another, I think we should consider the notion that there is a constant turnover of receptors on the granulosa cell membrane. Therefore what we are seeing with a decrease in the number of receptors during granulosa cell luteinization is probably related to either a more rapid degradation rate or a decrease in the synthesis rate. I do not think it is just a modification of a membrane protein.

D. T. Armstrong: With regard to the question of desensitization, or inhibition of response to a hormone by prior exposure of the cell to that hormone, we have obtained results with granulosa cells from sheep follicles that appear to differ slightly from those you have presented for the rat. Our technique has been to culture whole follicles for 18 hours in the presence or the absence of gonadotropins, as indicated by pretreatment in Fig. A. The follicles are then separated into granulosa and thecal components, and the isolated components are tested for responsiveness to FSH or hCG by measuring cAMP production during short-term incubation. As shown in Fig. A, granulosa cells from small (1–3 mm in diameter) follicles respond to FSH, but not to hCG, with increased cAMP production, indicating the presence of FSH, but not LH, receptors. Pretreatment with FSH markedly reduced their responsiveness to FSH, without affecting their response to hCG. Pretreatment with hCG had no significant effect on their response to FSH. In contrast, granulosa cells from large (4–6 mm) follicles responded equally well to both FSH and hCG in the absence of pretreatment. Pretreatment with FSH depressed the responsiveness to both FSH and hCG, the depression being considerably greater for FSH than for hCG. Pretreatment with hCG completely eliminated the subsequent response to hCG, while causing only a mild reduction of response to FSH. Thus, when using cAMP production as an indication of functional gonadotropin receptors or granulosa cells, it is evident that "homologous" inhibition of response can be demonstrated for each of the gonadotropins, a considerably lesser degree of "heterologous" inhibition being seen.

Theca preparations from the same sheep follicles exhibit similar inhibition of responsiveness to hCG as a result of pretreatment with hCG, but not with FSH. When androgen production is used as

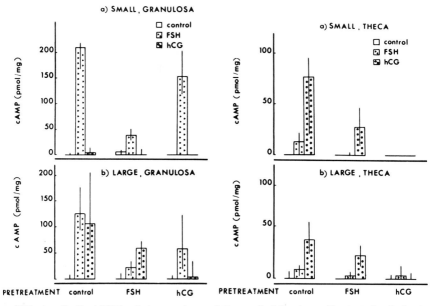

FIG. A.   Cyclic AMP levels in granulosa and theca cells following a 40-minute incubation in control media, or media containing NIH-FSH-S11, 5 μg/ml, or hCG, 5 IU/ml. Prior to separation into theca and granulosa fractions, the intact follicles were cultured for 18 hours in control media or in media containing FSH or hCG, as indicated by pretreatment. Data from T. J. Weiss, D. T. Armstrong, and R. F. Seamark, *Mol. Cell. Endocrinol.* (1979) (in press).

index of hCG responsiveness, we find a similar loss of responsiveness following pretreatment with hCG. Surprisingly, addition of exogenous cAMP (dibutyryl cAMP, 1 or 5 mM) will not overcome the inhibition of androgen caused by pretreatment with hCG. This suggests still another site of inhibition of hormone response. Thus it would appear that steroidogenic cells may have multiple sites of secondary inhibition of response to a hormone, following initial stimulation by that hormone: (1) "desensitization" at the binding site for the hormone at the level of the cell membrane, as you have shown for the rat granulosa cell; (2) decreased cAMP production, following prior stimulation by the hormone; and (3) refractoriness at a step subsequent to cAMP production—possibly at a key enzymic step in steroid biosynthesis. It would be interesting to know whether these are mutually independent mechanisms of inhibition, or, if not, which ones may be causes and which effects. Do you have any information or ideas concerning this question?

J. S. Richards: I think the whole problem of the activation of adenylate cyclase has yet to be resolved. One of the things we are looking at when we look at whole cells *in vivo* may be an activation of phosphodiesterase. In addition to phosphodiesterase there are other things that will modify adenylate cyclase activity. Activators and inhibitors of adenylate cyclase have been described in many systems. The desensitization to cAMP that you are seeing may reflect saturation of cAMP binding proteins and related protein kinase reactions. Once stimulated, the activated enzyme system may not be able to accomplish any more. Each enzyme system has a certain capacity to handle substrate or be modified. You may be seeing the saturation of an enzyme cascade system.

S. W. Spaulding: When you measured cAMP binding, did you also measure the ratio of saturated to unsaturated sites or else kinase activity ratio? When you say that there is a 20-fold increase in the binding protein and only a 2-fold increase in the cAMP, one might be able to detect a decrease in the activity ratio of the protein kinase rather than an increase.

J. S. Richards: I have looked at protein kinase activity and have not seen a parallel 20-fold increase in activity or even a shift of the ratios. One of the problems may be the protein kinase assay itself. Histone may not be the appropriate substrate. I believe that, in order to make any sense out of protein kinase assays, one has to find the right substrate, and I do not think that histone is the only one for all of them. Apparently in the granulosa cell it is not the ideal one, and it has been suggested that I try protamine. That may be a better substrate, and with protamine I may in fact see a shift in the ratio. Further I do not know that the cAMP binding is the regulatory subunit of protein kinase.

L. Birnbaumer: I should like to comment on your findings of desensitization to two hormones and on the semantics of the case. I feel that the word "desensitization" should be reserved to events that happen at the levels of receptor and translation of receptor activity, and that we should talk about "loss of responsiveness" or "refractoriness" when referring to changes in hormone action seen at the levels of cAMP accumulation or final steroid synthesis and secretion. The reasons that lead me to propose this go back to experiments performed in the late 1960s and early 1970s by Manganiello, Murad, and Vaughan [*J. Biol. Chem.* **246,** 2195 (1971)] in which they demonstrated a phenomenon very similar to the one shown by you in terms of obtaining refractoriness in response to one hormone not only to this hormone, but also to another hormone. In brief, what Manganiello *et al.* saw was that when isolated fat cells were incubated with epinephrine, cAMP levels first rose and then, within 10–15 minutes, fell back to control levels, and that addition of ACTH to such epinephrine-treated (and perhaps desensitized?) cells resulted in no response of cAMP accumulation, even though ACTH is known to affect the adenylyl cyclase of these cells through a receptor different from that with which epinephrine interacts. Two types of experiments showed that the lack of responsiveness to ACTH after epinephrine treatment is not one we would now call desensitization: (1) transfer of epinephrine-treated cells to a fresh medium immediately restored their capacity to respond by accumulating cAMP; (2) it was shown that the medium separated from epinephrine-treated cells contained a substance—not yet identified [Ho and Sutherland, *J. Biol. Chem.* **247,** 1071 (1972)]— that upon addition to fresh cells obliterated even their initial cAMP response to epinephrine. Thus, in these cells loss of responsiveness is something that appears to be happening at the metabolic level, very likely unrelated to down regulation of receptors and/or uncoupling of receptors from adenylyl cyclase, which would be events that we have come to associate with the term desensitization. Hence, my desire to establish a nomenclature leading to a little less confusion than that with which nature is already providing us.

With respect to rates of changes of responses as seen by determining cAMP levels, receptor levels, and hormone-responsive adenylyl cyclase, the differences you observe, in which the cAMP level response wanes before changes in cyclase response or receptor levels occur, can also be seen in other systems—the fat cells being one of them. The meaning and/or purpose for the existence of these differential rates of appearance of refractory states still escapes me.

J. S. Richards: We have stimulated *in vivo* and then taken these cells out and put them *in vitro*. *In vitro* they have *not* lost their responsiveness. I have been trying to look at something that is occurring *in vivo* in the follicle as opposed to what is occurring when the cells are isolated. The process of isolation disrupts the membrane/membrane contact. There may be a special theca–granulosa cell environment which is causing the desensitization *in vivo*.

L. Birnbaumer: I would like to add that, even in the same species, the rates at which refractoriness develops in hormonally induced increases of cAMP levels varies with the cell type. In fat cells refractoriness is established within 15 minutes, whereas in heart cells establishment of refractoriness takes up to 2 hours to develop.

A. L. Goodman: I would like to respond to a remark of Dr. Naftolin, comparing the rat and the primate. I think that there is more than a quantitative difference between monotocous and polytocous species. Our recent studies in the monkey indicate that there is a qualitative difference, as well, in species that elaborate only a single gamete. Namely, the monkey seems to use her two ovaries only one at a time in sequence. When we performed unilateral ovariectomy and removed the ovary opposite to the one that had the cyclic structure (the dominant follicle or the corpus luteum), the monkey did not seem to know that the ovary was gone. That is, no homeostatic or compensatory response was elicited by the removal of that ovary. That is in contrast to polytocous species in which both ovaries seem to be functional, and in which anatomical bilateral symmetry is reflected in functional bilateral symmetry. In the monkey at least, that does not seem to be obtained. A response to hemiovariectomy in the monkey was conditional on the surety of the ovary's dominant structure, the dominant follicle or the corpus luteum.

R. O. Greep: A question concerning transport: you show small box-labeled theca, a bigger one labeled granulosa, and you connect the two by an arrow that points from theca to granulosa. This means that the testosterone produced by the theca must somehow reach the aromatase produced by the granulosa. But hormones are transported through the bloodstream, and, there being no blood vessels in the granulosa at the time it is secreting estrogen, how do you visualize the transport of testosterone over into the granulosa? Perhaps the aromatase goes the other way—I think not. It seems strange to me that no one has investigated this matter, which is so amenable to resolution.

J. S. Richards: I think of it in terms of diffusion, but there may be a transport mechanism that allows testosterone to get into the granulosa cells. The only thing I can say is that if you incubate intact follicles with testosterone in the medium, testosterone becomes available to the intracellular aromatizing system of granulosa cells. I agree with you that it is important to know if and how steroids are transported actively across membranes.

K. J. Ryan: In response to that question, there are no tight junctions in the granulosa layer, so there is no blood–ovarian barrier like the blood–testis barrier. In point of fact, the follicular fluid is a transudate of the serum and has FSH, LH, prolactin, and other serum constituents in it. In the absence of the granulosa vascularity, a lot of things still get through into the granulosa and into the antral fluid. Dr. Armstrong, do you want to add to this? Do you have direct data?

D. T. Armstrong: The only direct data I have is the fact that follicular fluid does, of course, contain a great deal of testosterone. How the follicle transports this perhaps is not so important from the standpoint of availability of substrate for the granulosa cells, as the fact that clearly it does— there's ample evidence that it is there.

J. Vaitukaitis: I would like to respond to previous questions raised about the effect of desensitization on phosphodiesterase and cAMP-dependent protein kinase activities. In studies that Albertson and I reported [B. D. Albertson and J. L. Vaitukaitis, *Endocrinol. Res. Commun.* **4,** 295 (1977)], we observed no significant change in intracellular phosphodiesterase activity with desensitization. Moreover, after induction of desensitization, there was no significant change in cAMP-dependent protein kinase activity with subsequent hormonal stimulation *in vivo,* using the pseudopregnant rat model.

In a series of studies carried out over several years, we have usually observed a concomitant increase in the receptor number for LH or FSH, along with adenylyl cyclase and cAMP-dependent protein kinase activities and have never observed the kind of disparity that you suggest in terms of initial increase in cAMP binding protein, the regulatory subunit of cAMP-dependent protein kinase, followed by an increase in specific cell surface gonadotropin receptors.

J. S. Richards: First, I do not know if the increase in cAMP binding is protein kinase. Because I have not seen a 20-fold increase in protein kinase, I am not sure whether or not the binding protein reflects protein kinase. However, if I administer FSH intravenously, I can demonstrate an increase in binding within a 2–4-hour period, so it seems to be very rapid and does occur prior to a demonstrable increase in LH receptor.

RECENT PROGRESS IN HORMONE RESEARCH, VOL. 35

Studies on Atherogenesis and Corneal Transplantation Using Cultured Vascular and Corneal Endothelia

D. Gospodarowicz, I. Vlodavsky, G. Greenburg, J. Alvarado, L. K. Johnson, and J. Moran

Department of Medicine and Ophthalmology, Cancer Research Institute, University of California Medical Center, San Francisco, California

I. Introduction

Mesothelium and endothelium are tissues composed of a single monolayer of highly contact-inhibited and flattened cells. Although they are of deceptively simple morphological appearance, these tissues are located in places such that they perform vital functions and ensure the survival of the individual.

Endothelia are mostly, if not exclusively, found at the interface between a fluid and an organ, where they perform a barrier function. Such is the role of the vascular endothelium, which prevents the interaction of nucleated and anucleated cells (platelets) present in the bloodstream with the very thrombogenic subintimal surface. Endothelia can also be involved in active transport, being responsible for the creation and maintenance of the different ionic and macromolecular concentrations present in the extravascular and vascular spaces. Such functions are particularly well developed in the endothelia responsible for the blood–brain barrier and the blood–retina barrier, where macromolecules and inorganic compounds are present in different concentrations in the cerebrospinal fluid, the brain extravascular spaces, or in retinal tissues versus the intravascular fluid, all of which are direct results of the selective permeability barrier of the vascular endothelium.

Such a function is also well represented by the corneal endothelium, whose main function is to pump water out of the corneal stroma into the anterior chamber in order to maintain the corneal stroma in a state of deturgescence. Such a low water content is important in providing a nearly equal refractive index to the various proteins of the corneal stroma, and thus the endothelium is most important in maintaining the cornea clear. Local or total destruction of the corneal endothelium results in the formation of an edema and opacification of the cornea, which may lead to blood vessel invasions and loss of vision.

Due to their location, the physiological function of endothelial cells such as those present in the vascular systems has been particularly difficult to study *in vivo*. Therefore, in studies concerning the functions and property of those tissues, the *in vitro* approach involving the maintenance of these cells in tissue culture seems to be ideally suitable. However, limited success has been encountered in establishing long-term culture of endothelial cells possessing all the attributes of the endothelium *in vivo* and capable of being propagated *in vitro* for long-term periods.

In this regard, we tried using recently purified mitogens, such as fibroblast growth factor (FGF) or epidermal growth factor (EGF), to see if it is possible to develop cultures of vascular or corneal endothelial cells capable of dividing with a high mitotic index when maintained at a low or clonal density, and exhibiting upon reaching confluency the morphologic and metabolic activity characteristics of those tissues *in vivo* as expressed by the preservation of their original cellular shape, polarity, and their ability to produce a basement membrane. Ultimately, the demonstration that endothelial cells grown and maintained in tissue culture have not lost their original function is found in the observation that, when these cells are transplanted back to their original *in vivo* environment, they are still capable of resuming their normal function. For the corneal endothelium, it is that of the maintenance of the corneal transparency, while for the vascular endothelium, it involves among other functions, the prevention of thrombus formation.

II. Vascular Endothelial Cells

Endothelial cells constitute the inner lining of the blood vascular system. Because of their location at the interface between blood and tissue, they are the chief element involved in the permeability of blood vessels (Aursnes, 1974; Stemerman and Spaet, 1972). Abnormalities of the endothelial cell structure and function are prominent in the pathology of a number of diseases of the blood vessel wall, such as thromboangitis and microangiopathy (Bell, 1954). Since the continuity of the vascular endothelium is essential for the survival of the organism, the elucidation of the factors involved in the endothelial cell's survival and proliferation is important. This can best be examined in tissue culture.

Two observations have led us to examine the effect of FGF on vascular endothelial cells: (1) FGF is a potent mitogen for BALB/c 3T3 cells (Gospodarowicz, 1975; Gospodarowicz *et al.*, 1976a; Gospodarowicz and Moran, 1974, 1977). Although these cells are commonly referred to as fibroblasts, their morphology and the fact that they can produce vasoformative sarcomas *in vivo* suggest that they are derived from vascular endothelium (Boone *et al.*, 1976). FGF was first named fibroblast growth factor to emphasize its effect upon fibroblasts; subsequent studies, however, have shown that it is a mitogen for a wide variety of mesoderm-derived cells (Gospodarowicz *et al.*, 1976a, 1977b; 1978a, c,d,f,g; Gospodarowicz and Moran, 1977; Gospodarowicz and Zetter, 1977).

Since the vascular endothelium is derived from the embryonic mesoderm, one would expect endothelial cells also to be responsive to FGF.

We have examined the possibility that FGF is a survival factor as well as a mitogen for cultured vascular endothelial cells. These studies have demonstrated that FGF can be used to maintain and grow endothelial cells in tissue culture for prolonged periods (Gospodarowicz, 1976; Gospodarowicz et al., 1976a, 1977b,c, 1978a–d,f,g). Our first attempt to look at the effect of FGF on the proliferation of vascular endothelium started with bovine tissue. Bovine tissues, unlike human ones, are readily available, and with their use the characteristics of endothelial cells derived from different vascular territories, as well as from donors varying in age from fetal to adult, can easily be examined. Since we had intended to study at a later time the effect of FGF on capillary proliferation in vivo, and since capillaries originate from endothelial cells, we first examined the comparative mitogenic effects of FGF and EGF on endothelial cell cultures obtained from the bovine aorta. When primary cultures are started from bovine aortic endothelium using relatively few cells (i.e., 30 cells/cm²), the formation of a monolayer is dependent on the presence of FGF in the culture medium. In 10% calf serum alone, small colonies are formed from cell aggregates during the first few days, but these cells are apparently unhealthy, becoming heavily vacuolated, and dying within a few days. In contrast, when FGF was added, the cells proliferated vigorously and formed a monolayer (Gospodarowicz et al., 1976b, 1977c, 1978b) (Fig. 1).

These results with the bovine endothelium demonstrate that FGF is a mitogenic agent for bovine vascular endothelial cells and can be used to develop clonal cell lines, since it acts as a survival as well as a mitogenic agent when those cells are maintained at extremely low density (1 cell/cm²). Endothelial cells from similar fetal or adult vascular territories respond to FGF in the same way. Moreover, we did not observe any significant differences between cells from venous endothelium and those from aortic endothelium in their response to FGF (Gospodarowicz et al., 1978b,d). Since FGF stimulates both primary cultures and subcultures of endothelial cells in a similar way, it is unlikely that we are selecting a cell type responsive to FGF during the cloning procedure. Moreover, we have been able to develop cloned cell lines in tissue culture derived from fetal heart, umbilical vein, brain capillaries, as well as from the fetal and adult aortic arch. The adult bovine aortic arch endothelial cell line has been passaged weekly with a split ratio of 1:64 for over 65 weeks (390 generations) without loss of differentiated functions as expressed by the presence of AHF-antigen (Gospodarowicz et al., 1978b,d) and cell surface polarity. Karyotyping of the cultures revealed no chromosomal abnormality, and the chromosome number ($2n = 60$) was that of Bos taurus. Metabolic labeling of the cultures with ³⁵S methionine followed by double electrophoresis have shown that cultures at confluency were making the same proteins when analyzed either at a low or a

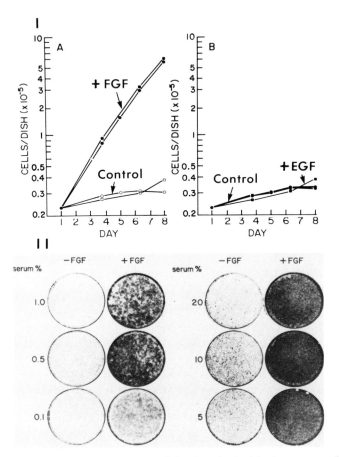

FIG. 1. (I) Growth rate of bovine endothelial cells maintained in the presence of fibroblast (FGF) or epidermal (EGF) growth factor with or without thrombin. Vascular endothelial cells derived from the adult aortic arch (56 passages, 336 generations) were plated at 740 cells/cm² in 6-cm dishes in DME supplemented with 10% calf serum. (A) The cells were maintained in the presence of FGF alone (●), FGF + thrombin (■), thrombin alone (□), or without addition (○). FGF was added every other day at a final concentration of 100 ng/ml, and thrombin every 4 days at a final concentration of 2 μg/ml. (B) Same as (A) but with EGF (100 ng/ml) instead of FGF. (II) Correlation between FGF and the serum concentration on the growth of fetal heart endothelial cell cultures. Fetal heart endothelial cells (15 passages, 125 generations) were plated at 14,000 cells per 6-cm dish and maintained in the presence or in the absence of FGF at 100 ng/ml with different concentrations of calf serum ranging from 0.1% to 20%. FGF (100 μg/ml) was added every other day and the medium was changed every 4 days; 8 days later, the plates were washed, fixed with formalin, and stained with 0.1% Giemsa.

high passage number. Furthermore, the proteins labeling pattern was strikingly different from that of vascular smooth muscles (Fig. 2), indicating that no contamination by vascular smooth muscles was present. When the vascular endothelial cells reached confluency, the cultures exhibited a morphological appearance similar to that observed *in vivo* (Figs. 3 and 4). This is concomitant with the formation of a basement membrane similar to that observed *in vivo* (Fig. 4). Particularly impressive was the ability to stain 1-month-old cultures when exposed to Alizarin Red, a stain for calcium deposits. This is further indication of the great degree of similarity between the basement membrane synthesized *in vitro* and *in vivo* (Fig. 4).

Each of the cell lines is used as a tool to study different properties of the vascular endothelium. The fetal heart endothelial cell, which shows an absolute requirement for FGF and responds to it even when the cells are maintained in serum concentrations as low as 0.1%, is used for the study of metabolic agents that interact with the endothelium but have a short half-life in high serum concentration. The adult bovine aortic endothelial cell line, which responds to FGF only in high serum concentration (10%) and does not proliferate at all in the absence of FGF, has been used to study the release of mitogens from transformed cells. In such experiments, the growth of low-density cultures of endothelial cells is monitored in the presence and in the absence of irradiated tumor cells (Birdwell *et al.*, 1977). Finally, the fetal aortic endothelial and calf aortic endothelial cell lines can be used to study the synthesis and secretion of components of the basement membrane, such as collagen and fibronectin (Birdwell *et al.*, 1978; Gospodarowicz *et al.*, 1978c–f, 1979c).

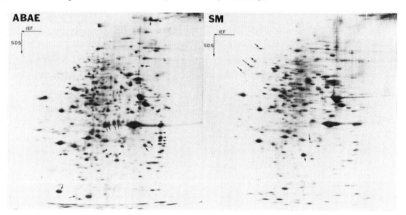

FIG. 2. Two-dimensional electrophoresis of proteins synthesized by vascular smooth muscle (SM) and endothelial cells (ABAE). Confluent cultures were exposed to [^{35}S]methionine (400 μCi/ml) for 30 minutes, washed with phosphate-buffered saline, and lysed directly with isoelectric focusing sample buffer (9.5 M urea, 2% NP-40, 2% ampholytes, pH 3.5–10, 5% β-mercaptoethanol). Then 500,000 cpm were subjected to two-dimensional electrophoresis according to O'Farrell *et al.* (1977). Arrows mark differences between the two autoradiograms. Exposure time was 10 days.

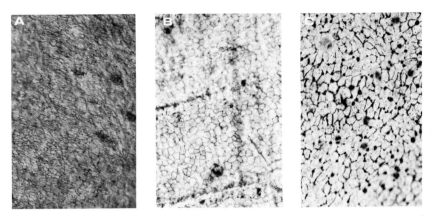

FIG. 3. Comparison of the morphological appearance of the vascular endothelium present in the rabbit vena cava (A), the aortic arch (B), and the vascular endothelium grown *in vitro* (C). After the removal of the rabbit vena cava and aortic arch by means of dissection, these tissues were cut to expose the endothelium. The tissues were then washed with 0.9% NaCl and stained with Alizarin Red. Owing to the contraction of the vena cava, the vascular endothelial cells look more elongated and packed than *in vivo*. Culture of vascular endothelial cells maintained at confluency for 3 weeks were submitted to the same treatment. Pictures were taken with a bright-field photomicroscope (A, × 28; B, × 70; C, × 70).

A. CULTURED VASCULAR ENDOTHELIAL CELLS PRESERVE THEIR CELL SURFACE POLARITY

The vascular endothelium is characterized *in vivo* by a polarity of cell's surfaces. Its apical surface exposed to the bloodstream is a nonthrombogenic surface whereas the basal surface produces and is in contact with a highly thrombogenic basement membrane. Vascular endothelial cells maintained in tissue culture have been examined to see if they will exhibit the same cell surface polarity as observed *in vivo*.

1. Preservation of the Nonthrombogenic Apical Surface by Vascular Endothelium in Vitro

When confluent cultures of vascular and smooth muscle cells are exposed to human platelets, it is found that, after the cultures have been washed, aggregated platelets remain tightly bound to the apical surface of smooth muscle cells (Fig. 5F), whereas similarly treated vascular endothelial cells show no visible platelets attached to its apical surface (Fig. 5A). In order to examine the basal surface, the cells were first removed by treating them with a nonionic detergent. When the remaining extracellular matrix at the base of vascular endothelial cells is exposed to platelets, they are seen to aggregate with each other and become tenaciously adherent to this matrix.

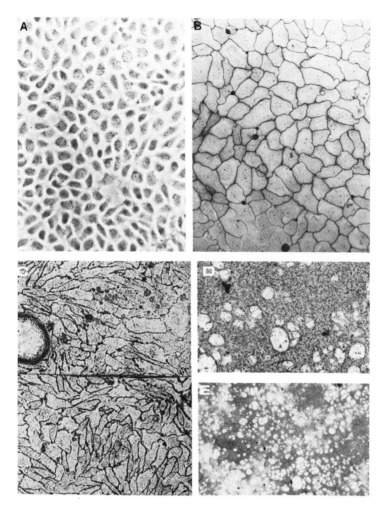

FIG. 4. Appearance of adult bovine aortic endothelial cells maintained in tissue culture in the presence of fibroblast growth factor (FGF). (A) Monolayer of endothelial cells maintained in the presence of 10% calf serum and 100 ng of FGF per milliliter for a week. The cells are polygonal, closely apposed, and with an indistinct border (phase contrast, × 128). (B) Same monolayer as in (A) but stained with silver nitrate to show the cell borders (× 187). The cells showed the same organization as did preparations of endothelium stained *in situ*. (C) Adult bovine aortic endothelial (ABAE) cells maintained in culture for 3 weeks. The cultures were then exposed to Alizarin Red. The intercellular border stained bright red (× 128). (D) ABAE cells were maintained in culture for a month and then exposed to 0.5% Triton X in phosphate-buffered saline. After the removal of the cell monolayer, the basement membrane was stained with Alizarin Red (× 85). (E) Same as (D), but × 34; the basement membrane stained bright red.

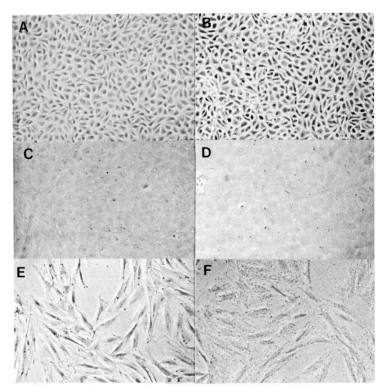

FIG. 5. Adherence of platelets to cultured corneal or vascular endothelial cells and vascular smooth muscle culture. Platelets (2×10^8 in 1 ml of culture medium containing 0.25% bovine serum albumin) were incubated with vascular (A), or corneal (C) endothelial cells, and vascular smooth muscle cells (E) for 30 minutes at 37°C. The cultures were then washed 10 times, and observed under phase contrast microscopy ($\times$ 150). No visible platelets attached to the upper surface of the vascular (B) or corneal (D) endothelial cells. In contrast, smooth muscle cells (F) have aggregated platelets bound tightly to their upper surface.

In order to determine whether the attached platelets can release their content, [^{14}C]serotonin-loaded platelets were incubated with vascular endothelial cells or vascular smooth muscle. The culture medium containing unattached platelets and any serotonin that might have been released during the binding period was then washed away, and the platelets were collected by centrifugation. Subsequently, the cells and attached platelets were washed and then hydrolyzed in 0.2 N NaOH. The cells, platelets, and platelet-free supernatants were counted separately to determine the distribution of [^{14}C]serotonin. As shown in Table I, vascular endothelial cells bind very few platelets (less than 0.5 platelet per cell), whereas smooth muscle cells bind platelets all over their cell surfaces, in which case [^{14}C]serotonin was released. This stands in contrast to the cultures of vascular

TABLE I

Binding of Platelets to Vascular and Corneal Endothelial Cells and
Vascular Smooth Muscle Cells[a]

Cell types	Cell-bound platelets (cpm [^{14}C]serotonin 10^6/cells)	Released [^{14}C]serotonin (cpm/10^6 cells)
Vascular endothelial cells	295	3290
Corneal endothelial cells	362	3290
Vascular smooth muscle cells	28500	75540
No cells	—	3015

[a] Platelets (2×10^8; 109,460 cpm) were incubated with confluent cell cultures for 30 minutes at 37°C. The binding of platelets to cells and the release of [^{14}C]serotonin from platelets were determined as described in the text. Treatment of 2×10^8 platelets with 10 units of human thrombin per milliliter caused release of 83,760 cpm of [^{14}C]serotonin.

and corneal endothelial cells, where no serotonin release was observed other than that which was spontaneously released by platelets incubated under the same conditions but in the absence of cells. The lack of serotonin release by platelets exposed to the apical surface of vascular endothelial cells was not due to their inability to release their contents, since when exposed to thrombin (10 IU/ml), 80–90% of the counts were released in the culture medium.

Vascular endothelial cell cultures, when maintained in the presence of arachidonic acid, were also capable of making prostacyclins (J. Bruno, private communication). This prostaglandin is a potent inhibitor of platelet aggregation and is known to be made *in vitro* in great quantities by the vascular endothelium (Gryglewski *et al.*, 1976). Therefore, *in vitro* as *in vivo*, the apical cell surface of the vascular endothelium is a nonthrombogenic surface and the cultured cells are capable of synthesizing prostacyclins, which have been shown by others (Weksler *et al.*, 1977) to inhibit platelet aggregation.

2. Basement Membrane Synthesis by the Basal Cell Surface of Vascular Endothelium in Vitro

As soon as vascular endothelial cells reach confluency and adopt the configuration of a highly contact-inhibited cell monolayer (Fig. 4), they start to secrete enormous amounts of an amorphous extracellular material which is localized on the basal part of the cells. As shown in Fig. 6, if one treats the vascular endothelial cell monolayer with a nonionic detergent, the monolayer is selectively removed and an amorphous matrix is left over underneath it (Fig. 6) (Gospodarowicz *et al.*, 1978e).

When the nature of the material coating the dishes was analyzed, it was found to consist, among other macromolecules, of collagen type IV. The basement

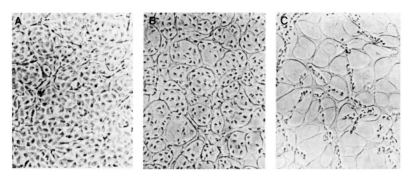

FIG. 6. Configuration of a monolayer of the bovine calf aortic arch endothelial cell culture maintained for a long period of time (phase contrast, × 116). Bovine calf aortic arch endothelial cell cultures were seeded at 100,000 cells per 10-cm dish in the presence of DME supplemented with 10% calf serum and 100 ng of fibroblast growth factor (FGF) per milliliter. When the cells reached confluence, the medium was changed to DME supplemented with 10% calf serum and 1 ng of FGF per milliliter. Two weeks later, an amorphous material appeared under the monolayer (A). When the monolayer was treated with phosphate-buffered saline containing 0.1% Triton X, the monolayer was dissolved and the nuclei of the cells as well as the basement membrane were left behind (B, C).

membrane produced *in vitro* was further analyzed using an indirect immunofluorescence technique for the presence of fibronectin (Birdwell *et al.*, 1978), a cell surface glycoprotein which has been shown to be related to cell adhesion and morphology (Yamada *et al.*, 1976; Ali *et al.*, 1977), and which has been shown to be present *in vivo* in the basement membrane of different tissues (Stenman and Vaheri, 1978). The result of such studies (Fig. 7) demonstrates that fibronectin coats, in an unparallel amount, the basement membrane produced by confluent vascular endothelial cells (Birdwell *et al.*, 1978; Gospodarowicz *et al.*, 1978e). Therefore, fibronectin can be considered as being one of the major constituents of the basement membrane synthesized *in vitro* by these cells. Previous studies done with other cell types, such as fibroblast or myoblast, maintained at high density, have shown that fibronectin could be localized in the areas of cell–cell contacts, as well as on the apical cell surface. In contrast, in confluent cultures of vascular endothelial cells, fibronectin can be detected only in the basal part of the cells, and in association with the basement membrane. No fibronectin can be detected either in the area of cell–cell contact or on the apical cell surface (Fig. 8). There is therefore, a unique polarity in the production of fibronectin by vascular endothelial cells when they reach confluency, since it will accumulate only in association with the basement membrane and will be conspicuously absent from the apical surface of the monolayer.

It thus seems that the vascular endothelium produces fibronectin in large quantities and with a unique polarity. One might then well wonder why vascular endothelial cells produce so much fibronectin. Since the vascular endothelium grows as a single layer of highly contact-inhibited and flattened cells; one could

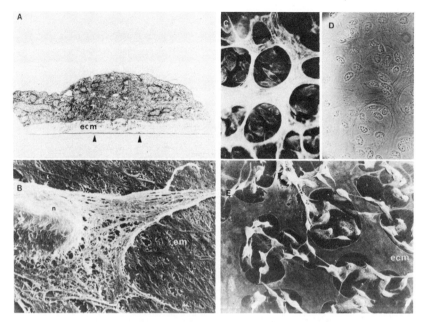

FIG. 7. Electron micrograph of vascular endothelial cells and immunofluorescence of LETS antigen. A clone of adult bovine aortic endothelial (ABAE) cell cultures in their 20th passage (107 generations) was used. (A) and (B) Electron micrographs of 2-week-old ABAE cultures. (A) Transmission electron micrograph of a thin section of an ABAE monolayer cut perpendicularly to the monolayer, which shows the extracellular matrix (ecm) underneath the cells. The dark line (arrowheads) along the bottom of the micrographs is the plastic substrate of the tissue culture dish. (B) Scanning electron micrograph of a 2-week-old ABAE culture treated briefly with 0.5% Triton X-100. This micrograph shows a single ABAE cytoskeleton (cs) and attached nucleus (n) stretched over the extracellular matrix (em). (C) and (D) Indirect immunofluorescence of LETS on ABAE cultures. (C) Staining of 2-week-old culture following Triton X-100 treatment shows areas of fluorescence that correspond to the basement membrane. (D) Phase-contrast micrograph of the same field as in (C). (E) Scanning electron micrograph of an ABAE monolayer treated very briefly with 0.5% Triton X-100. The extracellular matrix (ecm) is quite apparent, and many ABAE cytoskeletons are still attached to the substrate.

suggest that these cells would produce much fibronectin in order to help maintain their flattened and contact-inhibited morphology. Furthermore, the endothelial cells that form the inner lining of the arteries may need to secrete great amounts of fibronectin in order to stay attached to the basal lamina. If one considers the turbulence, the pressure variations, and the speed of the blood flow in the aortic arch, there are few cell types that could form a monolayer and remain attached to the basement membrane unless they developed a special means to stick to it. Such a means could be the production of fibronectin, which primarily functions to enforce cell adhesion. The presence of large quantities of fibronectin in the vascular endothelium could also provide a clue as to the site of synthesis of the

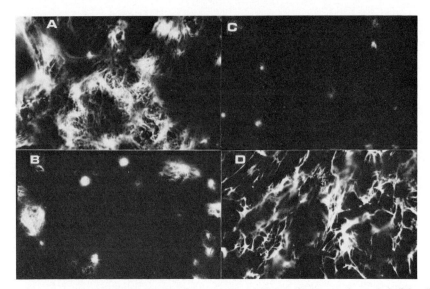

FIG. 8. Indirect immunofluorescence localization of fibronectin in vascular endothelial cell cultures. (A) Staining of a sparse culture showing the distribution of fibronectin on the apical (top) cell surfaces, and concentrated in the areas corresponding to cell junctions. (B) Staining of a subconfluent culture showing the fibronectin localized in areas restricted to the intercellular junctions. (C) Staining of a confluent culture (1–4 weeks) with little or no detectable fluorescence. (D) Staining of a confluent culture of vascular endothelium maintained in the absence of fibroblast growth factor and which has lost its contact-inhibited properties.

cold-insoluble globulin (CIG), a protein found in plasma in concentrations in excess of 300 μg/ml, and which is antigenically identical to fibronectin (Ruoslahti and Vaheri, 1975). Since the vascular endothelium, in order to stay attached to the basal lamina, makes great amounts of fibronectin, it makes sense that part of it will be shed into the bloodstream, where it will appear as CIG. It might, therefore, be concluded that, because of their situation (inner layer of the arteries and veins), vascular endothelial cells could be called upon to make a major contribution to the production of the fibronectin found in the basement membrane of the blood vessels as well as that found in the plasma as CIG. Since it is localized in the basal cell surface as well as the basement membrane, it can act as a glue that will make the vascular endothelium adhere firmly to its basement membrane (Zetter et al., 1978).

3. The Relationship between the Formation of the Basement Membrane and the Phenotypic Expression of the Vascular Endothelium

The ability of the vascular endothelial cells to make their basement membrane is in all likelihood involved in the expression of the differentiated status by these cells once they reach confluency. In this regard, it is important to note that the differentiation of various cell types maintained *in vitro* has been directly related to their ability to make a basement membrane upon reaching confluency. This is the stage at which, since the cells no longer divide, differentiated functions can be expressed (Gospodarowicz *et al.*, 1978e, 1979c). While vascular or corneal endothelial cells that make their own basement membrane *in vitro* exhibit all the characteristics of differentiation at confluency, cell types, such as epidermal or epithelial cells, that do not make their own basement membrane *in vitro*, do not express their phenotypic expression unless they are artificially provided with a basement membrane when maintained, for example, on either collagen-coated dishes or feeder layers of 3T3 (Liu and Karasek, 1978; Sun and Green, 1978; Rheinwald and Green, 1977; Gospodarowicz *et al.*, 1978e, 1979c).

Since vascular endothelium maintained *in vitro* can keep its ability to make a basement membrane similar in structure and composition (collagen type IV and fibronectin) to that made *in vivo*, it is not so surprising, then, that these cells should behave *in vitro* as they do *in vivo*, since they are resting on the same basement membrane in both conditions. Therefore, the environment is similar in both conditions, the cells being exposed on one side to the plasma or the tissue culture medium while being attached by their basal surface to the basement membrane coating the subintima *in vivo* or the plastic dishes *in vitro*.

4. The Role of Cell Surface Proteins in Dictating the Cellular Shape and the Morphological Appearance of the Vascular Endothelium: The Appearance of Fibronectin and CSP-60 as a Function of Cell Density

A partial restoration of the normal morphology, adhesiveness, and contact inhibition of cell migration can be induced by adding fibronectin to a transformed culture. It has therefore, been suggested that fibronectin is involved in the control of cell morphology (Yamada *et al.*, 1976; Ali *et al.*, 1977). However, in the case of vascular endothelial cells, fibronectin has no effect on their cellular organization, since its presence is neither correlated nor required for the formation of a monolayer composed of closely apposed and nonoverlapping cuboidal cells (Vlodavsky *et al.*, 1979b; Gospodarowicz *et al.*, 1979c). This role can, however, be assigned to a major cell surface protein of 60,000 MW, when unreduced, and 30,000 MW when reduced. This cell surface protein (CSP) is referred to as CSP-60. Under various normal and experimental conditions, CSP-60 showed a strict correlation with the establishment of a cell monolayer composed of highly packed, flattened, and nonoverlapping cuboidal or hexagonal cells. CSP-60 is present at confluence only in highly organized tissues, such as the vascular or corneal endothelium (Vlodavsky *et al.*, 1979b) but not in cell types, such as vascular smooth muscle cells, that grow in three dimensions.

The lactoperoxidase-catalyzed iodination of cell surface proteins was used to study how the appearance of fibronectin and CSP-60 in vascular endothelial and smooth muscle cells can be modulated by changes in the cell density and organization in culture. In particular, we have looked for changes in the pattern of surface proteins associated with disorganization and reorganization of a highly confluent endothelial cell monolayer. Exposure to either urea, EDTA, or trypsin was used to dissociate the cell monolayer into single round cells that remained attached to the substratum (Fig. 9d). The cells were then washed free of the

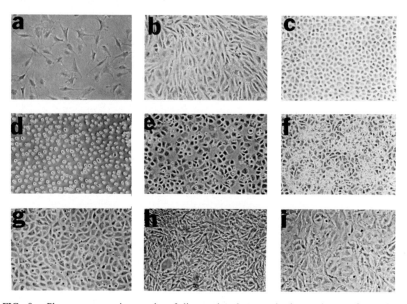

FIG. 9.   Phase-contrast micrographs of disrupted and reorganized monolayers of vascular endothelial cells. (a) Sparse, actively growing culture, 2 days after seeding. Single, well-spread, and elongated cells. (b) Subconfluent culture 5 days after seeding. Cells are in contact with each other but not yet organized into a two-dimensional monolayer. (c) A confluent, endothelial monolayer. Highly organized, flattened, and closely apposed cells that no longer proliferate. (d) A confluent monolayer treated with urea (1 M in DME, 1 hour, 37°C). The monolayer is disrupted into single round cells that remain attached to the tissue culture dish. (e) Urea-treated cells at an intermediate stage of reorganization 1 hour after washing the urea out and incubating it under growth conditions; cells in contact with each other are already flattened and closely apposed. (f) Urea-treated cells seeded at a high density and observed after 6 hours. Cells attached to the tissue culture dish adopt the configuration of a perfect cell monolayer. The excess of cells remain round, primarily floating, and do not adhere or grow on top of the attached cells. (g) Urea-treated cells seeded at a high cell density and observed 24 hours later after washing the excess cells. The cultures adopt the characteristic, two-dimensional organization. (h) Cells from a sparse culture seeded at a high density and observed 48 hours later. A multilayer culture composed of elongated cells that spread and grow on top of each other as well as in various directions. A similar morphology was adopted by the cultures described under (e), (f), (g), and (h) when calf serum free of fibronectin, rather then normal calf serum, was used. (i) Cells maintained in the absence of fibroblast growth factor (FGF). Endothelial cells after three passages in the absence of FGF lose their contact inhibition property and grow in various directions and on top of each other.

disruptive agent and allowed to reorganize by a 3–24-hour incubation in growth medium with or without reseeding the cells at a high density (Fig. 9g). Electrophoresis analysis of the various iodinated samples has demonstrated that the adoption of a perfect cell monolayer configuration after removal of the disorganizing agent (Fig. 9) was accomplished without reappearance of the fibronectin that was partially or completely removed from the cell surface by either trypsin, EDTA, or urea (Fig. 10). Similar results were obtained by using fibronectin-free serum rather than normal calf serum. In contrast, there was, with no exception, a clear correlation between the formation of a confluent cell monolayer (Fig. 9c) and the presence of a 60 K molecular weight surface component that we have called CSP-60. Following disorganization of a confluent endothelial cell monolayer by exposure to either urea, trypsin, or EDTA, CSP-60 became no longer susceptible to iodination by lactoperoxidase when the cells detached from each other (Fig. 10-1, lane E, and Fig. 10-2, lane B). In contrast, the adoption of a highly organized configuration by washing away the disruptive agents and by either incubating the cells for about 3 hours under growth conditions (Fig. 10-1, lanes B and F, and Fig. 10-2, lane C) or by reseeding the cells at a high cell density (Fig. 10-1, lanes C and G, and Fig. 10-2, lane D), was in each case associated with the reappearance of CSP-60 as a major cell surface protein accessible to the lactoperoxidase-catalyzed iodination. CSP-60 was, however, largely or almost completely missing when the cells of a disorganized monolayer were reseeded as single cells at a low density (Fig. 10-1, lanes D and H, and Fig. 10-2, lane E) and when cells from sparse cultures were pooled and reseeded at a high density (Fig. 9h). Both sparse and confluent cultures of vascular smooth muscle cells, which grow in multiple layers at confluence, contained large amounts of fibronectin (Fig. 11, lanes G and H). Fibronectin was also present as a major band in subconfluent cultures of vascular endothelial cells that did not yet adopt the typical, two-dimensional, monolayer configuration (Fig. 9b). In contrast, neither of these cultures showed the 60 K component, which is characteristic only of a highly confluent endothelial monolayer (Fig. 11). CSP-60, but not fibronectin, was also missing in vascular endothelial cells that were no longer maintained in the presence of FGF and had therefore lost their contact-inhibition property (Fig. 9i). In contrast, it was present (albeit to a lower extent than in confluent vascular endothelial cells) in samples derived from contact-inhibited, but not from sparse, cultures of corneal endothelial cells.

These results indicate that CSP-60, rather than fibronectin, correlates with the events that lead to the formation of a highly confluent and organized cell monolayer. CSP-60 was, however, not required for substrate adhesion and flattening of cells, since it was missing from cells that adhere and spread perfectly well after first dissociating a confluent monolayer and seeding the cells at a low density. In order to further characterize CSP-60, we have looked for its electrophoresis mobility before and after reduction with DTT. The results (Figs.

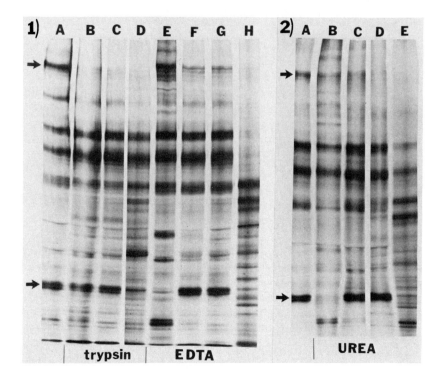

FIG. 10.   Appearance of a cell surface protein (CSP-60) and fibronectin after disruption and reorganization of a highly contact-inhibited endothelial cell monolayer. Confluent, endothelial cell monolayers were treated with either trypsin (0.05% Gibco, 3 minutes, 37°C), EDTA (0.03% in Ca^{2+}-, Mg^{2+}-free PBS, 30 minutes, 37°C), or urea (1 M in DME, 1 hour, 37°C) to disrupt cell-to-cell contacts. The disruptive agent was then washed out, and the cells were allowed to reorganize on the same plate or after reseeding at a high or low cell density. Similar results were obtained by using serum from which the fibronectin had been removed. Disrupted and reorganized cultures were labeled with ^{131}I by the lactoperoxidase/glucose oxidase technique, lysed, and analyzed after reduction with DTT, by a gradient (6 to 16%) polyacrylamide slab gel electrophoresis and autoradiography. (1) Confluent cell monolayers disrupted by trypsin or EDTA. (A) Confluent, endothelial cell monolayer. Both fibronectin (230 K) and CSP-60 (60 K) are present as major bands (arrows). (B) Confluent culture that was first trypsinized into single cells and then washed and incubated in the same plate for 12 hours under growth conditions to readopt its original monolayer organization. Fibronectin is largely missing, whereas CSP-60 appears as a major band. (C) Cells 12 hours after trypsinization and seeding at a high density. The cells fully adopt a monolayer organization and show CSP-60, but little or no fibronectin. (D) Cells 12 hours after trypsinization and seeding at a low density. Both fibronectin and CSP-60 are largely missing. (E) Confluent culture treated with EDTA and labeled after disruption when the cells detached from each other. CSP-60 is little or no longer exposed to lactoperoxidase, whereas the fibronectin of the endothelial basement membrane becomes available for iodination. (F) Confluent culture that was first disrupted by EDTA and then incubated in the same plate for 5 hours under growth conditions to readopt its original morphology. CSP-60 reappears as a major band, whereas the amounts of fibronectin are substantially decreased. (G) Cells 12 hours after EDTA dissociation and seeding at a high density. The cells adopt a gel pattern similar to that of lane F. (H) Cells 12 hours after EDTA dissociation and seeding at a low density. Fibronectin and CSP-60 are almost missing. (2) Confluent endothelial monolayer disrupted by urea.

11 and 12) indicate that nonreduced samples contained a 60 K component that is present in highly confluent and organized cell monolayers. After reduction, CSP-60 was missing from its original position, yielding a major band of an apparent molecular weight of about 30 K (Fig. 11, lanes A and E). The dimeric disulfide-bonded nature of CSP-60 was further demonstrated on two-dimension gels, nonreduced in the first dimension and reduced in the second. Samples derived from highly confluent and organized cultures of either vascular (Fig. 12B) or corneal (Fig. 12E) endothelial cells revealed a major, off-diagonal spot that had an apparent molecular weight of about 30 K and which at the first, nonreduced dimension, migrate as a 60 K component. There were no such components (30 K) in samples derived either from sparse, actively growing endothelial cells (Fig. 12C) or from sparse and confluent (Fig. 12F) cultures of smooth muscle cells. Control gels, running either nonreduced (Fig. 12A) or reduced (Fig. 12D) in both directions, showed no such off-diagonal spots, proving that the appearance of the low molecular weight, off-diagonal spot was caused by the reduction step between the two electrophoresis stages.

A mild treatment with trypsin (0.2 μg/ml, 1 hour, 37°C) under conditions that did not disrupt the cell monolayer completely removed the fibronectin from the cell surface but did not affect CSP-60 as long as the cells remained in contact with each other. In contrast, trypsin treatment, which induced dissociation of the monolayer and rounding of cells, largely eliminated CSP-60, which reappeared as soon as the cells again formed a highly organized cell monolayer (Fig. 10). Since protein synthesis was not required for this appearance of CSP-60 it is suggested that, after dissociation of a confluent endothelial monolayer, CSP-60 is no longer exposed to the lactoperoxidase-catalyzed iodination and that its exposure only in cells that adopt a highly organized monolayer configuration correlates with this type of morphology. The present results therefore suggest that, in confluent cultures, fibronectin serves mainly as a glue by which the cells are attached to the basement membrane, since, unlike CSP-60, it is secreted in large quantities and is a major component of the basement membrane. Fibronectin might also have a role in the restriction of the lateral mobility of various surface receptors and in the inhibition of adsorptive endocytosis (Vlodavsky et al., 1979a) but has no significant role in the establishment of a highly organized cell monolayer.

(A) Undisrupted confluent, cell monolayer. (B) Confluent culture treated with urea and labeled when the cells appeared as single round spheres. CSP-60 is no longer exposed to the lactoperoxidase-catalyzed iodination. (C) Confluent culture that was first treated with urea and then allowed to reorganize by a 3-hour incubation under growth conditions. CSP-60 reappears as in the control, undisrupted, culture. (D) Cells 24 hours after disruption with urea and reseeding at a high density. CSP-60 reappears as a major surface component. (E) Cells 24 hours after urea treatment and reseeding at a low density; little or no CSP-60 can be observed. The arrows point to fibronectin (230 K) and to CSP-60 (30 K).

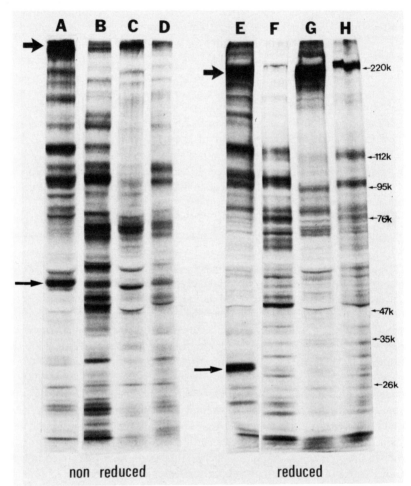

FIG. 11. Sodium dodecyl sulfate–polyacrylamide gel electrophoresis of lactoperoxidase-iodinated sparse and confluent cultures of vascular endothelial and smooth muscle cells with and without reduction with DTT. Autoradiogram of a slab gel. Washed cells were iodinated with ^{131}I by the lactoperoxidase/glucose oxidase technique, lysed, and analyzed by a gradient polyacrylamide slab gel electrophoresis either before (lanes A–D) or after (lanes E–H) reduction with 0.1 M dithiothreitol. (A, E) Confluent monolayers of bovine aortic endothelial cells. (B, F) Sparse culture of bovine aortic endothelial cells. (C, G) Confluent culture of bovine aortic smooth muscle cells. (D, H) Sparse culture of bovine aortic smooth muscle cells. Gels were standardized with T4 phage [^{35}S]-methionine labeled proteins, and arrows mark the position of fibronectin and CSP-60. The arrows point to fibronectin (unreduced, 400 K; reduced, 230 K) and to SCP-60 (unreduced, 60 K; reduced, 30 K). The appearance of CSP-60 in confluent cell monolayers has been demonstrated in all the vascular endothelial lines tested so far, regardless of their origins and ages. This includes cells derived from the fetal heart, fetal calf, and adult bovine aortic arches, bovine pulmonary artery, bovine umbilical vein, and pig aortic arch.

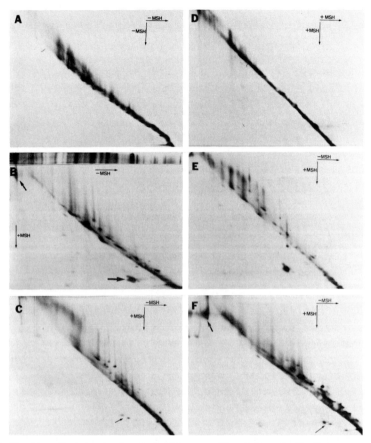

FIG. 12. Two-dimensional gel analysis of lactoperoxidase iodinated cells. Cultures were iodinated and the cells were lysed and harvested under nonreducing conditions. Aliquots were run on gradient (6.5–16%) polyacrylamide slab gel; the gel was cut into appropriate narrow strips, which were then placed each at the top of another 6.5–16% slab gel and sealed in place with 0.5% (v:v) agarose in electrophoresis buffer. A reducing agent (5% MSH, 2-mercaptoethanol) was present, as shown. After electrophoresis, the slab gel was fixed in 7% acetic acid, dried, and subjected to autoradiography on Kodak NS-2T X-ray film. (A) and (D) Confluent vascular endothelial cells. (A) Both dimensions without reduction. No off-diagonal spots are present. (B) A confluent monolayer of vascular endothelial cells. First dimension nonreduced, second dimension reduced; arrows mark the position of fibronectin (upper left) and CSP-60 (lower left). (C) Sparse actively growing vascular endothelial cells. First dimension nonreduced, second dimension reduced. Note the absence of fibronectin and CSP-60. (D) Both dimensions with reduction. (E) A confluent corneal endothelial cell monolayer. Nonreduced at the first dimension, and reduction at the second dimension. CSP-60 appears as a major off-diagonal spot. Fibronectin is little exposed or not exposed at all to the lactoperoxidase-catalyzed iodination. (F) Confluent vascular smooth muscle cells. First dimension nonreduced, second dimension reduced. Note the absence of CSP-60 and the presence of fibronectin.

B. SELECTIVE PERMEABILITY BARRIER PROPERTIES OF THE VASCULAR ENDOTHELIUM AS SHOWN BY STUDIES WITH LOW-DENSITY LIPOPROTEIN

The location of vascular endothelial cells, at the interface of two completely different extracellular compartments (the vascular and the interstitial compartment), means that these cells are exposed to various substances at concentrations and proportions far different on each of these regions and are therefore expected to possess unique properties, both as a barrier and as a transport system. Such properties are of particular significance in preventing an excess of plasma lipoproteins from accumulating in the subendothelial region and in the smooth muscle cells of the arterial wall. It is evident that breaches in the endothelial barrier, such as occur in endothelial injury, can initiate the atherogenic process, and it is also possible that exposure to abnormally high concentrations of lipoproteins can produce similar atherosclerotic lesions in the absence of endothelial damage.

A number of recent studies have identified a pathway in several cultured cell lines by which low density lipoprotein (LDL) is taken up into the cells via a specific receptor (Goldstein and Brown, 1977; Stein *et al.*, 1976). After internalization, the lipoprotein apoprotein is degraded in the lysosomes to low molecular weight material, and the cholesteryl ester content is hydrolyzed by a lysosomal cholesterol esterase and reesterified by the acyl-CoA:cholesterol acyltransferase pathway (Goldstein and Brown, 1977). The LDL pathway has been found to regulate the uptake, storage, and synthesis of cholesterol and thus to protect cells from an overaccumulation of sterols. Most of the studies reported so far have been carried out with cultured fibroblasts or smooth muscle cells. These cells display, under tissue-culture conditions, characteristics and growth properties different from those found *in vivo* and are exposed, under physiologic conditions, to only low concentrations of plasma lipoproteins such as are present in the extracellular spaces. In contrast, the vascular endothelium meets the full circulating concentrations of lipoproteins in the plasma and, when maintained in culture, mimics perfectly its *in vivo* counterpart in its monolayer organization, polarity, and function.

Two mechanisms have been proposed for the regulation of the cellular cholesterol content and metabolism in fibroblasts, lymphocytes, and smooth muscle cells. These involve (a) a receptor-mediated regulation of the enzymes of cellular cholesterol synthesis and esterification and (b) down-regulation of the number of receptor sites through which the uptake of plasma lipoprotein is mediated (Goldstein and Brown, 1977). It is of obvious interest to determine which of these pathways, if any, is significant in the vascular endothelium of large vessels, particularly because these cells provide the primary barrier against the high circulating levels of plasma LDL. A study of the LDL pathway in endothelial cells can also lead to a more general understanding of factors that regulate both the barrier and transport functions of cells that are located at the interface between fluid and tissue and adapt the configuration of a highly confluent cell monolayer.

1. LDL Interaction with Sparse Cultures of Vascular Endothelial Cells: Internalization of LDL and Its Effect on the Cell Cholesterol Metabolism

The establishment of clonal endothelial cell lines from different species and origins provides us with a well-defined and controlled system to study the interaction between plasma lipoproteins and the vascular endothelium. Using sparse and subconfluent endothelial cell cultures derived from bovine fetal heart and from calf and adult aortic arch, we have demonstrated the operation of a receptor-mediated LDL pathway in a manner similar to that described for fibroblasts and smooth muscle cells (Vlodavsky et al., 1978; Gospodarowicz et al., 1978c, 1979c). The presence on the cell surface of a specific high-affinity receptor site for LDL was indicated by the observations that the binding of ^{125}I-labeled LDL could be saturated (half-maximal binding obtained at 15 μg of protein per milliliter) (Fig. 13A), showing the characteristic competition with native LDL molecules, and the amount bound reached a plateau as time proceeded (Fig. 13B). Figure 13B demonstrates that, subsequent to LDL binding, the bound particles are internalized (and thus become resistant to heparin) and replaced at the receptor site by a new particle of LDL from the medium. As the amount of LDL within the cells increases with time, the lipoproteins begin to be degraded and the hydrolyzed acid-soluble products appear in the culture medium (Fig. 13B). When the rate of LDL degradation equals its rate of cellular uptake (3–4 hours), a final steady state is reached in which the total cellular content of LDL is constant. The degradation of ^{125}I-labeled LDL was competitively inhibited by unlabeled LDL and reached a maximal rate at the same LDL concentration as that required to saturate the high-affinity receptor binding site (Fig. 13A). It seems, therefore, that the high-affinity uptake and degradation of LDL by endothelial cells is, as in other cell systems (Goldstein and Brown, 1977; Stein et al., 1976), dependent upon the prior binding of LDL to its specific cell surface receptor site.

The internalization of the bound LDL was also reflected by its profound regulatory effect on the cellular cholesterol metabolism. It has been shown with cultured fibroblasts that, as a result of the degradation of LDL in the lysosomes, cholesterol synthesis is suppressed. This is the result of an inhibition of the enzyme 3-hydroxy-3-methylglutaryl coenzyme A reductase (HMG-CoA reductase). At the same time, cholesterol esterification is stimulated by increasing the activity of acyl-CoA: cholesterol acyltransferase (ACAT) (Goldstein and Brown, 1977). When subconfluent endothelial cells were incubated in the presence of increasing concentrations of LDL, incorporation of [^{14}C]acetate into cholesterol was progressively and specifically decreased (Table II). The amount of label incorporated into triglycerides, fatty acids, and phospholipids was not significantly different from that obtained in the absence of LDL (P. E. Fielding et al.,

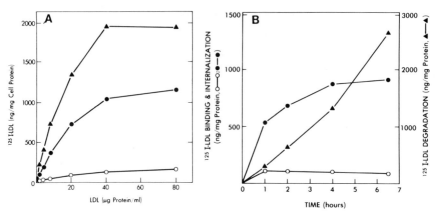

FIG. 13. Cell surface binding, internalization, and degradation of ^{125}I-labeled low-density lipo-proteins ([125I]LDL) as a function of (A) [125I]LDL concentration and (B) time of incubation with LDL. Subconfluent cultures of fetal bovine heart endothelial cells (FBHE) were incubated for 48 hours in growth medium containing LPDS (4 mg/ml), washed, and incubated for 3 hours (at 37°C) with various concentrations of human [125I]LDL (165 cpm/ng) (experiment A), or for various times with 10 μg of [125I]LDL per milliliter (experiment B). After the appropriate interval, the amounts of radioactive trichloroacetic acid-soluble material released into the medium (degradation) (▲) and the amounts of [125I]LDL accessible (○) (binding) and resistant (●) (internalization) to release by heparin were determined.

1979). These results indicate that there was a specific inhibition of the HMG-CoA reductase activity. Concomitant wih the reduction in cholesterol synthesis, increasing concentrations of LDL caused a 5- to 15-fold stimulation in choles-terol esterification, as indicated by an increased incorporation of either [14C]-acetate or [3H]oleate into cholesteryl esters (Table II). This indicates that there was a stimulated activity of ACAT. A maximum response was observed at 50–100 μg of LDL per milliliter, which is the concentration that saturates the LDL-specific receptor sites (Vlodavsky et al., 1978; Gospodarowicz et al., 1978c). Therefore, in sparse cultures of vascular endothelial cells, both the synthesis and esterification of cholesterol are regulated by LDL in a manner similar to that found with vascular smooth muscle cells (P. E. Fielding et al., 1979) and fibroblasts (Goldstein and Brown, 1977).

2. LDL Interaction with Confluent Monolayers of Vascular Endothelial Cells: The Lack of LDL Internalization Correlates with the Lack of Regulatory Effect of LDL on the Cell Cholesterol Metabolism

In vivo, vascular endothelium neither grows rapidly nor has the morphology of subconfluent endothelial cells culture. One of its main characteristics is its appearance as a single layer of highly flattened and contact-inhibited cells, which divide only slowly, if at all, except in response to endothelial injury. It is only by establishing conditions for the long-term maintenance of endothelial cells charac-terized by their unique morphology and growth properties at confluence that one

TABLE II

Regulation of Cholesterol Synthesis and Esterification in Sparse and
Confluent Cultures of Endothelial Cells[a]

| | Cholesterol synthesis: [^{14}C]acetate incorporation into free cholesterol | | | | Cholesterol esterification: [^{3}H]oleate incorporation into cholesteryl oleate | | | |
| | Sparse | | Confluent | | Sparse | | Confluent | |
Conditions	pmol/mg[b]	% Inhibition	pmol/mg[b]	% Inhibition	pmol/mg[b]	Fold increase	pmol/mg[b]	Fold increase
No lipoprotein	2750	—	170	—	708	—	345	—
+ Native LDL	673	76	153	10	8693	12.6	269	0.
+ Cationized LDL	148	95	58	66	7666	10.8	3327	9.0

[a] After incubation (48 hours) of sparse (actively growing) and confluent (highly contact inhibited) endothelial cultures in growth medium containing LPDS (4 mg/ml), the medium was replaced with fresh DME-LPDS medium with or without either native (100 µg/ml) or cationized (25 µg/ml) low-density lipoprotein (LDL). Cells were preincubated with the lipoproteins for either 5 hours or 12 hours and then with either [1-^{14}C]acetate (1 mM) or [^{3}H]oleate–albumin complex (0.1 mM) for a further 2 and 20 hours, respectively. Cells were then washed, harvested, and extracted with chloroform–methanol; the lower phase was taken for thin-layer chromatography on silica gel plates developed in hexane–ethylether–acetic acid (83:16:1). Lipids were identified by iodine vapor, and areas containing [1-^{14}C]cholesterol and cholesteryl [^{3}H]oleate were scraped into vials and counted in 10 ml of toluene-based scintillation fluid.

[b] Picomoles per milligram of cell protein.

can avoid misleading conclusions regarding the real capabilities of these cells. Using cells that fulfill this requirement (Fig. 14D), we have found that the early stage of the formation of a contact-inhibited cell monolayer was already associated, 24–48 hours after reaching confluence, with a 75% to 85% decrease in the capacity of the cells to internalize and degrade LDL particles. This inhibition was even more dramatic (90–95%) in cells that were tested 1–2 weeks after reaching confluence (Fig. 14A and D), although the cells still exhibited a specific binding of LDL to an extent that was approximately 2-fold lower than that obtained with subconfluent cultures (Vlodavsky et al., 1978; P. E. Fielding et al., 1979). This decrease in binding could, in fact, have resulted from the decrease in surface area available for LDL binding at confluence. In contrast, endothelial cells that have been cultured in the absence of FGF and have lost the property of contact inhibition (Vlodavsky et al., 1978; Gospodarowicz et al., 1978c) (Fig. 14E) or vascular smooth muscle cells which can grow on top of each other and form multilayers at high cell densities (Fig. 14F), were capable of internalizing LDL at either low or high cell density (Fig. 14B and C). In agreement with our results showing a lack of LDL internalization in confluent cultures of vascular endothelial cells and in contrast to results obtained with sparse endothelial cultures, cholesterol metabolism in confluent endothelial cells showed almost no regulating response to LDL, even at high concentrations of lipoprotein protein (up to 300 μg/ml) and after an extended incubation period (P. E. Fielding et al., 1979). Thus, confluent endothelial cells showed no decrease in the synthesis of free cholesterol when preincubated in the presence of 200 μg of LDL per milliliter, and there was no LDL-dependent increase in the formation of cholesteryl esters (Table II).

Since confluent endothelial cells specifically bind LDL, it is evident that the lack of regulatory response to native LDL could be due either to a lack of internalization and/or a defect in the degradation process. To study whether or not the degradative processes were operational in confluent cultures, we have used a modified type of LDL (cationized LDL), which is taken into the cells by endocytosis independently of the LDL receptor sites (Goldstein and Brown, 1977; Basu et al., 1977). The results obtained with cationized LDL have indicated that the uptake and lysosomal degradation of cationized LDL were not affected by the density and organization of the endothelial cell cultures. Once the cationized LDL is delivered to the lysosomes, it is broken down even by confluent cells, and the chloroquine-sensitive degradation products regulate cholesterol synthesis and esterification (Table II). Confluent endothelial cells must therefore, retain the lysosomal lipase and protease activities necessary for the hydrolysis of the protein and lipid moieties of LDL and for the subsequent regulation of cholesterol metabolism, although they will not internalize LDL (P. E. Fielding et al., 1978). This demonstrates that the lack of regulatory response to native LDL is due to the lack of internalization rather than to a defect in the degradation process. Thus, by using either the binding and degradation of LDL (Vlodavsky et al., 1978; Gospodarowicz et al., 1978c) or the inhibition and

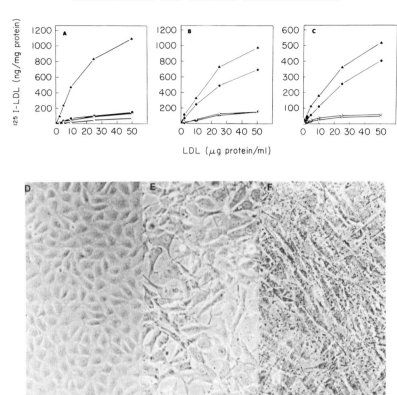

FIG. 14.   Binding and uptake of ^{125}I-labeled low-density lipoprotein ([^{125}I]LDL) by sparse and confluent cultures of endothelial and smooth muscle cells. (A) Adult bovine aortic endothelial cells. (B) Adult bovine aortic endothelial cells that have lost contact inhibition of growth. [This clone was derived from cells that were maintained in the absence of fibroblast growth factor (FGF) for four passages]. (C) Adult bovine aortic smooth muscle cells. (D), (E), and (F) Confluent cultures at the time of the experiments. The endothelial and smooth muscle cells were plated at an initial density of 2 × 10^4 cells per 35-mm dish and tested before (▲, △) and 8 days after (●, ○) reaching confluence. To obtain a highly confluent and contact-inhibited monolayer of endothelial cells, cells were seeded at low density and FGF was added every other day until the cells were nearly confluent (5–7 days). The cultures were then maintained for an additional 8–10 days to assume the distinct appearance of contact-inhibited cells (D). The growth medium was replaced with fresh medium containing LPDS (4 mg/ml) 32–48 hours before the experiments. Monolayers were then washed and incubated (3 hours, 37°C) with various concentrations of [^{125}I]LDL (412 cpm/ng) in 1 ml of the same medium. Specific binding (△ and ○, accessible for heparin release) and internalization (▲ and ●, heparin-resistant) of [^{125}I]LDL were determined. (D) Adult bovine endothelial cells, highly flattened and contact inhibited. (E) Adult bovine aortic endothelial cells—a clone that no longer shows contact inhibition of growth. These are elongated cells that can grow on top of each other; even at confluence, spaces are available between the cells. (F) Bovine aortic smooth muscle cells. Cells grow on top of each other as a multiple layer and in various directions.

stimulation, respectively, of HMG-CoA reductase and ACAT (P. E. Fielding *et al.*, 1979) as a criterion we have been able to demonstrate conclusively the lack of a receptor-mediated internalization of either the protein or cholesterol moiety in contact-inhibited cultures of vascular endothelial cells. Similarly, when cells were preincubated in a medium containing normal serum, rather than LPDS, and subsequently exposed to physiological concentrations of LDL (600 μg LDL protein per milliliter), the confluent endothelial cell monolayers exhibited a chloroquine-sensitive degradation that was only about 2–3% (0.1 μg LDL protein per 10^6 cells per 24 hours) of the amount of LDL degraded by sparse cultures.

3. The Down Regulation of LDL Receptor Sites Plays a Minor Role in the Inhibition of LDL Internalization in Confluent Endothelial Cells

In cultured fibroblasts and smooth muscle cells, the number of LDL receptors is diminished when the cells are incubated with LDL-containing medium over a period of days (Goldstein and Brown, 1977). It has been proposed that this feedback regulation is in response to increased levels of cellular cholesterol and is achieved via a diminished synthesis of the LDL receptor site itself. In both confluent and nonconfluent smooth muscle cells, a 24-hour preincubation with LDL produced a 70–80% decrease in ^{125}I-labeled LDL binding and uptake. On the other hand, while subconfluent endothelium showed a similar extent of down-regulation, confluent endothelium showed only a small (less than 30%) decrease in binding, even after preincubation with LDL for 72 hours (Vlodavsky *et al.*, 1978; Gospodarowicz *et al.*, 1978c).

Bulk phase pinocytosis can also be considered as a source of LDL cholesterol for endothelial cells. Using either [^{14}C]inulin or [^{14}C]sucrose we have observed a 2- to 3-fold inhibition of pinocytosis upon the formation of a confluent endothelial cell monolayer. However, as far as the uptake of LDL is concerned, this inhibitory effect seems to have little or no significance, since in sparse cultures bulk phase endocytosis does not account for more than 3% of the total LDL taken into the cells via the receptor-mediated pathway. These results indicate that the primary regulation of cholesterol metabolism in confluent aortic endothelium does not occur through down-regulation of the high-affinity surface receptor sites nor through inhibition of bulk phase pinocytosis but rather via an inhibition of the receptor-mediated internalization of LDL.

4. Clinical Significance of the Inability of Confluent Vascular Endothelial Cells to Internalize LDL

Since the vascular endothelium is exposed to large amounts of plasma lipoproteins, a control mechanism must exist to limit the uptake of LDL and to protect against the accumulation of cholesterol esters in both endothelial and smooth muscle cells of the arterial wall. The above results suggest that such a mechanism is provided by the strict contact-inhibited organization that enables the endothelium of the large vessels to function as a selective barrier to the high circulating levels of plasma LDL. It is, therefore, possible that the massive accumulation of cholesterol esters observed within aortic smooth muscle cells in natural or experimentally induced atherosclerosis results from a lesion at the endothelial level, leading to an unregulated uptake of LDL. This implies that in the *in vivo* situation, damage to the endothelial cell layer might stimulate the uptake of LDL and initiate the process of atherosclerosis. When a wound is made in the endothelium, the cells at the periphery of the wound start migrating into the wound. Those cells are then released from the restriction imposed by contact inhibition, become again capable of LDL uptake, and thus accumulate cholesterol. Cells far away from the wound, on the other hand, remain contact inhibited and do not gain the capacity to internalize LDL. Thus, after each wounding of the endothelium, the wound area will fill up with vascular endothelial cells laden with cholesterol. The accumulated lipids could in turn modify the cells and, if they are no longer contact inhibited, they could proliferate in multiple layers and thus produce the initial atherosclerotic plaque. That this could, indeed, be the case was demonstrated by the following experiment. A confluent monolayer of vascular endothelial cells was wounded and then exposed to a high concentration of LDL. Staining with Oil Red O revealed an accumulation of lipids only in those cells migrating into the wound (Fig. 15B) while the cells that remained contact inhibited did not contain any lipids (i.e., the cells located far away from the wound) (Fig. 15A). On the other hand, wounding of confluent smooth muscle cell cultures and exposure to high concentrations of LDL, showed accumulation of lipids in those cells migrating into the wound (Fig. 15D) as well as in cells located *far away* from the wound area (Fig. 15C). Any change in the cell morphology associated with a loss of contact inhibition resulted in a resumption of LDL internalization. By example, dissociation of a confluent endothelial monolayer by exposure to EDTA produced a 10-fold increase in the extent of LDL uptake and degradation 24 hours after seeding the cells at one-fifth of their density at confluence, although the cells did not proliferate in LPDS-containing medium. Similarly, removal of about 10% of the cells along an artificial wound in a confluent monolayer was associated with a migration of cells into the wound and gave, 24 hours later, a 2- to 2.5-fold increase in the uptake of LDL, although the rest of the cells remained highly contact inhibited and cell proliferation did not occur (Vlodavsky *et al.*, 1978; Gospodarowicz *et al.*, 1978c, 1979c). The formation of cell–cell contacts, rather than the inhibition of cell proliferation, seems, therefore, more likely to induce the inhibition of LDL uptake at confluence.

5. The Lack of LDL Internalization in Contact-Inhibited Endothelial Cells Correlates with a Restricted Surface Receptor Lateral Mobility and Production of a Fibronectin Meshwork

The cell surface and associated cytoskeletal elements are perturbed and actively involved in endocytosis, especially when the attachment of a particle to the plasma membrane is a prerequisite (Silverstein *et al.*, 1977). It has also been

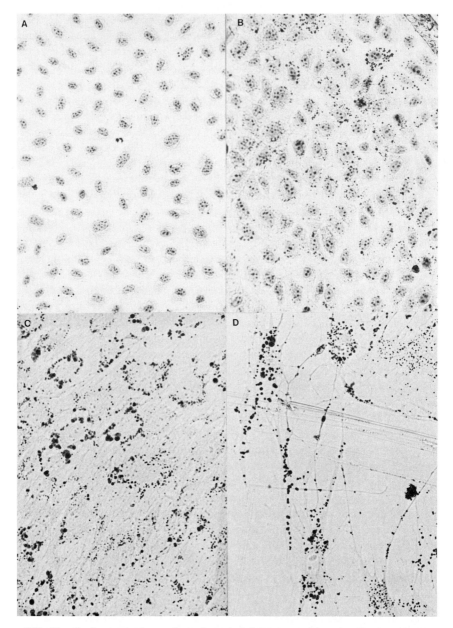

FIG. 15. Confluent monolayers of vascular endothelial and smooth muscle cells exposed to high levels of low-density lipoprotein (LDL) after wounding. Confluent monolayers of adult bovine aortic endothelial or smooth muscle cells were wounded and exposed for 5 days to LDL (300 μg of protein per milliliter added each day). The plates were then fixed and stained with Oil Red O and

shown that a directional lateral movement of various cell surface receptors from their original random distribution to form patches and caps is involved in the internalization of ligand–receptor complexes by various cell types, such as fibroblasts, polymorphonuclear leukocytes, and lymphocytes (Nicolson, 1976). It is, therefore, likely that changes in membrane fluidity and receptor lateral mobility could affect uptake processes. If this were the case with LDL, then it would be expected that surface receptor lateral mobility in contact-inhibited endothelial cells should be severely restricted in comparison to that of endothelial cells in sparse culture. We have therefore studied (1) whether or not the formation of a highly contact-inhibited endothelial cell monolayer is associated with changes in receptor distribution and lateral mobility, (2) what the structural basis for such changes, if they occurred, is, and (3) how these changes are related to the inhibition of LDL uptake in contact-inhibited cells that show specific binding of LDL but no subsequent internalization. By using fluorescein-conjugated anti-LDL (fl-Anti LDL) and fluorescein-conjugated concanavalin A (fl-Con A), we have examined the binding and distribution of LDL and Con A in sparse and confluent cultures of aortic endothelial and smooth muscle cells (Vlodavsky et al., 1979a). The results have demonstrated that, in sparse endothelial cells that internalize LDL, the LDL receptor sites are segregated into patches and caps (Fig. 16A and B). In contrast, monolayers of contact-inhibited cells that can no longer internalize the bound LDL show no receptor redistribution (Fig. 16D). This restricted mobility at confluence was also demonstrated by using the lectin Con A as a probe (Fig. 16F–J). With cell types, such as smooth muscle cells, that are not contact inhibited at confluence, there was almost no receptor clustering and no capping induced by LDL or Con A in either sparse or confluent cultures (Fig. 16E and J) (Vlodavsky et al., 1979a).

An aggregated but randomly distributed fluorescence pattern was observed with sparse endothelial cells that were preincubated with LDL at 4°C, rather than at 37°C, or that were first fixed with formaldehyde to inhibit the internalization of LDL (Fig. 16C and H). The higher degree of receptor lateral mobility in sparse (Fig. 17A and B), as opposed to confluent contact-inhibited endothelial cells (Fig. 17C), or to smooth muscle cells, was best demonstrated with cells that were incubated with LDL when attached to the tissue culture dish but then released, by an EDTA dissociation, from the restriction imposed by their attachment to the substratum (Vlodavsky et al., 1979a; Gospodarowicz et al., 1979e). Small clusters randomly distributed over the entire cell surface area were observed in

---

hematoxylin. (A) Endothelial cells—an area away from the wound. Contact-inhibited cells do not accumulate stained lipid droplets (lack of black dots). (B) Endothelial cells in the wound area. Cells migrating into the wound show large numbers of Oil Red O-positive inclusions. (C) Smooth muscle cells, an area away from the wound. Cells are labeled with stained particles reflecting the accumulation of lipid. (D) Smooth muscle cells in the wound area—large numbers of stained particles in cells migrating into the wound.

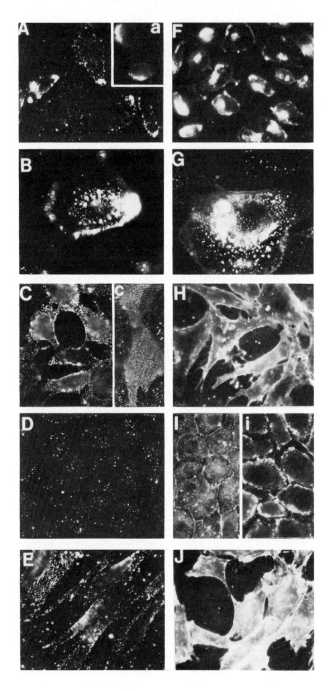

EDTA-dissociated, sparse endothelial cells that were prefixed to prevent the internalization process and then incubated in suspension with LDL and fl-Anti LDL (Fig. 17D).

Immunofluorescence microscopy has been used to show that late at confluence fibronectin disappears from the apical cell surface and is primarily produced toward the substrate underlying the endothelial cell layer (Fig. 8). This is associated with the appearance on the cell surface of a 60 K molecular weight component (CSP-60) not present in actively growing cells or in a disorganized cell monolayer (Figs. 10 and 11). A reorganization of the cellular microfibrillar system was also observed at confluence concomitant with the formation of a closely apposed cell monolayer. These structural changes might affect not only the freedom of surface receptor lateral mobility but the rigidity of the membrane in general, thus inhibiting processes such as invagination and formation of endocytotic vesicles. Since fibronectin can form disulfide-bonded complexes (Hynes and Destree, 1977), it might also restrict the lateral mobility of various surface receptors because of cross-linking with proteins in the cell membrane. It is therefore possible that a transmembrane interaction with an "exoskeleton" consisting of fibronectin and perhaps other proteins or glycoproteins might account for the present observations regarding the changes in membrane dynamics and organization at confluence. Sparse and contact-inhibited endothelial cells were labeled by the lactoperoxidase-catalyzed iodination tech-

---

FIG. 16. Cell surface distribution of low density lipoprotein (LDL) and concanavalin A (Con A) receptor sites in sparse and confluent vascular endothelial and smooth muscle cells attached to coverslips. Coverslip cultures of sparse and confluent bovine aortic endothelial and smooth muscle cells were labeled (1 hour, 4°C) either with fl-Anti LDL or with Anti-LDL and fl-Anti rabbit IgG, after first being incubated with LDL (100 μg/ml, 1 hour, 37°C) (A–E). Coverslips were also incubated directly with fl-Con A (50 μg/ml, 15 minutes, 37°C) (F–J) and mounted for fluorescence microscopy (Leitz Orthoplan, epi-illumination). (A–E) Cell surface distribution of receptor sites for LDL. (A, B) Sparse endothelial cultures exposed to LDL and then to fl-Anti-LDL (A, a) or successively to LDL, rabbit anti-LDL, and goat anti-rabbit IgG (B) as described. The LDL receptor sites are segregated into large aggregates (minicaps) located primarily in one pole of the cell. (a) Cells that were rounded up during the incubations but still remained attached to the substrate. (c) Sparse endothelial cells that were incubated with LDL at 4° rather than at 37°C, washed, and stained with fl-Anti-LDL at 4°C. A random distribution of fluorescence in small clusters. (D) Highly confluent and contact inhibited endothelial cells after preincubation with LDL at 37°C and with anti-LDL and fl-Anti-IgG at 4°C. The LDL receptor sites are distributed in small clusters over the entire cell surface area. (E) Sparse culture of smooth muscle cells treated with LDL, Anti-LDL, and fl-Anti IgG as in (D). A random, uniformly distributed LDL receptor clusters. (F–J) Cultures exposed to fl-Con A. (F, G) Sparse culture of endothelial cells. Surface receptor sites for Con A are segregated into large patches and form perinuclear caps (F, G). (H) Sparse endothelial culture fixed with formaldehyde (3.7%, 15 minutes, RT) before exposure to fl-Con A. A diffused fluorescence staining pattern over the entire cell surface area. (I) A highly confluent and contact inhibited monolayer of endothelial cells. A mostly peripheral, slightly aggregated, and random distribution of Con A receptor sites. (i) represents cells that contract during incubation and washing. (J) Sparse culture of smooth muscle cells. Cells display a random, slightly clustered receptor distribution.

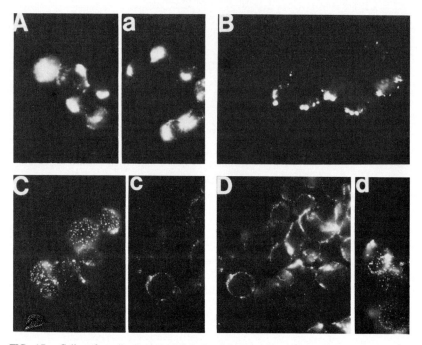

FIG. 17. Cell surface distribution of low-density lipoprotein (LDL) receptor sites in EDTA-dissociated sparse and confluent vascular endothelial cells. Cells attached to the tissue culture dish were incubated with LDL and fl-Anti LDL as described in the legend to Fig. 16, dissociated with 0.03% EDTA solution, and spun; single cells in suspension were observed for their fluorescence staining pattern. (A) and (B) represent cells from sparse endothelial cultures showing segregation of the LDL receptor sites into caps (A) or minicaps (B) in one pole of the cells. (C) Cells from a highly confluent and contact-inhibited monolayer of endothelial cells. The LDL receptor sites are randomly distributed in small clusters over the entire cell surface area. (D) Sparse endothelial cells that were first dissociated with EDTA, fixed (3.7% formaldehyde, 15 minutes) and then incubated in suspension with LDL and fl-Anti LDL. A clustered but random distribution of fluorescence.

nique, and the protein pattern analyzed by polyacrylamide gel electrophoresis either with or without reduction with dithiothreitol. Examination of the electrophoresis pattern of reduced (Fig. 11E–H) and nonreduced (Fig. 11A–D) samples revealed that, in confluent (Fig. 11A and E), endothelial cells, fibronectin is involved in the formation of disulfide cross-linked complexes whereas little or no fibronectin and no production of extracellular matrix were detected in sparse, actively growing endothelial cultures (Fig. 11B and F). Such disulfide-bonded complexes were also identified in either sparse (Fig. 11D and H), or confluent (Fig. 11C and G) cultures of smooth muscle cells that showed no ligand-induced receptor capping (Fig. 16E and J) but were still capable of LDL uptake (P. E. Fielding *et al.*, 1979; Vlodavsky *et al.*, 1978b). These cells might, therefore, internalize by means of binding to coated pits, as in the fibroblast model (Goldstein and Brown, 1977), rather than by means of a mechanism that involves receptor redistribution. These results suggest that receptor restriction in contact-inhibited endothelial cells might play a role in enabling the endothelium of the large vessels to function as an efficient barrier against the high circulating levels of LDL, which is the main carrier of cholesterol in the blood. Consequently, any disruption of the endothelial monolayer would release the cells from contact inhibition, increase the fluidity of the membrane, and initiate a chain reaction resulting in the eventual accumulation of LDL lipid in the endothelial layer.

The vascular endothelium may not be the only example of a cell layer whose metabolic function is dictated by its organization. It cannot be by chance that every time one encounters contact inhibition, it is correlated in most cases, if not all cases, with a tissue located at the interface between a fluid and other organs and whose functions are primarily that of a selective permeability barrier. On the other hand, when a tissue lacks contact inhibition (and this occurs even in the case of the vascular endothelium, e.g., the fenestrated capillary endothelium), it is in contact with an organ (kidney, liver, endocrine gland, etc.) whose role is to release hormones and proteins into the bloodstream.

6. Chylomicrons as a Possible Source of Cholesterol for Confluent Endothelial Cells

The above experiments have demonstrated that, in contact-inhibited endothelial cell monolayers, the bound LDL particles supply little or no cholesterol for the regulation of endogenous cholesterol metabolism or for maintenance of the cholesterol content of cellular membrane structures. Since high-density lipoprotein (HDL) is supposed either to remove or to lower the cholesterol content of the cell membrane (Craw *et al.*, 1976), and since the endogenous cholesterol synthesis is greatly reduced at confluence (P. E. Fielding *et al.*, 1979), another source for the cholesterol found in the vascular endothelium must be sought.

For endothelial cells, unlike fibroblasts or smooth muscle cells, an alternative source of lipoprotein cholesteryl ester is provided by the particles of dietary lipid (chylomicrons), which circulate only in the plasma compartment. It has been shown, in the isolated perfused heart, that the coronary vascular bed can clear and hydrolyze chylomicron cholesteryl ester. We have therefore, looked at the characteristics of chylomicron binding and lipid uptake to vascular endothelial cells in culture (C. J. Fielding *et al.*, 1979).

When ^{125}I-labeled chylomicrons were incubated with endothelial cells at 4°C or 37°C, the particles were bound to the cells by a specific high-affinity receptor site such that half-maximal binding (Fig. 18A) was obtained at a chylomicron protein concentration of approximately 5 μg/ml. At saturation, the bound chylomicrons (50–70 ng of protein per 10^6 cells) covered about 4.5% of the cell surface area, a result similar to that obtained with LDL (Vlodavsky *et al.*, 1978). The binding of ^{125}I-labeled chylomicron was reduced by 70% to 80% in the presence of a 20-fold excess of unlabeled chylomicrons. When binding was measured as a function of time, it was found to be almost maximal within 60

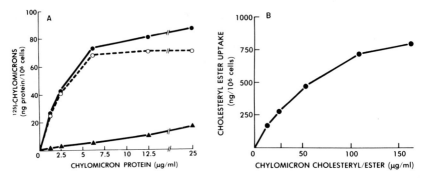

FIG. 18.   Chylomicron binding (A) and cholesteryl ester uptake (B) by confluent endothelial cells. Confluent cultures of fetal bovine heart endothelial cells (FBHE) were incubated for 3 hours at 4°C (A) or for 24 hours at 37°C (B) with various concentrations of ^{125}I-labeled chylomicrons (A) or cholesteryl [3H]oleate-labeled chylomicrons (B), respectively. Monolayers incubated with iodinated chylomicrons were extensively washed, solubilized, and measured for ^{125}I-radioactivity. Specific binding (O----O) to the cell surface was obtained by subtracting the values obtained in the presence of an excess (50–500 μg of protein per milliliter) of unlabeled lipoprotein (either chylomicrons or VLDL) (▲——▲) from the observed total cell-associated radioactivity (●——●). To measure the uptake of cholesteryl [3H]oleate from chylomicrons (B), monolayers were washed, incubated with heparin (10 mg/ml) for 1 hour at 4°C to remove surface-bound chylomicrons, washed again, and then scraped and extracted with chloroform–methanol. The lower layer was taken for thin-layer chromatography on silica gel-coated plates and developed in hexane–diethyl ether–acetic acid (83:16:1 v:v:v); the radioactivity in free and esterified cholesterol was counted in 10 ml of a toluene-based scintillation fluid. Cholesteryl ester values were corrected for surface particles bound nonspecifically as shown in (A), and these corrected values and free cholesterol radioactivity were added to represent total cholesteryl ester uptake into the cells (●). Uptake of cholesteryl ester under these conditions was linear for at least 48 hours.

minutes, at 37°C and within 3–4 hours at 4°C (C. J. Fielding *et al.*, 1979; Gospodarowicz *et al.*, 1979c).

   To further investigate the specificity of the chylomicron binding sites, cells were incubated with ^{125}I-labeled chylomicrons in the presence and in the absence of the various isolated plasma lipoprotein classes. These experiments have indicated that at a 10-fold excess of competing lipoprotein, chylomicron binding was reduced 65% by HDL, but only 35% by LDL. In contrast, the binding of labeled LDL was inhibited 70–75% by a 10-fold excess of LDL, but by only 10–15% by the same excess of HDL. To determine whether the chylomicron receptor sites can be down-regulated by preexposure to LDL, cells were preincubated for 24 hours in the presence of 50 μg of LDL protein per milliliter and tested for the subsequent binding of either LDL or chylomicrons. Under conditions that reduced LDL binding by 80%, there was almost no reduction in chylomicron binding and there was also no effect of preincubation in medium containing LPDS plus unlabeled chylomicron (25 μg of protein per milliliter) (C. J. Fielding *et al.*, 1979; Gospodarowicz *et al.*, 1979c). In contrast to the binding of LDL, the chylomicron receptor sites were equally expressed in cells exposed either to normal serum or to LPDS. These results, as well as the competition experiments, suggest that the chylomicron and LDL surface receptor sites are separate entities.

A second characteristic feature of chylomicron binding was that, in either subconfluent or contact inhibited endothelial cells, the protein moiety of the particle was neither internalized nor degraded. When binding was carried out at 4°C, chylomicrons, like LDL, were retained at the cellular surface, and neither lipid nor protein could be shown to be present in the cells. Under these conditions, 50–70% of the bound lipoprotein could be released by heparin or degraded by trypsin, thereby confirming the surface location of the particles. At 37°C, however, while protein was still excluded from the cell, the chylomicron triglycerides and cholesteryl esters (labeled with glyceryl tri-[³H]oleate or cholesteryl [³H]oleate, respectively) were taken into the cells (Fig. 18B) and were degraded to fatty acids and free cholesterol by a chloroquine-sensitive, presumably lysosomal, process. Furthermore, the internalized chylomicron cholesterol could be shown to inhibit the endogenous synthesis of cholesterol from acetate (C. J. Fielding et al., 1979). Thus, the interaction of chylomicrons with either sparse or confluent endothelial cells appeared to proceed by a process involving an initial temperature-independent binding to a high-affinity receptor site, followed by internalization of chylomicron lipid, but not protein, and presumably by generation of a lipid-depleted product particle.

Uptake of labeled cholesteryl ester at 37°C was linear for at least 48 hours, and at that time the cells took up more than the entire cholesteryl ester content of a chylomicron at each binding site. This is a completely new way to deliver lipids into cells, consisting of a repeated attachment and removal of particles from these sites, with net loss of lipid (but not protein) resulting from the adsorption incident.

The unique feature of chylomicrons as a potential source of cholesterol for contact-inhibited endothelial cells was further observed by staining with Oil Red O confluent monolayers that were first exposed (96 hours, 37°C) to either low and very low density lipoproteins (LDL and VLDL, respectively) or to either rat chylomicrons or a synthetic triglyceride-lecithin dispersion (intralipid). A massive accumulation of lipid droplets was only obtained in endothelial cells that were preincubated with chylomicrons (Fig. 19d), and there was no uptake of lipids from LDL, VLDL, or Intralipid (Fig. 19a–c). Similar experiments with confluent, non-contact-inhibited cultures of aortic smooth muscle cells showed lipid accumulation (Oil Red O-positive inclusions) in cells exposed to each of the lipoproteins or to Intralipid (Fig. 19e–h).

These results demonstrate that, compared with the negligible amounts of LDL cleared through its specific receptor sites in contact-inhibited endothelial cells, chylomicrons can contribute significantly to the overall endothelial cholesterol homeostasis. In normal metabolism, the level of circulating chylomicron cholesterol is limited by the ability of the liver to clear the remnant lipoprotein products

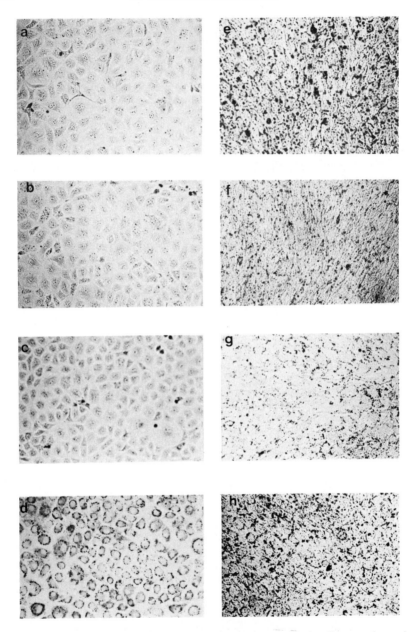

FIG. 19. Confluent cultures of vascular endothelial and smooth muscle cells exposed to various lipoproteins. Confluent cultures of vascular endothelial (a–d) and smooth muscle (e–h) cells in LPDS-containing medium were exposed (96 hours) to human low (a, e) or very low (b, f) density lipoproteins (LDL and VLDL, respectively) or to rat chylomicrons (d, h). Lipoproteins were added each day to a final concentration of about 400 μg of cholesteryl esters per milliliter (240 μg of LDL

of chylomicron catabolism. It seems possible that it is under conditions of degenerated hepatic clearance of remnant lipoproteins that the chylomicron cholesteryl ester receptor may play a dominant role in the uptake of cholesterol by the endothelial cell.

C. MEMBRANE CHANGES INDUCED BY FGF IN VASCULAR ENDOTHELIAL CELLS

Changes in growth properties and the induction of cell division by various mitogens and enzymes are often associated with structural and functional changes in the cell surface. Since glycoproteins and glycolipids are intimately involved in cell recognition, interaction, and growth control, lectins that bind specifically to these surface components can be used as probes to study the relationship between membrane changes and growth alterations.

The interaction between various lectins and glycoproteins that are capable of lateral diffusion in the plane of the membrane can lead to a selective redistribution of the lectin–receptor complexes in a process that results in so-called "patch formation" (passive clustering of cross-linked macromolecules) and subsequent "cap formation" (segregation of the cross-linked patches to one pole of the cell by an active, microfilament-dependent process). The capped complexes may undergo pinocytosis leading to extensive loss of the appropriate membrane receptors, a phenomenon referred to as "antigenic modulation." The long-range receptor movement involved in patching and capping can be directly observed by using fluorescein-labeled lectins (Nicolson, 1976). Short-range lateral movements like those involved in the lectin-mediated receptor clustering and cell agglutination can be indirectly quantified by measuring the ability of cells to bind to nylon fibers coated with different densities of lectin molecules (Vlodavsky and Sachs, 1975). This binding requires a short-range lateral mobility of the appropriate receptors to allow their alignment with the lectin molecules on the fiber. By using these techniques (fluorescence microscopy and binding of cells to fibers) with bovine endothelial cells and the lectin concanavalin A (Con A), we have demonstrated that both the short- and long-range types of receptor mobility were increased in response to preincubation with FGF (Fig. 20). These changes were not obtained by preincubation with EGF, which does not bind and has no mitogenic effect on the bovine endothelial cells (Gospodarowicz *et al.*, 1978b–d).

---

protein per milliliter, 800 μg of VLDL protein per milliliter, and 40 μg of chylomicron protein per milliliter. Cells were also exposed to Intralipid (synthetic triglyceride-lecithin dispersion) at about 3 mg of triglyceride per milliliter (c, g). Prior to staining with Oil Red O, cells were washed and fixed (3.7% formaldehyde, 1 hour, 22°C). Lipid accumulation (Oil Red O-positive inclusions) was observed in cultures of smooth muscle cells exposed to each of the lipoproteins (e, f, h) or to Intralipid (g), whereas contact-inhibited monolayers of endothelial cells showed a massive accumulation of lipid droplets only after exposure to chylomicrons (d) and little or no lipid uptake from LDL (a), VLDL (b), or Intralipid (c).

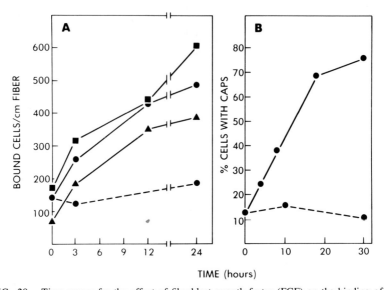

FIG. 20. Time-course for the effect of fibroblast growth factor (FGF) on the binding of fetal
bovine heart endothelial (FBHE) cells to nylon fibers coated with Concanavalin A (Con A) and for its
effect on the formation of caps by Con A. The cells for these experiments were seeded at high density
(10^6 cells/100-mm petri dish); FGF, 25 ng/ml (————), or EFG, 50 ng/ml (------------), was added
36–48 hours later. Cells were dissociated at the appropriate time with 0.03% EDTA solution to prepare
a single-cell suspension, spun, and washed with phosphate-buffered saline (PBS) before being used in
the experiments. (A) Binding of cells to fibers coated with Con A molecules. Nylon fibers were strung
in polyethylene frames, washed successively with petroleum ether and carbon tetrachloride, dried,
incubated (30 minutes, 21°C) with Con A solution (500 µg/ml) in PBS, and washed three times in
PBS. This procedure resulted in strong adsorption to the fiber surface of about 20 ng of Con A per
centimeter of fiber. In order to obtain fiber coated with lower densities of Con A molecules [2.5 (▲),
5 (●), and 10 (■) ng of Con A per centimeter of fiber)], the Con A solution was diluted in PBS
containing 500 µg of bovine serum albumin (BSA) per milliliter to keep the concentration of protein
constant (500 µg/ml). There was no binding of cells to fibers coated only with BSA. To measure the
binding of cells to fibers, a 4-ml cell suspension in PBS (4×10^5 cells/ml) was incubated with the
fibers (30 minutes, 21°C) with gentle shaking. Cells attached along both edges of a 1-cm fiber
segment were counted at 100 × magnification. The standard deviation of 3–5 independent cell-fiber
binding experiments was ± 10% over a range of 400–700 cells/cm. Below 100 cells/cm, the standard
deviation increased up to ± 25%. (B) Cap formation by Con A. To assay the formation of Con
A-induced caps, cells were incubated for 15 minutes at 37°C with 100 µg of fluorescein-conjugated
Con A (fl-Con A) per milliliter. Cells were washed with PBS and pipetted to dissociate aggregates; the
percentage of cells with a cap was determined with a Leitz Orthoplan fluorescent microscope fitted
with epi-illumination. Similar results were obtained with 10 µg of Con A per milliliter. Two hundred
cells were counted for each point, and only single cells were scored. When the percentage of
cap-forming cells was below 20%, the reproducibility of the results was ± 20–30%. With higher
percentages of cap-forming cells, the reproducibility ranged from 10 to 15%.

A 6–9-hour preincubation with FGF gave a nearly maximal increase (2- to 4-fold) in the binding of cells to Con A molecules on the fibers, and a significant effect was obtained already at 3 hours (Fig. 20A). A longer preincubation period (12–24 hours) with FGF was required to induce, in a large proportion (60–80%) of the cells, the ability to form caps upon addition of Con A (Fig. 20B). Redistribution and/or clustering of surface receptors are facilitated by a higher degree of receptor mobility and have been suggested as possible early events in mitogenesis. Our findings suggest that changes in the cell surface membrane are associated with the mitogenic activity of FGF, but it is not yet clear whether the induced alterations are actually required for and involved in the stimulation of cell division.

There are obvious advantages in obtaining a higher degree of membrane fluidity. It may facilitate the interaction of hormones and mitogens with their appropriate surface receptors and enable membrane enzymes and their substrates to come together and interact. A fluid membrane provides a simple means of distributing proteins and lipids to regions of the membrane remote from their point of insertion and for dividing membrane components evenly between daughter cells at the time of cell division (Bretscher and Raff, 1975). In this regard, it is of interest that the duration of preincubation with FGF required to induce a maximal effect on receptor capping is the same as that required for FGF to induce a stimulated synthesis of DNA and, ultimately, cell proliferation (Rudland et al., 1974; Gospodarowicz and Moran, 1977; Gospodarowicz et al., 1978c).

Endothelial cells are characterized by the ability to form a monolayer of flattened and highly contact-inhibited cells. In this stage, neither cell division nor the ability to form caps is induced by FGF (Fig. 21). This inability might be due to the massive accumulation of cross-linked fibronectin (Figs. 7, 8, and 11) that occurs in contact-inhibited endothelial cell monolayers making the surface membrane more rigid, thereby regulating such activities as cell division and membrane fluidity. Internalization of the mitogen-receptor complexes may be required for the induction of mitotic activity. Sparse endothelial cells which are free to internalize receptor-ligand complexes will therefore respond to FGF with an increased rate of proliferation. In contrast, confluent endothelial cells which can no longer internalize their mitogen-receptor complexes will no longer respond to FGF, although the mitogen binds to cell surface receptor sites. This could explain why contact inhibited cells which show a restriction of their cell surface receptor sites (internalization) are also unresponsive to a mitogenic stimulus.

III. Corneal Endothelial Cells

The corneal endothelium consists of a single layer of contact-inhibited and flattened cells attached to the inner surface of the cornea, which separates the corneal stroma from the aqueous humor. A viable endothelium is of primary importance if transplanted corneas are to remain transparent in the host eye

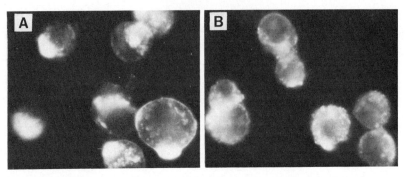

FIG. 21. Fluorescence micrographs of fl-Con A binding to cells derived from sparse and confluent endothelial cultures. Sparse (actively growing, 3 days after seeding) and confluent (highly contact inhibited, 2 weeks after seeding) cultures of fetal bovine heart endothelial cells were preincubated with fibroblast growth factor (FGF) (18 hours, 25 ng/ml), dissociated with 0.03% EDTA solution (5 minutes, 37°C), and incubated (15 minutes, 37°C) in suspension with fl-Con A (100 μg/ml). Formation of caps induced by Con A was determined as described in the legend to Fig. 17. (A) Cells derived from sparse cultures. A high frequency (70–80%) of cells with Con A caps. (B) Cells derived from contact-inhibited cultures. Con A surface receptors are slightly clustered but randomly distributed over the entire cell surface area.

(Stocker *et al.*, 1959), and the regenerative response of the endothelium is necessary for normal healing of penetrating corneal injuries (Inomata *et al.*, 1970). Numerous endothelial dystrophy have been recognized (Grayson and Keates, 1969). Elucidation of the factors involved in the survival of corneal endothelial cells and their proliferation in response to injury is therefore of interest for several reasons. As pointed out by other workers (Slick *et al.*, 1965; Perlman and Baum, 1974; Stocker *et al.*, 1958), the metabolic properties and proliferative characteristics of these cells can be examined most easily in tissue culture.

Since FGF has been shown to be a survival and mitogenic agent for vascular endothelial cells, which resemble corneal endothelial cells in several respects, including their *in situ* morphology as a monolayer and their functional importance in active transport, we have examined the possibility that, as with vascular endothelial cells, FGF could be a mitogenic agent for corneal endothelial cells, and we have compared its effect to that of EGF.

A. THE ESTABLISHMENT OF CORNEAL ENDOTHELIAL CELLS IN TISSUE CULTURE

Endothelial cells from bovine corneas can easily be established in tissue culture, and the morphology of the growing colonies closely resembles the description of endothelial cell cultures from rabbit corneas (Slick *et al.*, 1965; Perlman and Baum, 1974) and human corneas provided they are maintained in the presence of either EGF or FGF (Fig. 22) (Gospodarowicz *et al.*, 1977a). As shown in Fig. 22A, the mitogenic effect of FGF depended on the age of the

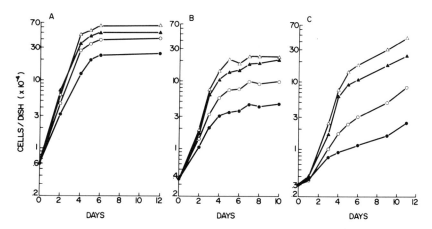

FIG. 22. (A) Growth curve of cultured corneal endothelial cells seeded at low density and maintained in tissue culture in the presence and in the absence of Dextran, fibroblast growth factor (FGF), or both. Primary culture of bovine endothelial cells seeded at 6000 cells per 35-mm gelatinized plate and maintained in the presence of DME supplemented with 10% calf serum (●——●), 10% calf serum + 5% Dextran (○——○), 10% calf serum + 100 ng/ml FGF (▲——▲), or 10% calf serum, 5% Dextran, and 100 ng/ml FGF (△——△). FGF was added every other day. Media were changed every 6 days. (B) and (C) are the same as (A), but the corneal endothelial cells were either at their second (B) or third (C) passage.

cultures. Although FGF had a minimal effect in primary culture (3-fold increase in cell number over control), cells in their second passage, when maintained in the absence of FGF, already began to lose their potential for proliferation (Fig. 22B), and the addition of FGF resulted in a 10- to 20-fold increase in their final density. Addition of FGF to cultures in their third passage (Fig. 22C) resulted in a 30-fold increase in the final cell density. The mitogenic effect of FGF further depended on the substrate upon which the cells were maintained. While cells maintained on gelatinized dishes responded better to FGF than did cells maintained on plastic (Gospodarowicz and Greenburg, 1979a,b), the addition of 5% Dextran alone to the medium greatly accelerated the proliferation of cultured cells maintained in the absence of growth factor (Fig. 22B and C). It also resulted in a higher final cell density when added to cultures maintained in the presence of FGF (Fig. 22B and C). The addition of Dextran affected not only the rate of proliferation of the cell population, but also the synthetic ability of the cells and their morphological appearance. Cultured cells maintained in the presence of Dextran and FGF produced an extensive basement membrane that appeared earlier and was more developed than that seen in cultures maintained in the absence of Dextran (Gospodarowicz et al., 1978d, 1979b; Gospodarowicz and Greenburg, 1979b). The morphological appearance of cultures maintained in the presence of FGF and Dextran was that of a highly contact-inhibited monomonolayer similar in appearance to that observed in vitro (Fig. 23).

The observation that FGF and EGF are potent mitogens for corneal endothelial cells has found a practical application in the development of cloned cell lines

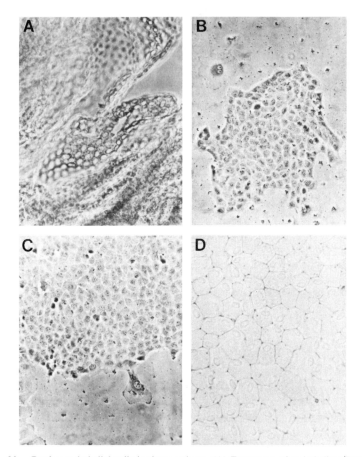

FIG. 23. Bovine endothelial cells in tissue culture. (A) Fragments of endothelium/Descemet's membrane immediately after explantation to tissue culture medium (phase contrast, × 150). (B) Colony of endothelial cells arising from a fragment of endothelium. A binucleated cell can be seen at the top (phase contrast, × 150). (C) Monolayer outgrowth from endothelium after 7 days in culture (phase contrast, × 150). (D) Endothelial cell monolayer after fixation and silver nitrate staining (phase contrast, × 300).

from the corneal endothelium. The finding that addition of FGF to the medium allowed the cells to divide at a density (about 0.6 cells/cm²) that permitted cloning has proved to be critical for the isolation of clonal cell strains of corneal endothelium used to study the control of differentiation and proliferation of that cell type. Clonal cell strains of corneal endothelial cells have been maintained for the past year in our laboratory and have been passaged every week with a split ratio of 1:64. The late-passage cultures have consistently shown the same sensitivity to FGF as secondary passages of endothelial cells and also exhibited the same characteristic differentiation at high density (Gospodarowicz *et al.*, 1977a, 1979b).

B. MORPHOLOGICAL APPEARANCE AND BASEMENT MEMBRANE FORMATION OF BOVINE CORNEAL ENDOTHELIAL CELLS GROWN IN CULTURE

1. Light Microscopy

Bovine corneal endothelial cells at confluence formed a very contact-inhibited monolayer similar in appearance to that observed *in vivo* (Fig. 23). At confluence, the cells started to secrete large amounts of an extracellular material covering the bottom of the dish and forming concentric layers two to four layers deep (Fig. 24). This amorphous material was best seen after treating the cultures with nonionic detergents, which selectively removed the cell monolayer and left the extracellular material adhering to the dish (Fig. 25). The corneal basement membrane produced *in vitro* could be stained with Alizarin Red in the same way that Descemet's membrane stains *in vivo* (Fig. 25).

2. Transmission Electron Microscopy

When confluent cultures of corneal endothelial cells were examined by transmission electron microscopy, they exhibited every one of the attributes shown by endothelial cells *in vivo*, including synthesis of Descemet's membrane. As shown in Fig. 26, an extracellular matrix typical of a basement membrane *in vivo*

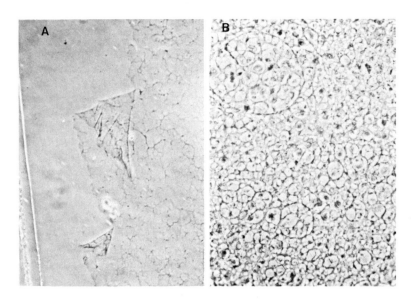

FIG. 24. Confluent cultured corneal endothelial cells (A) were treated with 1% Triton X-100 in phosphate-buffered saline (PBS) to expose the basement membrane. The tissue cultures were then scratched with a needle to remove part of the basement. (B) A zone of heavy deposit where the basement membrane is formed of multiple layers of collagenous material deposited on top of each other.

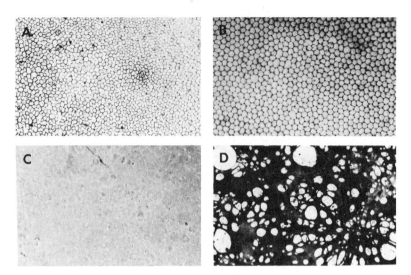

FIG. 25. Morphological appearance of long-term corneal endothelial cell culture and the synthesis of the basement membrane *in vitro*. (A) Corneal endothelial cell culture maintained for a month in tissue culture were stained with Alizarin Red. The intercellular border stained bright red, and the polygonal as well as the contact-inhibited morphology of the cell monolayer are readily apparent. (B) The morphology can be compared to that of the endothelium of a corneal button stained with Alizarin Red just after excision. (C) Corneal endothelial cell culture maintained for a month in tissue culture and photographed with a phase-contrast photomicroscope. The cells form a flattened and contact-inhibited cell monolayer where few details can be seen, owing to the lack of contours of the cell. The culture is then exposed to 0.5% Triton X in phosphate-buffered saline, and the cell monolayer is removed exposing the basement membrane (C), which stains bright red when processed through the Alizarin Red staining procedure.

is seen underneath the cell monolayer. Pinocytotic vesicles with an electron-dense coat are present near the base of these cells; it is presumed that these vesicles are involved in the secretion of collagenous and other proteins forming Descemet's membrane (Fig. 26B and C). Furthermore, cultured bovine corneal endothelial cells *in vitro* have a distinct polarization of their organelles. Bundles of microfilaments run parallel to the apical plasma membrane and delimit a zone free of organelles (Fig. 26A). A junctional complex is present at the apex of the cells (Fig. 26C). Microplicae and villi characterize the apical cell membrane as well as a marginal fold found adjacent to the junctional complex. The cell mitochondria exhibit the unique arrangement of the cristae mitochondriales (Fig. 26B) that is characteristic of corneal endothelial cells (Gospodarowicz *et al.*, 1979b).

3. Localization of Fibronectin at Various Cell Densities and following the Synthesis of a Basement Membrane

Earlier studies done with vascular endothelial cell cultures have shown that the fibronectin was mostly if not uniquely localized in the basal cell surface as well

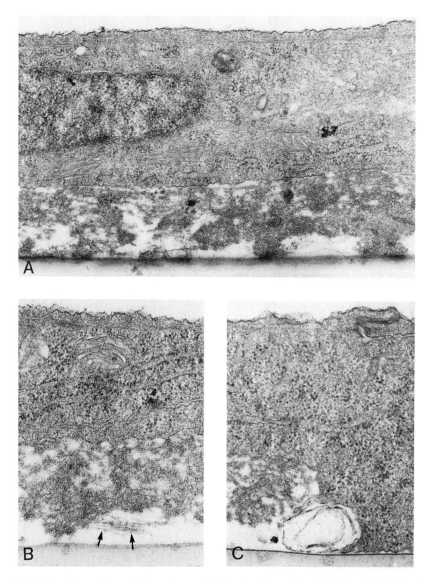

FIG. 26. Transmission electron micrographs of cultured corneal endothelial cells. (A) Bovine corneal endothelium. The nucleus is shown on the right. Deposited collagenous fibrils are accumulated between the endothelial cells and the dish. The apical cell zone is organelle-free and filamentous. The basal side contains mitochondria, rough endoplasmic reticulum, free ribosomes, and vesicle that are probably involved in the secretion of collagenous and other proteins ($\times$ 31,280). (B) A portion of bovine corneal endothelial cell showing rough endoplasmic reticulum cisterna and a mitochondrium with typical orientation of its cristae mitochondrialis. Collagenous material is deposited between the cell base and the dish. Larger collagen fibrils with striations are seen near the dish (arrows). Rough endoplasmic reticulum is more abundant in these cells than those *in vivo*, perhaps because these cells are in the process of forming a new Descemet's membrane ($\times$ 36,720). (C) A typical junctional complex is shown near the apical cell surface on the left side of the illustration. Note the presence of a "terminal web" along the apical surface of the cell ($\times$ 36,720).

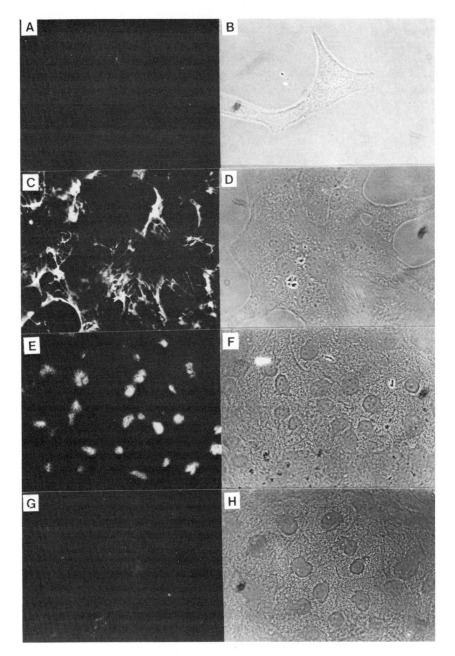

FIG. 27.   Indirect immunofluorescence localization of fibronectin in corneal endothelial cell cultures. (A) Staining of isolated cells shows the abasence of fibronectin. (B) Phase contrast micrograph of the same field as (A). (C) Staining of a sparse culture showing the distribution of fibronectin

as in the basement membrane of confluent cultures. We have repeated these studies with cultured corneal endothelial cells to see if the redistribution of fibronectin, which takes place at confluency, was a phenomenon characteristic of *all* endothelia or could only be observed with the vascular endothelium. Figure 27 shows the results of indirect immunofluorescent studies on corneal endothelial cell cultures using a monospecific rabbit antibovine plasma fibronectin antiserum. The localization and distribution of fibronectin vary as a function of the cell density. The importance of cell–cell contacts as a signal for the synthesis of fibronectin may be inferred from the apparent absence of fibronectin on isolated cells (Fig. 27A and B), and its presence on cells in contact with others (Fig. 27C and D). In sparse cultures (Fig. 27C and D), fibronectin could be seen covering the apical cell surfaces and was also concentrated in areas corresponding to cell junctions. When the cultures were subconfluent (Fig. 27E and F), the fibronectin was localized in areas restricted to the areas of cell–cell contacts and tended to disappear from the apical cell surfaces. The distribution of fibronectin was hexagonal in pattern, and only the angles of the hexagon fluoresced (Fig. 27E and F). After the cultures had been confluent for 1–4 weeks, little or no fluorescence was observed (Fig. 27G and H), but with careful focusing, the presence of scattered areas of fluorescence could be observed. This was related, in all cases, to areas where the extracellular matrix was exposed. Therefore, as with confluent vascular endothelial cell cultures, the fibronectin associated with the apical cell surface was not found at any time after the cells became confluent (1–4 weeks in culture). In sparse cultures, on the other hand, fibronectin was found on the apical surface of the cells and at regions of cell–cell contact. The association of fibronectin with the extracellular matrix of the corneal endothelial cells was very apparent when confluent monolayers of corneal endothelial cells were treated with nonionic detergents before labeling for immunofluorescence. Figure 28A shows labeling of the extracellular matrix in a 1-week culture, whereas Fig. 28B shows labeling in a 3-week culture. In both cases, extensive fibrillar labeling patterns were observed and the distribution of the label did correspond to the organization of the matrix.

In order to analyze whether fibronectin is in fact a major component of the corneal endothelial basement membrane and to what extent it is disulfide cross-linked into large complexes, the extracellular matrix, exposed after removing the cell layer with Triton X-100, was iodinated and the protein pattern was analyzed by gel electrophoresis (Fig. 29). In nonreduced samples, large amounts of labeled material remained at the very top of the running gels and a major band

on the dorsal (bottom) and apical (top) cell surfaces, and concentrated in the areas corresponding to cell junctions. (D) Phase-contrast micrograph of the same field as (C). (E) Staining of a subconfluent culture showing the fibronectin localized in areas restricted to cell–cell contact. (F) Phase-contrast micrograph of the same field as (E). (G) Staining of a confluent culture (1–4 weeks) with little or no detectable fluorescence. (H) Phase-contrast micrograph of the same field as (G). All photomicrographs × 400.

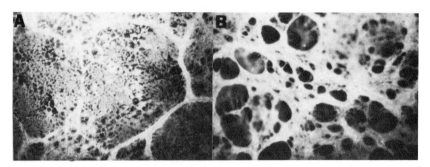

FIG. 28. Indirect immunofluorescence localization of fibronectin of Triton X-100-treated corneal endothelial cell cultures. (A) Staining of a 1-week-old culture after treatment with Triton X-100. Shows intense labeling of fibronectin, which corresponds to the extracellular matrix. ($\times$ 165) (B) Staining of a 3-week-old culture after treatment with Triton X-100 showing the very extensive fibrillar labeling that corresponds to the organization of the extracellular matrix ($\times$ 165).

had an apparent molecular weight that corresponded to that of fibronectin dimers (460 K) (Fig. 29B). Reduction with DTT decreased the amounts of these high molecular weight complexes and yielded a major band that comigrated with a fibronectin monomer (230 K) (Fig. 29D). Since no production of a basement membrane and no fibronectin were detected in growing cells that were not yet in contact, these results demonstrate that, concomitant with the formation of a confluent corneal endothelial cell monolayer, fibronectin becomes a major component of the extracellular matrix and forms a meshwork of disulfide-bonded fibrils that are closely associated with the basal cell surface.

The production of fibronectin by corneal endothelial cells maintained in culture for 2 weeks after reaching confluence was further studied by exposing the culture to [^{35}S]methionine (Fig. 30). The newly synthesized fibronectin was then specifically precipitated by a double antibody technique from the growth medium (Fig. 30A and G), cell extract (Fig. 30, C and I), and from the extracellular matrix underlying the confluent corneal endothelial cell monolayer (Fig. 30, F and L). These experiments have shown that most of the fibronectin produced at a late stage of confluence no longer remains as a cellular component but instead is largely released into the tissue culture medium and, to a lesser extent, toward the basement membrane underlying the cell monolayer (Gospodarowicz et al., 1979b).

As already shown with vascular endothelial cell cultures, when confluent cultures of corneal endothelial cells were exposed to human platelets, no visible platelets were attached to their upper surface (Fig. 5C, Table I). In contrast, when the extracellular matrix of these cultures was exposed, after detergent treatment, the platelets adhered very tenaciously to it. These results, therefore, show that corneal endothelial cells maintained in tissue culture exhibit at confluency a polarity of function and structure, since the cell surface exposed to

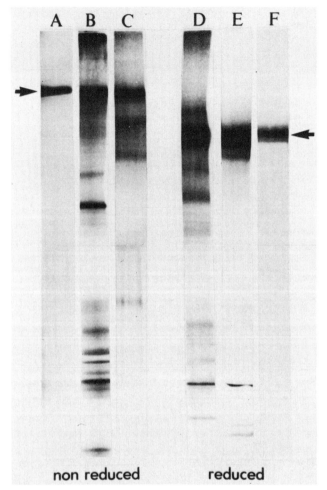

non reduced   reduced

FIG. 29. Sodium dodecyl sulfate–polyacrylamide gel electrophoresis of lactoperoxidase-iodinated corneal endothelial basement membrane before and after reduction with dithiothreitol. Corneal endothelial cells maintained in culture for 2 weeks after reaching confluence were treated with 0.5% Triton X-100 to remove the cell monolayer. The extracellular matrix was then iodinated with ^{131}I and lactoperoxidase and either dissolved in a sample buffer (lanes B and D) or subjected to double immunoprecipitation with antifibronectin (lanes C and E). Samples were analyzed by gradient polyacrylamide slab gel electrophoresis either before (lanes A–C) or after (lanes D–F) reduction with 0.1 M dithiothreitol. (A, F) Fibronectin purified from bovine plasma by affinity chromatography on a gelatin–Sepharose column followed by gel filtration on Sephadex G-200. (B, D) Extracellular matrix (basement membrane) underlying a confluent corneal endothelial cell monolayer. (B) Nonreduced; dimers (460 K molecular weight) and higher complexes (on top of the running gel) of fibronectin appear as a major component, and little or no fibronectin is present as a monomer. (D) Reduced sample; most of the high molecular weight material on top of the gel and the 460 K component (fibronectin dimers) are no longer present, whereas monomers of fibronectin (230 K) appear as the major and almost only band. (C, E) Fibronectin precipitated from the extracellular matrix by double immunoprecipitation; arrows mark the positions of fibronectin monomers (230 K) and dimers (460 K).

the medium is nonthrombogenic and free of fibronectin, while the basal cell surface is involved in the production of a thrombogenic basement membrane composed mostly of a fibronectin meshwork.

C. CONTACT INHIBITION AND THE REGULATION OF THE CORNEAL ENDOTHELIUM PERMEABILITY FUNCTION AS SHOWN BY STUDIES WITH LOW-DENSITY LIPOPROTEIN

Previous studies with cultured vascular endothelial cells derived from big vessels have shown that the formation of a highly contact-inhibited cell monolayer is associated with changes in the cell surface membrane, which impede the process of adsorptive endocytosis and allow the cells to form an efficient block against low-density lipoprotein (LDL) present in the medium (Vlodavsky et al., 1978a; Gospodarowicz et al., 1978c, 1979b,c; C. J. Fielding et al., 1979; P. E. Fielding et al., 1979). The barrier formed by the confluent endothelium results in part from the massive accumulation of disulfide cross-linked fibronectin (Birdwell et al., 1978; Vlodavsky et al., 1979a), which at confluency greatly restricts the lateral mobility of various cell surface receptors, and thus prevents the entire internalization of ligands specifically bound to the cell surface (Vlodavsky et al., 1978, 1979a,b; Gospodarowicz et al., 1978c, 1979b,c). From these studies, the notion emerged that the organization of tissues, like vascular endothelium, that exhibit a strict contact-inhibited morphology might by itself be responsible for its major function. The major function of the vascular endothelium is to be a selective permeability barrier controlling the passage of plasma components such as lipoproteins. However, the possibility exists that these studies done in tissue culture reflect the artificial conditions under which the cells were maintained. Therefore, the notion that the spatial organization of a tissue, contact inhibition in particular, is responsible for its ability to function as an effective barrier, should be considerably reinforced if one could show that another tissue similar in structure to the vascular endothelium, but obtained from a completely different organ, would at confluency exhibit the same metabolic properties shown by the vascular endothelium. Such a tissue might best be represented by the corneal endothelium, since at confluence it is even more contact inhibited than the vascular endothelium (Stocker, 1971; Gospodarowicz et al., 1977a, 1978c,d, 1979b,c).

By using corneal endothelial cells maintained in tissue culture, we have now further analyzed how the adoption of a contact-inhibited configuration and the associated accumulation of cross-linked fibronectin at confluency can affect the distribution and restrict the lateral mobility of Con A surface receptor sites, and how this restriction can, in turn, lead to a lack of receptor-mediated internalization of cell surface-bound molecules, such as LDL.

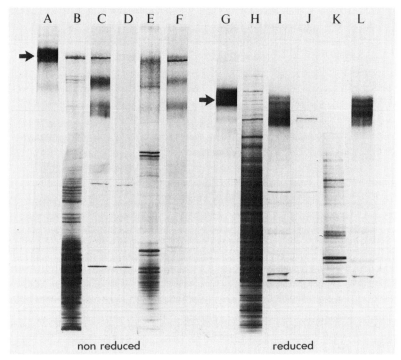

FIG. 30. Electrophoresis of L-[³⁵S]methionine-labeled proteins before and after immunoprecipitation from cell extracts, extracellular matrix, and growth medium of confluent corneal cell monolayers. Corneal endothelial cells maintained in culture for 2 weeks after reaching confluence were exposed to [³⁵S]methionine (65 μCi/ml, 24 hours) in a medium containing 10 μM methionine. The medium was collected, and the cell layer was either lysed or removed with 0.5% Triton X-100. Immunoprecipitation of the newly synthesized [³⁵S]fibronectin from the growth medium (lanes A and G), cell extracts (lanes C and I), and the extracellular matrix underlying the cell monolayer (lanes F and L) was carried out by the double antibody technique (rabbit anti-bovine plasma fibronectin followed by goat anti-rabbit IgG). Precipitates were dissolved in a sample buffer and analyzed on a gradient polyacrylamide slab gel before (lanes A–F) or after (lanes G–L) reduction with 0.1 M DTT. (A, G) Growth medium precipitated by anti-fibronectin. (B, H) Total cell extract. (C, I) Cell extract precipitated by anti-fibronectin. (D, J) Cell extract precipitated by nonimmune rabbit serum and goat anti-rabbit IgG. (E, K) Total [³⁵S]methionine-labeled proteins in the extracellular matrix after solubilization and removal of the cell layer. (F, L) Extracellular matrix after an immunoprecipitation with anti-fibronectin. Arrows mark the positions of fibronectin dimers (460 K, nonreduced samples) and monomers (230 K, reduced samples).

1. LDL Binding as a Function of Cell Density

As shown in Figs. 31 and 32, both sparse and confluent cultures of bovine corneal endothelial cells bind LDL at 4°C in a manner similar to that described for fibroblasts, smooth muscle cells, and vascular endothelial cells (Goldstein and Brown, 1977; Weinstein *et al.*, 1976; Stein and Stein, 1976; Vlodavsky *et*

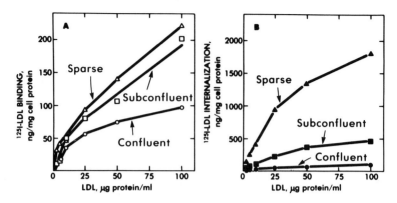

FIG. 31. Binding and uptake at 37°C of ^{125}I labeled low-density lipoprotein (^{125}I]LDL) by sparse and confluent cultures of bovine corneal endothelial cells. Bovine corneal endothelial cells were plated at an initial density of 2×10^4 cells per 35-mm dish and tested when sparse ($1.5-2 \times 10^5$ cells/dish) (△, ▲), subconfluent (4×10^5 cells/dish) (□, ■) or highly confluent (8×10^5 cells/dish; 8–10 days after reaching confluency) (○, ●). Similar results were obtained with cells that were seeded at different densities to obtain sparse, subconfluent, and confluent cultures on the day of the experiment. Forty-eight hours before the experiment, the growth medium was replaced with fresh medium containing LPDS (4 mg/ml). Monolayers were then washed and incubated (3 hours, 37°C) with various concentrations of ^{125}I]LDL (4.4×10^5 cpm/μg protein) in the presence and in the absence of a 10- to 50-fold excess of unlabeled LDL. Specific binding (A) (△, □, ○: accessible for heparin release) and internalization (B) (▲, ■, ●: heparin resistant) of ^{125}I]LDL were determined as described in Goldminz *et al.*, 1979.

al., 1978; P. E. Fielding *et al.*, 1979). The presence of specific high-affinity surface receptor sites was indicated by the observations that binding was saturable (half-maximum at 20 μg/ml of LDL protein per milliliter) (Fig. 31), and showed the expected competition with unlabeled LDL. At 10 μg/ml of ^{125}I-labeled LDL, a 5-fold excess of unlabeled LDL reduced the binding by 80%, whereas the same concentrations of HDL gave less than a 15% reduction. In both sparse and confluent cultures, 70–80% of the total radioactivity associated with the cells at 4°C was released by heparin. The maximum binding observed at saturation with confluent cultures was, per milligram of cell protein, about half that of sparse culture, an observation already made with vascular endothelial cell cultures (Vlodavsky *et al.*, 1978a). Since, at confluency, the cell surface area is 2- to 4-fold smaller than when the cells are sparse, it is evident that, if the density of LDL surface receptor sites remains the same with the two culture conditions, the total number of receptor sites per cell will be lower in confluent than in sparse cultures.

These results therefore, demonstrate that sparse and confluent corneal endothelial cell cultures can specifically and to a similar extent bind LDL and behave, in that respect, as sparse or confluent culture of vascular endothelial cells.

2. Cell Density Effects on the Internalization of LDL

In order to study the uptake of LDL into the cells, cultures were incubated at 37°C with various concentrations of ^{125}I-labeled LDL, and the amount of radioactivity resistant to heparin release was then determined. Although subconfluent cells bind LDL to an extent only 10% less than that observed with sparse cultures (Fig. 31A), the degree of LDL internalization was reduced by 75% (Fig. 31B). This demonstrates that, upon the formation of cell–cell contact, the subconfluent cells, although capable of binding the LDL, already showed a strong decrease in their ability to internalize the bound molecules. The decrease in LDL internalization was even more remarkable with confluent cultures of corneal endothelial cells, which form a highly contact-inhibited cell monolayer composed of closely apposed and flattened cells. Highly confluent cultures bind LDL to an extent about 60% of that observed with sparse cultures, whereas the extent of LDL internalization was less than 5% of that obtained with sparse cultures and about 20% of that of subconfluent cultures. Since confluent cultures of corneal endothelial cells are capable of binding LDL (although to a lesser degree than sparse or subconfluent cultures) and since the degree of internalization decreased strongly as soon as the cells started to adopt a contact-inhibited morphology, our results demonstrate that the cell density and organization pattern in culture strongly affects the degree of internalization of molecules specifically bound to the cell surface. The corneal endothelium in its normal configuration (which is that of a highly contact-inhibited cell monolayer) can therefore, form an effective block toward macromolecules present in the extracellular medium.

3. Release from Contact Inhibition and Its Effect on LDL Uptake

Since the lack of internalization exhibited by confluent corneal endothelial cells could become a permanent characteristic of the cells, we have analyzed what happens when the cells are released from contact inhibition. Confluent cultures of corneal endothelial cells, which have been analyzed for their ability to bind (Fig. 32A and B) and internalize (Fig. 32C) LDL, were dissociated with 0.05% trypsin/0.02% EDTA; the cells were plated at a split ratio of 1:5 and 48 hours later were tested for their capacity to bind and internalize LDL. The results (Fig. 32C) demonstrate that although these cells came from cultures that did not internalize the bound LDL molecules, the reseeding at a low density was associated with a complete reacquisition of their ability to internalize the cell-bound LDL. During the 48 hours of incubation in medium supplemented with lipoprotein-deficient serum, there was little or no proliferation of cells. At 6–8 days after again reaching confluency, cultures were retested for their ability to bind and internalize LDL (Fig. 32). From this, it was observed that, as with the original confluent cultures from which they were derived, the cells were no longer capable of internalizing LDL, although they did show specific binding of

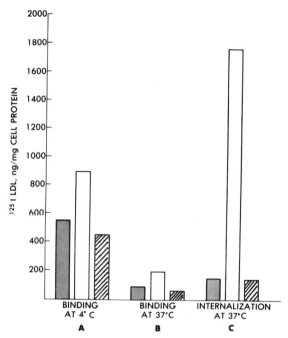

FIG. 32.   Gain and loss of low-density lipoprotein (LDL) uptake capacity after seeding confluent cells at a low density and resumption of a contact-inhibited organization. Contact-inhibited monolayers of corneal endothelial cells (■) were dissociated with 0.05% trypsin/0.02% EDTA, and the single cells were seeded at a 1:5 dilution. Cells were tested for [^{125}I]LDL binding and internalization prior to dissociation (■); when sparse (2 × 10^5 cells/dish) (□); and 6–8 days after again reaching confluency (▨). Cultures in LPDS containing medium were incubated with [^{125}I]LDL (50 μg/ml, 3.8 × 10^5 cpm/μg protein) at either (A) 4°C (90 minutes) or (B, C) 37°C (3 hours) and tested for specific [^{125}I]LDL binding (heparin-releasable radioactivity) (A, B) and internalization (heparin-resistant radioactivity) (C) as described in Goldminz et al., 1979.

lipoprotein particles. These results demonstrate that the ability of corneal endothelial cells to internalize LDL is, as already observed with vascular endothelial cell cultures, highly sensitive to changes in the cell density. Although the ability to internalize LDL is lost when the cells reach confluency, they can reacquire this capacity when they are reseeded under sparse conditions and are released from contact inhibition.

4. Restriction of Lateral Mobility of Surface Receptors is Correlated with the Inhibition of LDL Uptake

Since the formation of a contact-inhibited cell monolayer was associated with a complete lack of LDL internalization, while disruption of the cell monolayer resulted in a resumption of that process (Gospodarowicz et al., 1978c; Vlodavsky et al., 1978), and since cell surface dynamics is involved in adsorptive endocytosis (Silverstein et al., 1977), it occurred to us that the receptor-bound

LDL molecules have to be directed to specific regions on the cell surface prior to their internalization. If this were the case, one would expect that the lateral mobility of surface receptors of confluent corneal endothelial cells is severely restricted in comparison with that of corneal cells in sparse culture or in a wounded area.

Fluorescein-conjugated Con A (fl-Con A) was used to study the distribution and lateral mobility of Con A surface receptor sites on sparse and confluent cultures of corneal endothelial cells. Cells were incubated with fl-Con A either when attached to the tissue culture plastic (Fig. 33C and D) or in suspension after dissociation with EDTA (Fig. 33A and B). Sparse corneal endothelial cells that were first dissociated with EDTA and then incubated (15 minutes, 37°C) with fl-Con A showed a high percentage of cells (80–90%) in which the Con A receptor sites were induced to segregate and form a cap in one pole of the cell (Fig. 33A). In contrast, cells from contact-inhibited monolayers that were similarly dissociated with EDTA and incubated with fl-Con A showed a random, slightly clustered fluorescence pattern, but there was no sign of cap formation (Fig. 33B). Similar results were obtained with cells attached to the tissue culture dish. In sparse cultures of corneal cells that were incubated (30 minutes, 37°C) with fl-Con A, the Con A binding sites were drawn into large aggregates to form a "nuclear cap" at the center of the cells (Fig. 33C). In contrast, contact-inhibited corneal endothelial cells showed a dispersed or slightly aggregated fluorescence pattern over the entire cell surface (Fig. 33D). A higher freedom of receptor lateral mobility was observed after the cells of sparse cultures had been released from the restriction imposed by their attachment to the substratum, and, in both attached and dissociated cells, cap formation by Con A was prevented by aldehyde fixation before coating with fl-Con A. The present results therefore, demonstrate that the formation of cell-to-cell contacts and the adoption of a cell monolayer configuration is associated with a formation of an effective barrier to LDL in the medium so that the cells can no longer internalize the cell surface membrane-bound LDL molecules. This block is related to the organization of the corneal endothelial cell layer and is not intrinsic to the cells, since the LDL particles were actively taken in by sparse cells in the same way as described for fibroblasts and smooth muscle cells. We have further demonstrated that the inhibition of LDL uptake at confluence is due to the formation of cell–cell contacts rather than to the inhibition of cell proliferation, since it was released by disrupting the cell monolayer under conditions that did not stimulate cell division. Thus, after wounding, as with confluent cultures of vascular endothelial cells, there was a greatly increased uptake of LDL into cells located at the wound periphery but not into cells that remained contact inhibited, whereas after reseeding of confluent cells at low density, the LDL lipid was taken up by the entire culture (Goldminz et al., 1979). The barrier properties of the corneal endothelium, which at confluency was reflected by the inhibition of LDL uptake, may result from changes in the cell surface membrane that upgrade the process of

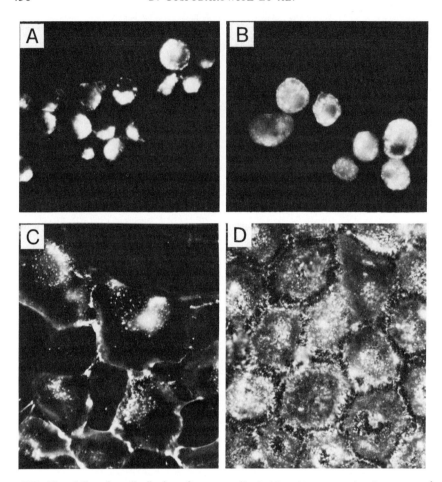

FIG. 33. Cell surface distribution of concanovalin A (Con A) receptor sites in sparse and confluent cultures of corneal endothelial cells. (A,B) Cells in suspension. EDTA-dissociated cells derived from sparse (A) or confluent (B) cultures of bovine corneal endothelial cells were incubated (30 minutes, 37°C) with fl-Con A (50 μg/ml), washed, and scored (single cells) for their fluorescence distribution pattern as described in the text. (A) Sparse cultures. In 80–90% of the cells, the Con A receptor sites are segregated into a cap in one pole of the cells. (B) Cells from a confluent, contact-inhibited monolayers. Con A receptor sites are randomly distributed over the entire cell surface area. (C, D) Cells attached to coverslips. Coverslip cultures of sparse (C) and confluent (D) corneal endothelial cells were exposed (30 minutes, 37°C) to fl-Con A (50 μg/ml), washed 5 times with PBS, fixed (3.7% formaldehyde, 1 hour, 22°C), and mounted for fluorescence microscopy. Similar results were obtained without fixation. (C) Sparse cultures. Surface receptor sites for Con A are segregated into large patches and form a "nuclear cap." (D) Confluent, contact-inhibited cells. Con A receptor sites are aggregated, but distributed over the entire cell surface area.

adsorptive endocytosis. By using the lectin Con A as a probe to detect membrane changes, we have demonstrated that in sparse corneal endothelial cells, which internalize LDL, receptor sites for Con A are free to move in the membrane plane and can be segregated into patches and caps. In contrast, monolayers of contact-inhibited cells that can no longer internalize the bound lipoprotein show no receptor redistribution. Figure 34 is a schematization of the different ways receptor–ligand complexes are distributed before being endocytosed by cell types that show no ligand induced receptor clustering or capping and by cell types that are capable of such receptor redistribution. It is to be noticed that if receptor redistribution takes place in surfaces where coated pits are present, a short range lateral displacement of the receptor-ligand complexes toward the coated pits will still be required before internalization proceeds.

5. Fibronectin and the Reorganization of the Microfibrillar System Can Play a Role in Controlling the Permeability Barrier Function of the Corneal Endothelium

Confluent contact-inhibited corneal endothelial cells produce underneath the cell monolayer an amorphous material of which fibronectin is a major component (Gospodarowicz *et al.*, 1978c,d, 1979b,c). Lactoperoxidase iodination of confluent corneal endothelial cultures had demonstrated that in contact-inhibited, *but not* in sparse cultures, fibronectin is involved in the formation of a disulfide

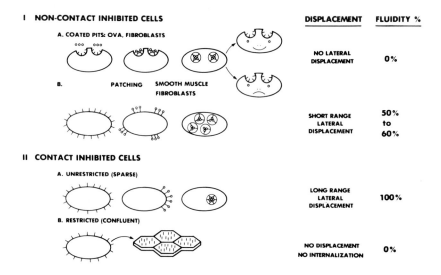

FIG. 34. Relationship between the fluidity of the cell surface membrane and internalization in the three different models of endocytose, which required neither lateral displacement (coated pits), short-range lateral displacement (patching), or long-range lateral displacement of the receptor–ligand complexes (capping).

cross-linked meshwork that might greatly reduce the freedom of receptor lateral mobility in the plane of the cell membrane. Cell surface components can thus be cross-linked to the underlying basement membrane, and this further limits the freedom of receptor lateral mobility in confluent monolayers.

Cytoskeletal structures associated with the plasma membrane have been implicated in the control of membrane dynamics and the distribution of surface receptors (Nicolson, 1976; Vlodavsky and Sachs, 1977). Therefore, the reorganization of the microfibrillar system that takes place when the cells reach confluency and became contact-inhibited is of paramount importance in restricting the lateral mobility of surface receptors. Under sparse conditions, the microfibrils are attached to the basal as well as to the apical cell surface, whereas at confluence, they are reorganized and lie parallel to the plane of the apical cell surface, delineating a zone free of organelles (Hogan et al., 1971; Gospodarowicz et al., 1979b). The microfibrils are furthermore attached to the terminal web at the lateral cell surface but no longer show any linkage with the apical cell surface (Fig. 26A). Therefore, in confluent, but not in sparse or subconfluent, corneal endothelial cultures, receptor mobility will be restricted on the one hand via cross-linked fibronectin, which attached the basal cell surface to the basement membrane, and on the other hand, by the reorganization of the microfibrillar system below the apical cell surface. One might suggest, then that receptor restriction in contact-inhibited corneal endothelial cells has a major role in enabling the endothelium of the cornea to function as an efficient barrier against macromolecules present in the aqueous humor following trauma, hyphema formation, or an inflammatory disease, such as uveitis.

D. IN VIVO TRANSPLANTATION STUDIES OF CORNEAL ENDOTHELIUM MAINTAINED IN TISSUE CULTURE

The ability of most corneal endothelial cells to repair themselves in vivo is severely limited by their lack of proliferative capacity (Van Horn and Hyndiuk, 1975; Van Horn et al., 1978). Although small endothelial wounds can be repaired through the process of endomitosis and cell enlargement (Stocker, 1972) extensive wounds will result in an edema of the corneal stroma that will render the cornea opaque and can be followed by vascularization of the stroma with a further loss of transparency. An intact endothelium is therefore essential for normal vision.

Corneal transplantation (keratoplasty) is one of the most important ophthalmic surgical procedures yielding a high degree of restoration of vision. It has, however, the intrinsic limitation of the number of corneas available possessing a suitable endothelium for keratoplasty. If a method could be found to replace the damaged endothelium with a viable one that would retain its capacity to proliferate, this would dramatically increase the use and success of keratoplasty. We have investigated the possibility of replacing damaged corneal endothelium with a new, vigorously growing endothelium that has been maintained in tissue culture for short (20 generations) or prolonged (200 generations) periods of time and that originates from bovine eyes (Gospodarowicz *et al.*, 1977a, 1979a; Gospodarowicz and Greenburg, 1979b).

1. Seeding or Coating of a "New" Corneal Endothelium

Because of our previous experience with bovine corneas and their ready availability, pilot studies *in vitro* were undertaken using steer eyes (chromosome number 60XY). It was found that, if one uses bovine cornea denuded of its endothelium and seeds bovine corneal cells previously maintained in tissue culture on it, within 15 minutes most of the cells attach and within 2 hours a new endothelium has settled upon the denuded Descemet's membrane (Fig. 35). For a corneal button of 7 mm, the ideal cell concentration, provided that the plating efficiency is 80%, is 75,000. Since female rabbits (chromosome number 44XX) were to be the object of the keratoplasty, rabbit corneas denuded from their endothelium were used to perform the endothelial transplantation. As shown in Fig. 36, similar results to that obtained using denuded cow cornea were obtained. One can therefore envision two possible approaches for the transplantation of cornea coated with a heterologous endothelium (Fig. 37). One can take the cornea of the animal 1 day before surgery, plate the cells on it, and transplant the cornea 12–18 hours later in other recipients (homologous transplant, as far as the corneal epithelium and stroma are concerned; heterologous, as far as the corneal endothelium is concerned). Alternatively, one can remove the cornea, plate the bovine endothelial cells, and graft the *same* cornea 2 hours later in the same animal. In this situation one will have an autologous transplant, as far as the corneal epithelium and stroma are concerned, while the tissue of foreign origin being transplanted is the bovine endothelium coating the rabbit cornea. When rabbits were used, most of the keratoplasty was done using corneal buttons maintained from 3 to 6 hours in organ culture. During that time, the corneal button, which does not have a rim of sclera, became edematous and opacified. Once grafted in the host, the progressive clearing of the donor tissue can be followed to determine the ability of the new endothelium to maintain the stroma deturgesced. This indicates the speed at which the coated endothelial cells resume their normal function *in vivo*, as well as to whether or not the whole transplanted endothelium or only part of it is functional. When cats were used instead of rabbits, because of the relative lack of availability of these animals, we had to use the same animal as donor and recipient. As soon as the corneal button was taken out of the eye, its endothelium was removed, the bovine corneal endothelial cells were then plated on it, and after being maintained for 2 hours at 37°C, the cat corneal button was grafted back into the same eye.

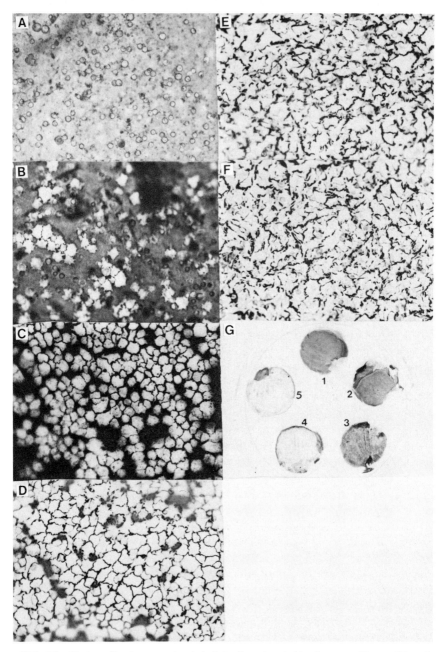

FIG. 35. Plating of bovine corneal endothelial cells to denuded bovine corneal button (11 mm). The cornea was first denuded of its endothelium as described by Gospodarowicz and Greenburg (1979a,b); bovine corneal endothelial cells (1.5×10^5) were then added in 60 μl of DME supplemented with 0.1% calf serum. The corneal button was then stained with Alizarin Red at 5 (A), 10 (B), 15 (C), and 30 (D) minutes, and at 1 hour (E) and 4 hours (F) (all pictures taken at × 40). G represents the corneal button stained with Alizarin Red: 1, corneal button at time 0; 2, at 5 minutes; 3, at 10 minutes; 4, at 30 minutes; and 5, at 2 hours.

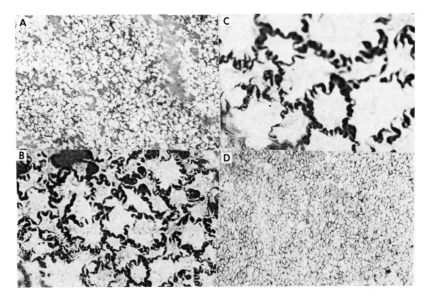

FIG. 36. Bovine corneal endothelial cells seeded on denuded rabbit cornea. Bovine corneal endothelial cells (2×10^5) were seeded on an 11-mm corneal button. The corneas were stained 30 minutes later (A, B, C) and 24 hours later (D) with Alizarin Red. (A) and (D) are photomicrographs taken at $\times$ 26; B and C were taken at $\times$ 130 and $\times$ 260, respectively.

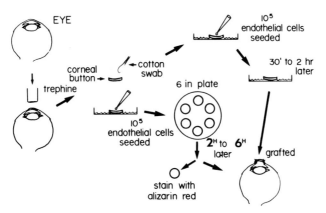

FIG. 37. Schematic representation of corneal endothelial cells seeded on corneal button. A corneal button is removed from the eye with an 11-mm trephine. It is then placed in a tissue culture dish with its endothelium facing upward. The endothelium is scraped off with a cotton swab. New endothelial cells are seeded on the corneal button, which is then incubated for 30 minutes to 2 hours prior to being grafted back into the same recipient or kept overnight in a CO_2 humid incubator to be grafted 2 to 6 hours later into another animal.

2. The Transplantation of Bovine Corneal Endothelial Cells in Rabbit

When rabbit corneal buttons coated with bovine corneal endothelial cells were maintained for 12–18 hours in organ culture and then grafted into a homologous recipient, the corneal button achieved a dramatic degree of clarity during the surgery. One day after the surgery, it was completely clear. The longest time a graft has remained clear is over a year, and prospects remain bright for these animals (Fig. 38A and B; Table III).

Unlike rabbit corneal buttons coated with bovine corneal endothelial cells, rabbit corneal buttons coated with bovine keratocytes became completely opaque within 3–5 days after surgery (Fig. 38C) and remained opaque thereafter (Table III).

These results therefore demonstrate that bovine corneal endothelial cells maintained in tissue culture are functional when coated on rabbit corneas previously denuded of their endothelium. They performed the same function as that of the native endothelium, namely that of an active pump that maintains the state of deturgescence of the cornea and will make the graft stay clear and transparent. Early-passage (20 generations) and late-passage (200 generations) corneal endothelial cells were equally functional (Table III, Gospodarowicz *et al.*, 1979a).

Statistical evaluation of our results reveals a low rate of failure, since, from a total of 24 transplants, 21 were successful (85% rate of success). A few transplants failed because of an excessive number of cells that became deposited in the aqueous outflow channels, causing a secondary glaucoma. Since this effect of

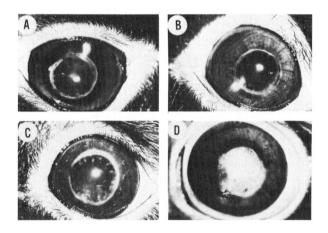

FIG. 38. Comparison of the clarity *in vivo* of corneal buttons coated with either corneal endothelial cells or keratocytes. Corneal buttons coated with bovine corneal endothelial cells became transparent within 48 hours after keratoplasty and remained transparent thereafter. Pictures were taken after 256 days (A, B) and 152 days (C). Corneal button coated with bovine keratocytes (D) 20 days after keratoplasty. The graft became completely opaque within 48 hours after surgery and remained so thereafter.

TABLE III

Comparison of the Clarity of Rabbit Corneal Buttons Coated with Either Bovine Corneal Endothelial Cells or Keratocytes and Grafted in Rabbit Recipients Considered as a Function of Time

Corneal endothelial cells				Keratocytes			
Case	Days[a]	Clarity of the cornea[b]	Karyotype[c]	Case	Days	Clarity of the cornea[b]	Karyotype
1	102	++++	$2n = 60$, XY	1	30	—	$2n = 60$, XY
2	101	++++	$2n = 60$, XY	2	25	—	$2n = 60$, XY
3	73	++++	$2n = 60$, XY	3	16	—	$2n = 60$, XY
4	62	++++	$2n = 60$, XY	4	12	—	$2n = 60$, XY
5	57	++++	$2n = 60$, XY	5	12	—	$2n = 60$, XY
6	50	++++	$2n = 60$, XY				
7	29	++++	$2n = 60$, XY				
8	13[d]	++++	$2n = 60$, XY				
9	10[d]	++++	$2n = 60$, XY				

[a] Number of days between the keratoplasty and the time when the animal was sacrificed.

[b] Clarity of the cornea: —, opaque; +, cloudy; ++, hazy; +++, slightly hazy; ++++, transparent.

[c] Karyotype of the cells obtained from the endothelial side of the graft at the time of sacrifice and maintained in culture.

[d] Rabbits 8 and 9 had developed a secondary glaucoma and were therefore analyzed at days 13 and 10, respectively.

excessive number of cells has been recognized, washing these cells off prior to keratoplasty has completely resolved this problem.

Since rabbit corneal endothelial cells are known to keep their ability to divide and to regenerate after trauma, it is of extreme importance to establish the nature and origin of the cells present in the graft after long-term heterologous transplantation. Since these studies were performed with recipient and donor tissues from different animals (steer versus rabbit), as well as from different sexes (female versus male), the identification of the cell types present in recipient and grafted tissues by karyotyping can be done easily. As shown in Table III, the karyotype of the cells present in the graft always had male sex chromosomes (XY) and a diploid number of chromosomes ($2n = 60$) with a chromosomal structure like that outlined by Hsu and Benirschke (1975) on *Bos taurus*. As shown in Fig. 39, the autosomes include 58 telocentric chromosomes with long arms that are even and decrease gradually in length. The readily distinguishable sex chromosomes consisted of an X, which is a large, submetacentric chromosome, associated with a Y, which is a very small submetacentric chromosome. In contrast, the karyotype of the corneal endothelial cells derived from the recipient territory always had female sex chromosomes (XX) and a diploid number of chromosomes ($2n = 44$) with a chromosomal structure like that outlined by

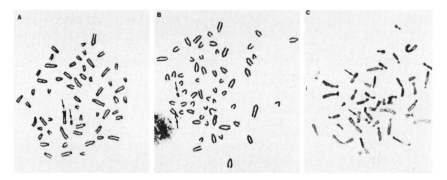

FIG. 39. Karyotypes of corneal buttons coated with bovine corneal endothelial cells, bovine corneal keratocytes, or rabbit corneal endothelium. Bovine corneal endothelial cells (A) and bovine corneal keratocytes (B) were put back in tissue culture after being maintained *in vivo* for 42 and 16 days, respectively. The cultures were exposed to colchicine for 12 hours. The cells were then karyotyped, and their karyotype was compared to that of the corneal endothelial cells (C) originating from the recipient, put in tissue culture at the same time as (A) and (B), and exposed to colchicine for 12 hours. The arrows indicate the respective sex chromosomes.

Nichols *et al.* (1965). As shown in Fig. 39, the autosome included 12 metacentric chromosomes, 24 submetacentric chromosomes with long arms decreasing gradually in length, and 8 telocentric chromosomes. Similar results were obtained when the karyotype of keratocytes coating the corneal button were compared to that of recipient corneal endothelium (Gospodarowicz *et al.*, 1979a).

This therefore, demonstrated that no invasion of the corneal button by the recipient endothelium took place, and conversely, no invasion of the recipient territory by the foreign endothelium or keratocytes coating the corneal button can be observed.

3. The Transplantation of Bovine Corneal Endothelial Cells in Cat

The previous results demonstrate conclusively that bovine corneal endothelial cells grown in tissue culture can be successfully transplanted back *in vivo*, all the while resuming their normal function. However, since rabbit endothelium can regenerate *in vivo*, it is desirable to repeat this experiment with species where the corneal endothelium does not regenerate. With the cat, in contrast to the rabbit, it has been conclusively demonstrated that the corneal endothelium does not regenerate (Van Horn *et al.*, 1978). Therefore, in this species, no recolonization of the grafted corneal button by the host cells is possible. When cat corneal buttons coated with bovine corneal endothelial cells were grafted in the same donor, as already observed with rabbits, the corneal button stayed clear (Fig. 40). This was the case in 8 animals out of 8. Those corneal buttons are still perfectly clear 382 days postoperatively. It therefore demonstrates that as with the rabbit, bovine corneal endothelial cells grown in tissue culture can replace the endothelium of the host since, as soon as they are placed in their *in vivo* environment, they will resume their normal function.

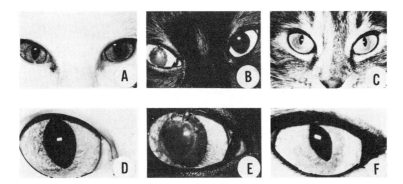

FIG. 40. Clarity *in vivo* of cat corneal buttons coated with bovine corneal endothelial cells. Corneal buttons coated with bovine corneal endothelial cells became transparent within 48 hours after keratoplasty and remained transparent thereafter. Pictures were taken 120 days (cat 1, A and D), 85 days (cat 2, B and E), and 235 days (cat 3, C–F) following keratoplasty. A, B, and C show the cat heads; keratoplasty was performed on the left eyes. D, E, and F show a close-up of the left eyes.

4. In Vivo Transplantation of Vascular Endothelium Maintained in Tissue Culture

The previous studies, in addition to demonstrating the feasibility of using corneal endothelial cells maintained in tissue culture for keratoplasty, allow us to develop new methods for the study of other types of endothelial cells, which are located in less accessible places, to permit the study of their physiological properties. Particularly interesting in this regard is the vascular endothelium of the large vessels which, in species such as the cat, monkey, and human, retains its proliferative capacity, while the corneal endothelium of the same animals does not proliferate. This type of vascular endothelium shares a number of characteristics with corneal endothelium. They both have the same morphology, being both composed of a highly contact-inhibited cell monolayer. They both function as a selective barrier and have a nonthrombogenic surface. They manufacture basement membranes that are similar in composition (type IV collagen and fibronectin). Although the principal difference between vascular and corneal endothelia resides in their transport polarities (from blood toward tissues in the vascular endothelium, as opposed to a transport from stroma toward aqueous humor for the corneal endothelium), this difference may not hold for the vascular endothelium of the large vessels, since denudation of the intima of the aorta will result in local edema. The vascular endothelium transplanted into the eye could therefore function as a corneal endothelium.

To investigate this possibility, we have transplanted in rabbit eyes, rabbit corneal buttons coated with bovine vascular endothelial cells. To date, out of 9 animals carrying these grafts, 8 have a clear cornea (Fig. 41), while one is slightly hazy. This demonstrates conclusively that vascular endothelial cells

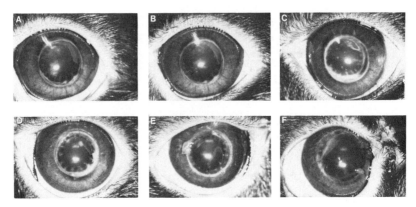

FIG. 41. Morphological appearance of rabbit corneal buttons grafted on rabbits and coated with bovine vascular endothelial cells. The grafted corneal button was coated with vascular endothelial cells for 4 hours, and became transparent 1 hour after keratoplasty (photographed 50 days after surgery). (A), (B), (C), (D), (E), and (F) represent 6 different rabbits.

derived from big vessels or from the heart and grown in tissue culture for an extended period of time can substitute *in vivo* the corneal endothelium. Therefore, these cells are capable of performing the same function as that of the corneal endothelium when transplanted on denuded cornea.

5. Significance of These Studies

Our results demonstrate that corneal endothelial cells maintained in tissue culture remain functional. As soon as they are transplanted *in vivo*, they resume their main function, which is that of maintaining the state of deturgescence of the cornea, thereby preventing edema formation. In this respect, early-passage corneal endothelial cells (20 generations) are as functional as late-passage corneal endothelial cell cultures (200 generations). If one considers that, after 200 generations, one original cell has given rise to a progeny of 10^{60} cells which cover a total surface area of 10^{44} km^2 (if one accepts that the surface area of one cell is 100 μm^2), the potential of the tissue culture approach for generating huge quantities of corneal endothelium suitable for transplantation studies in species in which corneal endothelial cells do not proliferate becomes obvious.

The capacity of the corneal endothelium grown in tissue culture to be transplanted is considerably enhanced by the rapidity with which the cells plated and reorganized themselves into a monolayer when placed on homologous or heterologous corneas denuded of their endothelium. This allowed new methods of transplantation, since one has only to wait 2 hours between the removal of a damaged cornea and its transplantation back into the same recipient. This technique was used infrequently with the rabbit, since we wanted to operate under the worst possible conditions (edematous cornea) so that we would be able to follow the progressive stages of the corneal clearing. However, with cats, where we transplanted an autologous cornea coated with heterologous endothelium, we used a 2-hour plating time, and this proved to be invariably successful. Transplantation of the cornea of the recipient back into the same recipient has enormous advantages. The corneal button thus prepared will be in perfect condition and free of edema from the outset. The possibility that the blood vessels will grow in the stroma of the cornea is therefore minimized. The rejection phenomenon, which could only involve the endothelium (since it is the only tissue of foreign origin) becomes, in turn, exceedingly unlikely. Under such conditions, it is feasible to transplant vigorously growing and functional endothelia into species, such as the human, in which corneal endothelium does not proliferate and therefore has only a limited capacity to participate in wound repair. The demonstration that the vascular endothelium can be substituted for the corneal endothelium when transplanted back *in vivo* may further simplify the keratoplasty since, instead of using a corneal endothelium of different species, one could use the vascular endothelium of the recipient grown in tissue culture to coat its own cornea and to replace the deficient corneal endothelium. Furthermore, since the cornea of the recipient coated with the vascular endothelium remains clear, one could easily perform physiological studies on it, now made impossible by lack of access to the vascular endothelium *in vivo*.

ACKNOWLEDGMENTS

This work was supported by Grants HL 20197 and EY 02186 from the National Institutes of Health. I. Vlodavsky is a recipient of the Chaim Weizmann Research Training Fellowship. We wish to thank Ms. Helene Guillemin for her invaluable assistance in the preparation of this manuscript.

REFERENCES

Ali, I. U., Mautner, V., Lanza, R., and Hynes, R. O. (1977). *Cell* **11**, 115.
Aursnes, I. (1974). *Microvasc. Res.* **1**, 283.
Basu, S. K., Anderson, R. G. W., Goldstein, J. L., and Brown, M. S. (1977). *J. Cell Biol.* **74**, 119.
Bell, E. T. (1954). "Diabetes Mellitus." Thomas, Springfield, Illinois.
Birdwell, C. R., Gospodarowicz, D., and Nicolson, G. (1977). *Nature (London)* **268**, 528.
Birdwell, C. R., Gospodarowicz, D., and Nicolson, G. (1978). *Proc. Natl. Acad. Sci. U.S.A.* **75**, 3273.
Boone, C. W., Takeichi, N., Paranjpe, M., and Gilden, R. (1976). *Cancer Res.* **36**, 1626.
Bretscher, M. S., and Raff, M. C. (1975). *Nature (London)* **25**, 43.
Craw, T. E., Koschinsky, T., Hayes, S. B., and Steinberg, D. (1976). *Lancet* **1**, 1315.
Fielding, P. E., Vlodavsky, I., Gospodarowicz, D., and Fielding, C. J. (1979a). *J. Biol. Chem.* **259**, 749.
Fielding, C. J., Vlodavsky, I., Fielding, P., and Gospodarowicz, D. (1979b). *J. Biol. Chem., in press.*
Goldminz, D., Vlodavsky, I., and Gospodarowicz, D. (1979). *Exp. Eye Res., in press.*

442   D. GOSPODAROWICZ ET AL.

Goldstein, J. L., and Brown, M. S. (1977). *Annu. Rev. Biochem.* **46**, 897.

Gospodarowicz, D. (1975). *J. Biol. Chem.* **250**, 2515.

Gospodarowicz, D. (1976). "Progress in Clinical and Biological Research Membranes and Neoplasia: New Approaches and Strategies" (V. T. Marchesi, ed.), pp. 1–19. Liss, New York.

Gospodarowicz, D., and Greenburg, G. (1979a). *Exp. Eye Res.* **28**, 147.

Gospodarowicz, D., and Greenburg, G., (1979b). *Exp. Eye Res.* **28**, 249.

Gospodarowicz, D., and Moran, J. S. (1974). *Proc. Natl. Acad. Sci. U.S.A.* **71**, 4584.

Gospodarowicz, D., and Moran, J. S. (1977). *In* "Cell Culture and Its Application" (R. T. Acton and J. D. Lynn, eds.), pp. 55–81. Academic Press, New York.

Gospodarowicz, D., and Zetter, B. (1977). "Joint WHO/IABS Symposium on the Standardization of Cell Substrates for the Production of Virus Vaccine," p. 109. Karger, Basel.

Gospodarowicz, D., Moran, J. S., and Bialecki, H. (1976a). *Int. Symp. Growth Horm. Related Pept. 3rd., Excerpta Med. Found., Int. Congr. Ser.* **381**, 141.

Gospodarowicz, D., Moran, J., Braun, D., and Birdwell, C. R. (1976b). *Proc. Natl. Acad. Sci. U.S.A.* **73**, 4120.

Gospodarowicz, D., Mescher, A. L., and Birdwell, C. R. (1977a). *Exp. Eye Res.* **25**, 75.

Gospodarowicz, D., Moran, J. S., and Mescher, A. L. (1977b). "Molecular Control of Proliferation and Cytodifferentiation" (J. Papaconstantinou and J. W. Rutter, eds.), Vol. 35, p. 33. Academic Press, New York.

Gospodarowicz, D., Moran, J., and Braun, D. (1977c). *J. Cell Physiol.* **91**, 377.

Gospodarowicz, D., Vlodavsky, I., Bialecki, H., and Brown, K. (1978a). *In* "Fifth Brook Lodge Meeting on Novel Aspects of Reproductive Biology" (C. H. Spilman and J. W. Wilks, eds.), p. 107. Spectrum, New York.

Gospodarowicz, D., Brown, K. D., Birdwell, C. R., Zetter, B. R. (1978b). *J. Cell Biol.* **77**, 774.

Gospodarowicz, D., Vlodavsky, I., Fielding, P., and Birdwell, C. R. (1978c). *In* "Birth Defects" (J. W. Littlefield and J. de Grouchy, eds.), Excerpta Med. Found., Amsterdam. pp. 233–271.

Gospodarowicz, D., Greenburg, G., Bialecki, H., and Zetter, B. R. (1978d). *In Vitro* **14**, 85.

Gospodarowicz, D., Greenburg, G., and Birdwell, C. R. (1978e). *Cancer Res.* **38**, 4155.

Gospodarowicz, D., Vlodavsky, I., Greenburg, G., and Birdwell, C. R. (1978f). "Growth Requirements of Vertebrate Cells in Vivo" (R. G. Ham, C. Waymouth, and P. J. Chapple, eds.), p. 688. Cambridge Univ. Press, London and New York.

Gospodarowicz, D., Mescher, A. L., and Birdwell, C. R. (1978g). *In* "Gene Expression and Regulation in Cultured Cells" *(Natl. Cancer Inst. Monogr.)* **48**, 109.

Gospodarowicz, D., Greenburg, G., and Alvarado, J. (1979a). *Proc. Natl. Acad. Sci. U.S.A.* **76**, 464.

Gospodarowicz, D., Greenburg, G., Vlodavsky, I., Alvarado, J., and Johnson, L. K. (1979b). *Exp. Eye Res.* (in press).

Gospodarowicz, D., Vlodavsky, I., Greenburg, G., and Johnson, L. K. (1979c). *In* "Hormones and Cell Culture." Cold Spring Harbor Laboratory Press, Cold Spring Harbor, New York (in press).

Grayson, M., and Keates, R. H. (1969). "Manual of Diseases of the Cornea." Little, Brown, New York.

Gryglewski, R., Banting, S., Moncada, S., Flower, R. J., and Vane, R. J. (1976). *Prostaglandins* **12**, 685.

Hogan, M. J., Alvarado, J., and Weddell, J. (1971). "Histology of the Human Eye. An Atlas and Textbook." Saunders, Philadelphia.

Hsu, T. C., and Benirschke, K. (1975). "An Atlas of Mammalian Chromosomes," Vol. 1, p. 47. Springer-Verlag, New York.

Hynes, R. O., and Destree, A. (1977). *Proc. Natl. Acad. Sci. U.S.A.* **74**, 2855.

Inomata, H., Smelser, G. K., and Polack, F. M. (1970). *Am. J. Ophthalmol.* **70**, 48.

Liu, S.-C., and Karasek, M. (1978). *J. Invest. Dermatol.* **71**, 157.

Nichols, W. W., Levans, A., Hansen-Melander, E., and Melander, Y. (1965). *Hereditas* **53**, 63.

Nicolson, G. L. (1976). *Biochim. Biophys. Acta* **458**, 1.

O'Farrell, P. Z., Goodman, H. M., and O'Farrell, P. H. (1977). *Cell* **12**, 1133.

Perlman, M., and Baum, J. L. (1974). *Arch. Ophthalmol.* **92**, 235.

Rheinwald, J. C., and Green, J. (1977). *Nature (London)* **265**, 421.

Rudland, P. S., Seifert, W., and Gospodarowicz, D. (1974). *Proc. Natl. Acad. Sci. U.S.A.* **71**, 2600.

Ruoslahti, E., and Vaheri, A. (1975). *J. Exp. Med.* **141**, 497–501.

Silverstein, S. C., Steinman, R. M., and Cohn, Z. A. (1977). *Annu. Rev. Biochem.* **46**, 669.

Slick, W. C., Mannagh, J., and Yuhaz, A. (1965). *Arch. Ophthalmol.* **73**, 229.

Stein, O., and Stein, Y. (1976). *Biochim. Biophys. Acta* **431**, 363.

Stein, O., Weinstein, D. B., Stein, Y., and Steinberg, D. (1976). *Proc. Natl. Acad. Sci. U.S.A.* **73**, 14.

Stemerman, M. B., and Spaet, T. H. (1972). *Bull. N. Y. Acad. Med.* **48**, 289.

Stenman, S., and Vaheri, A. (1978). *J. Exp. Med.* **145**, 1054.

Stocker, F. W. "The Endothelium of the Cornea and Its Clinical Implication," 2nd ed., p. 214. Thomas, Springfield, Ill.

Stocker, F. W., Eiring, A., Georgiade, R., *et al.* (1958). *Am. J. Ophthalmol.* **46**, 294.

Stocker, F. W., Eiring, A., Georgiade, R., *et al.* (1959). *Am. J. Ophthalmol.* **47**, 772.

Sun, T. T., and Green, H. (1977). *Nature (London)* **269**, 489.

Van Horn, D. L., and Hyndiuk, R. A. (1975). *Exp. Eye Res.* **21**, 113.

Van Horn, D. L., Hyndiuk, R. A., Seideman, S., Buco, P. J., and de Bruin, J. (1978). *In* "Proceedings of Scanning Electron Microscopy," Part V, pp. 285-290.

Vlodavsky, I., and Sachs, L. (1975). *Exp. Cell Res.* **96**, 202.

Vlodavsky, I., and Sachs, L. (1977). *Exp. Cell Res.* **105**, 179.

Vlodavsky, I., Fielding, P. E., Fielding, C. J., and Gospodarowicz, D. (1978). *Proc. Natl. Acad. Sci. U.S.A.* **75**, 356.

Vlodavsky, I., Johnson, L. K., Fielding, P., and Gospodarowicz, D. (1979a). *J. Cell. Physiol.*, in press.

Vlodavsky, I., Johnson, L. K., and Gospodarowicz, D. (1979b). *Proc. Natl. Acad. Sci. U.S.A.*, in press.

Weinstein, D. B., Carew, T. E., and Steinberg, D. (1976). *Biochim. Biophys. Acta* **424**, 404.

Weksler, B. B., Marcus, A. J., and Jaffe, E. A. (1977). *Proc. Natl. Acad. Sci. U.S.A.* **74**, 3922.

Yamada, K. M., Yamada, S. S., and Pastan, I. (1976). *Proc. Natl. Acad. Sci. U.S.A.* **73**, 1217.

Zetter, B. R., Martin, G. R., Birdwell, C. R., and Gospodarowicz, D. (1978). *Ann. N. Y. Acad. Sci.* **312**, 299.

DISCUSSION

A. White: I am surprised that I can speak because this splendid presentation and its implications leave me almost breathless. I hesitate to ask questions or make suggestions because I am certain that Dr. Gospodarowicz has thought of all the things that I have in mind. Obviously, the integrity of the endothelial cells in the vascular system will modulate the extent of plaque formation. Do you know what is the rate of fibronectin turnover and the factors that may control its synthesis and degradation? Is the concentration of this protein in the endothelial cell membrane a critical factor in determining the functional integrity of the endothelial cell?

D. Gospodarowicz: Thank you, Dr. White. I will first answer your question about fibronectin. Little is known about the rate of fibronectin turnover *in vivo*. Yamada has recently studied its synthesis and cellular transfer *in vitro* in chick fibroblasts [K. Y. Yamada, *J. Cell Biol.* **78**, 520 (1978)]. In cultures maintained at low density, fibronectin is localized to extracellular fibrillar structures under and between the cells, as well as to intracellular, diffusely granular structures. This intracellular localization is apparently due to recently synthesized fibronectin located in intracellular pools, such as endoplasmic reticulum, before export to the cell surface. By isotopic labeling procedures, such pools were found to contain 10% of the fibronectin synthesized over 24 hours. Treatment of cells with the protein synthesis inhibitors cycloheximide or puromycin results in a progressive decrease in this intracellular immunofluorescent staining, which is complete in 2 hours. The staining returns after removal of the protein synthesis inhibitors. These findings suggest that it is possible to analyze the kinetics and exact pathways of secretion of this glycoprotein.

As far as the factors that may control its synthesis are concerned, it is widely agreed that cellular contact appears to precede the formation of fibronectin protein networks. Because the fibronectin network appears to be interlinked throughout the confluent monolayer, cellular contact may be a physical prerequisite for the formation of such networks. In addition to cell–cell interaction, hormonal effect can also modulate the synthesis of fibronectin. Lai Bo Chen *et al*. [L. B. R. Chen, R. C. Gudor, T. T. Sun, A. B. Chen, and M. W. Mosesson, *Science* **197,** 776 (1977)] have reported that, while 3T3 cultures maintained in the presence of 0.7% serum had a low level of fibronectin, addition of EGF restored the normal 3-dimensional networks of fibronectin.

As concerns the factors that destroyed the fibronectin, obviously proteases, specifically those produced by cells *in vitro*, can destroy fibronectin. Whether such mechanisms are operational *in vivo* is questionable; further studies will be required in this field. As regards the production of prostacyclin *in vitro* by vascular endothelial cells, preliminary studies done at Syntex by Dr. J. Bruno have indicated that those cells produced prostacyclin *in vitro,* but that they required arachidonic acid in order to produce maximal amounts of the factor. We have not done any experiment of denudation with cultures exposed to platelets *in vitro* in order to determine whether the cells could release prostacyclin and thereby inhibit the aggregation of platelets and release phenomenon.

R. Levine: I want to add my own appreciation to that of Dr. White. It was an absolutely magnificent talk. I would just like to make some remarks and then ask some questions in relation to the LDL being internalized. For some time now we have been collaborating with Professor Wayland at California Institute of Technology, who has what he has called the whole-body microscope, which can observe the mesenteric blood vessels and the capillaries *in vivo*. We have utilized this to make some fluorescent lipoproteins; that is, the apoproteins are made fluorescent and therefore they become visible and we look at them on a TV screen. The most interesting finding we have had is that, when insulin is given, LDL goes into the endothelial cell; HDL does not. Without insulin there is very little penetration. The reason for doing these experiments is an old suspicion based on a long set of findings in the literature that insulin is proatherogenic. This stems from the work of Lyman Duff in 1951, which has been confirmed over and over again but has been neglected. This is, of course, important, especially in considering the therapy of the adult, obese diabetic who has a high insulin level. I wonder, then, whether you would try to see whether adding some insulin to the culture would improve the internalization of LDL?

D. Gospodarowicz: We never exposed the cultures to insulin. Therefore, I could not speculate on what would happen in this case. What you have observed with the capillary endothelium *in vivo* could also occur with the vascular endothelium maintained *in vitro*. In that context, I would like to point out that the vascular endothelium we work with is derived from the big vessels (aortic arch) or the heart and is therefore strictly contact inhibited. Capillary endothelia, with the exception of those of brain and muscles, are known not to be as contact inhibited as that lining the big vessels. In fact, in endocrine organs, kidney, or liver they are fenestrated and are not contact inhibited. Therefore, what could be observed with the capillary endothelium will be difficult to reproduce with the endothelium of the big vessels. Now, I can tell you one more thing. As soon as I return to the laboratory, I will add some insulin to the cultures to see what happens.

M. Sherman: Shinitzky and Inbar have demonstrated that lipid fluidity and protein mobility in biological membranes are functions of the ratio of cholesterol to phospholipid in the membrane [*Biochim Biophys. Acta* **433,** 133 (1976)]. Do you think it possible that one mechanism of FGF alteration of membrane fluidity is mediated by its effects on LDL binding and consequent cholesterol uptake, in addition to the mechanism involving the cross-linking of fibronectin that you proposed?

D. Gospodarowicz: I do not know. I cannot comment on that.

H. Friesen: Could you clarify for us the relationship between pituitary and brain FGF? I ask this question especially as, to my knowledge, myelinated fibers are not very extensively represented in the pituitary.

D. Gospodarowicz: There is no correlation between the primary structures of pituitary FGF and brain FGF, although both mitogens affect the same cell types as does EGF in some cases. Brain FGF has been shown to be a fragment (residues 44 to 153) of the myelin basic protein [F. C. Westall, V. A. Lennon, and D. Gospodarowicz, *Proc. Natl. Acad. Sci. U.S.A.* **75**, 4675 (1978)]. Tryptic mapping of the pituitary FGF has demonstrated that it is of a different structure. One of the reasons we first investigated the structure of the brain FGF is that a kilogram of brain costs 60 cents, while a kilogram of pituitary costs $110. More time will therefore be required to accumulate enough materials for structural studies.

F. Naftolin: Your beautiful talk brings to mind another tissue system that may be governed by the same principles and have a similar therapeutic and physiologic role. The placental membranes fit many of the criteria you describe and are being implicated in prostaglandin and cholesterol by-product metabolism. The amnion is a single layer with an interface with amniotic fluid and the chorion. It might use a fibronectin backing and function in an analogous way to other epithelia. This may give greater insight into the mechanisms of amniotic fluid kinetics, the onset of labor and furnish material for autografts as you described. Is there fibronectin in the placental membranes?

D. Gospodarowicz: I do not have any experience with amnion or amnionic cells and can therefore only speculate. I think that every time you have a single-cell monolayer exposed on one side to a tissue and on another side to a fluid, if that cell monolayer is contact inhibited, and if it plays the role of a selective barrier function, there can be a unique polarity in the distribution of fibronectin, which will be found on the cell side exposed to the tissue but not on that exposed to the amniotic fluid. Therefore, since it is likely that fibronectin will be extensively cross-linked, it could also play a role in attaching the cell monolayer to its substrate, thereby restricting the lateral mobility of receptor–ligand complexes and limiting their rate of internalization. If those cells, when maintained in culture, had an apical, nonthrombogenic cell surface, I would not be too astonished if fibronectin did accumulate on the basal part of the cells, establishing a cell polarity of structure and function. Interestingly enough, it has recently been reported that the amniotic fluid contains fibronectin [E. Crouch, G. Balian, K. Holbrook, D. Duksin, and E. Bornstein, *J. Cell Biol.* **78**, 701–715 (1978)]. The more I think about your comment, the more merit it appears to me to have.

J. Kellett: When you grow cells up in endothelial cell cultures with fibroblast growth factor, what happens to them when you withdraw the fibroblast growth factors?

D. Gospodarowicz: When you remove the FGF, the cells do not die. They simply either do not divide or divide at a much slower rate. The most striking thing is the morphological appearance of the cultures, which, at confluence, do not consist of a highly contact-inhibited cell monolayer but are composed of large cells growing in multiple layers. Concomitant with loss of contact inhibition is a loss in the nonthrombogenic properties of the cells and the appearance of fibronectin on the apical cell surface. Therefore, the cells have lost their polarity of cell surfaces and function which characterizes the vascular endothelium.

J. Kellett: Does any amount of serum prevent this from happening? Does that mean that there is no fibroblast growth factor in serum?

D. Gospodarowicz: With a particular batch of serum, if the cells look abnormal in 10% serum, they will look even more so in 50% serum. However, if you look hard enough, you always find a good batch of serum. According to Dr. Sorgente's laboratory, out of 10 batches of fetal calf serum, only 1 may be good for growing endothelial cells without FGF. We do not bother to look. We simply add FGF to any batch of calf serum. It could be in platelets. It may be that it is not released from organs (whatever they are) under normal circumstances, but only in case of wounds. If you cut a nerve, you will generate it locally.

J. Kellett: Does it react immunologically with platelets?

D. Gospodarowicz: One should pose this question to Dr. H. N. Antoniades and Dr. C. D. Scher *(Natl. Cancer Inst. Monogr.* **48**, 137 (1978)].

A. L. Southern: One of the major applications of your work could be to a study of the mechanism of glaucoma. In this particular condition there is an increased resistance to outflow of aqueous and cell surface phenomena and it may play a role in preventing the movement of the fluid through the trabecular meshwork, where it normally occurs. One of the substances that may interfere with the outflow of aqueous is a coating of fibronectin on the trabeculum, where it should not be present normally. It may occur, however, in patients with glaucoma due to some defective response to fibroblast growth factor. Also cortisol may be involved somehow, since most glaucoma patients are sensitive to cortisol in that they show an excessive increase in intraocular pressure in response to topical ocular administration of the steroid. When you visited my laboratory a few months ago, you mentioned that you have been able to obtain cell cultures from the trabecular area. I just wonder if you have more recent findings into the relationship of fibronectin, cortisol, and glaucoma?

D. Gospodarowicz: So that I may avoid any confusion with my colleagues at U.C.S.F., when I visited your laboratory I spoke on corneal endothelium, not on the trabecular cell.

A. L. Southern: I know that you have participated in studies in which you grew cells from the trabecular meshwork.

D. Gospodarowicz: That is correct. But I would like to say that this is not my work—it is the work of Jon Polansky, John Baxter and Jorge Alvarado. As a matter of fact, John Baxter could comment if he was not gone fishing. I will say that, on the basis of their work, it appears that trabecular cells do contain fibronectin between the cells and that they do respond to glucocorticoids. They seem to have a receptor site for glucocorticoids. However, I think the best way to obtain an answer to your question would be to ask Jon Polansky or Jorge Alvarado at U.C.S.F.

J. Kowal: It is obvious from the early part of your talk that the terms fibroblast growth factor and epidermal growth factor may be meaningless when we see the spectrum of cells they affect. Is there any pattern of activity of these two compounds you can discuss in relation to the embryonic origin of the cells?

D. Gospodarowicz: Work being done on epidermal growth factor and embryonic tissue covers two areas. One is the cleft palate, the work being done at the NIH by Dr. Pratt. The other area is the maturation of the embryonic lung, and this work is being done at Vanderbilt University. Otherwise, I do not know of any work on embryonic tissue done with growth factors.

L. Kornel: I would like to further extend the issue raised already briefly by one of the previous discussants, i.e., that of the possible hormonal control of the fascinating cellular growth phenomena discovered by you. Since fibroblasts are known to be one of the main target tissues to glucocorticoids, which dramatically inhibit growth and proliferation of these cells, and these steroids also have a well-known effect on vascular endothelium, I wonder if you would care to comment on the possibility that glucocorticoids may be involved in the control of fibronectin secretion.

D. Gospodarowicz: I do not have the slightest idea. I have never worked in that field, so I cannot comment. Your comments do, however, raise many interesting problems.

L. Kornel: I believe that it may be of considerable interest to study such a possibility. I would like to add that we have recently found specific, high-affinity receptors to glucocorticoids in the cytosol of arterial wall homogenate. Their precise location, regarding individual cellular components of the arterial wall (endothelium, smooth muscle, fibroblasts) is being presently investigated by us. The very presence of such receptors in the arterial wall (these cytoplasmic receptor–steroid complexes do translocate to cell nuclei, as shown by us recently [*Meet. Endocrine Soc. 60th,* Abstr. 119 (1978)]) strongly suggests that these steroids are involved in the control mechanism of some of the biological processes of arterial wall cells.

We have also found high-affinity receptors to mineralocorticoids in the cytosol of arterial wall homogenate, which are distinctly different from the glucocorticoid receptors. The question that comes to mind is the possible role of mineralocorticoids as demonstrated by your accumulation of low-density lipoproteins in the arterial smooth muscle following endothelial injury. If indeed a mechanism exists in the arterial wall, by means of which elevated plasma levels of mineralocorticoids would effect increased sodium ion and water flux into the cells, this may well result in a "swelling" of the endothelial cells, and, consequently their increased vulnerability to injurious factors.

G. Richardson: The fact that fibronectin is a normal basement membrane constituent suggests that it might be useful as a coating material on tissue culture flasks to promote the early adherence of epithelial cells. Has this been tried?

D. Gospodarowicz: Yes, cold insoluble globulin has been used for this purpose.

K. Sterling: In the beautiful data in which you showed that strictly contact-inhibited cells could internalize LDL only when the layer was disrupted, that is, "wounded," you drew the conclusion that vascular endothelium of large vessels are impervious to LDL, and hence, LDL does not get to the vascular smooth muscle cells ordinarily, but they are exposed to high concentration of LDL only in response to endothelial injury. Of course I would love to believe this, but what bothers me is that, under clinical circumstances such as in the homozygotic hereditary hypercholesterolemia, Brown and Goldstein have shown such enormous premature atherosclerosis in the homozygotes, whereas you would expect only isolated lesions as if it were isolated, occurring only at sites of endothelial injury. I wonder whether you definitely meant to extend these intriguing *in vitro* findings to the pathological situation *in vivo,* and how would you put it together, in human pathology—if you actually wanted to make that extension? I was not quite clear on that.

D. Gospodarowicz: Most of what I describe is within what we call "normal situations"—not pathological situations. I never had the occasion to work with endothelial cells derived from patients that have hypercholesterolemia, so I do not know what those cells would look like, nor what their metabolism would be. *In vivo* measurements have shown that in hypercholesterolemia a decreased number of LDL receptors is associated with an elevated rate of LDL synthesis and a lower rate of degradation. Both changes lead to an increased (6- to 10-fold) level of plasma LDL-cholesterol. This will certainly accelerate atherosclerosis, but the presence of a damaged endothelium is still believed to be a prerequisite [J. L. Goldstein and M. S. Brown, *Annu. Rev. Biochem.* **46,** 897 (1977)]. Once the smooth muscle cells are exposed to plasma, they are stimulated to proliferate and migrate into the intima, and the cholesterol released from the LDL ingested by these cells starts to accumulate as cholesteryl esters. In addition, receptor-negative cells show a much higher degree of *de novo* cholesterol synthesis despite the presence of high extracellular levels of LDL. This, together with a nonspecific uptake process that might become significant in view of the higher quantities of LDL in plasma, might further contribute to the depositing of cholesteryl esters on the artery wall. So, unless I examine these cells from those patients and know their characteristics, it would be extremely difficult for me to speculate on their nature.

H. Friesen: What is known of the mechanism of action of FGF? Are there, for example, receptors for FGF? Are these cAMP-dependent mechanisms? and so on? Could you elaborate please?

D. Gospodarowicz: The only thing firmly established is that FGF greatly increased nutrient transport, as demonstrated by D. C. Quinlan and J. Hochstadt [*J. Cell. Physiol.* **93,** 237 (1977)] and by M. Nilsen Hamilton and R. T. Hamilton [*J. Cell. Physiol.* **89,** 795 (1976)]. FGF also induces phosphorylation of specific cell surface proteins (Hamilton, personal communication). As far as nucleotides are concerned, cAMP was first shown to come down while cGMP was going up [P. S. Rudland, D. Gospodarowicz, and W. E. Seifert, *Nature (London)* **250,** 761 (1974)], when cells were maintained in the presence of serum. Pastan's group obtained exactly the reverse effect with cells maintained in the presence of plasma [W. B. Nesbitt, W. B. Anderson, Z. Miller, T. R. Russell, D. Gospodarowicz, and I. Pastan, *J. Biol. Chem.* **251,** 2344 (1976)]. Therefore, I do not think that the problem of the effect of FGF or even that of EGF on nucleotides has yet been resolved.

H. Friesen: What about receptors for FGF?

D. Gospodarowicz: We did work extensively on the EGF receptor sites using the granulosa cell–luteal cell model [I. Vlodavsky, K. Brown, and D. Gospodarowicz, *J. Biol. Chem.* **253,** 3744 (1978); D. Gospodarowicz, I. Vlodavsky, H. Bialecki, and K. Brown, *in* "Novel Aspects of Reproductive Biology" (C. H. Spilman and J. Wilks, eds.), p. 107. Spectrum, New York, 1978]. EGF binds in granulosa cells to specific receptor sites.

After binding, the EGF receptor site complexes are internalized and degraded. Luteal cells, which do not respond to EGF, have 10 times as many receptor sites and internalize as well as degrade the EGF receptor complexes. Since cells that do not respond to a mitogen will internalize the mitogen as well as cells that do respond, we are left with a lot of questions but very few answers.

As far as FGF is concerned, we were precluded from doing binding studies because of the high

(9.6) isoelectric point of the factor, which binds to everything and gives a very high background. I believe that Dr. Todaro has done some binding studies with FGF using cells in suspension.

H. Friesen: Could you tell us about the tissue distribution of receptors for FGF in normal tissues? Are they widely distributed or not?

D. Gospodarowicz: I can guess, but I cannot answer specifically because we do not have any binding studies with FGF. We do it mostly with EGF. Depending upon the cell type, we see which responds to FGF. The results are quite varied, and the same thing is true with EGF, as shown by Frati and his group.

F. Naftolin: Since the amnion may be important as I described in an earlier comment, and since the onset of labor is timed by an unknown event, it would be important to know what controls the entry of things like LDL into amniotic cells. You mentioned dextran, but do you know of other factors, either hormonal or nonendocrine, that could control the increased entry of LDL into otherwise normal appearing cells?

D. Gospodarowicz: We have observed *in vitro* that any denatured material that will stick to the cell membrane in an unspecific way and will bypass the high-affinity receptor site for that agent will automatically induce a massive endocytosis by the cell. It's like tickling a cell—they will start to absorb everything—so whatever agent does not have the right conformation and can bypass its normal receptor site by sticking in an unspecific way to the cell surface will get inside the cell within 15 minutes. Whether it will be transported through the cells I do not know, but in the process of getting inside it will take in its wake any agent binding to specific receptor sites, if the latter are localized next to the nonspecific binding sites. As examples, one could cite dextran, which induces tremendous endocytosis, or cationized LDL [S. K. Basu, R. G. W. Anderson, J. L. Goldstein, and M. S. Brown, *J. Cell Biol.* **74,** 119 (1977)].

Testis-Organizing H-Y Antigen and the Primary Sex-Determining Mechanism of Mammals

Susumu Ohno, Yukifumi Nagai, Salvatrice Ciccarese, and Hikaru Iwata

Department of Biology, City of Hope National Medical Center, Duarte, California

I. Introduction

Admittedly, a rather large number of fish species, such as sea basses, practice a synchronous or an asynchronous form of hermaphroditism. Furthermore, all-female parthenogenic or gynogenic species are found even among reptiles. Nevertheless, one should not be misled by the above-noted exceptions, for the fact remains that a great majority of the vertebrates, including fish and amphibians, have always been gonochorists having the chromosomal sex-determining mechanism based on either the XX/XY scheme of male heterogamety or the ZW/ZZ scheme of female heterogamety. While the antiquity of the vertebrate chromosomal sex-determining mechanism is beyond question, the genetic sex of fish and amphibians can easily be reversed to either direction by larval exposure to sex steroid hormones. Even in avian species, the administration of estradiol-17β or its precursors appears to induce ovarian development of the genetically male ZZ gonad.

The uniqueness of mammals lies in the clear partitioning of their sex-determining mechanism into two components: the primary or gonadal determination, and the secondary or extragonadal sex determination. By this partitioning, the first component became independent and beyond the reach of sex steroids. The gene product or products responsible for the organogenesis of heterogametic gonads must be as ancient as vertebrates themselves. At the stage of fish, amphibians, and possibly also of reptiles and even birds, the expression of this gene product has remained inducible in the homogametic sex and suppressible in the heterogametic sex by sex steroids. Only in mammals did its expression become constitutive and heterogametic sex specific.

As to the secondary sex-determining mechanism, since mammalian fetuses of both sexes develop in a maternal environment dominated by female sex steroids, the estradiol dependence of feminine differentiation would have necessitated a new evolutionary innovation that renders the genetically male fetus estradiol insensitive. Quite understandably, extragonadal differentiation toward the feminine direction became an inherent and consitutive process not requiring induction by female steroids. Although masculine extragonadal differentiation of mammalian male fetuses has to be induced by testosterone, since genetically female fetuses are incapable of fetal testosterone synthesis, there was no need to render them androgen nonresponsive. Inasmuch as XX extragonadal cells are as androgen responsive as their XY counterparts, their sex chromosome constitution plays no role in the secondary sex-determining mechanism. Thus, we see a reasonable evolutionary economy in the partitioning of the mammalian sex-determining mechanism into two components.

The one that initiates the mammalian sex determination obviously is the male-specific, constitutive gene product responsible for testicular organogenesis, for testosterone production by fetal Leydig cells and antimüllerian hormone production by fetal Sertoli cells are programmed consequences of the testicular organogenesis. This product has been identified as the evolutionary conserved plasma membrane component serologically detectable as H-Y antigen (Wachtel et al., 1975b). Thus, in a very strict sense, the primary sex of mammals is determined not so much by the presence or the absence of the Y chromosome, but rather by the expression or nonexpression of H-Y antigen; witness H-Y antigen positive XX males in man (Wachtel et al., 1976a), the mouse (Bennett et al., 1977), the dog (Selden et al., 1978), and the goat (Wachtel et al., 1978). The cause of testicular organogenesis in the absence of the Y may be an autosomal dominant gene as in the mouse (Cattanach et al., 1971) or autosomal recessive gene as in the goat (Hamerton et al., 1969). In one rodent species, Ellobius lutescens, the H-Y antigen positive male normally lacks the Y chromosome, having the XO sex chromosome constitution (Nagai and Ohno, 1977). Conversely, fertile XY females of another rodent species, Myopus schisticolor, apparently caused by an X-linked mutation (Fredga et al., 1976) failed to express H-Y antigen (Wachtel et al., 1976b).

At a more experimental level, a free suspension of newborn testicular cells of the mouse and the rat from which H-Y antigen had been lysostripped by an excess of H-Y antibody readily reaggregated to form ovarian primordial follicle-like structures, instead of testicular seminiferous tubule-like structures (Ohno et al., 1978a; Zenzes et al., 1978). Conversely, a free suspension of bovine fetal ovarian cells exposed to H-Y antigen reaggregated to form seminiferous tubule-like structures (Ohno et al., 1979), XX gonadal cells that became Sertoli and Leydig cells in XX/XY chimeric testes of the mouse were endowed with H-Y antigen (Ohno et al., 1978b), and so were XX gonadal cells of testis-like bovine freemartin gonads (Ohno et al., 1976).

The following constitutes a progress report from this laboratory on the study of testicular organogenesis under the direction of H-Y antigen.

II. Male Specific but Ubiquitous Expression of H-Y Antigen and Its Consequences

Although we suspect that different organogenesis-directing roles will be assigned to many of the so-called minor histocompatibility antigens that have thus far been defined only by various immunological means, this class of developmentally important plasma membrane antigens, as of today, is represented only by testis-organizing H-Y antigen. Accordingly, the study of H-Y antigen gives us a considerable insight into the general rule that governs the behavior and function of organogenesis-directing plasma membrane components.

Any plasma membrane antigen that directs an organogenesis should express itself before the commencement of that organogenesis, and in embryonic development, organogenesis occurs very early, preceding the differentiation of component cell types or histiogenesis. Furthermore, since an organogenesis-directing gene is likely to occupy the top of a regulatory hierarchy consisting of many genes, such a gene by definition is not placed under the stringent control of any other gene. All in all, one thus expects the expression of organogenesis-directing antigens that begins very early in the embryonic development to be ubiquitous, instead of being cell-type specific. H-Y antigen indeed becomes detectable as early as at the 8-cell stage of preimplantation male embryos (Krco and Goldberg, 1976), and its subsequent expression is quite ubiquitous, being found on all the cell types of male bodies that have been subjected to the study.

The consequence of the above-noted ubiquitous expression verified on H-Y antigen and presumed to be the general rule applicable to all other organogenesis-directing antigens is that the plasma membrane of early embryonic cells must be occupied by multitudes of organogenesis-directing antigens. It follows then that, at the commencement of testicular organogenesis, H-Y antigen has to drive out most of the irrelevantly expressed organogenesis-directing antigens from the plasma membrane of future male gonadal cells, virtual monopolization by H-Y antigen of the plasma membrane constituting the initial commitment toward testicular organogenesis. Such monopolization requires the dissemination of H-Y antigen by gonadal cells. Indeed, our quantitative H-Y antibody obsorption tests revealed that, compared to adult male spleen cells, fetal and newborn testicular cells of the mouse are endowed with 5 to 10 times greater numbers of H-Y antigen sites. In addition, free H-Y antigen disseminated by testicular cells has been found in the epididymal fluid of adults rats (Müller et al., 1978).

Quite obviously, H-Y antigen does not exist as an integral component of the plasma membrane. As it enjoys the freedom of leaving from and returning to the male gonadal plasma membrane, it must stay on the male plasma membrane via its anchorage site. Furthermore, unless all organogenesis-directing antigens utilize the same plasma membrane anchorage site, a competitive displacement of irrelevantly expressed organogenesis-directing antigens with a relevant one at the onset of each organogenesis becomes impossible. This plasma membrane anchorage site function for all organogenesis-directing antigens has been assigned to ubiquitously expressed β_2-microglobulin major histocompatibility (β_2-m-MHC) antigen dimers (Ohno, 1977).

III. Physical Association between H-Y Antigen and β_2-m-MHC Antigen Dimers

H-2 dependence or restriction of the cell-mediated immune response directed against H-Y antigen became known soon after its discovery as one of the minor histocompatibility antigens (Eichwald and Silmser, 1955). The consistent rejection of male skin grafts by females with the mean graft survival time of 25.6 days was observed only within the inbred strains of the H-2^b haplotype, whereas within the H-2^k inbred strains, females accepted male skin grafts 87% of the time. More recently, it has been shown again in the mouse that lysis of male targets by anti-H-Y cytotoxic T lymphocytes of the female is as H-2 dependent or restricted as that of virally infected or transformed targets by cytotoxic T cells (Simpson and Gordon, 1977; Ciccarese and Ohno, 1978). While the above suggests the physical association on the male plasma membrane between H-Y antigen and the β_2-m-H-2 (MHC of the mouse) antigen dimer, this suggestion would not be acceptable to those who advocate the two T-cell receptor model as the cause of H-2 restriction in T-cell killings. Fortunately, there are other more convincing evidences of the proposed physical association that do not involve T lymphocytes.

In the presence of complements, mouse H-Y antibody raised in the H-2^b (e.g., C57BL6 or C57BL10) strain is potently cytotoxic to spermatozoa and male epidermal cells of H-2^b and H-2^d haplotypes, while it is hardly cytotoxic to male H-2^k targets (Scheid et al., 1972). In man, an even more stringent HLA restriction has been observed on the male specific cytotoxicity of H-Y antibody. Human H-Y antibody is generated only when HLA compatible male donors and female recipients share HLA-A2 determinant, and that human H-Y antibody, so obtained, lyse only those male targets that carry HLA-A2 determinant (Goulmey et al., 1977; van Leeuwen et al., 1977). The above clearly indicate that humoral H-Y antibody is directed against a hybrid antigen consisting of H-Y and β_2-m-MHC dimers. Yet, this MHC restriction in the male-specific cytotoxicity of H-Y antibody contrasts sharply with the same antibody's capacity to absorb H-Y antigen of all mammalian species (Wachtel et al., 1975a). It would appear that evolutionary conserved H-Y antigen attached to any variant of its plasma membrane anchorage site can readily be absorbed by H-Y antibody because of the general conformational similarity among all variants of the β_2-m-MHC antigen dimer even of different species. To be cytotoxic, by contrast, a portion of the amino terminal antigen-binding site of H-Y antibody has to find the exact fit with the characteristic conformation of a particular MHC allelic variant against which it was raised.

For reasons that are not very clear, antigen–antibody complexes, formed on the plasma membrane of live cells, gather over one pole of the cell. This is known as the capping phenomenon. The capped antigen–antibody complexes are subsequently autophagocytized—the lysostripping phenomenon. Thus, by the use of an appropriate anti-plasma membrane-antigen antibody, one can denude the plasma membrane of a particular antigen for a period determined by the half-life of that antigen. When the male plasma membrane was capped with regard to β_2-microglobulin, H-Y antigen was also found within the cap (Fellous et al., 1978). The observed cocapping indicated that β_2-microglobulin and H-Y antigen are in physical association on the male plasma membrane. H-2 antigen of the mouse and HLA antigens of man, however, did not cocap with H-Y antigen (Geibs et al., 1977; Fellous et al., 1978). Taken at the surface value, the above can be taken to mean that on the plasma membrane of male cells, H-Y antigen directly forms a dimer with β_2-microglobulin. This, however, makes no sense. It is the hydrophobic core of MHC antigens (M. W. 45,000) that renders β_2-m-MHC antigen dimers to be the integral component of the plasma membrane. Since β_2-microglobulin, being made of only 110 amino acid residues, has no hydrophobic core of its own, only the possession of a hydrophobic core by H-Y antigen would anchor β_2-m-H-Y antigen dimers to the plasma membrane. Yet, by having a hydrophobic core, H-Y antigen forfeits the freedom of leaving from the plasma membrane to function as a short-range hormone. We shall now show that the reason for the failure of H-Y antigen to cocap with H-2 antigens of the mouse is found in the masking effect of H-Y antigen. By associating, H-Y antigen covers many of the antigenic determinants of H-2 antigens, rendering them inaccessible to anti-H-2 antibody.

One unique feature of lymphocytes and other free wandering cells is that they do not engage in organogenesis of any sort. Consequently, their plasma membrane anchorage sites are only sparsely occupied by ubiquitously expressed organogenesis-directing antigens, all of which are totally irrelevant to these cells. Accordingly, most of their β_2-m-MHC antigen dimer sites are in the unoccupying state that permits the full exposure of MHC antigenic determinants. Indeed, anti-H-2 antibodies are extremely cytotoxic to mouse spleen cells; nearly 100% killing up to 1:128 antibody dilution. In sharp contrast, when confronted with constituent cells of any solid organ, anti-H-2 antibody's much vaunted cytotoxicity becomes an acute embarrassment. For example, anti-H-2 antibody is no more cytotoxic than H-Y antibody toward male epidermal cells; 50% killing up to 1:16 dilution. Not surprisingly, the presence of H-2 antigens is not demonstrable on much of fetal and neonatal cells by the cytotoxicity test.

In the presence of complements, anti-H-2^d (B6/AKR anti-BALB Meth. A sarcoma) antibody is not at all cytotoxic to a free suspension of newborn H-2^d

testicular cells of the BALB/c strain (Fig. 1). Yet when 60 μl of the above-noted anti-H-2^d antibody in 1:16 dilution was repeatedly absorbed with the total of 28 × 10^6 BALB newborn testicular cells, roughly 75% of anti-H-2K^d activity and roughly 25% of the anti-H-2D^d activity were removed from anti-H-2^d antibody. It should be recalled that mammalian species are endowed with two closely linked gene loc for ubiquitously expressed MHC antigens; H-2D and H-2K loci of the mouse and HLA-A and HLA-B loci of man. In the mouse, the availability of recombinant strains enabled us to measure separately anti-H-2D^d activity and anti-H-2K^d of this anti-H-2^d (H-2D^{d}H-2K^d) antibody on spleen cells of two recombinant strains: B10A (5R) which is H-2D^{d}H-2K^b and BALB-H-2^g which is

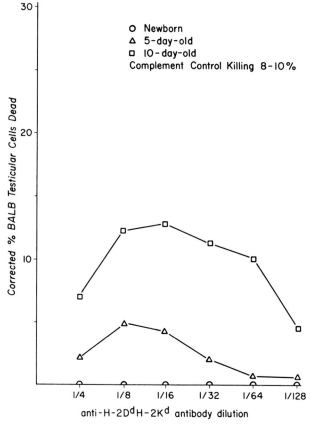

FIG. 1. The total cytotoxic insensitivity to anti-H-2^d (B6/AKR vs. BALB Meth. A sarcoma) antibody of BALB newborn testicular cells and a gradual postnatal acquisition of the anti-H-2^d cytotoxic sensitivity by these testicular cells are shown. Agarose-absorbed guinea pig complements were used in all cytotoxicity tests. A free suspension of testicular cells was obtained by the double enzyme treatment: First with 0.5% collagenase and then with 0.5% trypsin (Ciccarese and Ohno, 1978). The dead cell percentage did not exceed 10%.

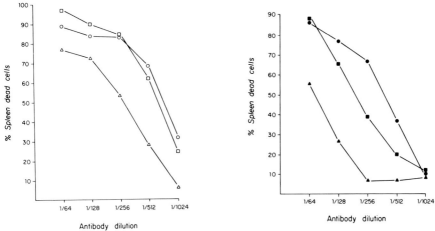

FIG. 2. The total resistance of newborn BALB/c mouse testicular cells to the cytotoxic effect of anti-H-2D^{d}H-2K^d (B6/AKR vs. BALB Meth. A sarcoma) antibody is not due to the absence of H-2^d antigenic determinants on their plasma membrane, as evidenced by the capacity of these cells to absorb many of the specificities of anti-H-2^d antibody noted above. *Left:* The cytotoxicity of unabsorbed anti-H-2D^{d}H-2K^d antibody toward adult female spleen cells of BALB/c (H-2D^{d}H-2K^d) ($\square$) and two recombinant strains; B10A (5R) (H-2d^{d}H-2K^b) ($\bigcirc$) and BALB-H-2^g (H-2D^{b}H-2K^d) ($\triangle$). This antibody was as cytotoxic to B10A (5R) target cells as to BALB/c cells, although only H-2D^d antigenic determinants were recognized on the former. Its cytotoxicity directed only against H-2K^d antigenic determinants of BALB-H-2^g targets, however, was considerably less. *Right:* Reduced cytotoxicities toward the same set of three targets caused by the absorption of the same anti-H-2D^{d}H-2K^d antibody with BALB/c newborn testicular cells: 28 × 10^6 cells per 60 µl of 1:16 diluted antibody. The absorption more markedly reduced the antibody's anti-H-2K^d activity as measured on BALB-H-2^g targets ($\blacktriangle$) (roughly 75% reduction) than anti-H-2D^d activity as measured on B10A (5R) targets ($\bullet$) (roughly 20% reduction). Of the two types of anchorage sites (β_2m-H-2D^d and β_2m-H-2K^d) on the BALB testicular plasma membrane, associating H-Y antigen apparently masked more H-2D^d antigenic determinants than H-2K^d antigenic determinants. $\blacksquare$, BALB/c (H-2D^{d}H-2K^d) targets.

H-2D^{b}H-2K^d. Figure 2 compares the cytotoxicity toward spleen cells from BALB/c and the two above-noted recombinant strains of unabsorbed anti-H-2^d antibody (left) with that of the same antibody repeatedly absorbed with BALB newborn testicular cells (right). It should be noted that the absorption reduced markedly more of anti-H-2K^d activity as measured on BALB-H-2^g cells than anti-H-2D^d activity measured on B10A (5R) cells. The above apparently established not only the presence on the BALB newborn testicular plasma membrane of β_2-m-H-2D^d as well as β_2-m-H-2K^d antigen dimer, but also the masking effect of H-Y antigen, which is markedly uneven with regard to H-2D^d and H-2K^d antigenic determinants.

As the reciprocal experiment of the above, we then immunized male B6 (H-2D^{b}H-2K^b) mice with BALB newborn testicular cells. If more of the antigenic determinants of H-2D^d are made inaccessible by associating H-Y antigen, we then expect anti-H-2^d activity of the antibody so obtained to be directed primarily against H-2K^d antigenic determinants. This indeed was found to be so (Fig. 3). While this antibody was weakly cytotoxic to B1OA (5R) spleen cells that measured anti-H-2D^d activity, it was nearly as cytotoxic to BALB H-2^g spleen cells as to BALB/c cells. Indeed, most of the anti-H-2^g activity of this B6 anti-BALB-newborn-testicular antibody was directed against H-2K^d antigenic determinants (Fig. 3).

From the above, one can deduce with reasonable certainty that, on the plasma membrane of BALB newborn testicular cells, nearly all the β_2-m-H-2D^d and β_2-m-H-2K^d antigen dimer sites are occupied by testis-organizing H-Y antigen and that this association renders a large portion of H-2D^d and a smaller portion of H-2K^d antigenic determinants inaccessible to anti-H-2^d antibody. The total resistance of fetal and newborn testicular cells to the cytotoxic effect of anti-MHC antibodies has now been explained. Although the observation noted above can be

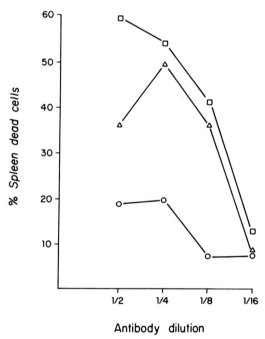

FIG. 3. The cytotoxicity toward the same set of three targets of anti-BALB newborn testicular cell antibody raised in 2-month-old male B6 (H-2d^{b}H-2K^b) mice by four weekly injections of 5 × 10^6 newborn testicular cells. In the presence of guinea pig complements, this antibody was not cytotoxic to newborn BALB testicular cells against which it was raised. Neither was it cytotoxic to adult spleen cells of wrong H-2 haplotypes; e.g., H-2D^{k}H-2K^k of C3H. It was a form of anti-H-2^d antibody directed mostly against H-2K^d antigenic determinants measurable on BALB-H-2^g targets. This was expected from the absorption data summarized in Fig. 1. Targets: □, BALB/c (CH-2K^{d}H-2D^d); ○, B1OA (5R) (H-2K^{b}H-2D^d); △, BALB-H-2^g (H-2K^{d}H-2D^b).

explained by the following two alternatives, neither can account for the total resistance to the cytotoxic effect of anti-H-2^d antibody displayed by H-$2D^d$H-$2K^d$ newborn testicular cells: (1) On the BALB newborn testicular plasma membrane, H-Y antigen preferentially associates with β_2-m-H-$2D^d$ antigen dimer sites, leaving β_2-m-H-$2K^d$ antigen dimers in the unoccupied state. (2) On the same plasma membrane, the expression of H-$2D^d$ antigen is suppressed, while existing β_2-m-H-$2K^d$ antigen dimers are either not in association with H-Y antigen or such an association does not interfere with the accessibility of H-$2K^d$ antigenic determinants. It should be pointed out here that in spite of the masking effect by H-Y, the number of H-$2K^d$ sites per BALB newborn testicular cells detected by the absorption capacity appeared not much less than that per adult BALB spleen cells, for 21×10^6 adult spleen cells were required to achieve the degree of absorption of anti-H-$2K^d$ activity achieved by 28×10^6 newborn testicular cells, shown in Fig. 2 right. The above finding is schematically summarized in Fig. 4.

IV. β_2m($-$), HLA($-$) Daudi Human Male Burkitt Lymphoma Cells as the Source of Free H-Y Antigen

This requirement of testis-organizing H-Y antigen to have its plasma membrane anchorage site implies that, in a mutational absence of β_2m-MHC antigen dimers, the stable plasma membrane expression of H-Y antigen by male cells should become impossible. The $\beta_2$microglobulin gene of man is located near the long-arm distal end of chromosome 15, and this position appears to be particularly vulnerable for a deletion. Accordingly, a number of established human cell

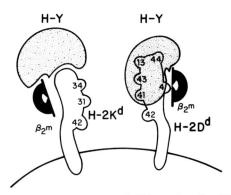

FIG. 4.   H-Y antigen that occupied all the β_2m-H-$2D^d$ as well as β_2m-H-$2K^d$ antigen dimer sites during the act of testicular organogenesis (gestational day 12) continue to monopolize these anchorage sites on the plasma membrane of BALB newborn mouse testicular cells. H-Y antigen by association masks all the antigenic determinants of H-$2D^d$ as well as H-$2K^d$, rendering them totally inaccessible to anti-H-2^d antibody as its cytotoxic targets. The association of H-Y antigen with β_2m-H-$2K^d$ antigen dimer, however, is not as tight as that with β_2m-H-$2D^d$ antigen dimer. Accordingly, H-$2K^d$ antigenic determinants 31, 34, 42 can still function as immunogens as well as absorptogens, but not as cytotoxic targets.

lines are characterized by a complete or partial mutational deficiency of β_2-microglobulin which apparently causes the suppression of HLA antigen expression (Nilsson *et al.*, 1974). The above fact and the availability of totally β_2m($-$), HLA($-$) Daudi human male Burkitt lymphoma line as well as partially deficient Simpsson 8226 human male myeloma line were kindly pointed out to us by George Klein of Stockholm. Quantitative mouse H-Y antibody absorption tests were performed on the above two cell lines and their appropriate controls, and the number of cells required for 50% absorption of the male-specific cytotoxicity contained in 50 μl of 1:4 diluted H-Y antibody was determined on each. The number of H-Y antigen sites on the Daudi plasma membrane was found to be only 20% of the control. Reduction to 30% of the control value was also noted in Simpsson 8226. Inasmuch as somatic hybridization with HeLa D98 human female cell line simultaneously restored the expression of Daudi HLA antigens A10 and BW17 and that of the control H-Y antigen level, the mutational lack of β_2m-HLA antigen dimer anchorage sites was clearly responsible for 80% deficiency of H-Y antigen sites on the Daudi plasma membrane (Beutler *et al.*, 1978). Subsequently, the absence of H-Y antigen sites on the Daudi plasma membrane was reported by Fellous *et al.* (1978). Thus, we were left with two possibilities. The total absence of its anchorage sites is causing either a drastic reduction in the H-Y antigen synthesis or continuous excretion of H-Y antigen by Daudi human male Burkitt lymphoma cells. In the event of the latter proving true, Daudi becomes an excellent source of free H-Y antigen. Accordingly, we devised the following method to collect excreted proteins of Daudi cells. Exponentially growing Daudi cells were transferred to the protein-free RPM1 1640 culture medium at the concentration of 0.67 to 1 million cells per milliliter and maintained for the period of 16 hours. While no increase in the percentage of dead cells was noted at the end, each 1 million Daudi cells excreted on the average 10 μg of proteins into the culture medium during the above period. These culture media containing excreted proteins of Daudi were stored frozen. Subsequently, they were pooled and concentrated 50-fold in cold. When the concentrated Daudi culture medium so obtained was used as the organ culture medium for bovine XX embryonic indifferent gonads after adding Ig-free fetal calf serum to the concentration of 20%, it passed the ultimate test of containing active H-Y antigen, as we shall shortly see.

V. Identification of Daudi H-Y Antigen in Solution and the Property of Gonad-Specific H-Y Antigen Receptors

In order to identify free H-Y antigen among the Daudi excreted proteins, we first labeled these proteins with [³H]lysine. To the protein-free RPM1 1640 culture medium in which Daudi cells were to be maintained for the period of 16 hours, 5 μCi of [³H]lysine were added per milliliter to make the labeled-to-cold lysine ratio in the medium 1:74. In one particular series of experiments to be

described here, 104 ml of RPMl 1640 culture medium in which a total of 147 ×
10^6 Daudi cells excreted their proteins was concentrated in the cold to 2.0 ml by
ultrafiltration. Unincorporated [^{3}H]lysine was removed from the above concentrated Daudi medium by passing it through a Sephadex G-25 column; 6.8 ml of
void volume eluates were then concentrated to 2.0 ml and subjected to ultracentrifugation at 100,000 g for 1 hour to remove membrane fragments and other
particulates. At this point, we were thus in the possession of 1.428 mg of Daudi
excreted proteins in solution labeled with 1.004 × 10^6 cpm of tritium counts.

As the next step, these labeled Daudi proteins were loaded on a Sephadex
G-200 column equilibrated with 0.15 M Nacl, Tris·HCl buffer pH 7.2 isotonic
solution. The G-200 elution profile thus obtained is shown in Fig. 5. These
eluates were separately pooled to form four fractions, and each fraction was
again concentrated to 3.0 ml. It should be noted that fraction II (tubes 13–40) and
fraction III (tubes 41–57) contained most of the Daudi proteins; 48.9% and
23.0%, respectively. As there apparently were virtually no Daudi excreted
proteins in the 8–9 S range, fraction I virtually a cleanly separated void volume
peak containing 13.9% of the total proteins. Fraction I apparently contained not
so much proteins of very large molecular weights, but rather a collection of
hydrophobic proteins that formed large aggregates, for when 3.0 ml concentrate
of fraction I was subjected to ultracentrifugation again at 100,000 g for 1 hour,

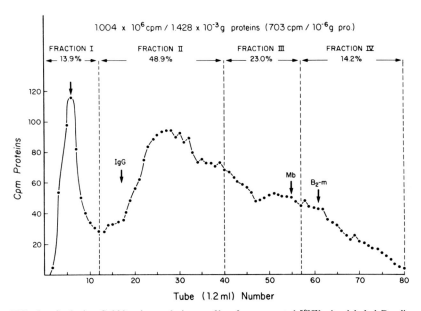

FIG. 5.   Sephadex G-200 column elution profile of concentrated [^{3}H]lysine-labeled Daudi excreted proteins. Aside from Dextran blue used as a void volume marker, molecular weight markers
used were IgG of MW 150,000, Mb (myoglobin) of MW 17,800, and β_2-microglobulin of MW
12,000. Counts per minute were for 1/10 of each tube containing 1.2 ml.

30% of the total counts per minute was lost in the precipitates. Fractions II, III, and IV formed no appreciable precipitates. Most of the small proteins and polypeptides contained in fraction IV appeared to be of molecular weights less than 10,000, for during the concentration procedure two-thirds of fraction IV counts per minute passed through the ultrafiltration membrane to be eliminated with dialyzates.

For the identification of Daudi H-Y antigen in one or more of the above four fractions, we decided to use primarily the gonad-specific H-Y antigen receptor residing on the plasma membrane of bovine fetal ovarian cells. Daudi H-Y antigen thus absorbed on the ovarian cell surface can then be studied by the absorption test using H-Y antibody. As befits its role as the master determiner of the mammalian primary (gonadal) sex, the H-Y antigen expression by males is not stringently regulated, being constitutive as well as ubiquitous. What is it then that confines the developmental role of H-Y antigen to the gonad? Inasmuch as organogenesis requires not only a relevant plasma membrane antigen, but also its specific membrane-bound receptor, an evolutionary economy of not adding an unnecessary complication to the already taxed regulatory system dictates that only one of the two components noted above be made organ-specific by the stringent regulation. Thus, it was proposed that the expression of specific membrane-bound H-Y antigen receptors is confined to gonadal cells only, but of both sexes (Ohno, 1976). The bisexual expression of the H-Y antigen receptor was predicated by the observation that, if endowed with exogenous H-Y antigen, XX gonadal cells readily differentiate into testicular Leydig and Sertoli cells as already noted (Ohno, 1976; Ohno et al., 1978b).

Such specific membrane-bound H-Y antigen receptors should not be confused with the ubiquitously present anchorage site provided by β_2m-MHC antigens dimers. Because of a difference in their assigned roles, we expect the former's binding affinity toward H-Y antigen to be several orders of magnitude greater than that of the latter. Indeed, in a balanced XX/XY chimeric male mouse whose entire body was made of roughly one-to-one mixture of male and female cells, we witnessed the XY to XX transfer of H-Y antigen only among testicular Leydig and Sertoli cells, but not among spleen and epidermal cells (Ohno et al., 1978b). After finding an immunologically measurable quantity of free H-Y antigen in the epididymal fluid of adult male rat, Müller et al. (1978) demonstrated the specific absorption of epididymal H-Y antigen by the ovarian membrane preparation and also to a lesser extent by the testicular membrane preparation, while the extragonadal preparations from liver, kidney, brain, and epidermis absorbed no appreciable amount of epididymal H-Y antigen.

While the H-Y antigen receptor sites of bovine fetal testicular cells are nearly saturated by endogenous H-Y antigen, those on the plasma membrane of fetal ovarian cells should be in the unoccupied state. For the receptor assay of Daudi H-Y antigen in fractions I to IV, we have accordingly prepared a suspension of free bovine fetal ovarian cells in the following manner. Fresh ovaries removed from female bovine fetuses near the end of the gestation period were finely minced into cubes of roughly 1 mm^3. These cubes derived from a single ovary (50–100 mg wet weight) were first incubated in 5 ml of 1.0% trypsin solution for 30 minutes at 37°C. Free ovarian cells obtained by this first treatment were discarded; softened cubes that remained were then incubated with 5 ml of 1.0% hyaluronidase solution for another 30 minutes at 37°C. On the average, this second treatment yielded a suspension of 5–15 × 10^6 free ovarian cells per ovary.

For the first series of H-Y antigen tests by the receptor assay, protein concentrations of four fractions were equalized, so that 600 μl of each fraction now contained 4500 cpm (6.7 μg) of Daudi excreted proteins of different kinds. Then 600 μl of each fraction was layered on the top of 7 × 10^6 tightly packed free ovarian cells. After resuspending ovarian cells, each mixture was kept on ice for 30 minutes and then incubated for an additional 30 minutes at 37°C. Ovarian cells were then washed twice in a great excess (10 ml) of 0.15 M NaCl, Tris·HCl buffer pH 7.2 isotonic solution. Tightly cell-bound cpm were then determined. Results of this and the next series of experiments are tabulated in Table I. While marginal absorptions shown by ovarian cells exposed to fractions II, III, and IV could be dismissed as representing trivial low-affinity, high-capacity bindings, the absorption of 161 cpm (0.23 μg of protein) per 7 × 10^6 ovarian cells seen in fraction I was indicative of the high-affinity, limited-capacity binding between Daudi H-Y antigen and the bovine H-Y antigen receptor residing on the fetal ovarian membrane. Accordingly, the next series of experiments was performed by decreasing the number of ovarian cells to 4 × 10^6, while increasing the

TABLE I

H-Y Antigen Surveys of Four Fractions at a Concentration 7500 cpm (10.67 × 10^{-6} gm of Proteins)/ml

	Ovarian receptor assay (membrane-bound cpm)		H-Y antibody absorption (4 × 10^6 exp. ovarian cells per 10 μl ½ H-Y antibody)	
Fraction	At 7 × 10^6 cells per 0.6 ml (cpm)	At 4 × 10^6 cells per 2.2 ml (cpm)	Max. % corrected lysis	Percent absorption[a]
I	161	115	21.5	53.8% (S)
II (N.S.)	62	38	48.5	6.3% (N.S.)
III (N.S.)	14	5	46.2	11.8% (N.S.)
IV	23	13	52.4	0%
		Unabsorbed H-Y antibody	52.4	—

[a] S, significant; N.S., not significant.

volume of each fraction to 2.2 ml. The protein concentration was kept as before. As expected of trivial low-affinity, high-capacity bindings, this condition did not increase marginal absorptions per cell in fractions II, III, and IV. By contrast, the absorption per cell of fraction I increased by 24%, from 23 cpm/10^6 cells to 28.8 cpm/10^6 cells. When these 4×10^6 ovarian cells that bound 115 cpm Daudi fraction I protein were mixed with 10 μl of 1:2 diluted mouse H-Y antibody, incubation for 50 minutes in ice absorbed out 53.8% of the male specific cytotoxicity of H-Y antibody toward male BALB/c mouse epidermal cells. This absorption capacity was roughly equal to that of bovine fetal testicular cells. Thus, it became clear that 115 cpm represented Daudi H-Y antigen that saturated all the available receptor sites offered by 4×10^6 bovine fetal ovarian cells. By contrast, the same number of ovarian cells exposed to other fractions in the second series of experiments acquired only negligible H-Y antibody absorption capacity (Table I).

The above tests showed that the concentration of H-Y antigen in 7500 cpm/ml of fraction I solution was sufficiently above K_d between Daudi human H-Y antigen and the bovine ovarian H-Y antigen receptor so that the complete saturation of all the available receptor sites occurred in the second series, which represented the condition of H-Y antigen being in considerable excess of the available receptor sites. By contrast, 7×10^6 ovarian cells/0.6 ml of fraction I solution of the first series represented the opposite condition of the number of receptor sites exceeding the availability of Daudi H-Y antigen. The last observation indicated to us that, by the use of a very large number of bovine fetal ovarian cells, the complete and selective removal of H-Y antigen from fraction I is possible.

For this purpose, 1 ml of fraction I solution containing 8330 cpm (11.85 μg of proteins) was incubated with 40×10^6 bovine fetal ovarian cells. Saturation of all the available H-Y antigen receptor sites should have transferred 1150 cpm of H-Y antigen to the ovarian plasma membrane. As shown in Table II, however, the actual count obtained was only 416 cpm. The presence in great excess of receptor sites has apparently succeeded in removing most, if not all, H-Y antigen

TABLE II

The Complete Removal of H-Y Antigen from Fraction I by an Excess of Ovarian Receptors [8330 cpm (11.85 $\times$ 10^{-6} gm)/ml]

| | Membrane-bound counts per minute | |
Absorbed cell number	Observed	Expected at the receptor saturation
1st Absorption 40×10^6 cells	416	1150
2nd Absorption 4×10^6 cells	3	115

from fraction I. Indeed, when the supernatant of fraction I was recovered and reincubated with 4×10^6 fresh ovarian cells, appreciable binding to the ovarian plasma membrane no longer occurred (Table II).

In order to identify H-Y antigen as a missing protein subunit in the sodium dodecyl sulfate (SDS) gel, two 1-ml fraction I solutions, one before and the other after the selective removal of H-Y antigen by a large excess of ovarian cells, were differentially concentrated to equalize the counts per minute per milliliter, and 100 μl of each, pretreated with 5% β-mercaptoethanol and 1% SDS, were subjected to electrophoresis in a 0.4×9.2 cm SDS gel. Subsequently, a cylindrical gel was sliced into 45 2-mm-long pieces, and the counts per minute of each slice were determined. Two profiles obtained are superimposed to each other in Fig. 6. A striking peculiarity of fraction I Daudi proteins is that, in apparent contradiction to their elution as a void volume peak, they consisted mostly of smaller subunits of MW less than 50,000. This peculiarity supports our suspicion that fraction I consisted mainly of large aggregates of smaller hydrophobic proteins rather than very large proteins. Larger protein subunits were far more prominent in fraction II. Figure 6 shows that the most prominent peak has a molecular weight of 25,000, which corresponds to Ig-light chains. Daudi lymphoma cells, being of B-cell origin, are known to synthesize a considerable amount of Ig κ-type light chain. However, Ig-light chains eluting as a G-200 void volume peak must have existed as subunits of Ig-M. A subunit peak corresponding in molecular weight to Ig μ-type heavy chain, however, is not readily discernible in Fig. 6. Thus, the identity of the most prominent MW 25,000 peak remains a mystery. Figure 6 (top) shows that only one conspicuous difference separates the two superimposed profiles of fraction I. Disappearance of one rather prominent subunit peak immediately to the left of the MW 12,000 peak coincided with the selective removal of H-Y antigen from fraction I, and this correlation was observed in three repeat experiments. It was thus established that when interchain disulfide bridges were disrupted by the β-mercaptoethanol pretreatment, H-Y antigen dissociated into the monomeric subunit of MW 18,000. We, however, believe that all the H-Y antigen excreted by Daudi cells existed only in polymeric forms, at the saturating concentration, forming huge aggregates of greater than 280,000 MW. It would be recalled that during the concentration of fraction I from 14.4 ml to 3.0 ml immediately following Sephadex G-200 separation, one-third of the total counts per minute precipitated out. Indiscriminate formation of interchain disulfide bridges was responsible for the generation of these irreversibly water-insoluble precipitates. When these precipitates were forcibly dissolved by 5% β-mercaptoethanol, at least 7 hydrophobic subunits were identified in an SDS–gel electrophoresis profile, the H-Y antigen subunit being the smallest.

Once bound to its specific receptor sites, however, the H-Y antigen quickly reverted back to the monomeric form of MW 18,000. By feeding [^{3}H]lysine only to Daudi cells, we were able to label Daudi excreted proteins with 69.9×10^6

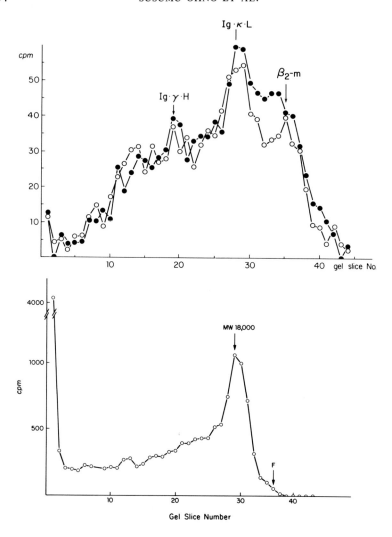

FIG. 6. *Top:* Two sodium dodecyl sulfate (SDS)–polyacrylamide gel electrophoresis profiles of fraction I Daudi excreted proteins are superimposed upon each other. The pretreatment included 5% β-mercaptoethanol and 1% SDS. ●: Fraction I not exposed to bovine fetal ovarian cells. It contained 8330 cpm (11.85 μg) Daudi excreted proteins. ○: Fraction I from which all the H-Y antigen (468 cpm) was removed by 40×10^6 bovine fetal ovarian cells. The selective removal of H-Y antigen resulted in the disappearance of an MW 18,000 protein subunit peak immediately to the right of MW 22,000 Ig κ-type light-chain marker and to the left of MW 12,000 β_2-microglobulin marker.

Bottom: SDS-gel electrophoresis of profile of the membrane fraction of 7.5×10^6 bovine fetal ovarian cells whose receptors were saturated with 33,078 cpm of highly labeled Daudi H-Y antigen. Without the prior disruption of interchain disulfide bridges by β-mercaptoethanol, the MW 18,000 peak, 1073 cpm high, of monomeric H-Y antigen is clearly seen.

cpm/mg in contrast to 1.004×10^6 cpm/mg proteins in the previous experiment. When 7.5×10^6 bovine fetal ovarian cells whose receptors were saturated with 33,07S cpm of highly labeled Daudi H-Y antigen were disrupted by sonication, their membrane fraction without the benefit of 5% βmercaptoethanol pretreatment readily released the monomeric H-Y antigen of MW 18,000 (Fig. 6, bottom).

Going back to the previous experiment, Table II shows H-Y antigen to have comprised 5% of fraction I Daudi proteins (416 cpm/8330 cpm). Accordingly, the two series of experiments summarized in Table I were performed at the H-Y antigen subunit concentration of 0.53 µg/ml. Knowing its subunit molecular weight, the above concentration now becomes $2.67 \times 10^{-8} M$. Inasmuch as at this concentration the saturation of the bovine ovarian H-Y antigen receptor sites occurred, K_d of H-Y antigen toward its gonad-specific receptor is likely to be at least one order of magnitude less than $2.67 \times 10^{-9} M$. This is a rather respectable binding affinity that befits H-Y antigen's organogenesis-directing role. Table I also shows that at saturation 4×10^6 bovine fetal ovarian cells absorbed 115 cpm of H-Y antigen. Since each microgram of Daudi excreted proteins was labeled with 703 cpm of tritium, 115 cpm meant 0.164 µg of H-Y antigen. If the one-to-one binding is assumed between each H-Y antigen monomeric subunit and its specific receptor, it follows that each bovine fetal ovarian cell was endowed with 1.23×10^6 H-Y antigen receptor sites. The above number appears quite reasonable.

Needless to say, in a mutational absence of the gonad-specific H-Y antigen receptor presently defined, testicular organogenesis should fail in H-Y antigen (+) XY individuals. ^{3}H-labeled fraction I Daudi excreted proteins provide us with a means to identify a predicted receptor defect.

VI. Testicular Conversion of Bovine XX Embryonic Gonads by Human Daudi H-Y Antigen

Encouraged by the successful identification of human H-Y antigen subunit among Daudi excreted proteins, we decided to perform the ultimate test of H-Y antigen's biological activity—its ability to induce testicular organogenesis in embryonic indifferent gonads preferably of the XX sex chromosome constitution.

As the source of indifferent gonads, the cattle became a species of choice for the following reasons. (1) In the chromosome complement of the cattle, all 29 pairs of autosomes are acrocentrics; thus, the large metacentric X and the small metacentric Y stand out from the rest. This enabled us to identify the chromosomal sex of early embryos from mitotic figures of hemopoietic cells in the liver (Gropp and Ohno, 1966). (2) Indifferent gonads of bovine embryos 20–30 mm in crown-rump (CR) length (roughly 30–45 gestational days) are large enough (1.2 mm in length) to permit easy isolation from surrounding tissues and subsequent removal. Yet they are small enough to survive 5 days of organ culture.

In the development of bovine embryos, the emergence of gonadal ridges coincides with the abundance of migrating primordial germ cells in the dorsal mesentery in embryos of 10–12 mm CR length; approximately gestational day 28. While the migration of primordial germ cells continues, the gonad remains in the indifferent stage until embryos reach the 30-mm CR length. The first sign of sexual differentiation is seen in the distribution pattern of primordial germ cells; most of the germ cells of XX embryos remain in the periphery, keeping at a distance from the central somatic blastema of the gonad, whereas most of the germ cells of the XY embryo invade the central somatic blastema and soon a few testicular cords emerge deep within the central somatic blastema. Nevertheless, male gonads do not acquire the true testicular characteristics in the form of tunica albuginea and seminiferous tubules until embryos reach the 45-mm CR length stage (Gropp and Ohno, 1966). For the present organ culture experiment, we have used only indifferent gonads from chromosomally verified XX embryos of CR lengths 25–30 mm.

For the source of Daudi excreted proteins, RPM1 1640 culture median in which Daudi cells have been maintained in the protein-free state for a period of 16 hours were pooled and then concentrated by the ultrafiltration 50-fold. Accordingly, each milliliter came to contain roughly 500 μg of proteins excreted by 50×10^6 Daudi cells. Judging from our findings already discussed, each milliliter must have contained 69.5 μg of fraction I proteins—therefore, 3.5 μg of the MW 18,000 H-Y antigen subunit; the amply high concentration of $1.74 \times 10^{-7} M$ should have saturated all the available H-Y antigen receptor sites of bovine embryonic XX gonadal cells. For organ culture, Ig-free fetal calf serum was added to the above to concentration of 20%, and an embryonic indifferent gonad was maintained in 1 ml of the above culture medium daily refreshed for 5 days.

Each bovine XX indifferent gonad maintained for 5 days in 50-fold concentrated Daudi excreted proteins underwent complete and very precocious testicular differentiation, becoming equipped not only with seminiferous as well as rete tubules, but also with tunica albuginea (Fig. 7). By contrast, its left or right partner maintained for 5 days in 20% Ig-free fetal calf serum with added RPM1 1640 culture medium as the control remained in the indifferent state (Fig. 9). The presence of MW 18,000 H-Y antigen subunit appeared to have immediately stimulated the metabolic activity of an XX indifferent gonad, 1 ml of the Daudi culture medium turning acidic at the end of first 24 hours. Yet not much histological change occurred during the first days. Suddenly at day 4, germ and somatic elements on the surface area that had been degenerating were rapidly replaced by mesenchymal cells that formed an apparent tunica albuginea, by day 5, leaving only scattered patches of coelomic or germinal epithelia at the gonadal surface. The emergence of tubular structures was equally sudden beginning at the end of 3 days. Sertoli cells of the tubular wall as well as the presence of basement

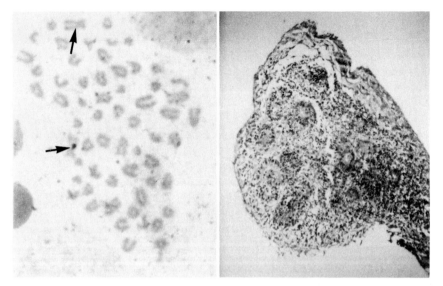

FIG. 7. A hepatic metaphase figure (left) and an embryonic left gonad that underwent precocious testicular transformation (right) of a bovine XX embryo 27 mm in crown–rump length. Lenses used: 100 × 10 (left) and 25 × 6 (right). The presence of two metacentric X-chromosomes and no Y is evident in this mitotic figure (left). Yet, the organ culture for 5 days in 1 ml of daily refreshed 50-fold concentrated Daudi culture medium (RPM1 1640 + 20% Ig-free fetal calf serum) caused the precocious testicular transformation of this XX indifferent gonad. Tunica albuginea, seminiferous tubules as well as rete tubules are seen (right).

membrane became more conspicuous and readily recognizable if transformed gonads were allowed to degenerate a little by maintaining them a little longer in the last milliliter of exhausted culture medium, for degeneration selectively affected interstitial elements (Fig. 7 and 8). Admittedly, the type of testicular transformation induced upon bovine XX embryonic indifferent gonads by concentrated Daudi excreted proteins was very precocious therefore abnormal. This degree of testicular development does not occur even in XY embryonic gonads until embryos reach 45 mm in CR length, as already noted. Nevertheless, the observed transformation verifies the remarkable biological potency of the MW 18,000 H-Y antigen subunit present among Daudi excreted proteins.

In view of the extreme evolutionary conservation of H-Y antigen (Wachtel *et al.*, 1975a), the ability of human H-Y antigen to interact successfully with the bovine gonad-specific H-Y antigen receptor is no surprise. Quite surprisingly, the same Daudi excreted proteins caused no visible alteration on slightly older XX gonads derived from fetuses of 35–45 mm in CR length. It should be recalled that in the Moscona-type reaggregation experiment, an exposure to the concentrated Daudi excreted proteins caused a free suspension of ovarian cells from far older bovine fetuses (170 mm CR length) to reform seminiferous

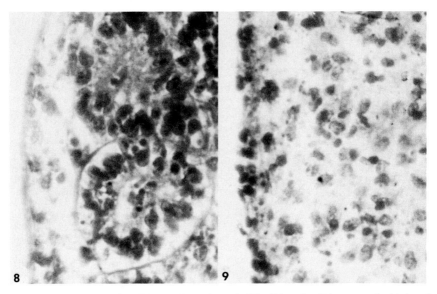

FIGS. 8 and 9.   A portion of the transformed gonad of Fig. 7 (see Fig. 8) is compared with that of
its right partner gonad (Fig. 9) at a higher magnification; lenses used: 45 × 10. The control gonad was
also organ cultured for 5 days in 1 ml of RMP1 1640 + 20% fetal calf serum. The RMP1 1640 culture
medium, however, did not contain proteins excreted by Daudi. Seminiferous tubules of the transformed gonad are lined with Sertoli-like cells having the nuclear morphology of postpubertal Sertoli
cells. Because of the formation of tunica albuginea, germinal or coelomic epithelia disappeared (Fig.
8). The control gonad, by contrast, remained totally indifferent (Fig. 9).

tubule-like structures (Ohno *et al.*, 1979). Perhaps the older fetal gonadal
surface is no longer penetrable by MW 18,000 H-Y antigen active-site fragments.

VII. Summary

Embryonic indifferent gonads of mammals have the inherent tendency to
develop toward the ovary. The precise meaning of this general statement is likely
to be the bisexual expression of the ovary-organizing plasma membrane component and its specific membrane-bound receptor. Testicular organogenesis that
normally, but not always, depends upon the presence of the Y-chromosome is the
responsibility of the two plasma membrane components; the male-specific but
ubiquitously expressed H-Y antigen and its specific receptors expressed only by
gonadal cells, but of both sexes. Of these four components for mammalian
gonadal organogenesis, only the expression of H-Y antigen is confined to the
heterogametic male sex. Accordingly, this plasma membrane component, which
has been conserved in evolution to the extreme, emerges as the master regulator
of the primary (gonadal) sex-determining mechanism of mammals. Its ubiquitous

as well as constitutitve expression in the male reflects its master regulatory role, since a master by definition is not under genetic subjugation.

Testis-organizing H-Y antigen is not an integral component of the plasma membrane. Instead, it utilizes β_2-microglobulin-MHC (H-2 of the mouse and HLA of man) antigen dimers as its plasma membrane anchorage sites. This enables H-Y antigen to play a hormonelike role during testicular organogenesis. By so doing, H-Y antigen drives out the bisexually expressed, rival ovary-organizing antigen from the plasma membrane and virtually monopolizes the β_2m-MHC antigen dimer anchorage sites of male gonadal cells. In the mouse, this monopolization by H-Y renders much of H-2 antigenic determinants inaccessible to anti-H-2 antibody. Hence, fetal and newborn testicular cells are totally resistant to the cytotoxic effect of anti-H-2 antibody.

In the absence of its anchorage sites, H-Y antigen synthesized by β_2m($-$) HLA($-$) Daudi human male Burkitt lymphoma cells is not stably maintained on the plasma membrane. Instead, it is excreted into the culture medium. Accordingly, the concentrated protein-free RPM1 1640 culture medium in which Daudi cells have been maintained for the period of 16 hours served as the starting material for the identification of H-Y antigen in solution. All the biological activities of H-Y antigen were found to be embodied in the monomeric subunit of MW 18,000, although the above subunit forms polymers by interchain disulfide bridges. As H-Y antigen is extremely hydrophobic, at saturation it forms very large aggregates of molecular weight greater than 280,000, thus eluting in a void volume peak from the Sephadex G-200 column. At the saturation concentration of $2.67 \times 10^{-8} M$, this H-Y antigen, after becoming the monomer, saturated the gonad-specific H-Y antigen receptor sites residing on the plasma membrane of bovine fetal ovarian cells, each of which possessed 1.26×10^6 H-Y antigen receptor sites.

Organ culture for 5 days of bovine XX embryonic indifferent gonads in the presence of concentrated Daudi excreted proteins containing roughly $10^{-7} M$ of the H-Y antigen induced precocious testicular organogenesis; the formation of seminiferous as well as rete tubules and of tunica albuginea.

ACKNOWLEDGMENTS

The authors are grateful for the assistance and advice received from Drs. E. A. Boyse, G. C. Koo, S. S. Wachtel, and U. Wolf. This work was supported in part by NIH grant RO1 AG00042, NIH Contract NO1-CB-33907, and the Wakunaga Pharmaceutical company.

REFERENCES

Bennett, D., Boyse, E. A., Mathieson, B. J., Scheid, M., Wachtel, S. S., Yanagisawa, K., and Cattanach, B. M. (1977). *Nature (London)* **265**, 255.

Beutler, B., Nagai, Y., Ohno, S., Klein, G., and Shapiro, I. (1978). *Cell* **13**, 509.

Cattanach, B. M., Pollard, C. E., and Hawkes, S. G. (1971). *Cytogenetics* **10**, 318.

Ciccarese, S., and Ohno, S. (1978). *Cell* **13**, 643.

Eichwald, E. J., and Silmser, C. R. (1955). *Transpl. Bull.* **2**, 148.

Fellous, M., Günther, E., Kemler, R., Wiels, J., Berger, R., Guenet, J. L., Jakob, H., and Jacob, F. (1978). *J. Exp. Med.* **148**, 58.

Fredga, K., Gropp, A., Winkling, H., and Frank, F. (1976). *Nature (London)* **261**, 255.

Geibs, R., Goldberg, E. H., and Klein, J. (1977). *Nature (London)* **270**, 352.

Goulmy, E., Bradley, B. A., van Leeuwen, A., Lansberg, Q., Munro, A., Termijtelen, A., and van Rood, J. T. (1977). *Tissue Antigens* **10**, 248.

Gropp, A. and Ohno, S. (1966). *Z. Zellforsch. Mikrosk. Anat.* **74**, 505.

Hamerton, J. L., Dickson, J. M., Pollard, C. E., Grieves, S. A., and Short, R. V. (1969). *J. Reprod. Fertil.* Suppl. **7**, 25.

Hayman, D. L., and Martin, P. G. (1965). *Genetics* **52**, 1201.

Krco, C. J., and Goldberg, E. H. (1976). *Science* **193**, 1134.

Müller, U., Aschmoneit, I., Zenzes, M. T., and Wolf, U. (1978). *Human Genet.* **43**, 151.

Nagai, Y., and Ohno, S. (1977). *Cell* **10**, 729.

Nilsson, K., Erwin, P. E., and Welsh, K. I. (1974). *Transpl. Rev.* **21**, 53.

Ohno, S. (1976). *Cell* **7**, 315.

Ohno, S. (1977). *Immunol. Rev.* **33**, 59.

Ohno, S., Christian, L. C., Wachtel, S. S., and Koo, G. C. (1976). *Nature (London)* **261**, 597.

Ohno, S., Nagai, Y., and Ciccarese, S. (1978a). *Cytogenet. Cell Genet.* **20**, 351.

Ohno, S., Ciccarese, S., Nagai, Y., and Wachtel, S. S. (1978b). *Arch. Androl.* **1**, 103.

Ohno, S., Nagai, Y., Ciccarese, S., and Smith, R. (1979). *In Vitro* **15**, 11.

Scheid, M., Boyse, E. A., Carswell, E. A., and Old. L. J. (1972). *J. Exp. Med.* **135**, 938.

Selden, J. R., Wachtel, S. S., Koo, G. C., Haskins, M. E., and Patterson, D. F. (1978). *Science,* **201**, 646.

Simpson, E., and Gordon, R. D. (1977). *Immunol. Rev.* **35**, 59.

van Leeuwen, A., Goulmy, E., Bradley, B. A., and van Rood, J. T. (1977). *Tissue Antigens* **10**, 249.

Wachtel, S. S., Koo, G. C., and Boyse, E. A. (1975a). *Nature (London)* **254**, 272.

Wachtel, S. S., Ohno, S., Koo, G. C., and Boyse, E. A. (1975b). *Nature (London)* **257**, 235.

Wachtel, S. S., Koo, G. C., Breg, W. R., Thaler, H. T., Dillard, G. M., Rosenthal, I. M., Dosik, H., Gerald, P. S., Saenger, P., New, M., Lieber, E., and Miller, O. J. (1976a). *N. Engl. J. Med.* **295**, 750.

Wachtel, S. S., Koo, G. E., Ohno, S., Gropp, A., Dei, V. G., Tantravahi, R., Miller, D. A., and Miller, O. J. (1976b). *Nature (London)* **264**, 638.

Wachtel, S. S., Basrur, P., and Koo, G. C. (1978). *Cell* **15**, 279.

Zenzes, M. T., Wolf, U., Günther, E., and Engel, W. (1978). *Cytogenet. Cell Genet.* **20**, 365.

DISCUSSION

W. Hansel: Dr. Ohno, there is a paper soon to be published from Israel in which steroid production by gonads from bovine embryos has been measured. Although, in general, the results seem to agree with what you have been saying, in some cases it appears that bovine embryos younger than 40 days already knew their sex; that is to say, those with male chromosomes were already producing testosterone, females were already producing estrogens. Would you comment on this?

S. Ohno: We too have noted the earlier sign of gonadal differentiation. In the case of XX bovine embryos, migrated primordial germ cells tend to distribute themselves on the surface area of the gonadal ridge directly beneath the coelomic (germinal) epithelium. Whereas, XY primordial germ cells tend to invade that which Alfred Gropp and I identified as the emerging central somatic blastema of the gonad [A. Gropp and S. Ohno, *Z. Zellforsch. Mikrosk. Anat.* **74**, 505 (1966)].

M. New: I want to ask how you envision this HLA in terms of development. Do you envision that all the Y chromosome-containing cells secrete H-Y antigen and that this material circulates as a hormone, or that it diffuses locally? How do you explain the paradox of the situation in which you have individuals in which one gonad is an ovary and the other is a testicle?

S. Ohno: In one ideal XX/XY chimeric male mouse whose whole body was roughly a one-to-one mixture of XX and XY cells, we witnessed the XY-to-XX transfer of H-Y antigen in his testes but not in his spleen and epidermis [S. Ohno, S. Ciccarese, Y. Nagai, and S. S. Wachtel, *Arch. Androl.* **1**, 103 (1978)]. It would appear that only male gonadal cells (more precisely Sertoli cells) actively disseminate H-Y antigen. Accordingly, the effectiveness of H-Y antigen as a short-range hormone must be confined to an individual gonad.

M. New: Then if the Sertoli cells are secreting this, it therefore acts only locally.

F. Naftolin: Dr. Ohno, since you have given mingled H-Y antigen-containing and non-H-Y antigen-producing cells on your allophenic experiment without inducing a freemartin, can we now infer more about the genesis of freemartinism? Also, since H-Y antigen is present in adult cells, one might ask if it has any (regulatory) function after differentiation?

S. Ohno: First of all, I should clarify the bovine freemartin condition based on our own experience. The extreme testislike virilization of freemartin gonads is a rare event, and such a testicular transformation, if it is to occur, begins very late; i.e., after gestational day 90. All that we have shown thus far is that extremely virilized testislike freemartin gonads are characterized by the abundance of H-Y antigen [S. Ohno, L. C. Christian, S. S. Wachtel, and G. C. Koo, *Nature (London)* **261**, 597 (1976)].

F. Naftolin: In this context, why is the marmoset, which regularly has fraternal twins and interplacental transfer of cells and other materials, now showing freemartinism?

S. Ohno: Inasmuch as the same condition (early vascular anastomosis between heterosexual, dizygotic twins) does not affect the ovarian development in marmoset monkeys and man, there must be something peculiar to Bovidae i.e., dissemination of H-Y antigen to the fetal circulation by bovine male fetuses. While we studied the above-noted XX/XY chimeric mouse testis at the adult stage, our study on testislike bovine freemartin gonads was confined to the fetal stage.

F. Naftolin: Are there actions of H-Y antigens later in life?

S. Ohno: I believe that the H-Y antigen expression by extragonadal somatic cells of the male is redundant as well as irrelevant. Witness the observation that males of marsupial species belonging to two genera, *Isoodon* and *Paerameles,* eliminate the Y from many of their extragonadal somatic cell types [D. L. Hayman and P. G. Martin, *Genetics* **52**, 1201 (1965)]. As to the persistent expression of H-Y antigen by adult testicular cells, S. S. Wachtel and I observed that H-Y antigen disappears from spermatozoa of very old mice that became sterile. The above may or may not suggest the necessity of H-Y antigen expression for the maintenance of male fertility.

M. M. Grumbach: We owe a great debt to Dr. Ohno and his associates for providing these fresh insights into a major mystery of the mechanisms of sex determination and differentiation, namely gonadogenesis. Their observations have profound implications for developmental biology, especially organogensis, and they have provided a hypothesis that can be tested. Early in his lecture, Dr. Ohno mentioned the possibility that there is an ovary-organizing antigen—perhaps a counterpart to the H-Y antigen in the female, or a cell membrane component present in both sexes but not effective in the presence of H-Y antigen. Could you discuss this aspect further?

S. Ohno: The general statement that mammalian embryonic indifferent gonads have the inherent tendency to organize ovaries can be equated with the bisexual expression of a yet to be defined ovary-organizing antigen and its specific membrane-bound receptor. Indeed, when deprived of H-Y antigen, newborn testicular cells reorganized ovarian structures as noted in the text. Furthermore, XX/XY chimeric mouse gonads, on rare occasions, develop into functional ovaries [Evans *et al.,* *Nature* **267**, 430 (1977)]. It would appear that, in a favorable circumstance, an ovary-organizing antigen disseminated by XX gonadal cells succeeds in driving out H-Y antigen from neighboring XY gonadal cells and by so doing entices the latter to engage in ovarian organogenesis.

M. M. Grumbach: What is your concept of the interaction of β_2-microglobulin and the H-Y antigen? Is β_2-microglobulin a component of H-Y antigen or is it a ligand for H-Y on the plasma membrane?

S. Ohno: MHC (major histocompatibility) antigens (H-2 of the mouse and HLA of man) having a molecular weight of 45,000 form dimers with β_2-microglobulin (MW 12,000) on the plasma membrane of every cell type of the mammalian body. Striking conformational similarities between β_2m-MHC antigen dimers and half the immunoglobulin molecules (LH dimers) suggest that the amino-terminal region of β_2m-MHC antigen dimers conveniently exposed on the plasma membrane exterior is also endowed with the binding affinity to a certain class of macromolecules. On the basis of the above and many other considerations, I have proposed that the original function of β_2m-MHC antigen dimers has always been to serve as the plasma membrane anchorage site of testis-organizing H-Y antigen and other organogenesis-directing antigens. Rather numerous evidences that support the above notion are discussed in the text. At any rate, in order to function as a short-range hormone, H-Y antigen cannot remain as an integral component of the plasma membrane; hence, the requirement for its anchorage site.

P. K. Donahoe: First, Dr. Simpson equated the H-Y antigen with the weak histocompatibility transplantation antigens and has proposed that a linkage of the H-2 locus with the H-Y antigen is required for expression of the H-Y antigen. Could you elaborate further on the mechanism involved, particularly in reference to β_2-macroglobulin? Second, the ovary of the patient with mixed gonadal disgenesis, contralateral to the dysgenetic testis, often has many changes, particularly in the medullary area, of seminiferous tubular formation. Do you think in that case that H-Y antigen is acting at a distance on the ovary on the contralateral side?

S. Ohno: Dr. Simpson and her colleagues have shown that lysis of male target cells by female anti-H-Y T-cells is as H-2 restricted in the mouse as that of virally infected targets by cytotoxic T cells. The above can be taken to mean that on the male target plasma membrane, the cytotoxic T-cell receptor is recognizing a hybrid antigen made of H-Y and β_2m-MHC antigen dimers. However, there are those who believe in the two T-cell receptor model. As to the second question, with a possible exception of male bovine fetuses already discussed in connection with freemartinism, I do not believe that H-Y antigen can telegraph its message via blood stream. However, in view of extensive genetic polymorphism prevalent in all mammalian species, one cannot exclude the possibility that extragonadal somatic cells of certain exceptional male individuals may actively disseminate H-Y antigen as Daudi β_2m$(-)$, HLA$(-)$ human male Burkitt lymphoma cells indeed do *in vitro*. The blood stream of such individuals may indeed contain a significant level of H-Y antigen.

W. F. Crowley: In the studies that have correlated clinical expression of masculinity with cytogenetic studies of the Y chromosome, the H-Y antigen has been assigned a position near the acrosome of the Y chromosome. If that is true, where is it in the XX male and the XO male?

S. Ohno: While the so-called testis-determining gene of man has been localized in the vicinity of the Y centromere, whether the above denotes the H-Y structural gene itself or the activating regulator of the H-Y structural gene is still debatable. In the case of wood lemmings, it would be recalled that it was an X-linked mutation that produced XY females by suppressing H-Y antigen expression, their paternally derived Y's, by definition are normal. As to the second question, in man the β_2-microglobulin gene resides on chromosome 15, whereas chromosome 6 carries the HLA gene complex.

In man, in a mutational absence of β_2-microglobulin, HLA genes are not expressed, thus resulting in β_2m$(-)$, HLA$(-)$ phenotype of Daudi human male Burkitt lymphoma cells. When Daudi is hybridized with human female cells, such as HeLa D98, however, β_2-microglobulin supplied by the latter restores the expression of Daudi HLA antigens A10 and BW 17. With this restoration of the anchorage site, the normal male H-Y antigen level is also regained by the hybrid plasma membrane.

The XX male condition can be inherited either as an autosomal dominant as in the mouse, the dog, and man or as an autosomal recessive trait as in the goat and man. If one has always to invoke Y-autosome translocations as the cause of the above condition, it becomes necessary to assume the presence in multiple copies of the Y-linked H-Y structural gene; an insufficient number of H-Y gene copies going to an autosome creates a recessive trait, whereas a sufficient number of H-Y gene copies going to an autosome creates an autosomal dominant trait. If, on the other hand, the H-Y structural gene resides on the X, both autosomal dominant and recessive mutations can be viewed as mimics of the Y-linked activating regulator gene.

K. Sterling: I was very intrigued by this, and it raised a number of questions. The beginning of the talk was very interesting. I note your statement that the two sexes of hyenas look almost the same. Am I correct that they can be distinguished only by another hyena?

S. Ohno: I hope so.

K. Sterling: I gathered that hermaphrodites that have a testis on one side and an ovary on the other would exclude any circulation of the "organizer" and the H-Y antigen is local, from the Sertoli cell. Now how about the occasional occurrence of an ovotestis on one side (which often becomes malignant). Does that fit in, and how would it happen?

S. Ohno: My view is as follows: In the XX/XY mosaic or chimeric gonad, testis-organizing H-Y antigen and an yet to be defined ovary-organizing antigen are placed in the competing position vying for the occupation of anchorage sites provided by β_2-m-MHC antigen dimers. Most often, H-Y antigen emerges victorious, causing the mosaic gonad to become a testis. Occasionally, an ovary-organizing antigen manages to defeat H-Y antigen causing the mosaic gonad to become an ovary. Ovotestis develops as a consequence of the rare stalemate, each antigen managing local victories. In fact S. S. Wachtel compared cultured cells derived from a testicular part with those derived from an ovarian part of the human ovotestis and found H-Y antigen only in the former.

K. Sterling: My last question really reflects some confusion. I have not thought about genetics since I studied under the late J. G. Mendel. I was a little confused, I have to admit, about the antibody to H-Y antigen versus the β-2 microglobulin, which I thought I understood you to say becomes a dimer. Now if this is β-2 microglobulin, is this the antibody and would you make it all plain for me?

S. Ohno: My understanding is as follows: H-Y antigen stays on the male plasma membrane by attaching itself to the amino-terminal region of β_2m-MHC antigen dimers. Of the two subunits of this dimer, a smaller β_2-microglobulin is fully exposed on the plasma membrane exterior. It is a hydrophobic core of a larger MHC antigen that makes this dimer an integral component of the plasma membrane.

Your confusion about antigen vs. antibody is quite understandable, for β_2m-MHC antigen dimers have served both as the primodial antigens and as the primordial antibodies. N. K. Jerne's view is that the germ-line gene for antigen-recognizing variable regions of B-cell immunoglobulin as well as T-cell receptors are designed to recognize MHC antigens of the species [N. K. Jerne, *Eur. J. Immunol.* **1,** 1 (1971)]. Thus, β_2m-MHC antigen dimers are primordial antigens against which the immune system pays the greatest attention. On the other hand, light-chain as well as heavy-chain immunoglobulin molecules are made of domains, each consisting of 110 amino acid residues forming one disulfide bridge. For example, each amino-terminal variable region of both light-chain and heavy-chain as well as each light-chain constant region is represented by a single domain, whereas each heavy-chain constant region is made of three tandemly fused domains. Inasmuch as β_2-microglobulin too is made of 110 amino acid residues forming a single disulfide bridge, there is a little doubt that β_2-microglobulin served as the ancestral molecule from which antibody molecules have been derived. In this sense, β_2m-MHC antigen dimers are primordial antibodies.

U. K. Banik: In one of the slides you have a diagram of a mosaic mouse. Can you please tell us if it is possible to produce mosaic mice experimentally by perfusion of male and female blastocysts and transferring them to pseudopregnant animals.

S. Ohno: Since the original experiment by A. K. Tarkowski in 1961, thousands of chimeric mice have been produced by fusing two blastocysts.

F. Naftolin: It seems worth trying to understand the timing and mechanism of the control of H-Y antigen because of the implications for normal and abnormal development. Can we learn something from individuals who have an excess of sex chromosomes. Are there abnormal amounts of H-Y antigen present in these individuals? Similarly is a particular (endocrine) milieu necessary for proper H-Y antigen production and action? You said that if you administered ring A-reduced androgens you were able to change the amount of H-Y antigen in some of your experiments. Could you expand your remarks to include generalities of the endocrine milieu of very early preimplantation? In this regard, perhaps androgen-insensitive individuals might give us some insight. The androgen-insensitive individual develops testes that are very much like prepubertal testes in later life. This occurs despite properly functioning androgen receptors. This would imply that androgens are not important in the very early function of H-Y androgen in organizing the testes.

S. Ohno: In the mouse, the male-specific expression of H-Y antigen begins as early as at the 8-cell stage of preimplantation embryos, and its subsequent expression is ubiquitous as well as constitutive. The androgen independence of H-Y antigen expression is substantiated by the observation that the H-Y antigen level is not affected by *testicular feminization* mutation both in the mouse [D. Bennett *et al., Nature (London)* **257,** 236 (1975)] and man [G. C. Koo *et al., Science* **196,** 655 (1977)]. If Leydig cells of the H-Y antigen organized testis failed to synthesize a sufficient amount of H-Y antigen, a defect should be sought not in H-Y, but elsewhere, e.g., mutational deficiencies of gonadotropins and their releasing factors, of Leydig cell LH receptors, and of steroid synthesizing enzymes.

M. New: One comment in answer to Dr. Naftolin's question: I am fortunate to have heard Dr. Ohno and to have Dr. Wachtel working with me. Dr. Wachtel has examined the H-Y antigen in a genetic male with 17-α-hydroxylase deficiency who was totally androgen deficient and nonmasculinized. In this patient the H-Y antigen was positive. Therefore it is not only the receptor defect in testicular feminization, but also testosterone deficiency, which seems to be unassociated with the expression of H-Y antigen. This brings me to the question that I wanted to ask. Are you safe in considering normal XX females to be truly H-Y antigen negative when one considers that the assays available for measuring H-Y antigen are still rather imprecise bioassays?

S. Ohno: I have already noted that the XX male condition can be inherited as an autosomal recessive trait. The fact that a low level of H-Y antigen expression is quite compatible with the normal female development is implicit in this finding, for heterozygous mothers must be expressing half as much H-Y antigen as their homozygous XX sons.

J. A. Tata: In amphibians and other cold-blooded vertebrates, like fish, sexual differentiation not only occurs late in life, but is reversible, depending on environmental conditions and also steroid hormones. I would therefore like to ask you whether H-Y antigen is needed just to initiate the process of sexual differentiation or whether it is also necessary for maintenance of the sexually differentiated state throughout adult life.

S. Ohno: My understanding is as follows: In fish, amphibians, reptiles, and possibly also in birds, the H-Y antigen expression is suppressible in the heterogametic sex and inducible in the homogametic sex by steroid hormones and other means. Only in mammals did it become male-specific as well as constitutive. By so doing, H-Y antigen elevated itself to be the master regulator of the primary sex-determining mechanism. H-Y antigen is a social climber of a sort. All we know is that the primary function of H-Y antigen in mammals is to induce testicular organogenesis in the embryonic indifferent gonad. However, the fact that adult Sertoli cells continue to disseminate H-Y antigen into the seminal fluid may indicate its later function. I have already noted our observation that spermatozoa of very old, sterile male mice lack H-Y antigen.

G. Richardson: In female birds, the ovary develops on one side only. If that gonad is removed the other gonad sometimes differentiates as a testis. Since the bird is an XX animal, what is the source of the presumed H-Y antigen that is involved?

S. Ohno: You are absolutely correct; as to the cause, I stand by my answer given in response to Dr. Tata's question.

G. Richardson: So the steroid hormone is an H-Y antigen inducer in these animals?

M. M. Grumbach: Y-linkage of the structural gene or genes that code for H-Y antigen is a concept that is rapidly becoming the new central dogma of sex determination. Before we adjourn with this concept firmly imprinted, would you briefly review the critical evidence that the expression of H-Y antigen is linked to the Y?

We have talked previously of the evidence in the Scandinavian wood lemming that the expression of H-Y antigen also is under the control of a gene on the X chromosome. In this species with a skewed sex ratio, Fredga et al. [K. Fredga, A. Gropp, H. Winking, and F. Frank, *Nature (London)* **261**, 255 (1976)] have shown that fertile females can be either XX or XY; the XY females produce only female offspring. You and your associates reported that the XY fertile females are H-Y antigen negative and supported the role of an X-linked gene which restrains or suppresses the expression of H-Y antigen by the Y. In the human being we have advanced the hypothesis that a similar X-linked gene may be operative in the expression of H-Y antigen. Patients who have familial XY gonadal dysgenesis are (but not invariably) phenotypic females, of normal stature, and have bilateral streak gonads; the pattern of inheritance is consistent with an X-linked recessive trait. H-Y antigen has not yet been determined in this clinical disorder, but, should these patients be H-Y antigen negative despite the presence of a Y chromosome, it would add additional support favoring an activator of H-Y antigen on the X chromosome and afford a possible explanation for the pathogenesis of this disorder and the effect of the putative X-linked mutant gene.

S. Ohno: There are essentially two lines of evidence that favor the Y-linkage of H-Y structural gene. In earlier days of skin grafts, Bill Hildemann obtained some evidence that suggested a possible allelism of mouse H-Y antigen [W. H. Hildemann et al., *Transpl. Proc.* **2**, 24 (1970)]. S. S. Wachtel found that the H-Y antigen level of XYY human males was noticeably higher than that of ordinary XY males [S. S. Wachtel et al., *N. Engl. J. Med.* **293**, 1070 (1975)]. My prejudice at the moment, however, is inclined toward the X-linkage of H-Y structural gene.

L. Bullock: The question of whether H-Y antigen is needed for the initial onset of testicular differentiation or its continued maintenance prompts me to ask whether you have had the opportunity to look at H-Y antigen in the rat which carries the H^{re} gene. The young adult male rat is fertile but thereafter develops progressive seminiferous tubular failure similar to the syndrome of adult onset seminiferous tubular failure in man. You usually have an opportunity to study as testis in man only after use of the H^{re} rat, since it can be identified shortly after birth by its coat color pattern, would allow studies early on and might further the understanding of the role of H-Y antigen in the differentiated testis.

S. Cohen: I am a little confused about the antigen–antibody business here. Is this acting as an antigen, or is it produced as an antigen? Why is it called an antigen and how does it act?

S. Ohno: Too much discussion about β_2m-MHC antigen dimers appeared to have caused a confusion about antigen and antibody, and now androgen has been introduced. I hope that we are still talking about testis-organizing H-Y antigen. Any plasma membrane component detected by immunological means shall be defined as an antigen. So long as the immunological means remains as the most sensitive detection method, one should be content with the use of antigens.

S. Cohen: I am talking about the immunological antigen. Does it act immunologically?

S. Ohno: H-Y antigen was discovered by Ernst Eichwald in 1955 as a male-specific, minor histocompatibility antigen in the mouse.

J. C. Beck: How generalizable are your observations with respect to H-Y antigen, and the differentiation of the gonads to other organs? Are there other surface materials that you have been able to identify that control development in other organ systems?

S. Ohno: One great advantage of working with sex-related development is that there are females that possess no testis. This enabled us to identify testis-organizing H-Y antigen. Although there must be a kidney-organizing antigen, liver-organizing antigen, etc., since no viable animals without kidney or liver exist, there is no way of identifying them. In view of their extreme functional importance, I expect this class of antigens to be extremely conserved in evolution displaying little or no allelic or even species differences.

J. C. Beck: So it's an article of faith.

B. E. P. Murphy: I am with Dr. Cohen. I do not understand why you continue to call this the H-Y antigen when you have demonstrated that it has a very important physiological function; if it actually were antigenic and produced antibodies under physiological conditions, you would have no males.

S. Ohno: In our experience, circulating H-Y antibody is found in many multiparous females. These females also generate far more potent anti-MHC antibodies. Yet, even the latter do not kill MHC incompatible fetuses.

K. Sterling: To return to Fred Noftolin's provocative question about freemartinism, which I gather is a dizygotic bovine fraternal twinning with a male and female embryo sharing the same placenta; the female member tends to overcome and cause considerable atrophy of the gonad of the male, which I think has been known to embryologists for many decades, if I have it right. My question is: Assuming that this H-Y antigen is the long-sought organizer of the testis, would you then say that it can be overcome and suppressed by circulating estrogens and that "they" (females) really are more powerful? The old quote from Queen Elizabeth I is no longer relevant. She said, if I remember correctly: "Nuts" said the Queen, "if I had them, I'd be King." It would circulate estradiol conquering all? Is that right?

S. Ohno: In mammals, the expression of H-Y antigen is male-specific, ubiquitous, and constitutive. H-Y antigen can neither be induced in females by testosterone nor be suppressed in males by estradiol. The virilization of bovine XX freemartin gonads is due to the XY-to-XX transfer of H-Y antigen. One exception is the androgen-dependent dissemination of H-Y antigen by adult Sertoli cells as already noted.

F. Naftolin: I think that Dr. Sterling is referring to the observations that the male co-twin of a freemartin is somewhat less masculinized or less fertile than would be expected.

S. Ohno: In the testicular environment, XX primordial germ cells are incapable of undergoing the neonatal differentiation toward definitive spermatogonia; thus, they are eliminated from the testis at this stage. Some years ago, we found evidence of germ cell chimerism in bovine chimeric dizygotic twins. The loss of XX germ cells from the testis may be the cause of reproductive difficulties often encountered by bulls born twins to freemartins.

F. Naftolin: Since these fraternal twins have cross-communication between their placenta, they are both chimeras. Cells, antigens, and other blood-borne material are exchanged. It is a sort of cross circulation of embryos. Since the male is also chimeric, its development may also be abnormal, and this could or could not be due to some continuing influence by the female.

O. P. Ganda: I would like to return to the question of H-Y antigen being a true antigen or not. I think whether or not it is a true antigen, as you mentioned, the β-2-microglobulin dimer, which itself is located on chromosome number 15, does influence the histocompatible antigen (HLA) locus, which is on chromosome number 6. Could you go into this in more detail and tell us what is the teleologic significance of the β_2-microglobulin influencing the HLA loci on chromosome 6?

S. Ohno: This time, there seems to be a confusion between testis-organizing H-Y antigen and its plasma membrane anchorage site provided by β_2m-MHC antigen dimers. Nevertheless, we should push on. As to the reason why a mutational deficiency of β_2-microglobulin causes the suppression of HLA antigen expression in Daudi human male Burkitt lymphoma cells, I offer the following explanation: A nascent HLA antigen polypeptide chain, being so hydrophobic, cannot be peeled off its *messenger* RNA until more hydrophilic β_2-microglobulin comes to a rescue.

Recent Studies of the 3T3-L1 Adipocyte-Like Cell Line[1]

Ora Mendelsohn Rosen,*,†,[2] C. J. Smith,* Allen Hirsch,* E. Lai,*
and Charles S. Rubin*,‡,[3]

*Departments of *Molecular Pharmacology, †Medicine, and ‡Neuroscience,
Albert Einstein College of Medicine, Bronx, New York*

I. Introduction

To pursue our interest in the mechanism of action of hormones and the regulation of cAMP-dependent protein kinases, we sought a cell culture system that would be sensitive to hormone regulation and afford a variety of differentiated functions amenable to biochemical analysis. We decided to study the 3T3-L1 cell line that possesses the unusual property of differentiating from fibroblasts into adipocyte-like cells *in vitro*. The 3T3-L1 cell line was established and cloned from the original stock of Swiss mouse 3T3 cells by Dr. Howard Green and his associates (Green and Kehinde, 1974, 1975, 1976). During exponential growth and the approach to confluence, 3T3-L1 cells appear indistinguishable from other 3T3 cells with respect to growth rate, sensitivity to density-dependent inhibition, and morphological and biochemical properties. When the cells are maintained at confluence, some cells spontaneously enter a differentiation program that parallels the development of mammalian adipose tissue. The cells accumulate triglycerides, ultimately becoming engorged with lipid droplets (Green and Kehinde, 1976); they coordinately induce the enzymes of fatty acid biosynthesis including ATP: citrate lyase, acetyl-CoA carboxylase, fatty acid synthetase, and glycerol phosphate acyltransferase (Mackall *et al.*, 1976; Kuri-Harcuch and Green, 1977). Their content of lipoprotein lipase (Wise and Green, 1978; Spooner *et al.*, 1978) and glutamine synthetase (Miller *et al.*, 1978) also change dramatically. Concomitant with these biochemical changes the cells retract their processes and enter a morphological program that ultimately yields enlarged spherical cells that remain attached to the culture dishes (Green and Kehinde, 1976). Although no information is currently available regarding the genetic or epigenetic factors controlling the switchover from preadipocyte to

[1] This research was supported by National Institutes of Health Grants AM-09038, GM-22792, and AM-21248, NIH Training Grant 5732GM-7288 from the National Institute of General Medical Sciences, and Grant BC-12H from the American Cancer Society.

[2] Recipient of an Irma T. Hirschl Career Scientist Award.

[3] Recipient of Research Career Development Award from National Institutes of Health (K04 AM-00190).

adipocyte, the 3T3-L1 system is amenable to biochemical and physiological measurement and manipulation at all stages of development. Since mammalian fat cells respond to a wide variety of hormones, the 3T3-L1 cells also offered the potential for studying the development, regulation, and physiological coupling of hormone receptors and affector systems.

II. Acceleration of Adipocyte

To perform biochemical and physiological experiments it is desirable to have a near homogeneous population of cells. However, in the spontaneous differentiation process originally described (Green and Kehinde, 1974, 1975, 1976), fat cells appeared in a limited number of colonies accounting for 20–40% of the total cells, and the process of differentiation occurred over a 20–30-day period. Treatment of confluent monolayers with either 20–30% serum (Green and Meuth, 1974), supraphysiological concentrations of insulin (0.18 μM) (Green and Kehinde, 1975), 0.5 mM 1-methyl-3-isobutylxanthine (Russell and Ho, 1976), 0.3 μM prostaglandin F_{2a} (Russell and Ho, 1976), 33 μM biotin (Mackall et al., 1976), or combinations of insulin and any of the other agents (Mackall et al., 1976; Russell and Ho, 1976) have been reported to accelerate the expression of the adipocyte phenotype. However, differentiation induced by these procedures still requires several weeks (post-confluence) and results in 50–60% conversion.

Finally, since we intended to study the binding and physiological effects of insulin, a procedure for converting the cells in the absence of this hormone was desirable. An empirical search for stimulators of differentiation was carried out by examining the effects of various hormones and potential growth regulators on 3T3-L1 cells. We found that a combination of the glucocorticoid dexamethasone and an inhibitor of cAMP phosphodiesterase, 1-methyl-3-isobutylxanthine (MIX), evoked the rapid and uniform differentiation of approximately 80–90% of the cells (Rubin et al., 1978) (Fig. 1). Cells were incubated in the presence of 0.25 μM dexamethasone and 0.5 mM MIX for 48 hours. At the end of this time, the medium was changed and the cells were allowed to continue their developmental process for 96 hours. Figure 1 shows that, during the course of dexamethasone–MIX treatment, the cells assume a spindly shape and decrease their surface area. Cells do not appear differentiated during this period and retain the ability to undergo cell division. Following removal of the drugs after 48 hours, the cells are refed and never again exposed to drugs. On day 3 (the first day after drug removal) the cells regain their fibroblastic morphology and small triglyceride droplets appear within the cells. These are identified as triglyceride by Oil Red O staining and by direct measurement of triglyceride glycerol (Rubin et al., 1978). On day 4, the cells exhibit a very characteristic pattern of adipose development. Triglyceride droplets ring the nucleus, and the cells assume polygonal shapes. On days 5 through 7, triglyceride droplets continue to enlarge as

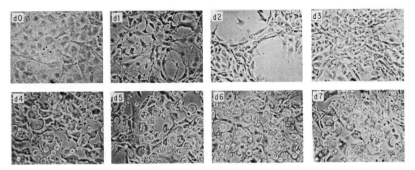

FIG. 1. Photomicrographs of differentiating 3T3-L1 cells. Confluent monolayers (d0; d = day) were treated with dexamethasone and methylisobutylxanthine (d1, d2) as described by Rubin *et al.* (1978). Typical areas were photographed with phase optics at a total magnification of × 160. After 48 hours treatment, cells were refed with fresh medium lacking drugs, and differentiation was allowed to proceed without any further manipulation (d3 to d7).

the cells become more spherical. As originally described (Green and Kehinde, 1974, 1975, 1976), differentiation is terminal and irreversible. However, during the course of differentiation with dexamethasone and MIX, approximately two cell divisions take place.

Although we do not understand how dexamethasone and MIX facilitate adipocyte conversion, we have addressed the question of whether the steroid effect is nonspecific, or falls into a definable subclass of steroid hormones. Figure 2 shows the dose-response curve for dexamethasone-stimulated differentiation. In this experiment the rate of appearance of fat cells was measured, usually at day 4, in the absence of MIX. The amount of triglyceride produced by the cells represented only 5–10% of the maximal capacity for triglyceride biosynthesis normally observed after 7 days of development. A definite order of potency among the various categories of steroids was established. Dexamethasone was the most potent, exhibiting a half-maximal stimulation at 65 nM and an optimal effect at 1 μM. Deoxycorticosterone and progesterone were half-maximally active at 1.3 and 6.0 μM, respectively. Progesterone, in turn, was more potent than testosterone, insulin, and other polypeptide hormones that had no effects over the time course studied.

Since preliminary experiments indicate the presence of cytosolic receptors for dexamethasone in 3T3-L1 cells, glucocorticords may act by the classical steroid receptor mechanism with ultimate transport of an activated form of receptor into the nucleus. They could also act by inhibiting phospholipases, thereby limiting the availability of arachidonic acid, the precursor of endoperoxides, prostacyclin, and prostaglandins (Hong and Levine, 1976a,b; Peters *et al.*, 1977). This view must be considered in light of the observation of Williams and Polakis (1977) that indomethacin (10 μM) potentiates insulin-mediated differentiation of 3T3-L1 cells. One approach to studying this would be to monitor prostaglandin

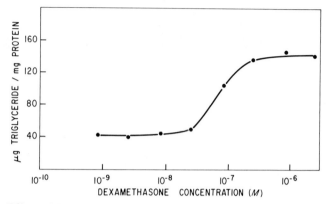

FIG. 2. Effects of dexamethasone on triglyceride accumulation in differentiating adipocytes. Confluent 3T3-L1 cells (100-mm dishes) were exposed to the indicated dexamethasone concentrations in the presence of 0.175 μM insulin in 8 ml of medium for 48 hours. Subsequently, cells were maintained in standard medium until 40–50% of the preadipocytes differentiated at the highest concentration of drug (total time = 96 hours). Cells were then washed, harvested, and extracted as described by Rubin *et al.* (1978). After saponification, the triglyceride content of the extract was determined in a couple enzymic assay (Rubin *et al.*, 1978). Methylisobutylxanthine was eliminated from the differentiation procedure because it independently stimulates some adipocyte differentiation, thus obscuring the effects of steroid alone. Insulin was included during the first 48 hours because it potentiates the effects of the steroids but induces no differentiation when the same procedure is carried out in the absence of steroid. Each point is the average of triplicate determinations that did not differ from each other by greater than 5%. The data reported in this figure are within 20% of those obtained in two other independent experiments of this kind.

production during drug treatment and differentiation. Another approach, pioneered by Dr. Gordon Sato (Hayashi and Sato, 1976), is to grow the cells in completely defined medium and then determine the hormonal requirements for the differentiation program.

The mechanism by which MIX stimulates the differentiation process is also unknown. We do know that cAMP, cGMP, or their analogs cannot substitute for MIX whereas the nonpurine inhibitor of phosphodiesterase, 4-(3-butoxy-4-methoxybenzyl)-2-imidazolidinone (Sheppard and Wiggan, 1971), can. It is conceivable that MIX has a more dynamic effect. For example, inhibition of phosphodiesterase activity would lead to an elevation of intracellular cAMP. The rise in cAMP might, in turn, induce the synthesis of phosphodiesterase, thus providing a transient or oscillating increase and decrease of cyclic nucleotide levels.

In summary, the method of accelerating adipocyte conversion with dexamethasone and MIX offers several advantages: (1) differentiation is consistent; (2) the time course of differentiation is compressed into 7 days; (3) the physiological and binding properties of insulin can be studied with cells that have not been exposed to high concentrations of this hormone; (4) differentiation is uniform rather than focal, facilitating biochemical analysis.

III. Hormone Sensitivity during Adipocyte Development

Mature mammalian fat cells have been studied in great detail and are known to respond to a variety of hormones, including catecholamines, ACTH, FSH, LH, glucagon, and TSH, with a significant increase in the conversion of triglycerides to glycerol and free fatty acids. All these hormones activate adenylate cyclase and increase intracellular cAMP (Steinberg et al., 1975). Activation of cAMP-dependent protein kinase and the phosphorylation and activation of hormone-sensitive triglyceride lipase (Huttunen et al., 1970) subsequently lead to an enhanced rate of lipolysis. Since mammalian preadipocytes are difficult to isolate, little is known about the biochemistry of differentiating fat cells. As a result undifferentiated and differentiated 3T3-L1 cells were compared to develop some notions about hormone-receptor development and coupling (Rubin et al., 1977). Hormone sensitivity was evaluated by assessing adenylate cyclase activity in broken-cell preparations using homogenates or crude membrane fractions. Adenylate cyclase activity was measured by monitoring conversion of $[\alpha\text{-}^{32}P]$-ATP to cyclic $[^{32}P]$AMP using the assay of Salomon et al. (1974). The accumulation of cAMP in intact cells was measured by radioimmunoassay (Steiner et al., 1972).

Table I shows that basal adenylate cyclase activity is approximately equivalent in preadipocytes and adipocytes, but total activity, represented by sodium fluoride-stimulated activity, increased approximately 2-fold during the course of differentiation. In preadipocytes, both isoproterenol and prostaglandin E_1 stimulated adenylate cyclase approximately 2-fold. In the adipocytes, however, isoproterenol stimulated the cyclase 15-fold to a level higher than that observed with fluoride. This activation, like that seen in the preadipocytes, was blocked by the β-adrenergic blocker propranolol. Second, an ACTH-sensitive adenylate cyclase activity appeared de novo. ACTH and its biologically active 1–24 amino-terminal analog stimulated adipocyte cyclase 6- to 7-fold. More recent studies have shown that the rise in ACTH-sensitivity is evident as early as day 3, preceding by at least 24 hours the development of increased sensitivity to β-adrenergic amines. Prostaglandin E_1 stimulated 4-fold in the differentiated cells, but this could reflect the 2-fold increase in total cyclase activity rather than an enhancement of hormone sensitivity. No effect was seen on either cell type with glucagon, TSH, FSH, or LH.

Table II shows the cAMP accumulation in preadipocytes and adipocytes in response to hormones. In preadipocytes, isoproterenol and prostaglandin E_1 elevated cAMP levels about 2-fold, and ACTH and glucagon had no effect. In the adipocyte, both isoproterenol and ACTH stimulated 25-fold. The potency of prostaglandin E_1 was approximately equivalent in the adipocyte and preadipocyte. Thus, during adipocyte development several categories of alterations in hormone responsiveness were discernible: for β-adrenergic agonists, there was intensification of a preexisting response; in the case of ACTH, a new sensitivity

TABLE I

*Effects of Hormones on Adenylate Cyclase Activity in Homogenates of
Adipocytes and Preadipocytes[a,b]*

	Adenylate cyclase activity (pmol cAMP formed/min/mg protein)	
Addition	Preadipocytes	Adipocytes
None (basal activity)	3.5	4.5
Isoproterenol, 2.5 μM	8.9	65.2
Isoproterenol, 2.5 μM plus propranolol, 10 μM	3.9	8.4
ACTH, 2 μM	3.5	17.6
ACTH (1–24), 2 μM	3.8	26.5
Glucagon, 2 μM	3.1	3.9
PGE$_1$, 3 μM	7.3	16.6
NaF, 20 mM	21.2	47.5

[a] From Rubin *et al.* (1977).

[b] Growth medium was removed from 2–4 100-mm culture dishes (3.2 to 4.0 $\times$ 10^6 cells) by aspiration. Cells were then washed twice with 5 ml of 0.15 M NaCl, 5 mM sodium phosphate buffer, pH 7.4 (phosphate-buffered saline) and removed from the dishes by scraping with a rubber policeman in the presence of two additional 2-ml aliquots of phosphate-buffered saline. Cells were harvested by sedimenting them at 300 g for 5 minutes, and the supernatant was discarded. The cells were resuspended in 1 ml of 5 mM Tris buffer, pH 7.5, containing 5 mM NaCl and 1 mM mercaptoethanol at 0°C and were allowed to swell for 2 minutes. One microliter of 0.25 M MgCl$_2$ was then added, and the cells were transferred to a Dounce homogenizer and disrupted at 0°C with 20 strokes, using a tight-fitting pestle. Aliquots of cell homogenates containing 40 μg of protein were then assayed for adenylate cyclase activity. The concentrations of hormones and NaF used in these experiments elicited maximal responses in adenylate cyclase activity as determined from dose-response curves. The data presented are average values from four separate experiments.

to a polypeptide hormone developed. Finally, there was no significant change in responsiveness to prostaglandin E$_1$. Enhanced responsiveness to β-adrenergic amines, and the appearance of ACTH sensitivity could result from the biosynthesis and integration of new cell surface receptors and their coupling to the catalytic component of adenylate cyclase and/or the coupling of preexisting receptors to the cyclase. We are currently in the process of distinguishing between these possibilities by independently assaying the presence of β-adrenergic and ACTH receptors.

IV. Insulin Receptors and Responsiveness

The questions that we are considering are: What is the nature of the insulin receptor in undifferentiated and differentiated 3T3-L1 cells? When and how do receptors become coupled to metabolic systems? What is the temporal relationship between the appearance of insulin responsiveness and the conversion of

TABLE II

Effects of Hormones on cAMP Content of Preadipocytes and Adipocytes[a,b]

Addition	cAMP content (pmol/mg protein)	
	Preadipocytes	Adipocytes
None (basal)	11.9	7.7
Isoproterenol, 2.5 μM	28.1	192.0
ACTH 1–24, 2 μM	13.3	206.0
Glucagon, 2 μM	10.8	6.9
PGE$_1$, 3 μM	34.5	40.3

[a] From Rubin *et al.* (1977).

[b] Hormones were directly added to 60-mm culture dishes containing standard growth medium and 0.1 mM 1-methyl-3-isobutylxanthine. After 5 minutes, the medium was aspirated, and the cells were washed once with 5 ml of phosphate-buffered saline (< 10 seconds) and then extracted with 3 ml of 5% trichloroacetic acid. Acid-insoluble macromolecules were sedimented at 2000 g for 5 minutes at 4°C. Pellets were dissolved in 0.1 N NaOH for protein determinations. The supernatant fluid was extracted repeatedly with H$_2$O-saturated ethyl ether (8 volumes of ether : 1 volume of acid-soluble extract) until the pH was 4–5. cAMP content was measured by radioimmunoassay. The data are averages of four separate experiments.

preadipocytes to fat cells? The insulin receptor of the 3T3-L1 cell was characterized by a series of equilibrium binding and kinetic experiments (Rubin *et al.*, 1978). Insulin was labeled with ^{125}I using the chloramine T procedure (Roth, 1975) and then purified on cellulose (Yalow and Berson, 1960). To avoid binding of [^{125}I]insulin to the culture dishes, cells were removed from the plates with Joklik's spinner medium containing 1 mM EDTA (Rubin *et al.*, 1977), washed and resuspended in HEPES-buffered saline solution containing 10 mg of bovine serum albumin per milliliter, tracer [^{125}I]insulin, and Bacitracin (Rubin *et al.*, 1978), an inhibitor of insulin degradation. Incubations were carried out at 18°C for 100 minutes and then assayed according to the procedure of Thomopoulos *et al.* (1976) as described (Rubin *et al.*, 1978).

The kinetics of binding are shown in Fig. 3. The half-time for maximal binding was approximately 3 minutes in the preadipocytes and 12 minutes in adipocytes. All samples reached equilibrium by 85 minutes. [^{125}I]insulin was displaced by native pork insulin, fish insulin, and desalaninyl-desasparaginyl insulin in accordance with their respective biological potencies. Anti-insulin receptor antibody [kindly donated by Drs. H. R. Kahn and J. Roth (NIH)] diminished the binding of insulin to its receptor by 83% at a final dilution of 1:500. Thus, [^{125}I]insulin appeared to be binding to physiologically relevant insulin receptors.

Figure 4 shows the effects of pH on insulin binding. Undifferentiated and differentiated cells bind little insulin below pH 7.0. Binding activity rises sharply above pH 7.0 and is maximal at pH 7.9. To demonstrate that receptor-bound

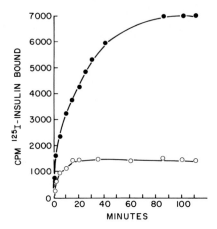

FIG. 3.   Kinetics of association of insulin with 3T3-L1 preadipocytes and adipocytes (Rubin *et al.*, 1978). Preadipocytes (5.5×10^6/ml) and adipocytes (4×10^6/ml) were incubated in the presence of 0.53 nM [^{125}I]insulin. Samples (0.15 ml) were removed at the indicated times, and binding was determined by the centrifugation assay. Duplicates tubes containing the same concentration of [^{125}I]insulin and 5 μM nonradioactive insulin were assayed in parallel to determine the extent of nonspecific binding. Nonspecific binding was less than 9% of total binding at all points. The data presented have been corrected for nonspecific binding. The specific activities of [^{125}I]insulin were 1332 cpm/fmol in the preadipocyte experiment and 940 cpm/fmol in the adipocyte study. ●———●, Adipocytes; ○———○, preadipocytes.

[^{125}I]insulin is not degraded or converted to another form, advantage was taken of the lower avidity of the receptor for hormone at pH 6.0. Cells were first allowed to come to equilibrium with [^{125}I]insulin at pH 7.9 at 18°C, then washed at pH 7.9 at 0°C and resuspended in the same insulin-binding medium adjusted to pH 6.0. Cells were incubated at pH 6.0 for 60 minutes at 18°C, during which time more than 90% of the bound insulin was released into the medium. The cells

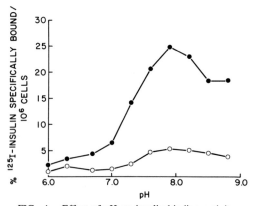

FIG. 4.   Effect of pH on insulin-binding activity.

were then removed by sedimentation, and the supernatant fluid was subjected to gel filtration in $6 M$ urea and $1 M$ acetic acid on a calibrated column of Sephadex G-50. The major fraction (85%) of insulin was recovered with monomeric, native hormone.

Equilibrium binding studies were performed with $10^{-11} M$ to $10^{-7} M$ insulin to compare the properties of the hormone receptors in differentiated and undifferentiated cells. Scatchard analysis of both adipocyte and preadipocyte binding yielded curvilinear plots compatible with either heterogeneity of sites (Kahn *et al.*, 1974; Pollet *et al.*, 1977), or negatively cooperative interactions among one type of binding site (DeMeyts *et al.*, 1973, 1976) (Fig. 5). Since the marked curvature observed in our binding curves occurred at insulin concentrations above the physiological range, i.e., greater than 10 nM, we analyzed the data by graphical resolution of the Scatchard plots into independent, high-affinity, low-capacity sites because they should participate in mediating the physiological actions of insulin, while the low-affinity, high-capacity sites may reflect the interaction of insulin with receptors for other hormones and growth

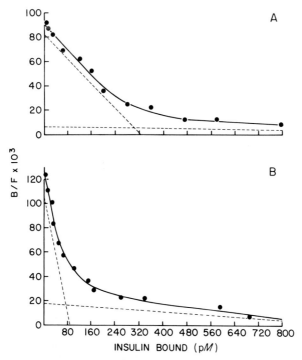

FIG. 5.   Scatchard plots of insulin-binding data for adipocytes (A) and preadipoctyes (B) (Rubin *et al.*, 1978). Preadipocytes (8×10^6 cells/ml) and adipocytes (8.3×10^5 cells/ml) were incubated to equilibrium at 18°C in HEPES binding buffer containing mixtures of [^{125}I]insulin (1750 cpm/fmol) and nonradioactive insulin over the concentration range 0.01 to 100 nM.

factors. We concluded that the preadipocytes contain 7000 sites per cell with a dissociation constant (K_d) of 0.8 nM. During the course of differentiation insulin receptor number increased 35-fold to 250,000 sites per cell accompanied by an increased K_d of 4 nM. This is consistent with an overall 7- to 10-fold increase in insulin-binding capacity in the physiological range (Rubin *et al.*, 1978). Reed *et al.* (1977) have also reported an increase in insulin-binding activity from 35,000 sites per cell in 3T3-L1 preadipocytes to 170,000 sites per cell in adipocytes.

Figure 6 portrays the binding data according to a plot described by Gammeltoft and Gliemann (1973). The curve in panel A is calculated using 250,000 sites per cell and a dissociation constant of 4 nM for the adipocytes. The curve in panel B is calculated using 6500 sites per cell and a K_d value of 0.9 nM. The points were experimentally derived from the raw data and fit the calculated curves well. To strengthen these observations, we also applied a kinetic approach. Using initial velocity data and the equation $V_1 = k_a$ (Ro) (insulin) where Ro is receptor concentration, we estimated the association constant (k_a) to be 4×10^7 mol^{-1} min^{-1} in preadipocytes and 0.7×10^7 mol^{-1} min^{-1} in adipocytes. The first-order dissociation constant (k_d) was determined at 18°C by following the release of [^{125}I]insulin after allowing the cells to achieve equilibrium with 0.5 nM [^{125}I]-insulin. Figure 7 shows that the first-order dissociation constants for the

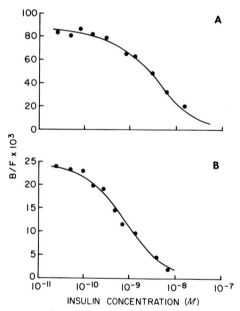

FIG. 6.   Insulin binding as a function of total insulin concentration (Rubin *et al.*, 1978). The data are presented according to the format suggested by Gammeltoft and Gliemann (1973). The data points were determined experimentally, and the curves were calculated as indicated in the text. Parameters used for adipocytes (A) were K_d = 4 nM, number of sites = 250,000/cell; for preadipocytes (B) K_d = 0.9 nM, number of sites = 6500/cell.

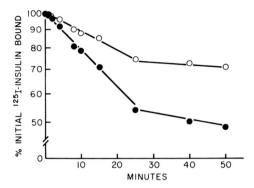

FIG. 7. Dissociation of bound insulin from preadipocytes and adipocytes (Rubin *et al.*, 1978). 3T3-L1 preadipocytes (3×10^6 cells/ml) and adipocytes (1.4×10^6 cells/ml) were incubated with 0.5 nM [^{125}I]insulin at 18°C for 100 minutes to achieve equilibrium binding. Then the suspension was diluted with 10 volumes of HEPES binding buffer (0°C), and the medium was removed by sedimentation. Cells were washed by resuspension in 20 volumes of HEPES binding buffer (0°C) and pelleted by centrifugation. Finally, cells were resuspended in 30 volumes of HEPES binding buffer (18°C), and the amounts of cell-bound and free [^{125}I]insulin were determined at the indicated times by sedimenting the cell suspension at 300 g for 1 minute at 0°C, collecting both the cells and medium, and determining the radioactivity in each fraction. Nonspecific binding and dissociation were monitored in samples containing 5 μM nonradioactive insulin. All data were corrected for specific binding. ●——●, Adipocytes; ○——○, preadipocytes.

preadipocytes and adipocytes were 0.014 per minute and 0.025 per minute, respectively.

Table III summarizes the parameters of insulin binding determined in equilibrium and kinetic studies. The results are consistent with the possibility that a single set of noninteracting high-affinity sites can account for the physiologically relevant binding of insulin to its cell surface receptors. It will be important to determine whether the change in affinity of the receptor for insulin during differentiation reflects the synthesis of a new type of receptor characteristic of fat cells. The estimated number of receptors in the differentiated adipocyte (250,000/cell) is about 5-fold higher than the number of sites reported for rat epididymal fat cells (Gammeltoft and Gliemann, 1973). It is possible that the number of insulin-binding sites and their affinity for insulin might change if cells were permitted to "age" in culture.

Insulin binding activity during the course of differentiation was correlated with the development of physiological insulin responsiveness (Rosen *et al.*, 1978). Three parameters of insulin action were followed: The conversion of [^{14}C]-glucose to $^{14}CO_2$ or ^{14}C-labeled lipid; the uptake of [^{3}H]2-deoxy-D-glucose, which in these cells is a reliable measure of transport; and the uptake of the nonmetabolizable glucose analog [^{3}H]3-O-methyl glucose. Figure 8 shows the development of insulin-binding activity during differentiation. Insulin binding capacity begins to rise above control values after day 3, achieving a maximum on

TABLE III

Parameters of Insulin Binding in Preadipocytes and Adipocytes[a]

	K_d (equilibrium)	Sites/cell	k_a	k_d	K_d (k_d/k_a)
Preadipocytes	0.8 nM	~ 7,000	4.1×10^7 min^{-1} mol^{-1}	0.014 min^{-1}	0.34 nM
Adipocytes	4.0 nM	~ 250,000	0.7×10^7 min^{-1} mol^{-1}	0.025 min^{-1}	3.6 nM

[a] From Rubin et al. (1978).

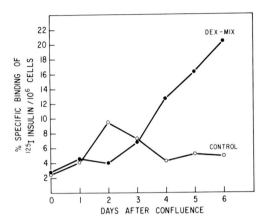

FIG. 8. Development of insulin binding activity in differentiating 3T3-L1 adipocytes (Rubin *et al.*, 1978). Control cells received fresh medium on days 0 and 2, whereas differentiating cells received fresh medium containing 0.5 m*M* methylisobutylxanthine (MIX) and 0.25 μ*M* dexamethasone (DEX) on day 0 and fresh medium alone on day 2. The [^{125}I]insulin concentration was 0.022 n*M*. Nonspecific binding was equal to 7–10% of specific insulin binding and was subtracted from the total amount bound. Data are presented as percent specific binding per 10^6 cells, where percent specific binding is calculated as (total [^{125}I]insulin bound-nonspecific binding) ÷ (total [^{125}I]insulin present in the assay). ●———●, Differentiating adipocytes; ○———○, control 3T3-L1 cells. Each point is the average of triplicate determinations that differed from each other by less than 10%. The pattern presented is typical of many experiments. From one experiment to another, insulin binding in the adipocytes may vary as much as 100% during days 1 to 3; after day 3, the interexperimental variability is reduced to 20–30%.

day 6 that is 5- to 10-fold greater than that observed in the control cells. This level is retained through days 7 to 10 (data not shown). When the nondifferentiating 3T3C cells were treated with dexamethasone and MIX, no differentiation occurred and insulin-binding capacity failed to increase (Table IV). Thus modifications in insulin-binding activity appear to correlate with adipocyte conversion, not with the dexamethasone and MIX treatment. The appearance of increased binding activity was not precisely congruent with the development of hormone responsiveness. Panel A in Fig. 9 shows insulin stimulation of the conversion of [^{14}C]glucose to ^{14}CO$_2$ and to ^{14}C-labeled lipid. Hormone responsiveness became apparent on days 2 and 3, before insulin-binding capacity was significantly altered. One day later, heightened responsiveness coincided with a rise in insulin-binding activity. Similar results were obtained when [^{3}H]-deoxyglucose uptake was assayed. The observations suggest that the development of insulin sensitivity may not be precisely coordinated with the appearance of elevated insulin binding activity and that the development of additional insulin binding capacity during differentiation may provide the cells with a mechanism for augmenting a preexisting physiological response to a level consistent with the metabolic and regulatory demands of the mature adipocyte. It is possible, but by

TABLE IV

Insulin Binding Activities in 3T3-L1 and 3T3-C Cells[a,b]

Cells		[125I]Insulin specifically bound/10⁶ cells (%)	
		Treatment	
		0.02 mM insulin	0.2 nM insulin
3T3-L1	Control	2.6	2.1
3T3-C	Control	4.0	2.0
3T3-L1	Dexamethasone 1-methyl-3-isobutylxanthine	21.2	22.1
3T3-C	Dexamethasone 1-methyl-3-isobutylxanthine	3.5	2.4

[a] From Rubin *et al.* (1978).

[b] 3T3-L1 and nondifferentiating 3T3-C cells, which also originated from Swiss mouse embryos, were grown to confluence and were either maintained at confluence (controls) or exposed to differentiating conditions (0.25 μM dexamethasone, 0.5 mM 1-methyl-3-isobutylxanthine) as described. Cells were assayed for insulin binding activity using 0.02 and 0.2 nM [125I]insulin 4 days after the removal of dexamethasone and 1-methyl-3-isobutylxanthine.

no means documented, that preexisting insulin receptors in confluent preadipocytes might couple to metabolic response systems during the early stages of adipocyte conversion.

The phenomenon of insulin-mediated depletion of insulin receptors, or "down regulation," has been described in detail by Gavin *et al.* (1974). Incubation of cells with supraphysiological concentrations of insulin for 16–48 hours brought about a reversible 50–70% decrease in receptor number. Since studies on down regulation of the insulin receptor *in vitro* have been performed with cells that do not exhibit dramatic responses to insulin (e.g., human lymphocytes), it seemed worthwhile to study this phenomenon in the insulin-responsive 3T3-L1 cells. A procedure was developed to remove cell-bound insulin subsequent to exposure to high concentrations of hormone and prior to the binding or physiological assays, which are carried out at low concentrations of hormone. This procedure is presented in the legend to Table V. Cells were incubated at 37°C with 0.2 μM insulin for the indicated periods of time, washed free of insulin, and assayed for [125I]insulin-binding activity at a concentration of 0.2 nM. A surprising result was that there was no change in receptor number of either insulin-sensitive adipocytes or insulin-insensitive preadipocytes. The physiological measurements (Table VI) also proved to be interesting. Cells treated for 15 minutes with 0.2 μM insulin exhibited the same basal and insulin-stimulated deoxyglucose uptake as control, untreated cells. In contrast, cells treated with supraphysiological levels of insulin for 24 hours exhibited a persistent, enhanced basal level of deoxyglucose uptake that sometimes reached a higher level than the maximal insulin-stimulated deoxyglucose uptake observed in the controls. Furthermore,

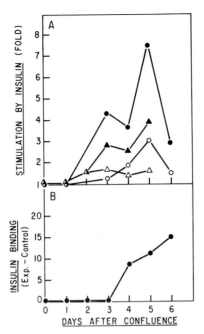

FIG. 9. Effects of insulin on the conversion of glucose to CO_2 and lipid during the early phase of differentiation (Rubin *et al.*, 1978). (A) $^{14}CO_2$ (▲———▲) and ^{14}C-labeled lipid (●———●) formation in response to 0.8 n*M* insulin was assayed daily for the first 4 days of differentiation. Basal $^{14}CO_2$ production was 450–1350 cpm/10^6 cells per 90-minute incubation, and basal ^{14}C-labeled lipid formation varied between 200 and 450 cpm/10^6 cells per 90-minute incubation. Fold stimulation by insulin was calculated from points representing the average of triplicate incubations differing from each other by less than 10%. The open symbols are for confluent undifferentiated cells. Although the pattern depicted in this figure is typical, the data obtained in independent experiments using different batches of cells have varied as much as 50–75%. (B) Specific insulin binding of the differentiating cells measured at 0.4 n*M* [^{125}I]insulin. Binding is expressed as percent of specific binding per 10^6 cells.

these cells were now quite refractory to further stimulation by insulin. Persistent elevation of basal hexose transport was maintained for a period of hours following removal of insulin from the medium. Table VII shows that elevation of basal hexose transport was dependent upon the concentration of insulin during treatment. Blockade of the insulin effect by anti-insulin serum confirmed that the effect was not due to a contaminant or metabolic degradation product in the insulin preparation. The development of elevated hexose transport activity was blocked by cycloheximide and partially inhibited by actinomycin D, suggesting that new protein synthesis may be required for the effect. The phenomenon was not observed with preadipocytes. Table VIII shows that the same results are obtained using uptake of [^3H]3-*O*-methylglucose to measure hexose transport.

Previous investigations (Rosen *et al.*, 1978; Gavin *et al.*, 1974; Martineau *et al.*, 1972; Kletzien and Perdue, 1975) have shown that glucose starvation

TABLE V

Effect of Prolonged Insulin Treatment on Insulin-Binding Activity[a,b]

Cells	Time of treatment with 0.2 μM insulin	[125I]Insulin specifically bound/10^6 cells (%)
Preadipocytes	Control (—insulin)	2.4
	10 min	3.0
	5 hr	2.3
	16 hr	2.2
	48 hr	3.0
Adipocytes	Control (—insulin)	14.4
	10 min	14.0
	5 hr	14.3
	16 hr	14.9
	48 hr	12.9

[a] From Rubin *et al.* (1978).

[b] Monolayer cultures of preadipocytes and adipocytes were treated with 0.2 μM insulin in standard medium for the indicated periods of time. In the case of 48-hour exposure, cells were fed with fresh medium containing 0.2 μM insulin after 24 hours. Insulin treatment was terminated by removing the medium and washing the cells with three 10-ml aliquots of phosphate-buffered saline (0.15 M NaCl, 10 mM sodium phosphate, pH 7.4), which was prewarmed to 37°C. Cells were then incubated with HEPES binding buffer at pH 6.0 for 30 minutes at 37°C. After washing with phosphate-buffered saline, the cells were incubated an additional 15 minutes in standard medium at 37°C. Cell suspensions were then prepared, and insulin-binding activity was assayed as described in the text. The rigorous washing procedure outlined here effectively removes assayable cell-bound insulin as indicated by the complete recovery of insulin binding capacities in preadipocytes and adipocytes and the retention of a control level of insulin-stimulated deoxyglucose uptake in adipocytes[6] pretreated with 0.2 μM insulin for 10 minutes. Control samples were treated as described above except that insulin was omitted from the medium. Data are presented for the 16-hour control. All other controls were not significantly different from the 16-hour value.

TABLE VI

Effectiveness of Standard Cell Washing Procedure in Removing Insulin[a,b]

Conditions	Deoxyglucose uptake (pmol/min/200,000 cells)			
	0[c]	0.5[c]	1.5[c]	5.0[c]
Control	9.9	23.9	32.7	33.6
Insulin-treated, 15 min	12.0	27.9	36.9	41.2
Insulin-treated, 24 hr	54.8	53.0	63.0	67.0

[a] From Rosen *et al.* (1978).

[b] Differentiated cells were fed with fresh complete medium and incubated at 37°C in either the absence of insulin or the presence of 1 μg/ml of insulin for 15 minute or 24 hours. Following the standard cell washing procedure, cells were assayed for [3H]deoxyglucose uptake in the presence of 0, 0.5, 1.5, and 5.0 ng/ml insulin.

[c] Amount of insulin in assay (nanograms per milliliter).

TABLE VII

Effect of Insulin Concentration on Subsequent Uptake of Deoxyglucose[a,b]

Additions during pretreatment	Deoxyglucose uptake (pmol/min/200,000 cells)
None	7.9
Insulin	
0.01 μg/ml	11.4
0.10 μg/ml	20.3
1.0 μg/ml	29.1
Insulin (1.0 μg/ml) plus anti-insulin serum	7.8

[a] From Rosen *et al.* (1978).

[b] Adipocytes were fed with fresh medium and incubated in the presence or the absence of insulin for 3 hours. The concentration of anti-insulin in serum used in this experiment (37 μl/ml) produced 70% inhibition of the acute effects of 0.5 μg/ml of insulin on deoxyglucose transport in untreated cells. This would be equivalent to less than 0.5 ng/ml of free insulin.

elevates hexose transport in fibroblasts. Since insulin stimulates glucose metabolism, the possibility that the effects observed here might arise from insulin-mediated glucose starvation were considered. Table IX compares treatment of cells with and without glucose in the presence or in the absence of insulin. Cells treated with high concentrations of insulin in the presence of glucose exhibited a 5- to 6-fold increase in basal hexose transport in 24 hours. In fact, these cells exhibited a larger effect than cells treated with insulin in the absence of glucose. In contrast, cells treated with insulin in the absence of supplementary glucose

TABLE VIII

Effect of Insulin Treatment on Subsequent basal 3-O-Methylglucose Uptake[a,b]

Pretreatment	3-O-Methylglucose uptake (pmol/min/200,000 cells)
Control	0.80
Insulin	3.69
Cycloheximide	0.85
Cycloheximide + insulin	1.31

[a] From Rosen *et al.* (1978).

[b] Adipocytes were fed with fresh medium in the presence of the absence of 1.5 μg of cycloheximide per milliliter. One-half hour later, insulin (1.0 μg/ml) was added where indicated, and the incubation was continued for 5 hours. Cells were then washed and assayed for uptake of [³H]3-O-methylglucose (164 cpm/pmol). The concentrations of cells used were between 1.20 and 1.85 $\times$ 10⁷/ml. The values presented are the means of triplicate determinations that differed from each other by less than 20%. The accumulation of radioactivity occurring in the presence of 3 μM cytochalasin B was subtracted from the total accumulation. Total uptake was generally at least twice that occurring in the presence of 3 μM cytochalasin B; accumulation of radioactivity in the presence of cytochalasin B was not different in control and insulin-treated cells.

TABLE IX

Deoxyglucose Uptake following Insulin Treatment in the Presence or the Absence of Glucose[a,b]

Pretreatment		Deoxyglucose uptake (pmol/min/200,000 cells)	
Glucose, 20 mM	Insulin, 1 μg/ml	−Insulin	+Insulin
−	−	9.7	18.5
+	−	7.7	28.4
−	+	26.6	32.3
+	+	53.7	60.7

[a] From Rosen *et al.* (1978).

[b] Differentiated cells were incubated for 24 hours in either complete medium (20 mM glucose) or medium lacking glucose in the presence or the absence of 1 μg/ml of insulin. After the standard washing procedure, [^{3}H]deoxyglucose uptake was measured in the presence or the absence of 25 ng/ml of insulin. In cultures treated with medium containing glucose and insulin, the glucose concentration remaining at the end of the 24-hour period was $\geq$ 15 mM.

showed a much greater enhancement of hexose transport, attributable at least in part to depletion of medium glucose and the development of glucose starvation in the insulin-treated culture (Rosen *et al.*, 1978). Finally, the enhanced basal transport of hexose results from an increase in V_{max} with no apparent change in the affinity of the transport system for deoxyglucose (Rosen *et al.*, 1978).

These studies show that prolonged exposure of the hormone-sensitive 3T3-L1 adipocytes to high concentrations of insulin does not elicit a fall in receptor number (down regulation). On the other hand, long-term treatment with high concentrations of insulin provokes a persistent state of elevated basal hexose transport during which cells become refractory to additional stimulation by insulin. The effects of prolonged insulin treatment are insulin-concentration dependent, blocked by cycloheximide, and independent of medium glucose depletion. The increase in transport appears to be ascribable to an increase in the number of activity of transport sites rather than to an altered affinity of existing sites. In fibroblasts, glucose starvation is associated with the induction of two membrane proteins with molecular weights of 78,000 and 95,000 (Shiu *et al.*, 1977; Pouyssegur *et al.*, 1977). Recently, Shanahan and Czech (1977a,b) have partially purified the glucose transport complex from mature fat cells and found it to consist predominantly of 78,000 and 95,000 dalton protein components. We are currently investigating the relationship between these observations and those related to the state of elevated basal hexose uptake in insulin-treated 3T3-L1 adipocytes. The possibility that chronic states of hyperinsulinism may affect hexose transport *in vivo* has been suggested by studies with short-term human adipose tissue cultures (Smith, 1974) and, more recently, by studies carried out *in vivo* in rats (Kobayashi and Olefsky, 1978). Studies of the 3T3-L1 system in this and other laboratories confirm and extend the original promise of the system as a relevant model for investigating the development of hormone receptors, the coupling of these receptors to their appropriate physiological effector systems, and the long-term effects of hormones on adipocyte metabolism and function.

REFERENCES

DeMeyts, P., Roth, J., Neville, D. M., Gavin, J. R., and Lesniak, M. A. (1973). *Biochem. Biophys. Res. Commun.* **55,** 154.

DeMeyts, P., Bianco, A. R., and Roth, J. (1976). *J. Biol. Chem.* **251,** 1877.

Gammeltoft, S., and Gliemann, J. (1973). *Biochim. Biophys. Acta* **320,** 16.

Gavin, J. R., III, Roth, J., Neville, D. M., Jr., DeMeyts, P., and Buell, D. N. (1974). *Proc. Natl. Acad. Sci. U.S.A.* **71,** 84.

Green, H., and Kehinde, O. (1974). *Cell* **1,** 113.

Green, H., and Kehinde, O. (1975). *Cell* **5,** 19.

Green, H., and Kehinde, O. (1976). *Cell* **7,** 105.

Green, H., and Meuth, M. (1974). *Cell* **3,** 127.

Hayashi, I., and Sato, G. H. (1976). *Nature (London)* **259,** 132.

Hong, S. L., and Levine, L. (1976a). *J. Biol. Chem.* **251,** 5814.

Hong, S. L., and Levine, L. (1976b). *Proc. Natl. Acad. Sci. U.S.A.* **73,** 1730.

Huttunen, J. K., Steinberg, D., and Mayer, S. E. (1970). *Biochem. Biophys. Res. Commun.* **41,** 1350.

Kahn, C. R., Freychet, P., Roth, J., and Neville, D. M. (1974). *J. Biol. Chem.* **249,** 2249.

Kletzien, R. F., and Perdue, J. F. (1975). *J. Biol. Chem.* **250,** 593.

Kobayashi, M., and Olefsky, J. M. (1978). *J. Clin. Invest.* **62,** 73.

Kuri-Harcuch, W., and Green, H. (1977). *J. Biol. Chem.* **252,** 2158.

Mackall, J. C., Student, A. K., Polakis, S. E., and Lane, M. D. (1976). *J. Biol. Chem.* **251,** 6462.

Martineau, R., Kolbacher, M., Shaw, S. N., and Amos, H. (1972). *Proc. Natl. Acad. Sci. U.S.A.* **69,** 3407.

Miller, R. E., Hackenberg, R., and Gershman, H. (1978). *Proc. Natl. Acad. Sci. U.S.A.* **75,** 1418.

Peters, H. D., Peskav, B. A., and Schonhofer, P. J. (1977). *Arch. Pharmacol.* **296,** 131.

Pollet, R. J., Standaert, M. L., and Haase, B. A. (1977). *J. Biol. Chem.* **252,** 5828.

Pouyssegur, J., Shiu, R. P. C., and Pastan, I. (1977). *Cell* **11,** 941.

Reed, B. C., Kaufmann, S. H., Mackall, J. C., Student, A. K., and Lane, M. D. (1977). *Proc. Natl. Acad. Sci. U.S.A.* **74,** 4876.

Rosen, O. M., Smith, C. J., Fung, C., and Rubin, C. S. (1978). *J. Biol. Chem.* **253,** 7579.

Roth, J. (1975). *Methods Enzymol.* **37,** 223.

Rubin, C. S., Lai, E., and Rosen, O. M. (1977). *J. Biol. Chem.* **252,** 3554.

Rubin, C. S., Hirsch, A., Fung, C., and Rosen, O. M. (1978). *J. Biol. Chem.* **253,** 7570.

Russell, T. R., and Ho, R. (1976). *Proc. Natl. Acad. Sci. U.S.A.* **73,** 4516.

Salomon, Y., Londos, C., and Rodbell, M. (1974). *Anal. Biochem.* **58,** 541.

Shanahan, M. R., and Czech, M. P. (1977a). *J. Biol. Chem.* **252,** 6554.

Shanahan, M. F., and Czech, M. P. (1977b). *J. Biol. Chem.* **252,** 8341.

Sheppard, H., and Wiggan, G. (1971). *Mol. Pharmacol.* **7,** 111.

Shiu, R. P. C., Pouyssegur, J., and Pastan, I. (1977). *Proc. Natl. Acad. Sci. U.S.A.* **74,** 3840.

Smith, U. (1974). *J. Clin. Invest.* **53,** 91.

Spooner, P. M., Chernick, S. S., Garrison, M. M., and Scow, R. O. (1978). *J. Biol. Chem.* in press.

Steinberg, D., Mayer, S. E., Khoo, J. C., Miller, E. A., Miller, R. E., Fredholm, B., and Eichner, R. (1975). *Adv. Cyc. Nucl. Res.* **5,** 549.

Steiner, A L., Packer, C. W., and Kipnis, D. M. (1972). *J. Biol. Chem.* **247,** 1106.

Thomopoulos, P., Roth, J., Lovelace, E., and Pastan, I. (1976). *Cell* **8,** 417.
Williams, I. H., and Polakis, S. E. (1977). *Biochem. Biophys. Res. Commun.* **77,** 175.
Wise, L. S., and Green, H. (1978). *Cell* **13,** 233.
Yalow, R. S., and Berson, S. (1960). *J. Clin. Invest.* **39,** 1157.

DISCUSSION

J. Kowal: I have one question concerning the 3T3 cells. Some work that was done by Rick Miller in our Department and recently published [*Proc. Natl. Acad. Sci. U.S.A.*], if I interpreted it correctly, suggested that insulin was actually involved in the differentiation to adipocytes. Miller has been working on glutamine synthetase induction. Does the addition of insulin enhance the conversion to adipocytes, or are the effects of insulin secondary?

O. M. Rosen: That is an important question—one that is not neatly resolvable without genetics. Insulin certainly promotes the morphological changes that accompany adipocyte conversion. Clearly you can get differentiation in the absence of insulin. All our studies were done in the absence of insulin during the course of differentiation. My feeling is that insulin is not required for differentiation per se, but that since it promotes fat synthesis the cells accumulate more lipid when they have been exposed to insulin for a long period of time. To answer you properly, one would have to have a cell that basically had no insulin receptors and differentiated just fine. Then one might be able to discriminate between effects on differentiation and effects on specific protein induction. We do not have that.

J. Carter: As you know, it has been very attractive to think that insulin should carry out many of its actions by activating phosphatases. It certainly would be very logical, but it has also been very hard to show. (1) Getting back to your heart protein kinase system, have you purified the phosphatase? (2) How specific is it for the phosphorylated protein kinase? (3) Do you have any direct evidence that insulin has any effect on either phosphatase activity or amount?

O. M. Rosen: (1) Yes, it has been purified; and (2) it is not specific for phosphoprotein kinase. It acts on a number of phosphoproteins. However, one can make it selective by virtue of different requirements. There are, for example, different metal requirements for activity on phosphoprotein kinases and protamine phosphate, for example. cAMP affects its activity on protein kinase, but not its ability to catalyze the dephosphorylation of other phosphoproteins. Thus, even though to my knowledge there is no specific phosphoprotein kinase phosphatase, the one that exists has been purified and can be made to act selectively *in vitro*. (3) That of course is the difficult question, and the one that we are very actively looking at now. It has been difficult to document an effect of insulin on phosphatase activity in crude extracts—or at least I have never been convinced that anybody has truly found that. I think that what one has to do is look at a specific substrate and assay a change in the phosphorylation state of that substrate. So we are now examining cells that are sensitive to insulin and looking to see whether we can alter the state of phosphorylation of the cyclic nucleotide binding protein.

E. Pavlik: With regard to the phosphorylation of the R subunit, is it possible that dimerization may play some role? In particular does C phosphorylate R or does an RC:RC dimer exist where an R subunit is phosphorylated not by its adjacent C subunit, but by the C subunit in the "neighboring" holoenzyme? The dilution approach that you described would not affect phosphorylation within the dimer. Hence, while it is clear that phosphorylation of the R subunit is not intermolecular, your approach has not distinguished between autophosphorylation within the RC holoenzyme or phosphorylation occurring between neighboring RC holoenzymes in the dimer.

O. M. Rosen: I am not quite sure that I understand what you mean by dimer. Are you talking about RC as a dimer?

E. Pavlik: Yes.

O. M. Rosen: As opposed to R_2 and C_2?

E. Pavlik: 2 R's and 2 C's; two holoenzymes forming a dimer.

O. M. Rosen: You are postulating that there is such a thing as an RC?

E. Pavlik: Yes.

O. M. Rosen: We have never found it.

E. Pavlik: Did'nt you show on your gel that there was a dimer and a monomer?

O. M. Rosen: In the figures, I used RC as a shorthand for holoenzyme. We have never found anything that would suggest that RC is free *in vivo*.

E. Palvik: What about the turnover of each subunit? Are the half-lives of the R subunits different from the half-lives of the C subunit? Are they transcribed and synthesized in a coordinated fashion of separately? Is it possible that the information for both is located in a gene cluster?

O. M. Rosen: That's a very good question, and one that we are just about to start studying. It really has not been looked at yet.

G. Aurbach: How general is phosphorylation of the R subunit? Would you suppose that it is general in tissues that are carrying out transport functions, in response to hormones mediated by cAMP? I am thinking in particular about Greengard's observations on apparent cAMP-stimulated protein phosphates. Was he actually observing in the toad bladder essentially the same phenomenon you are with cAMP, apparently simulating phosphatase?

O. M. Rosen: I cannot be sure because I have not repeated his experiments precisely but, on reading them, I believe that he could have been looking at a cAMP-mediated dissociation of protein kinase and a consequent dephosphorylation of the R subunit.

G. Aurbach: Have you been in communication with him about possibly checking out that question in the toad bladder system?

O. M. Rosen: I have not been in recent communication with him about this, so if there are new data I do not know about them.

G. Aurbach: In view of the relatively low insulin sensitivity of the macrophages, as well as the converted 3T3 cells, is it possible that some of those receptors might be somatomedin or NSILA receptors rather than insulin receptors?

O. M. Rosen: First of all, with respect to the 3T3 cells, transport is affected very sensitively by insulin. The concentration of insulin that enhances glucose transport is exactly the same as in normal adipocytes, i.e., 1–25 μU/ml. The effects of high insulin concentrations in these cells could very well have nothing to do with the insulin receptors that are involved in acute hexose transport. In the macrophages, we have not studied the receptors enough to know whether the higher concentrations of insulin required are occupying receptors made for something else. What we have done operationally in our analysis of the receptors in the fat cells is try to distinguish those that pertain to physiological concentrations of insulin. The rest of the curvilinear Scatchard could reflect other sorts of things including other receptors.

J. L. Vaitukaitis: Teleologically, why should there be two different forms of protein kinase—one phosphorylated, and the other one not? Second, when one monitors holoenzyme activity among hormonally responsive tissues, one initially observes a marked decrease in cAMP protein kinase holoenzyme activity in response to endogenously generated cAMP, and then a rapid regeneration of the holoenzyme within an hour or so. What do you think that reflects? De novo synthesis of R and C, or reassociation of the subunits? In addition, several laboratories have suggested that perhaps either the regulatory and/or the catalytic subunits may be translocated to the nucleus. Please comment.

O. M. Rosen: I do not know why there should be two kinds of protein kinases. I think we'll find that out. My hunch is that they are going to be in discrete parts of the cell, physiologically doing very different kinds of things. However, the hard evidence for that is not available.

A number of people have shown what you describe, namely, that exposure of cells to high concentrations of cAMP, leads to a diminution in the activity of protein kinase in the cytosol, and some investigators have claimed that they can recover the units in other particulate fractions, including the nucleus. These are difficult experiments to do; I think the answers could be right, but the data are hard to interpret. The components of protein kinase are extremely sticky, and if one dissociates protein kinase, the C and the R can adhere to a variety of intracellular particles, giving the impression that they have translocated. We need to study more protein kinase variants. It would be nice to have mutants analogous to the ones in steroid metabolism with defects in translocation. One should also look, using tools such as quantitative immunocytochemistry developed for protein kinases by Alton Steiner. I think it is very hard to use just one approach, namely, the measurement of catalytic activity, and be sure that what you are measuring is real, not some kind of peculiar artifact. Ultimately one is going to have to put together the fact that one of the things cAMP does in some cells is induce new proteins. If so, one would presume that it has to have some kind of nuclear effect—whether that means that protein kinase has to get into the nucleus is not really clear to me.

M. Saffran: There are more than two different kinds of protein kinases in the skeletal muscle. Reimann and Schlender have pointed out that the cAMP-independent protein kinases are far more important than the cAMP-dependent kinases. Is that true in heart as well as in skeletal muscle?

O. M. Rosen: The work I have been talking about has been restricted to the cAMP-dependent protein kinases, and even there your first comment is correct. I do not think there are two—I think that there are two broad families of cAMP-dependent protein kinases. There are also a number of highly substrate-specific cAMP-independent protein kinases. These are completely different enzymes. They are not regulated by cAMP. Clearly in skeletal muscle, glycogen synthesis and breakdown are affected by both kinds of kinases. It is not yet clear which of these prevails in various physiologic situations. There are also cAMP-independent protein kinases that are critically involved in other functions e.g., protein synthesis. In fact it has become evident in the last few years that cAMP-independent protein kinases are involved in a host of biological reactions. I have not studied glycogen metabolism in cardiac muscle, so I cannot directly answer your question as to the relative importance of these two kinds of kinases in that tissue.

K. Sterling: There was one figure—the dilution experiment in the first third of your talk, which had more on it than you discussed. It was largely unlabeled, you had a straight line with three sets of points: circles, triangles, and squares to give the dilution, but you also had a lower straight line and also a curvilinear line above. Will you please explain it more fully?

O. M. Rosen: The different symbols were for different dilutions, and the point was that they all fell on the same line. What I showed up here is the fact that if you add cAMP you convert this from an intra- to an intermolecular reaction, and then it becomes dilution sensitive.

J. Carter: In discussing the difference between physiological and superphysiological levels of insulin, you indicate that you could not wash away the insulin effect when you were using very large doses for prolonged periods of time. It has been clearly shown in isolated fat cells that the rate at which the insulin effect disappears is dependent both on the concentration and the time of the preincubation of the cells with insulin before you wash them, but I am not aware of any evidence that the change in glucose transport is qualitatively different under those circumstances. How long does this effect persist, and do you have any kinetic evidence to suggest that it is a qualitatively different change in the membrane than is induced by acute exposure at physiological levels?

O. M. Rosen: This effect lasts for many hours. One can treat cells for up to 24 hours with the high concentrations of insulin and the decay is very slow. It takes one or two days of bathing in non-insulin-containing medium until one even begins to approach preinsulin treatment values. The induction by insulin of the prolonged glucose uptake effect is cycloheximide sensitive, so that it appears to involve protein synthesis at some level. This would then make it very different from the acute effects that traditionally, and also in our hands, do not involve protein synthesis. As you may know, when fibroblasts are starved for glucose, their transport of glucose goes up enormously and is dependent upon protein synthesis. Pastan and his group have evidence that this effect involves the biosynthesis of two or more glucose-related proteins. In other words, there is the synthesis of some new proteins, which are in the particulate fraction of the cell and also on the cell membrane, one of which has a molecular weight of about 92,000 and another of which has a molecular weight of about 78,000. What they have to do with glucose transport and the possibility of new synthesis of glucose carrier sites under those conditions is not yet clear, but it is something that a number of people are working on. One of the things that we are interested in is whether or not the chronic effects of insulin are in fact doing something similar. We are looking at those two proteins to determine whether long-term treatment with high concentrations of insulin is enhancing the activity or the formation of proteins involved in hexose transport.

L. Birnbaumer: I am curious about your phenotypically AC⁻ variant cells. Have you done any studies on their cyclase system? Do they perhaps respond to GMP-P(NH)P?

O. M. Rosen: I really have not studied them with respect to GMP-P(NH)P. I think that they do have catalytic cyclase activity. The evidence for this is as follows: They have basal cAMP levels that are anywhere from perhaps one-fourth to three-fourths normal. Therefore, they can make cAMP, but they cannot enhance synthesis in response to hormones. If you assay adenylate cyclase in these mutants *in vitro* using the standard magnesium-dependent reaction that we all know about, one sees very little activity—perhaps one-sixteenth or so of the activity seen in wild-type cells, and this activity is not enhanced by any of the hormones that activate the wild-type extracts. If you carry out the adenylate cyclase reaction in manganese instead of in magnesium, you find that the variants are able to make cAMP at a rate better than in magnesium, but still in a hormone-insensitive fashion. I think that this is very analogous to the S49 lymphoma mutants, which have been studied in more detail. The macrophage variants have the ability to make cAMP from ATP, but have probably lost another regulatory component that renders them hormone insensitive. We really have not analyzed them enough to say more than that.

Hormonal Interactions in the Regulation of Blood Glucose

Philip Felig, Robert S. Sherwin, Vijay Soman, John Wahren,
Rosa Hendler, Luigi Sacca, Neil Eigler, David Goldberg, and
Mary Walesky

Department of Internal Medicine, Yale University School of Medicine, New Haven, Connecticut

I. Introduction

Regulation of the blood glucose concentration is a well recognized function of the endocrine system. The efficacy of the various control mechanisms is reflected by the very limited excursions in blood glucose observed in normal humans. In healthy subjects ingesting mixed meals, the blood glucose concentration generally remains between 70 and 110 mg/100 ml over the course of 24 hours (Service *et al.*, 1970). The preeminent role of insulin in this regulatory process has long been established. In addition to insulin, a variety of other hormones, particularly glucagon, catecholamines, cortisol, and growth hormone, have been implicated as having major roles in glucose homeostasis. In contrast to the action of insulin, each of these latter hormones tends to raise the blood glucose concentration and antagonizes one or more actions of insulin. For example, while insulin enhances glucose uptake and glycogen synthesis, epinephrine has the reverse effect. Interference with insulin-mediated glucose uptake (insulin resistance) is observed not only with increased levels of epinephrine (Altzuler *et al.*, 1967), but also in association with hypercorticism (Perley and Kipnis, 1966) and with growth hormone excess (Beck *et al.*, 1965). Insulin also differs from other glucoregulatory hormones with respect to the regulation of its secretion. In normal man, plasma insulin levels show moment to moment fluctuations in association with variations in blood glucose incident to mixed-meal ingestion (Tasaka *et al.*, 1975). In contrast, plasma glucagon level remain unchanged over 24 hours in healthy subjects ingesting mixed meals (Tasaka *et al.*, 1975). Stimulation of glucagon, epinephrine, or growth hormone secretion requires the development of frank hypoglycemia (DeFronzo *et al.*, 1977) or the presence of stimuli that operate via signals other than altered blood glucose levels (e.g., exercise, protein ingestion, stress). A clear distinction thus exists between insulin on the one hand and a variety of other hormones on the other hand with respect to effects on glucose metabolism as well as sensitivity to changes in circulating glucose. This distinction allows for a functional classification of hormonal control of carbohydrate metabolism in which insulin may be viewed as the prime regulatory

501

hormone while the other endocrine factors are considered counterregulatory hormones (Table I).

Among the various counterregulatory hormones, glucagon has been the focus of extensive investigative interest in the last 5–10 years (Unger, 1978; Sherwin and Felig, 1977). The development of radioimmunoassay procedures for the measurement of plasma glucagon, the infusion of crystalline glucagon into intact humans in physiological amounts, and the availability of an agent (somatostatin) that inhibits glucagon secretion have markedly increased our understanding of glucagon physiology. It is the purpose of this discussion to review (1) the role of glucagon in normal physiology, (2) the circumstances in which glucagon contributes to hyperglycemia in various disease states, and (3) evidence of a synergistic interaction of physiologic increments in counterregulatory hormones which provides an endocrine basis for the syndrome of stress hyperglycemia.

II. Glucagon: Physiologic Effects

Although glucagon was discovered more than 50 years ago, recognition of its physiologic role was long hampered by the absence of data concerning plasma concentrations as well as secretory rates. It is now recognized that total secretion in a 24-hour period in normal man amounts to no more than 100–150 μg (Fisher et al., 1976). Consequently, studies in which bolus injections of glucagon in doses of 1.0 mg or 0.1 mg are employed are clearly pharmacologic and provide little insight into glucagon's role in glucose homeostasis. Elucidation of glucagon's physiologic effects requires administration of the hormone in amounts similar to those that exist in nature.

The major physiologic stimuli of an increase in circulating glucagon are protein feeding (Unger et al., 1969), prolonged or severe exercise (Felig et al., 1972, Ahlborg et al., 1974), and brief starvation (Aguilar-Parada et al., 1969). Interestingly, the rise in plasma glucagon observed during a 1–3-day fast, is not

TABLE I
Hormonal Regulation of Blood Glucose

Regulatory hormone	Counterregulatory hormones
Insulin	Glucagon
↑ Glucose uptake	↑ Glycogenolysis
↑ Glycogen synthesis	↑ Gluconeogenesis
↓ Glycogenolysis	Catecholamines
↓ Gluconeogenesis	↑ Glycogenolysis
	↓ Glucose uptake
	Cortisol
	↑ Gluconeogenesis
	↓ Glucose uptake
	Growth Hormone
	↓ Glucose uptake

due to an increase in secretion but is a result of a reduction in glucagon catabolism (Fig. 1) (Fisher *et al.*, 1976). With prolonged starvation (beyond 3 days), glucagon levels return to baseline concentration as secretion well as catabolism declines (Fig. 1). The magnitude of the increment in plasma glucagon in these various hyperglucagonemic states is generally in the range of 100–200 pg/ml. With respect to glucose homeostasis, the significance of such a rise in glucagon is dependent on its ability to stimulate hepatic glucose production or antagonize the effects of physiologic hyperinsulinemia.

A. INSULIN ANTAGONISM

In the case of protein-stimulated glucagon secretion, Unger *et al.* (1969) suggested that the rise in glucagon prevents the hypoglycemia that would other-

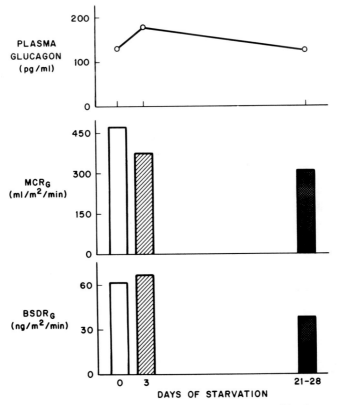

FIG. 1. Plasma glucagon levels, metabolic clearance rate (MCR_G), and basal systemic delivery rate ($BSDR_G$) of glucagon during prolonged fasting. The initial rise in plasma glucagon early in fasting is due to a fall in hormone clearance (catabolism) rather than an increase in secretion. Based on the data of Fisher *et al.* (1976).

wise accompany the hyperinsulinemia induced by protein feeding. Direct support
for this thesis has been provided by studies in which the rise in insulin as well as
glucagon induced by protein feeding were simulated.

As shown in Fig. 2, infusion of glucose at a rate of 2 ng/kg per minute results
in a 50–100% increase in plasma insulin, which is comparable to that observed
with a protein meal (Wahren *et al.*, 1976). This degree of hyperinsulinemia is
sufficient to cause virtually total inhibition of hepatic glucose output. However,
when glucagon is infused in amounts (3 ng/kg per minute) that simulate the
hyperglucagonemia of protein feeding, there is a prompt reversal of the insulin-
induced inhibition of hepatic glucose production (Fig. 2) (Felig *et al.*, 1976).
Thus the hyperglucagonemia induced by protein feeding permits ongoing hepatic
glucose output in the face of hyperinsulinemia. Protein ingestion thus constitutes
a physiologic example of glucagon-mediated insulin antagonism.

It should be recalled that ingestion of mixed meals (containing carbohydrate
and fat as well as protein) fails to alter plasma glucagon levels (Tasaka *et al.*,

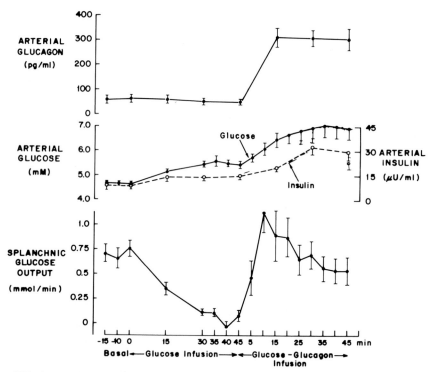

FIG. 2.   Arterial plasma glucagon, glucose, and insulin concentrations and splanchnic glucose
output in the basal state and in response to infusion of glucose (2 ng/kg per minute), followed by
infusion of glucose plus glucagon (3 ng/kg per minute). The addition of glucagon in a physiologic
dose promptly reversed the inhibition in splanchnic glucose production associated with a rise in
endogenous insulin. From Felig *et al.* (1976).

1975). From the standpoint of evolution, one may speculate that glucagon's role in survival of the organism may relate primarily to circumstances in which the diet was largely carnivorous. With pure protein feeding, glucagon permits a hyperinsulinemic response which is necessary for the assimilation of the ingested amino acids (Wahren *et al.*, 1976) without subjecting the organism to the risk of hypoglycemia.

B. EVANESCENCE OF GLUCAGON

When physiologic hypergluconemia is induced in the absence of antecedent hyperinsulinemia, an absolute increase in hepatic glucose production is observed (Fig. 3). The rise in glucose production occurs within 5–7 minutes and amounts to a doubling of hepatic glucose output. However, the stimulatory effect of hyperglucagonemia persists for 30 minutes or less (Fig. 3) (Felig *et al.*, 1976).

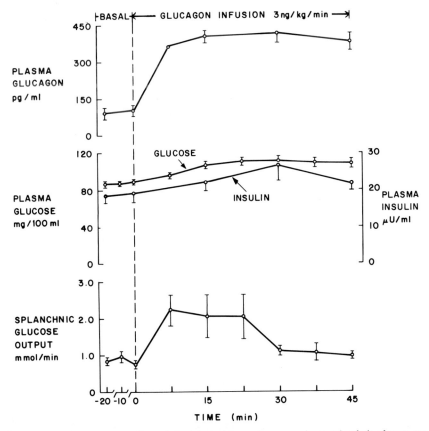

FIG. 3.   The evanescent effect of physiological hyperglucagonemia on splanchnic glucose output. Despite ongoing hyperglucagonemia, splanchnic glucose output returns to baseline within 30 minutes. Based on the data of Felig *et al.* (1976).

This evanescence of the action of hyperglucagonemia cannot be ascribed to depletion of liver glycogen, since the total glucose output amounts to less than 10 gm whereas total liver glycogen stores after an overnight fast amount to 70–90 gm. The fall in glucose output occurs in the face of stable insulin levels and is equally demonstrable in diabetic patients (Wahren *et al.*, 1976). The evanescent hepatic response to glucagon is thus not dependent upon increased insulin secretion. The transient nature of the stimulatory response suggests the rapid development of inhibition or reversal of glucagon action in man. Interestingly, this loss of glucagon action is not observed when pharmacological doses (50 ng/kg per minute) are infused (Liljenquist *et al.*, 1974), emphasizing further the need to differentiate physiologic from pharmacologic effects of glucagon.

To examine the nature and specificity of the hepatic refractoriness to hyperglucagonemia, the hepatic response to sequential infusions of glucagon and epinephrine was examined (Sacca *et al.*, 1978). Conscious dogs were infused with glucagon (3 ng/kg per minute) alone for 120 minutes followed by glucagon plus epinephrine (0.1 μg/kg per minute) for 60 minutes. As expected, glucagon alone caused an increase in glucose production, which returned to baseline by 75–120 minutes. After addition of epinephrine, glucose production rose again by 80% (Fig. 4). When the order of hormonal infusion was reversed, epinephrine alone caused a rise in glucose production, which returned to baseline by 60–120 minutes. When glucagon was added, glucose output promptly rose again by 85% (Fig. 5).

These observations indicate that evanescence with respect to hepatic glucose production is not unique to glucagon but is also observed with epinephrine, as first noted by Altszuler *et al.* (1967). Furthermore, hepatic refractoriness to persistent physiologic elevations of glucagon or epinephrine is selective for the particular hormone that is increased in concentration, since the liver remains responsive to other hormones that augment glucose production. As will be discussed below, a major aspect of the synergistic interaction between cortisol and other counterregulatory hormones involves the transformation of the evanescent action of glucagon and epinephrine to a persistent stimulatory effect on glucose production (Eigler *et al.*, 1979).

C. DOWN REGULATION OF THE GLUCAGON RECEPTOR

It is now well established that the first step in the action of glucagon as well as a variety of other polypeptide hormones is its binding to a receptor on the cell membrane (Cuatrecasas *et al.*, 1975). In the case of insulin, down regulation of the insulin receptor has been observed to occur in hyperinsulinemic states (Roth *et al.*, 1975). The question thus arises whether the rapid development of hepatic refractoriness to the action of physiologic increments in glucagon can be ascribed to a decrease in glucagon binding. To answer this question, hyperglucagonemia was induced in intact rats by the infusion of glucagon (3 ng/kg per minute) via an

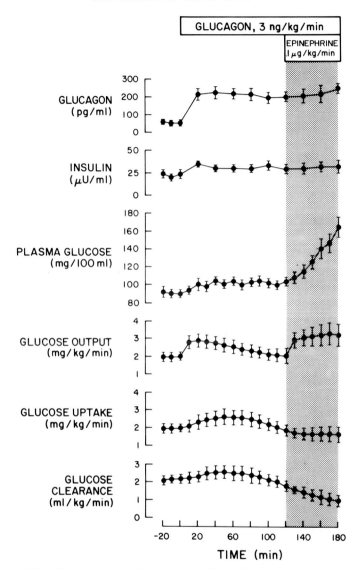

FIG. 4. The effect of glucagon alone and the addition of epinephrine on plasma glucagon, insulin, and glucose concentration, and glucose kinetics in six normal conscious dogs. Despite the development of hepatic refractoriness to glucagon (as indicated by the return of glucose output to baseline levels), there is a prompt response to the addition of epinephrine. From Sacca *et al.* (1978).

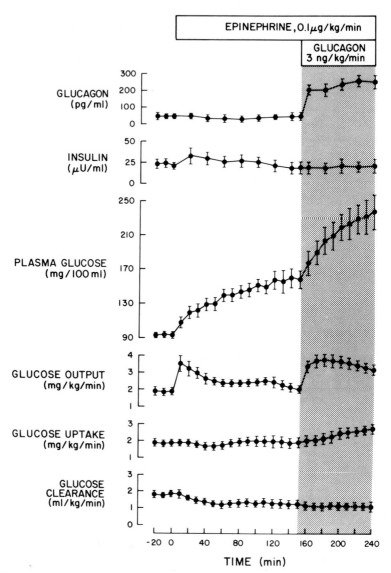

FIG. 5. Effect of epinephrine alone and after the addition of glucagon on plasma glucagon, insulin, and glucose concentration, and glucose kinetics in six normal conscious dogs. Despite the development of hepatic refractoriness to epinephrine (as reflected by the return of glucose output to basal levels), there is a prompt response to addition of glucagon. Coupled with the data in Fig. 4, the findings indicate that hepatic refractoriness develops to persistent physiologic increments in epinephrine as well as glucagon, and is specific for the particular hormone that has been infused. From Sacca *et al.* (1978).

indwelling catheter in the jugular vein. The animals were sacrificed after 1, 3, or 5 hours of the glucagon infusion, and specific binding of glucagon to liver membranes was determined (Soman and Felig, 1978).

Infusion of glucagon resulted in persistent increments in plasma glucagon of 250–300 pg/ml but only a transient 20–25 mg/100 ml rise in plasma glucose, which returned to baseline between 1 and 3 hours and was comparable to that observed in humans. As shown in Fig. 6, specific binding of glucagon to liver membranes was unchanged after 1 hour, tended to decrease slightly (12%), but insignificantly at 3 hours ($P > 0.5$), and fell significantly to values 45% below control at 5 hours. The glucagon infusion failed to alter specific binding of insulin or growth hormone, indicating the specificity of the effect of hyperglucagonemia on glucagon binding. Of note was the observation that glucagon-stimulated adenylate cyclase activity was reduced in the animals infused with glucagon for 5 hours but not after 1 or 3 hours. As shown in Fig. 7, there was close correspondence between glucagon binding and glucagon-stimulated adenylate cyclase activity in response to varying concentrations of glucagon in the control rats and the rats receiving the 5-hour glucagon infusion. Scatchard analysis of the glucagon binding data revealed a 45% reduction in binding capacity whereas binding affinity remained unchanged.

These observations thus indicate a role for hyperglucagonemia in the regulation of the glucagon receptor. Furthermore, the accompanying reduction in glucagon-stimulated adenylate cyclase activity suggests that diminished glucagon binding may have a role in diminishing the effects of physiological increments in plasma glucagon on target cells. On the other hand, the time course of

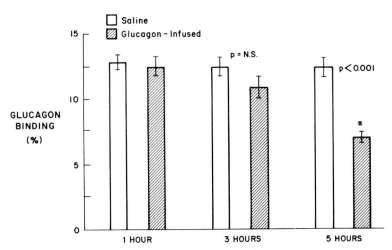

FIG. 6.   Specific binding of ^{125}I-labeled glucagon to liver membranes in saline- and glucagon-infused rats. A significant reduction in glucagon binding was observed after 5 hours, but not after 3 hours, of physiologic hyperglucagonemia. From Soman and Felig. (1978).

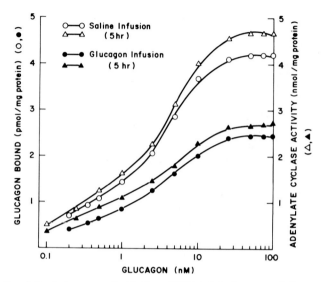

FIG. 7. Correlation between specific binding of ^{125}I-labeled glucagon and glucagon-stimulated adenylate cyclase activity in liver membranes from rats receiving a 5-hour infusion of saline (control) or a 5-hour infusion of glucagon. The data are expressed as the amount of glucagon specifically bound or the activity of adenylate cyclase at each concentration of unlabeled glucagon employed in the assay system. The glucagon infusion resulted in comparable decreases in glucagon binding and in glucagon-stimulated adenylate cyclase activity at all concentrations of glucagon. From Soman and Felig. (1978).

the changes in glucagon binding suggests that postreceptor mechanisms may be of more immediate importance. In humans (Felig *et al.*, 1976) and dogs (Sacca *et al.*, 1978), as well as in rats (Ganguli and Sperling, 1978), the hepatic glucose response to hyperglucagonemia is totally dissipated by 30–90 minutes. The data thus suggest dual modulation of tissue responsiveness to glucagon. Acute refractoriness (rapid evanescence) to physiologic hyperglucagonemia occurs via a postreceptor mechanism, whereas receptor-mediated modulation occurs via a slower process.

III. Glucagon: Diabetogenic Effects

Much of the interest in glucagon in recent years has derived from the hypothesis that glucagon has an essential role in the pathogenesis of diabetes mellitus (Unger and Orci, 1975). Such a role for glucagon was of more than passing concern, since it raised the possibility that suppression of glucagon (as can be achieved by somatostatin) might provide an improvement in the management of·the diabetic patient that is not achievable with insulin therapy alone. While this area remains controversial (Unger, 1978), many of the recent data underscore the primary role of insulin in the pathogenesis of spontaneous diabetes.

A. HYPERGLUCAGONEMIA AND GLUCOSE TOLERANCE IN NORMAL MAN

When a glucose load is ingested or administered intravenously, in addition to the rise in plasma insulin there is a fall in plasma glucagon (Unger *et al.*, 1970; Muller *et al.*, 1970). The failure to observe a comparable decline in diabetics led to the notion that the ratio of insulin to glucagon (I:G ratio) rather than the absolute concentration of insulin per se is the major determinant of glucose tolerance (Unger, 1976). By this reasoning, a rise in glucagon should bring about a deterioration in glucose tolerance independent of a lack of insulin. This hypothesis was tested by simulating in normal man the hyperglucagonemia that occurs in such diverse conditions as diabetic ketoacidosis, severe trauma or sepsis, and cirrhosis. Infusion of glucagon (3 ng/kg per minute) to normal subjects resulted in hyperglucagonemia of 350 pg/ml, yet failed to cause a diminution in glucose tolerance (Fig. 8) (Sherwin *et al.*, 1976a). The maintenance of normal glucose tolerance could not be ascribed to a "compensatory" rise in insulin (Fig. 8). Similar findings were observed after intraportal rather than peripheral glucagon administration (Holst *et al.*, 1977). Thus despite a 5- to 6-fold fall in the peripheral I:G ratio (from 34:1 to 6:1) during the glucagon infusion, no change in glucose tolerance occurred. The argument has been raised that glucose intolerance would not be expected unless the I:G ratio had been reduced to levels well below 6:1 (Unger, 1976). However, to achieve such a ratio would require either absolute insulin deficiency or hyperglucagonemia in excess of that observed in most disease states (i.e., pharmacologic hyperglucagonemia).

It should be noted that massive elevations in glucagon can bring about glucose intolerance even in the presence of insulin, as is observed in the glucagonoma syndrome (Mallison *et al.*, 1976). However, even in such circumstances the degree of hyperglycemia is extremely mild and is not accompanied by ketosis.

B. GLUCAGON IN DIABETES

In addition to failure of suppression of glucagon secretion after glucose ingestion, the diabetic patient demonstrates absolute hyperglucagonemia after the ingestion of protein meals (Wise *et al.*, 1973). Furthermore, moderate to marked elevations in glucagon are observed in diabetic ketoacidosis (Muller *et al.*, 1973). Whether such elevations in glucagon are responsible for deterioration of diabetic control in the face of ongoing insulin availability has been the subject of extensive investigation. In two juvenile-onset, ketosis-prone diabetics who were given their usual daily doses of of insulin and were infused with glucagon for 2–3

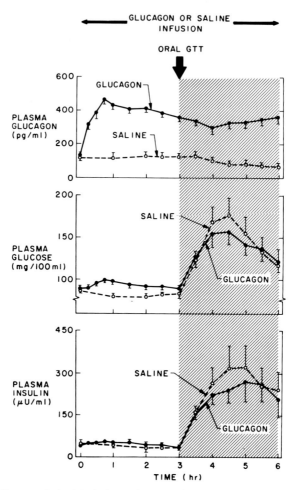

FIG. 8. Influence of physiologic hyperglucagonemia on the response to an oral glucose-tolerance test in normal subjects. Infusion of glucagon failed to alter the plasma glucose response. Plasma insulin levels were also the same in the saline (control) and glucagon infusion studies. From Sherwin *et al.* (1976a).

days in doses up to 9 ng/kg per minute, we failed to observe any deterioration in diabetic control as reflected by plasma glucose or blood ketones (Fig. 9) (Sherwin *et al.*, 1976a). Using a somewhat different protocol, in which insulin was infused continuously and glucagon was added, Raskin and Unger (1977) reported a marked increase in glycosuria. However, close perusal of their data reveals that mean plasma glucose levels generally did not increase by more than 40–60 mg/100 ml and the effect of the glucagon on plasma glucose was generally apparent for only the first 6–12 hours of the infusion. Furthermore, in a subsequent study, Clarke *et al.* (1978) found that infusion of glucagon failed to

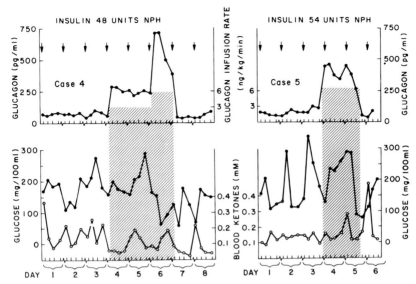

FIG. 9. Influence of glucagon infusion on plasma glucose and blood ketone levels in insulin-treated diabetics. The arrows indicate administration of insulin in the patient's usual dose. Hyperglucagonemia failed to cause a deterioration in metabolic control as reflected by plasma glucose and blood ketone concentrations. From Sherwin *et al.* (1976a).

alter plasma glucose levels or increase insulin requirements in diabetic patients treated with an artificial endocrine pancreas. Thus the overall data indicate that, in the insulin-treated diabetic, hyperglucagonemia is not of itself sufficient to bring about any substantial deterioration in glucose control.

While physiologic hyperglucagonemia has little glycemic effect in the face of endogenous or exogenous insulin, in the insulin-withdrawn diabetic glucagon clearly contributes to hyperglycemia. In such circumstances, hyperglucagonemia causes a markedly greater rise in plasma glucose than is observed in normal subjects or in insulin-treated diabetics (Sherwin *et al.*, 1976a). Nevertheless, the rise in hepatic glucose output is no greater in insulin-withdrawn diabetics than in healthy controls (Bomboy *et al.*, 1977). Thus the greater rise in blood glucose in the insulin-deficient diabetic is due to failure of glucose utilization.

C. EFFECTS OF SOMATOSTATIN

The discovery that somatostatin inhibited glucagon secretion (Koerker *et al.*, 1974) opened new opportunities for examining the physiologic as well as possible diabetogenic role of glucagon. With respect to diabetes, somatostatin administration resulted in a marked blunting of the glycemic rise to carbohydrate-containing meals even in the absence of insulin administration (Gerich *et al.*, 1974). Furthermore, somatostatin markedly reduced the insulin requirement in patients treated with the artificial pancreas (Meissner *et al.*, 1975). Such observations were generally interpreted as indicative of the essential role of glucagon for the full expression of diabetic hyperglycemia. On the other hand, subsequent studies have demonstrated that the action of somatostatin on blood glucose may reflect not its inhibition of glucagon secretion, but inhibitory effects on nutrient absorption. In addition, somatostatin may increase sensitivity to hyperglucagonemia independent of insulin availability.

1. Nutrient Absorption

In insulin-dependent diabetic subjects, administration of somatostatin markedly blunts the blood glucose rise after oral glucose administration but not after intravenous glucose infusion (Wahren and Felig, 1976). This dissociation between oral and intravenous glucose tolerance raised the possibility of an effect on carbohydrate absorption. Indeed, somatostatin dramatically reduced blood xylose levels after ingestion of this pentose, and the peak increment was delayed by 1–2 hours (Wahren and Felig, 1976). Administration of glucagon (3 ng/kg per minute) or intraduodenal administration of xylose failed to reverse the effect of somatostatin on xylose absorption. These observations suggest that somatostatin reduces postprandial hyperglycemia in diabetes primarily by decreasing and/or delaying carbohydrate absorption, rather than by enhancing carbohydrate disposal. The failure to improve glucose disposal provides further evidence for the primary role of insulin deficiency rather than glucagon excess in the pathogenesis of glucose intolerance in diabetes.

To counter these observations on carbohydrate absorption, subsequent studies were undertaken in which insulin-dependent diabetics were fed low-carbohydrate diets in which the protein content of the diet was increased (Raskin and Unger, 1978). Despite the virtual lack of carbohydrate in the diet, somatostatin administration was observed to improve blood glucose control (Raskin and Unger, 1978). While the effect of somatostatin was attributed to glucagon suppression, it is equally explainable on the basis of diminished protein absorption (Sherwin and Felig, 1978). In diabetic patients there is an exaggerated hyperglycemic response to protein ingestion and augmented hepatic uptake of gluconeogenic amino acids (Felig *et al.*, 1977). However, when somatostatin is infused, there is a marked reduction in amino acid availability after a protein meal (Goldberg *et al.*, 1979) (Fig. 10). This effect of somatostatin is not due to augmented metabolism of absorbed amino acids since somatostatin exaggerates rather than suppresses the plasma response to intravenous administration of leucine (Goldberg *et al.*, 1979). These observations thus provide evidence of an inhibitory effect of somatostatin on protein digestion and/or absorption. Similar conclusions have been reached on the basis of the effects of somatostatin on intraduodenally administered amino acids (Krejs *et al.*, 1978). Accordingly, the improved glucose response in somatostatin-treated diabetics fed a low-carbohydrate, high-protein diet may reflect reduced absorption of gluconeogenic nutrients rather than the conse-

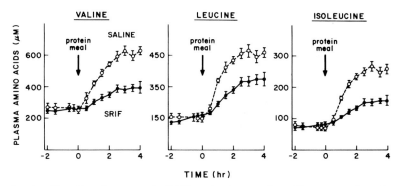

FIG. 10.   The effect of somatostatin (SRIF) on the plasma amino acid response to ingestion of a protein meal in healthy subjects. Somatostatin blunted the plasma rise of each of the branched-chain amino acids. A similar effect was not observed when amino acids were given intravenously, indicating interference by somatostatin in the absorption and/or digestion of a protein meal. From Goldberg *et al.* (1979).

quences of glucagon lack per se. With respect to the mechanism whereby somatostatin influences nutrient digestion and/or absorption, somatostatin has been observed to decrease the secretion of a variety of gastrointestinal hormones (gastrin, secretin), as well as exocrine pancreatic secretion, gut motility, and splanchnic blood flow (Gerich, 1977; Wahren and Felig, 1976).

2. Sensitization to Glucagon

Studies with somatostatin not only have involved the institution of a hypoglucagonemic state, but also have permitted an examination of the effects of reintroduction of hyperglucagonemia in the face of ongoing somatostatin infusion. For example, in insulinopenic dogs addition of physiologic doses of glucagon together with somatostatin results in a prompt restoration of hyperglycemia (Dobbs *et al.*, 1975; Cherrington *et al.*, 1978). Furthermore, in diabetic patients on low-carbohydrate, high-protein diets, addition of glucagon to the somatostatin results in a partial return of hyperglycemia (Raskin and Unger, 1978). Such observations have been interpreted as providing evidence that the hypoglycemic effects of somatostatin are due entirely to glucagon lack rather than other actions (e.g., gastrointestinal) of somatostatin. However, those studies fail to take into account the possibility that somatostatin increases the hepatic response to glucagon independent of insulin availability.

To examine the latter possibility, conscious dogs were infused with glucagon alone (3 ng/kg per minute) or with glucagon plus somatostatin together with replacement doses of insulin (Fig. 11) (Sacca *et al.*, 1979). Infusion of glucagon alone resulted in the expected transient increase in glucose output. When somatostatin and insulin were added, a 4- to 5-fold greater rise in glucose production was observed (Fig. 11). The greater hepatic glucose response occurred despite plasma glucagon levels comparable to those achieved with infu-

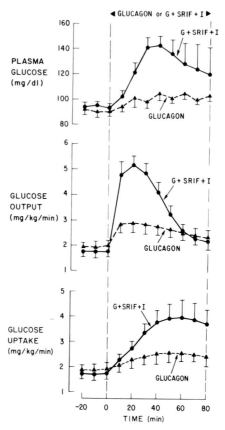

FIG. 11. Changes in plasma glucose, glucose output, and glucose uptake induced by infusion of glucagon alone or glucagon (G) plus somatostatin (SRIF) and replacement doses of insulin (I) in normal conscious dogs. The infusion of somatostatin markedly increased the stimulatory effect of glucagon on glucose output despite the presence of insulin in replacement doses. From Sacca *et al.* (1979).

sion of glucagon alone, and in the face of 3- to 4-fold increments in peripheral insulin levels (Fig. 12), indicating adequate repacement of portal insulin concentration. Furthermore, even if mild portal insulin deficiency were present, the exaggerated hepatic response to glucagon when administered together with somatostatin cannot be ascribed to insulin lack. As noted above, the stimulatory effect of glucagon on hepatic glucose output is no greater in insulin-withdrawn diabetics than in nondiabetic controls (Bomboy *et al.*, 1977).

Thus the observations with combined infusions of glucagon and somatostatin indicate that the latter potentiates the stimulatory effect of glucagon on hepatic glucose output independent of insulin availability (Sacca *et al.*, 1979). Consequently the hyperglycemia observed in insulin-treated diabetics when

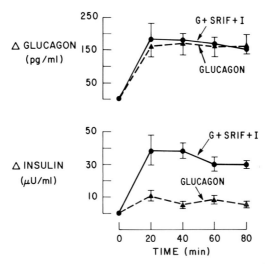

FIG. 12.   Changes in plasma glucagon and insulin concentrations during the infusion of glucagon alone or glucagon (G) plus somatostatin (SRIF) and insulin (I) in normal, conscious dogs. The rise in plasma glucagon was the same whether glucagon was given alone or with somatostatin. The 3- to 4-fold greater rise in peripheral insulin levels when somatostatin plus insulin were given together with glucagon suggests adequate replacement of portal insulin levels during the study. From Sacca *et al.* (1979).

physiologic doses of glucagon are added to somatostatin (Raskin and Unger, 1978), may reflect the potentiating effect of somatostatin on the action of glucagon rather than a diabetogenic effect of glucagon per se (Sherwin and Felig, 1978).

D. HYPERSENSITIVITY TO GLUCAGON IN UREMIA

In addition to the importance of absolute insulin deficiency, recent studies suggest that in certain disease states altered tissue responsiveness to glucagon may contribute to the hyperglycemic effect of this hormone. The importance of augmented tissue sensitivity to glucagon in the pathogenesis of glucose intolerance is suggested by observations in uremic man (Sherwin *et al.*, 1976b). Chronic renal failure is characterized by an increased incidence of glucose intolerance, insulin resistance (DeFronzo, 1978), and a 3- to 4-fold increase in circulating glucagon (Bibrey *et al.*, 1974). Although some of the increase in circulating glucagon is due to proglucagon, the concentration of true pancreatic glucagon (MW 3500) is elevated at least 2-fold in uremia (Kuku *et al.*, 1976). After chronic dialysis, glucose tolerance and insulin sensitivity return to normal in the absence of changes in plasma glucagon. On the basis of these observations, hyperglucagonemia did not appear to contribute to uremia-induced glucose intolerance. However, the role of glucagon in uremia is evident when tissue responsiveness to this hormone is examined. When glucagon is infused to uremic subjects (nondialyzed) in physiological doses, the glycemic effect is increased 3- to 4-fold as compared to healthy controls (Sherwin et al., 1976b) (Fig. 13). Furthermore, a direct linear correlation is observed between performance on glucose-tolerance testing and the glycemic response to glucagon infusion. This augmented glycemic response to glucagon returns to normal after dialysis (Fig. 13), thereby accounting for improved glucose tolerance despite persistence of the hyperglucagonemia.

Studies with a uremic rat model provide a cellular mechanism for these changes in responsiveness to glucagon. In 70% and 90% nephrectomized rats, the hyperglucagonemia, hyperglycemia, and hyperinsulinemia observed in uremic subjects are reproduced (Soman and Felig, 1977). In such animals glucagon binding to liver membranes and cyclic AMP generation in response to glucagon are increased 2- to 3-fold (Soman and Felig, 1977) (Fig. 14). Thus, changes in glucagon responsiveness in uremia may result from augmented binding of this hormone by target cells. These findings thus provide evidence of an important role of glucagon receptors in a syndrome of carbohydrate intolerance.

IV. Synergistic Interactions of Counterregulatory Hormones: A Mechanism for Stress Hyperglycemia

As noted above, each of the counterregulatory hormones has long been noted to have hyperglycemic, insulin-antagonistic effects (Table I). In stressful condi-

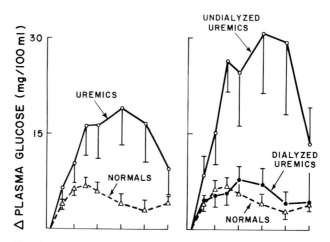

FIG. 13.   The glycemic response to physiologic doses of glucagon (3 ng/kg per minute) in undialyzed and dialyzed uremic patients and in healthy control subjects. In the undialyzed uremics, sensitivity to the hyperglycemic effect of glucagon is increased and returns to normal after dialysis. Based on the data of Sherwin et al. (1976b).

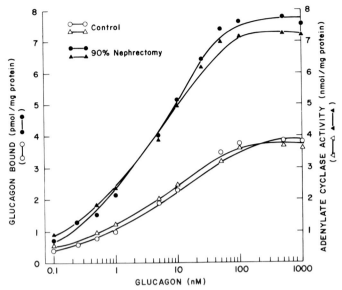

FIG. 14. Correlation between glucagon binding and glucagon-stimulated adenylate cyclase activity in control rats and uremic rats (90% nephrectomy). Specific binding of glucagon and glucagon-stimulated adenylate cyclase activity are shown as a function of glucagon concentration in the assay medium. Nephrectomy resulted in an increase in glucagon binding at all concentrations of glucagon, indicating an increase in binding capacity. There was a comparable increase in glucagon-stimulated adenylate cyclase activity. From Soman and Felig (1977).

tions such as severe burns, skeletal trauma, or sepsis, hyperglycemia and decreased glucose tolerance are observed in association with increased plasma levels of glucagon, epinephrine, norepinephrine, cortisol, and growth hormone (Batstone *et al.*, 1976; Kinney and Felig, 1979). However, physiologic elevations in glucagon and epinephrine cause only transient increments in hepatic glucose production and only modest increments (15–30 mg/100 ml) in blood glucose (Fig. 15). Furthermore, *acute, physiologic* increments in cortisol fail to alter glucose kinetics or plasma glucose (Fig. 15). Acute physiologic elevations in growth hormone also have little effect on plasma glucose (Gerich *et al.*, 1976). Thus, individually, each of the counterregulatory hormones has at best, a minor effect on glucose homeostasis in healthy subjects. The precise relationship between stress-induced increments in counterregulatory hormones and stress-induced hyperglycemia thus had not been established. The hypothesis was consequently considered that the response to any one counterregulatory hormone may be influenced by simultaneous elevations in one or more other members of this group of hormones (Eigler *et al.*, 1979).

Normal conscious dogs were studied during infusions of glucagon (3.5 ng/kg per minute), epinephrine (0.05 μg/kg per minute), or cortisol (400 μg/kg per hour for 90 minutes followed by 200 μg/kg per hour for an additional 5 hours), in

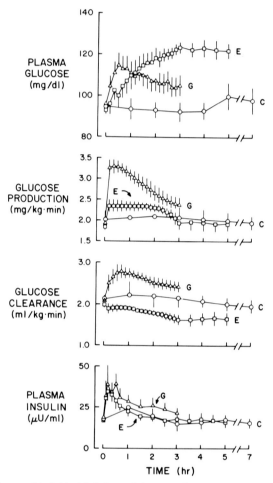

FIG. 15.   Influence of individual infusions of glucagon (G), epinephrine (E), and cortisol (C) on plasma glucose, glucose kinetics, and plasma insulin in normal, conscious dogs. From Eigler *et al.* (1979).

double or triple combinations. The infusion doses were chosen so as to simulate the increments in these hormones observed in circumstances of stress. The increments in plasma hormone concentrations were the same whether a given hormone was infused singly or in combination with one hormone or two others (Fig. 16).

As shown in Fig. 15, when infused singly, physiologic doses of glucagon cause a greater increment in glucose output than is observed with physiologic doses of epinephrine. On the other hand, epinephrine causes a reduction in glucose clearance, reflecting its antagonism of insulin-mediated peripheral glu-

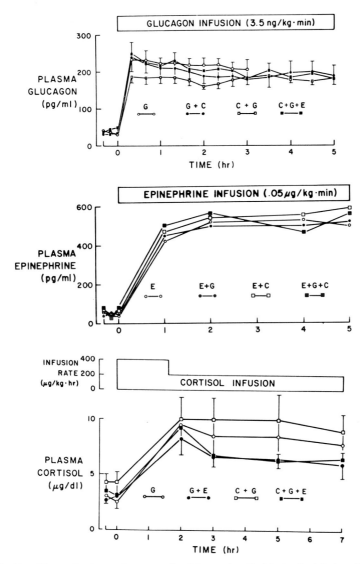

FIG. 16. Changes in plasma glucagon, epinephrine, and cortisol during the infusion of glucagon (G), epinephrine (E), and cortisol (C) alone or in various combinations. The data demonstrate that, for each of the hormones infused, the plasma increment achieved was the same whether the hormone was given alone or in various combinations. From Eigler *et al.* (1979).

cose utilization. In contrast, glucose clearance is augmented during glucagon infusion, presumably as a consequence of the rise in insulin. When glucagon and epinephrine are infused jointly (Fig. 17), the rise in plasma glucose (58 ± 3 mg/100 ml) is 50% greater than the sum of the individual responses to glucagon (10 ± 2 mg/100 ml) and epinephrine (20 ± 3 mg/100 ml). Concerning the mechanism of this synergism, the rise in glucose output was no more than additive and remained transient in nature. On the other hand, the rate of glucose clearance was not midway between that observed with epinephrine and glucagon when given singly, but declined to the same extent as that induced by epinephrine

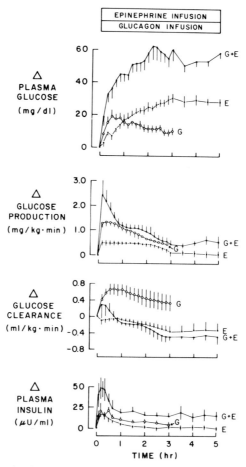

FIG. 17. Changes in plasma glucose, glucose kinetics, and plasma insulin during combined infusion of glucagon and epinephrine (G + E) as compared with infusion of glucagon (G) and epinephrine (E) individually. The plasma glucose increment with the combined infusion was 50% greater than the sum of the individual infusions.

alone. Thus, addition of epinephrine to glucagon has an additive effect on glucose production but a more than additive effect in reducing glucose utilization. The net result is a more than additive increase in blood glucose.

The effect of the addition of cortisol to infusion of glucagon or infusion of epinephrine is shown in Fig. 18. The rise in plasma glucose when cortisol was added to either hormone was markedly greater than the sum of the individual responses. In the case of cortisol plus glucagon, the response in plasma glucose (41 ± 8 mg/100 ml) was 215% greater than the sum of the individual glucose responses (10 ± 2 and 3 ± 4 mg/100 ml). When cortisol was added to epinephrine, the rise in plasma glucose (50 ± 7 mg/100 ml) was 100% greater than the sum of the individual plasma glucose increments. The synergistic interaction between cortisol on the one hand, and epinephrine or glucagon on the other hand, was not due to effects on glucose clearance or plasma insulin. The potentiating effect of cortisol was a consequence of an increase and, more important, a prolongation of the stimulatory effects of glucagon and epinephrine on hepatic glucose production (Fig. 18). Whereas the effects of glucagon and

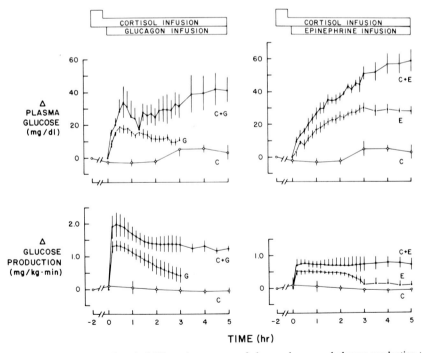

FIG. 18. Influence of cortisol (C) on the response of plasma glucose and glucose production to glucagon (G) or epinephrine (E). Cortisol had the effect of increasing and, more important, sustaining the stimulatory effects of glucagon and epinephrine on glucose production. As a result, the effects of the combined hormone infusions (C + G and C + E) on plasma glucose were more than additive. From Eigler et al. (1979).

epinephrine on hepatic glucose production are dissipated in 3 hours or less, when given alone, added cortisol causes a sustained increase in glucose production that persists for at least 5 hours.

In Fig. 19 the response to simultaneous infusion of all three hormones is shown. Noteworthy is the fact that within 5 hours, in previously healthy dogs, fasting plasma glucose levels exceeded 200 mg/100 ml, glucose production was 150% above basal levels, and glucose clearance was reduced. The metabolic criteria for a diabetic state were thus rapidly fulfilled as reflected by the presence of fasting hyperglycemia, absolute glucose overproduction, and reduced glucose

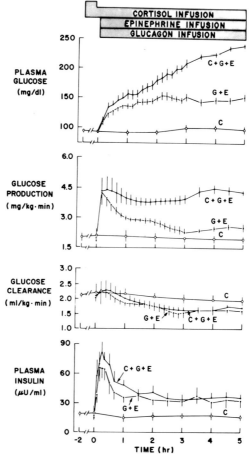

FIG. 19.   Effect of the addition of cortisol (C) on the metabolic response to glucagon plus epinephrine (G + E) infusion. The triple hormone infusion (C + G + E) resulted in hyperglycemia in excess of 200 mg/100 ml, a 2- to 3-fold, sustained increase in glucose production, and a fall in glucose clearance. From Eigler *et al.* (1979).

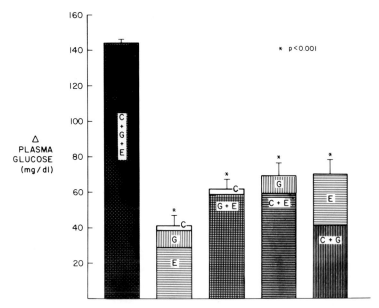

FIG. 20.   Synergistic effect of combined hormone infusion on plasma glucose concentration. The rise in plasma glucose produced by the simultaneous infusion of all three hormones (C + G + E) was 2- to 4-fold greater ($P < 0.001$) than the sum of the responses to infusion of cortisol (C), glucagon (G), and epinephrine (E) individually, or the sum of the responses to each combination of two counterregulatory hormones and the respective complementing single-hormone infusion. From Eigler *et al.* (1979).

utilization. The synergistic nature of the response to the triple hormone infusion is reflected by the fact that the rise in plasma glucose was 2- to 4-fold greater than the sum of the responses to individual infusions or the sum of responses to any double- plus single-hormone infusion (Fig. 20).

The current observations thus indicate that the effects of counterregulatory hormones cannot be predicted from responses to individual hormones but are determined by the hormonal milieu in which their hypersecretion occurs. Each hormone has particular effects, which may be enhanced or antagonized by the others. From the individual as well as combined responses, an overall scheme of counterregulatory hormone action may be constructed (Table II). Glucagon acts primarily to increase glucose production but this effect is transient and is offset by an accompanying rise in glucose utilization. Consequently, the net effect is a modest rise (10–15 mg/100) in plasma glucose. Epinephrine is also evanescent and less potent than glucagon in stimulating glucose output, but causes a sustained decrease in glucose utilization. As a result, its hyperglycemic effect exceeds that of glucagon. The combined presence of elevated levels of glucagon and epinephrine results in an additive but transient increase in glucose production

TABLE II

Actions and Interactions of Counterregulatory Hormones on Glucose Kinetics

Parameter	Glucagon	Epinephrine	Glucagon + epinephrine	Glucagon + epinephrine + cortisol
Glucose production				
Magnitude	↑ ↑	↑	↑ ↑ ↑	↑ ↑ ↑ ↑
Duration	Transient	Transient	Transient	Persistent
Glucose utilization	↑	↓ ↓	↓ ↓	↓ ↓

in association with decreased glucose utilization. Finally, addition of cortisol to either glucagon or epinephrine or to both hormones combined, converts a transient increase in glucose output to one of sustained glucose overproduction.

It should be noted that with the multiple-hormone infusions plasma insulin levels failed to rise in concert with the progressive increment in plasma glucose (Figs. 17 and 19). The inhibitory effect of epinephrine on insulin secretion is thus an important component of the hyperglycemic response. On the other hand, since plasma insulin never fell below basal levels, it is clear that absolute insulin lack is not a requirement for the hyperglycemia produced by multiple-hormone infusions.

The implications of these findings with respect to stress hyperglycemia are readily apparent. The data suggest that stress hyperglycemia cannot be ascribed to a single hormone but is a consequence of hormone–hormone interactions in a setting of hypersecretion of a variety of hormones. Furthermore, stress hyperglycemia does not require a preexisting abnormality in insulin secretion nor more than a few hours (3–5) in which to develop. It should also be noted that the combined hormone infusions caused substantial increments in plasma glucose, yet failed to raise plasma ketones (Eigler *et al.*, 1979). This is in keeping with observations in traumatized patients in whom elevations in plasma glucose exceeding 200 mg/100 ml occur in the absence of ketosis (Batstone *et al.*, 1976). The development of hyperketonemia may require an absolute deficiency of insulin.

V. Concluding Remarks

Our studies have attempted to examine insulin–glucagon interactions as well as the interactions among a variety of counterregulatory hormones (glucagon, epinephrine, and cortisol). In normal man, bursts of glucagon secretion precipitated by feeding pure protein prevent the inhibition in glucose production and the hypoglycemia that would otherwise accompany protein-stimulated insulin secretion. In contrast, sustained hyperglucagonemia fails to cause glucose intolerance or worsening of preexisting diabetes so long as endogenous or exogenous insulin is available. Glucagon-induced hyperglycemia can, however, be observed either in circumstances of absolute insulin deficiency (insulin-withdrawn diabetes) or when tissue sensitivity to this hormone is increased (as in undialyzed uremics). Data suggesting a major role for glucagon in the pathogenesis of spontaneous diabetes based on studies with somatostatin may reflect the latter's interference with nutrient absorption as well as its potentiation of the hyperglycemic action of glucagon. Finally, the glycemic response to any one of the counterregulatory hormones is dependent on whether there are simultaneous elevations in other counterregulatory hormones. The synergistic nature of these hormone–hormone interactions with respect to raising circulating plasma glucose levels may constitute the mechanism for stress hyperglycemia.

ACKNOWLEDGMENTS

This work was supported in part by Grants AM13526, AM20495, AM21158, and RR125 from the National Institutes of Health. Dr. Felig is an Established Investigator of the American Diabetes Association. Dr. Sherwin is recipient of a Research Career Development Award (AM00334) from the National Institutes of Health. Dr. Soman is recipient of a Clinical Investigator Award (AM00356) from the National Institutes of Health. Dr. Sacca was recipient of a North Atlantic Treaty Organization Fellowship.

REFERENCES

Aguilar-Parada, E., Eisentraut, A. M., and Unger, R. H. (1969). *Diabetes* **18,** 717.

Ahlborg, G., Felig, P., Hagenfeldt, L., Hendler, R., and Wahren, J. (1974). *J. Clin. Invest.* **53,** 1080.

Altszuler, N., Steele, R., Rathget, I., and DeBodo, R. C. (1967). *Am. J. Physiol.* **212,** 677.

Batstone, G. F., Alberti, K. G. M. M., Hinks, L., Smythe, P., Lang, J. E., Ward, C. M., Ely, D. W., and Bloom, S. R. (1976). *Burns* **2,** 207.

Beck, P., Schalch, D. S., and Parker, M. L. (1965). *J. Lab. Clin. Med.* **66,** 366.

Bilbrey, G. L., Faloona, G. R., White, M. G., and Knochel, J. P. (1974). *J. Clin. Invest.* **53,** 841.

Bomboy, J. D., Lewis, S. B., Lacy, W. W., Sinclair-Smith, B. C., and Liljenquist, J. E. (1977). *Diabetes* **26,** 177.

Cherrington, A. D., Lacy, W. W., and Chiasson, J. L. (1978). *J. Clin. Invest.* **63,** 664.

Clarke, W. L., Santiago, J. V., and Kipnis, D. M. (1978). *Diabetes* **27,** 649.

Cuatrecasas, P., Hollenberg, M. D., Chang, K.-J., and Bennett, V. (1975). *Recent Prog. Horm. Res.* **31,** 37.

DeFronzo, R. (1978). *Metabol. Clin. Exp.* **27,** 1866.

DeFronzo, R., Andres, R., Bledsoe, T. A., Boden, G., Faloona, G. A., and Tobin, J. D. (1977). *Diabetes* **26,** 445.

Dobbs, R. H., Sakurai, H., Sasaki, H., Faloona, G., Valverge, I., Baetens, D., Orci, L., and Unger, R. H. (1975). *Science* **187,** 544.

Eigler, N., Sacca, L., and Sherwin, R. S. (1979). *J. Clin. Invest.* **63,** 114.

Felig, P., Wahren, J., Hendler, R., and Ahlborg, G. (1972). *N. Engl. J. Med.* **287,** 184.

Felig, P., Wahren, J., and Hendler, R. (1976). *J. Clin. Invest.* **58,** 261.

Felig, P., Wahren, J., Sherwin, R. S., and Palaiologos, G. (1977). *Arch. Int. Med.* **137,** 507.

Fisher, M., Sherwin, R. S., Hendler, R., and Felig, P. (1976). *Proc. Natl. Acad. Sci. U.S.A.* . **73,** 1735.

Ganguli, S., Sperling, M., Franie, C., and Christensen, R. (1979). *Am. J. Physiol.* **236**, E358.

Gerich, J. (1977). *Arch. Int. Med.* **137**, 659.

Gerich, J. E., Lorenzi, M., Schneider, V., Karam, J. H., Revier, J., Guillemin, R., and Forsham, P. H. (1974). *N. Engl. J. Med.* **291**, 544.

Gerich, J. E., Lorenzi, M., Bier, D. M., Tsalikian, E., Schneider, V., Karam, J. H., and Forsham, P. (1976). *J. Clin. Invest.* **57**, 875.

Goldberg, D., Walesky, M., and Sherwin, R. S. (1979). *Metab. Clin. Exp.* in press.

Holst, J. J., Guldberg-Madsen, O., and Knop, J. (1977). *Diabetologia* **13**, 487.

Kinney, J., and Felig, P. (1979). *In* "The Biochemical and Metabolic Basis of Endocrinology" L. DeGroot, ed.). Grune & Stratton, New York. In press.

Koerker, D. L., Ruch, W., Chideckel, E., Palmer, J., Goodner, C. J., Ensinck, J., and Gale, C. C. (1974). *Science* **184**, 482.

Krejs, G. J., Raskin, P., and Fordtran, J. S. (1978). *Clin. Res.* **26**, 420A.

Kuku, S. F., Jaspan, J. B., Emmanouel, D. S., Ziedler, A., Katz, A. L., and Rubenstein, A. H. (1976). *J. Clin. Invest.* **58**, 742.

Liljenquist, J. E., Bomboy, J. D., Lewis, S. B., Sinclair-Smith, B. C., Felts, P. W., Lacy, W. W., Clifford, O. B., and Liddle, G. W. (1974). *J. Clin. Invest.* **53**, 198.

Mallinson, C. N., Bloom, S. R., Warin, A. P., Salmon, P. R., and Cox, B. (1974). *Lancet* **2**, 1.

Meissner, C., Thum, C., Beischer, W., Winkler, G., Schroder, K. E., and Pfeiffer, E. F. (1975). *Diabetes* **24**, 988.

Muller, W. A., Faloona, G. R., Aguilar-Parada, E., and Unger, R. H. (1970). *N. Engl. J. Med.* **283**, 109.

Muller, W. A., Faloona, G. R., and Unger, R. H. (1973). *Am. J. Med.* **54**, 52.

Perley, M. and Kipnis, D. M. (1966). *N. Engl. J. Med.* **274**, 1237.

Raskin, P., and Unger, R. H. (1977). *Diabetes* **26**, 1034.

Raskin, P., and Unger, R. H. (1978). *N. Engl. J. Med.* **299**, 433.

Roth, J., Kahn, C. R., Lesniak, M. A., Gorden, P., De Meyts, P., Megyesi, K., Neville, D. M., Jr., Gavin, J. R., III, Soll, A. H., Freychet, P., Goldfine, I. D., Bar, R. S., and Archer, J. A. (1975). *Recent Prog. Horm. Res.* **31**, 95.

Sacca, L., Sherwin, R. S., and Felig, P. (1978). *Am. J. Physiol.* **235**, E287.

Sacca, L., Sherwin, R. S., and Felig, P. (1979). *Am. J. Physiol.* **236**, E113.

Service, J. S., Molnar, G. D., Roseveau, J. M., Ackerman, E., Gatewood, L. C., and Taylor, W. F. (1970). *Diabetes* **19**, 144.

Sherwin, R. S., and Felig, P. (1977). *In* "International Review of Physiology, Endocrine Physiology II" (S. M. McCann ed.), Vol. 16, p. 151. Univ. Park Press, Baltimore, Maryland.

Sherwin, R. S., and Felig, P. (1978). *N. Engl. J. Med.* **299**, 1366.

Sherwin, R. S., Fisher, M., Hendler, R., and Felig, P. (1976a). *N. Engl. J. Med.* **294**, 455.

Sherwin, R. S., Bastl, C., Finkelstein, F. O., Fisher, M., Black, H., Hendler, R., and Felig, P. (1976b). *J. Clin. Invest.* **57**, 722.

Soman, V., and Felig, P. (1977). *J. Clin. Invest.* **60**, 224.

Soman, V., and Felig, P. (1978). *Nature (London)* **272**, 829.

Tasaka, Y., Sekine, M., Wakatsuki, M., Lhgawara, H., and Shizume, K. (1975). *Horm. Metab. Res.* **7**, 205.

Unger, R. H., and Orci, L. (1975). *Lancet* **1**, 14.

Unger, R. H. (1976). *Diabetes* **25**, 136.

Unger, R. H. (1978). *Metab. Clin. Exp.* **27**, 1691.

Unger, R. H., Ohneda, A., Aguilar-Parada, E., and Eisentraut, A. M. (1969). *J. Clin. Invest.* **48**, 810.

Unger, R. H., Aguilar-Parada, E., Muller, W. A., and Eisentraut, A. M. (1970). *J. Clin. Invest.* **49**, 837.

Wahren, J., and Felig, P. (1976). *Lancet* **2**, 1213.

Wahren, J., Felig, P., and Hagenfeldt, L. (1976). *J. Clin. Invest.* **57**, 987.
Wise, J. K., Hendler, R., and Felig, P. (1973). *N. Engl. J. Med.* **288**, 487.

DISCUSSION

S. Marx: These are extremely elegant studies, typical of the work that you and your co-workers have been doing for many years. This is a very interesting model of the stress response, and obviously it has many implications for human stress. I am particularly curious to know whether you have seen any subjective concomitants suggestive of a stress or arousal reaction in the subjects while they receive these combined hormonal infusions.

P. Felig: In the human studies, when we reduce our doses to the range that results in plasma catecholamine levels of no more than about 300 pg there is some sensation of tingling but no tachycardia. We have not noticed any symptoms when the other hormones (glucagon and cortisol) are added. I should emphasize that in our most recent work with catecholamines we have been infusing epinephrine in amounts that raised the circulating levels to no more than that observed with a venipuncture—namely, a rise from 25 to 75 pg. With such doses the response in terms of glucose tolerance is such that a normal subject's postprandial blood sugar may increase to 200 mg/dl. In other words, we think the effect of epinephrine on glucose uptake is so marked as to be demonstrable with plasma changes that are comparable with those induced by standing or smoking a cigarette and a variety of seemingly nonstressful circumstances [*Clin. Res.* **27**, 252A (1979)].

G. Baumann: Do you have any data or speculations about the molecular mechanisms of synergism among these hormones?

P. Felig: We do not at this point have any speculation as to the mechanism(s) of our findings. With regard to the effect of cortisol in sustaining glucose output, one of the immediate questions is whether a glycogenolytic response mediated by epinephrine and glucagon is being sustained as a gluconeogenic response. We do not as yet know the answer to that.

J. Geller: A very nice presentation with very impressive logic in your data. In the past, some human studies have reported that in acute myocardial infarction norepinephrine and epinephrine values in blood are high enough to almost completely suppress plasma insulin. I was a little surprised that in your dog studies insulin levels actually went up at least transiently and initially. I am wondering whether you have any insulin studies in humans under acute stress; second, what might be the role for free fatty acid elevations in the course of stress—since all these stress hormones also increase free fatty acids.

P. Felig: Your point is well taken. As concerns the changes in insulin, there may be some species differences. In humans we do not obtain the initial increase in insulin that we see in the dogs when we infuse epinephrine. The data on glucose intolerance after myocardial infarction have generally been attributed to an interference with glucose-stimulated insulin secretion. We would emphasize that in our studies in the dog there is also some interference with insulin secretion because the late, marked hyperglycemia is not accompanied by an appropriate rise in insulin. The point that I was emphasizing in the presentation was that a lack of normal basal insulin levels (as occurs in the decompensated diabetic) was unnecessary for the induction of "stress hyperglycemia" in a previously normal individual.

With regard to fatty acid measurements, we have not looked at that parameter in detail. However, we have examined the plasma ketone response. Interestingly, despite the severity of hyperglycemia the combined hormone infusions fail to bring about a rise in blood ketone acids. My interpretation is that one must have absolute hypoinsulinemia to induce hyperketonemia. I recognize that the data of McGarry and Foster have emphasized the importance of changes in insulin as well as glucagon. However, I believe that in the *in vivo* circumstance, unless you have absolute insulin lack, you will not observe hyperketonemia.

O. P. Ganda: It is known that epinephrine *in vivo* itself would stimulate glucagon secretion, and studies from your own laboratory have shown that cortisone administration can stimulate glucagon by itself. Even though in these studies you used rather smaller doses, did you look at the glucagon levels after combined stimuli, in comparison with the studies with glucagon infusion alone?

P. Felig: Yes, as I pointed out in the slide showing hormone levels, the glucagon level was the same when the glucagon was infused alone or with cortisol and/or epinephrine. It is clear that physiologic amounts of epinephrine as previously shown by Dr. Muller and Cahill from your laboratory fail to change glucagon levels in the dog. We have observed the same response. Our previous data showing that cortisol raises plasma glucagon involved studies with pharmacologic amounts of glucocorticoids administered for at least 3 days. Acutely, we do not observe an effect of physiologic increments in cortisol on plasma glucagon.

O. P. Ganda: One technical point in reference to your clearance data. I was not clear how you calculated the glucose clearance.

P. Felig: The studies of glucose kinetics were performed using [^{3}H]glucose. The metabolic clearance rate of glucose is calculated from the glucose uptake divided by the plasma glucose concentration. This is a useful parameter because it has been shown that hyperglycemia per se will increase glucose uptake.

O. P. Ganda: Would you care to speculate about any possible role of somatostatin itself on the liver glucose output?

P. Felig: I think that remains an open question. Our data have shown that somatostatin can augment the response to glucagon as well as blunt the response to epinephrine independent of changes in the availability of insulin or glucagon (L. Sacca, R. S. Sherwin, and P. Felig, *Am. J. Physiol.*). Whether the *in vivo* effects of somatostatin in sensitizing the liver to glucagon and blunting the liver's response to epinephrine are direct effects or are mediated through other hormonal perturbations, remains to be established.

A. Charles: In your initial models of starvation, exercise, and protein feeding, I can understand starvation and exercise associated with enhanced glucagon-mediated release of liver glucose, but in the protein-feeding model, you are infusing peripheral levels of insulin when portal vein levels of insulin would probably be 2- to 3-fold higher. I am not sure what portal vein glucagon levels might be, but if you take those facts into consideration, would you still assume that the glucagon has a role in protein feeding?

P. Felig: In our experimental model we were dealing with endogenous hyperinsulinemia in the portal vein; we demonstrated that a rise in insulin (stimulated by glucose infusion) that inhibited glucose output from the liver by 90–100% was overcome by a rise in glucagon. Teleologically, I think the basis for having a glucagon response with a protein meal relates to the fact that insulin is the anabolic hormone for mediating amino acid uptake and utilization after protein feeding. The rise in glucagon assures that the anabolism induced by insulin occurs without hypoglycemia.

A. Charles: My second question relates to the uremic model and infusions of glucagon at levels that you find present as immunoreactive glucagon. In uremia, nonbioreactive immunoreactive glucagon substances are increased; would you could comment on the quantitative aspects of that concept with respect to the infusions of glucagon.

P. Felig: Yes; Dr. Rubinstein and his colleagues have clearly demonstrated the heterogeneity of circulating glucagon, and an increment in a 9000 molecular weight or glucagon immunoreactive component (probably proglucagon) which accounts for a substantial proportion of hyperglucoganemia in uremia. Nevertheless, there is a substantial increment (2- to 4-fold) in true, pancreatic glucagon in uremia.

A. D. Kenny: Would you care to predict what would happen to the glucose balance in a patient in a state of stress hyperglycemia who is placed on a β-blocking drug such as propranolol (Inderal®)?

P. Felig: That is an interesting question. We have not done that type of experiment as yet. My impression is that much of the effect of epinephrine on glucose clearance is mediated by β-receptors. However, the situation becomes quite complex when evaluated with β-blockers because these are vasoactive agents. Thus, when studied *in vivo*, the β-blockers may be interfering with blood flow, which could be exerting an effect independent of hormone antagonism at the cellular level.

T. G. Muldoon: With respect to the cortisol-induced persistence of the actions of epinephrine and glucagon, you have indicated that this is due to increased glucose production. In wonder if you might have done the experiment where you are constantly infusing all three hormones and at the maximal level you would stop infusing cortisol and see if the levels fell to what they would have been with glucagon and epinephrine, and how quickly they would do this. Have you done this experiment?

P. Felig: We have not done that experiment. The problem is that it takes 5–7 hours to observe the marked hyperglycemia that accompanies the infusion of all three hormones. It becomes technically difficult to extend the experiments for an even longer time period.

J. A. Parsons: I think you have put your finger on an extraordinary important physiological mechanism—in fact, about the only thing that I would really take issue with is your use of the word counterregulatory, which seems to me to suggest that it acts against regulation, whereas in fact it is a beautiful finely tuned system for effecting glucose regulation in the absence of changes in endogenous insulin production.

As you know, we have been treating insulin-dependent diabetics with a continuous subcutaneous infusion of crystalline insulin as their only source of the hormone, using a miniature electromechanical pump (Parsons, Rothwell, and Sharpe, *Lancet* **1**, 77 (1977)). The special dual-rate version of this pump constructed for use with insulin has a low basal rate and an 8-fold higher mealtime rate, which is engaged by a push button and returns automatically to the basal level after 17 minutes.

When starting these studies, we though we might run into difficulty with hypoglycemia, particularly overnight. However, we have seen it in only one out of more than 20 patients, and this was a man treated early in the series whose glucose was so badly regulated that we began with more insulin than we would now recommend. We have found that the insulin requirement usually falls 20–30% during the first few days as carbohydrate metabolism returns toward normal. Once the basal rate is set, it has been possible to maintain excellent control for many months using this simple regime (Pickup *et al.*, *Br. Med. J.* **1**, 204 (1978)). It is particularly encouraging that not only glucose but lactate, pyruvate, β-hydroxybutyrate, and alanine all return to the normal range, which, of course, does not usually happen when insulin is given by conventional means. We intend to use this technique to test empirically whether the development of complications will be slowed or even reversed by such close metabolic control. In the first 7 patients whose renal function was studied by a radioimmunoassay for microalbuminuria, albumin loss decreased in every case, and in three of them it fell to values within the normal range (Viberti *et al.*, *Eur. J. Clin. Invest.* **8**, 336 (1978)).

I believe the noninsulin mechanisms for glucose regulation that you have discussed must provide the explanation why such good control of blood sugar is obtained during fasting in spite of the invariant rate of insulin delivery. It should be possible to learn much about the impairment of these mechanisms in poorly controlled diabetes by following the levels of glucagon, catecholamines, and corticosteroids during the run-in days of insulin infusion while carbohydrate metabolism is returning toward normal.

P. Felig: We too have undertaken studies with a portable infusion system in which insulin is administered subcutaneously at basal rates with preprandial increments infused by pressing a button on the pump. We have employed our system in seven juvenile diabetics who are very difficult to control with conventional subcutaneous insulin. Our results are such that we can maintain the blood sugar generally between 60 and 120 mg/dl (W. V. Tamborlane, R. S. Sherwin, M. Genel, and P. Felig, *N. Engl. J. Med.* **300**, 573 (1979)).

L. S. Jacobs: The question as to whether gluconeogenesis might be involved in the glucocorticoid mechanism of interaction, as opposed to glycogenolysis, may be answerable in part by examination of the concentrations of gluconeogenic precursors. Have you measured amino acid concentrations during the last half of your study period, in particular alanine and glutamine?

P. Felig: We do not as yet have data on the effects of the combined hormone infusions on plasma amino acids.

J. W. McArthur: I would like to ask a clinical question regarding stress hyperglycemia. Would you be willing to speculate about the relative importance of the various counterregulatory factors in, say, the stressed juvenile (insulin-deficient) diabetic?

P. Felig: I think the point is very well taken. In the diabetic, we may be dealing not only with the synergistic interactions of contra insulin hormones, but also with an inherent hypersensitivity to these hormones, perhaps because of the liver being underinsulinized or not having a continuously in-sulinized liver. Obviously, these types of studies are now being extended to the diabetic with and without insulin replacement. The data suggest that there are exaggerations of these responses in the diabetic. One would thus anticipate that the brittleness we see in juvenile diabetics related to stress may be explained on that basis.

L. Birnbaumer: These are very elegant data, Dr. Felig, and I would like to make a comment and pose a question at the end if I may. The actions of glucagon on glucose production are assumed to be cyclic AMP-mediated, and when you perfuse a liver or incubate hepatocytes with glucagon and lose your glucose production response, there are three steps that can be involved: loss of receptor, loss of adenyl cyclase stimulation, and loss of response in terms of accumulation of cAMP. In our laboratory, Dr. Iyengar and I have been working with isolated liver membranes prepared by the same method as that you use, and we have developed the conditions to obtain desensitization of adenylyl cyclase to glucagon stimulation in the test tube. Desensitization required high levels of ATP (1–3 mM), about 5 mM MgCl$_2$, 10 μM GTP, and about 30 minutes of incubation at 30–37°C. Under these conditions, the system becomes totally desensitized, to the extent that lags in progress curves seen with GMP-P(NH)P before glucagon addition have returned. Since one can also have loss of responsiveness because the cAMP levels have dropped rather than having desensitization of adenylyl cyclase, I wonder whether you have looked at the time course of development of refractoriness in your uremic model in terms of appearance of loss of cyclase stimulability versus appearance of loss of binding. I ask this because your observations were made after a given time, probably hours afterward, and while at this time changes in receptor levels and cyclase response go hand in hand, it may be that a dissociation can be seen if the development of the changes is studied as a function of time.

P. Felig: Your point is well taken, Dr. Birnbaumer. In those studies done by preparing mem-branes from uremic rats, we do not have data on the time course of changes in receptor binding and cAMP levels. We have begun to do studies with cultured hepatocytes looking at the effects of glucagon addition to the incubation medium. In that system there is good correspondence of the time course of the "down regulation" of binding and changes in adenylate cyclase activity.

C. A. Snipes: Does stress influence the output of possible hormones from the gut, like GIP, that may influence metabolism?

P. Felig: I do not know the answer to that. We have recent data to suggest that there is a gut hormone that modulates insulin action on the liver (R. DeFronzo, E. Ferrannini, R. Hendler, J. Wahren, and P. Felig, *Proc. Natl. Acad. Sci. U.S.A.* **75**, 5173 (1978). Whether the secretion of such hormones is altered in "stress" has not been established. However, since we are dealing with hyperglycemia in the fasted state, I doubt that gut hormones are of importance in our experimental model.

C. A. Snipes: I think counterregulatory is a beautiful term for the purpose of teaching medical students, who come to us firmly convinced that insulin and glucagon are exactly equal in all respects.

N. Varsano-Aharon: Dr. Felig, I wonder whether you have any data on, or could perhaps offer a novel explanation for, an interesting clinical observation in nondiabetic chronic renal dialysis patients. We observe that occasionally these patients, even when not on β-blockers, develop, following dialysis, a profound sustained hypoglycemia unilateral to insulin overproduction. Is this an expression of a lack of substrate as in kwashiorkor, or do you have any other thoughts?

P. Felig: There have been reports, particularly from Dr. Kipnis' group in St. Louis, that hypoglycemia in uremia may be related to reduced levels of plasma alanine.

SUBJECT INDEX

A

ACTH, effect on adrenal cholesterol metabolism, 249, 253–256
Adipocyte cell line, *see* 3T3-L1 adipocyte cell line
Adipocytes, development of hormone sensitivity during, 481–482
Adrenal cortex
  cholesterol metabolism in, 245–247
  LDL metabolism in, 219
    bovine, 233–239
    membranes, 239–244
Adrenal steroids, cholesterol as precursor of, 215–216
Adrenal tumor cells, LDL receptor pathway in, 219–223
Affinity chromatography
  of thyroid hormone receptors, 132–139
    elution, 135–139
    support matrices, 133–135
Albumin
  synthesis of
    on polyribosomes, 72–76
    translational control, 79–82
    in *Xenopus,* 76–77
Aldolase, androgen induction of, 2
Amide bond, in circular dichroism, 155
4-Aminopyrazolopyrimidine, effect on LDL pathway, 224–235
Androgens
  proteins induced by, 2
  synthesis of, 307–308
Antiestrogens
  in breast cancer therapy, 294
  effect on
    mammary tumors, 275–280
    uterus, 269–275
  mode of action of, 269–290
    model, 284–290
  radiolabeled, studies with, 280–284
  structures of, 269
ApoVDL-II, estrogen induction of, 2
Atherogenesis, 375–448
  vascular endothelial cells in studies of, 380–413
Avidin, progesterone induction of, 2

B

Basement membrane
  formation in corneal endothelial cells, 417–424
  synthesis by vascular endothelium, 383–386
Blood, glucose in, hormonal regulations of, 502–510
Breast cancer, antiestrogen therapy of, 294
Burkitt lymphoma cells, as H-Y antigen source, 457–458

C

Cat, transplantation of corneal epithelial cells in, 438
cDNA, prolactin-specific, 149
$cDNA_{ov}$, synthesis of, 14–18
Cell cultures, response to thyroid hormones, 98–120
Cell surface proteins, effect on vascular epithelium, 387–394
Cerebroside sulfate, structure of, 169
Cholesterol
  as adrenal steroid precursor, 215–216
  from LDL, 217–218
  metabolism in cell, LDL levels and, 395–396
Chromatin
  thyroid hormone binding proteins in, 127–129, 142
  thyroid hormone effects on, 117–120
Chylomicron, role in cholesterol levels, 407–411
Circular dichroism (CD)
  of pituitary hormones, 155–213
    dynamic studies, 187–207
    static studies, 165–187
  principles of, 155–165
    amide bond, 155
    aromatic chromophores, 159–164
    disulfide bonds, 164–165
Clomid, effect on uterus, 292–293
Conalbumin, estrogen induction of, 2
Corneal endothelial cells
  in atherogenesis studies, 413–441
  basement membrane formation in, 417–424
  LDL levels and, 424–432

DATE DUE